Health, Illness, and Health Care in Canada

Health, Illness, and Health Care in Canada

Edited by

B. Singh Bolaria
UNIVERSITY OF VICTORIA

Harley D. Dickinson
UNIVERSITY OF SASKATCHEWAN

Fourth Edition

NELSON EDUCATION

NELSON EDUCATION

Health, Illness, and Health Care, Fourth Edition
by B. Singh Bolaria and Harley D. Dickinson

Associate Vice President, Editorial Director:
Evelyn Veitch

Editor-in-Chief:
Anne Williams

Senior Acquisitions Editor:
Scott Couling

Marketing Manager:
Heather Leach

Developmental Editor:
My Editor Inc.

Permissions Coordinator:
Sandra Mark

Production Service:
PrePress PMG

Copy Editor:
Colleen Shea

Proofreader:
PrePress PMG

Indexer:
PrePress PMG

Manufacturing Coordinator:
Ferial Suleman

Design Director:
Ken Phipps

Managing Designer:
Katherine Strain

Interior Design:
PrePress PMG

Cover Design:
Jarrel Breckon

Cover Image:
"Untitled" (from Cyclic series) by Susan Cunningham, screenprint & chine collé on paper / Open Studio

Compositor:
PrePress PMG

Printed and bound in Canada
6 7 8 9 18 17 16 15

For more information contact Nelson Education Ltd., 1120 Birchmount Road, Toronto, Ontario, M1K 5G4. Or you can visit our Internet site at http://www.nelson.com

Library and Archives Canada Cataloguing in Publication

Health, illness, and health care in Canada / [edited by] B. Singh Bolaria, Harley D. Dickinson.—4th ed.

First ed. published under title: Sociology of health care in Canada.

Includes bibliographical references and index.
ISBN-13: 978-0-17-640694-3
ISBN-10: 0-17-640694-8

1. Medical care—Canada—Textbooks. 2. Social medicine—Canada—Textbooks. I. Bolaria, B. Singh, 1936– II. Dickinson, Harley D., 1951–

RA395.C3H424 2008 362.10971
C2008-900412-4

DEDICATION

In memory of my late mother, Audrey, and for my father,
Leslie, both of whom gave me unconditional love and support.
–H.D.D.

In memory of my late brothers Baldev and Jagmohan
and my late sister Rattan.
–B.S.B.

CONTENTS

PART 7

PREFACE

Health, illness, injury, and death, and the ways we as a society experience, understand, and respond to these realities of human existence affect us all. It is not surprising, therefore, that these issues are receiving an increasing amount of sociological attention in the form of new research, journals, books, and university courses. The publication of the fourth edition of *Health, Illness, and Health Care in Canada* serves in a small way to confirm the coming of age of both the sociology of health and illness and the sociology of medicine and health care in Canada.

In this revised fourth edition, we have tried to be responsive to comments and observations of those who have used the book, both instructors and students, as well as those of reviewers. We hope we have succeeded.

In this edition we have added new subjects and new contributions. The inclusion of new subjects has expanded the scope of health issues covered in this edition. These include: the emergence of the public health system in Canada; migration of physicians and nurses into and out of Canada; complementary and alternative medicine; mid-life health; and the safety of Canada's blood supply. Additionally, new contributions in areas such as environmental and occupational health and safety; ethnicity; aging and health; and population and health status with fresh perspectives add to the scope and strength of this edition. The revised and updated chapters from the third edition incorporate new developments, emerging research perspectives, and debates in their respective areas. All chapters are the result of original research and analysis written for this book by leading experts in the field.

This edition contains an introduction to each section, study questions, recommended readings, and glossaries of important terms intended to facilitate its use as a textbook and to direct readers to key texts and articles in each area covered.

In the final organization of the content of this edition, we benefited from the feedback of our colleagues who have used the previous editions in their teaching and research and from the suggestions of anonymous reviewers. We hope that our colleagues find both the pedagogical material and organization of the text helpful and useful in their work, particularly in the presentation of material for their courses.

ACKNOWLEDGEMENTS

With this fourth edition we hope that we have once again succeeded in bringing to instructors, students, and policy-makers alike an accessible and timely examination of key issues facing Canadians in the areas of health, illness, and health care. We could not have done it alone. Bringing this book together depended on the kind cooperation and consideration of a multitude of people. Of course, the authors who contributed their expertise to their endeavour must be acknowledged for their hard work – we would like to thank them for their efforts. We are particularly grateful for their patience and perseverance throughout the long time frame it took to complete this project. We hope that they will be pleased with the final outcome. We would also like to thank the many instructors and students who have used the previous three editions and thereby made the fourth edition both possible and necessary. We wish to acknowledge the constructive comments and suggestions made by anonymous reviewers, which proved extremely helpful for the authors and editors of this book. We are certain that their comments and suggestions contributed to the overall quality of the content and analysis presented here.

We must thank several people at Nelson. This project has taken a long time to complete and required the efforts of many people. The professionalism, commitment, and patience shown by the many people at Nelson were major components in the completion of this book. We are grateful to all those who started at the beginning of this project and to those who stuck with it to finalize the manuscript. First, we wish to mention Cara Yarzab and Sandra Green who initiated the work on the fourth edition, conducted meticulous review of the third edition, solicited the comments of external reviewers, produced summaries of reviewers' comments, and developed the initial table of contents and organization of the subject matter for the fourth edition. Sandra also initially worked as the development editor before passing this responsibility to Leslie Mann, who carried on these responsibilities superbly. We are especially grateful for her professionalism, enthusiasm, support, and above all, her patience. We both appreciate that she maintained her cool through missed deadlines. We also acknowledge her contributions in the development of the final table of contents and organization of the book. We must also thank the copy editor, Colleen Shea, whose editorial work provided consistency and improved the quality of presentation. We are also thankful to Susan Calvert, who brought the manuscript to publication.

Finally, we would like to thank our families yet again for their continued support. We all rejoice in this work's completion.

B. Singh Bolaria
Harley D. Dickinson
University of Victoria
University of Saskatchewan

PART 1

THE CANADIAN HEALTH CARE SYSTEM AND THE HEALTH STATUS OF CANADIANS

Sociological studies of health, illness, and health care cover a wide range of issues, such as the structure and organization of the health care sector, medical institutions, inequalities in health status, and social, political, and economic determinants of the nature and composition of the health care delivery system. These issues are pursued and examined from a variety of perspectives and paradigms. Despite this diversity, certain paradigms and orientations are still dominant in medicine and the study of health, illness, and health. These perspectives have profound influence on these areas, such as definition and etiology of health and illness, funding, organization and delivery of health services, research directions, and health policies and reforms. Four readings in this section address some of these issues. In Chapter 1, Bolaria examines the evolution and prevalence of the dominant paradigms in medicine and their implications with regard to etiology as well as treatment of health and illness. Other sections of the chapter focus on social epidemiology and on some recent trends in the scope and theme of sociological inquiry.

Bolaria notes that the mechanistic-individualistic clinical approach remains the dominant paradigm in medicine. This paradigm attributes disease to the "malfunctioning" of the human body and the treatment focuses on surgical or chemical interventions to restore normal functioning. Individuals receive treatment outside of and abstracted from their "normal" social and material contexts. A similar reductionist approach "blames" illness on individual lifestyles, behaviour, and consumption patterns. Both approaches, Bolaria notes, obscure the social nature of disease; that is, human health and illness are embedded in social, economic, political, and cultural contexts and these factors produce social variability in the health and illness status of individuals.

This chapter also presents an overview of studies that deal with the medical behaviour of consumers, the health sector and its contradictions, and the literature that focuses on the linkages between social forces in the broader society and in the health care system. The policy implications that flow from these latter studies are quite instructive. It is argued that because of the close link between medicine and social, economic, political, and class forces in the broader society, attempts to reform and transform medicine must be tied to wider strategies of change in the social structure.

The goal of a health policy and health reforms is to improve the health status of the population. How this goal should be achieved is often a matter of vigorous debate. There appears to be a growing consensus that the current medically dominated system, with its reductionist orientation, hospital-based medicine, and health care system, is no longer the best means to achieve better health for all Canadians. Although there is general agreement that the current system needs to be reformed, there is no agreement as to what those reforms should be and how those reforms should be implemented. Chapter 2 addresses trends and issues regarding health care and health reforms.

Dickinson, in Chapter 2, describes historical and contemporary issues and trends associated with the developments and reforms of the Canadian medicare and health care system. In the first part, he provides a brief account of the introduction of medicare and some of its structural and fiscal problems. Medicare originated in the failure of the market to ensure that people received necessary medical care and hospital services. The introduction of medicare for the most part removed the financial barriers to health care. Medicare, however, has been undergoing reforms since its inception. He argues that the impetus of these reforms were the structural characteristics of medicare itself, which include the scope of medicare and the initial intergovernmental funding arrangements. The original cost-sharing agreement between the federal and provincial governments discouraged experimentation with non-medical and non-hospital forms of treatment, and it discouraged provincial governments from improving efficiency in delivery of services. The reforms in funding arrangements during the 80s and 90s encouraged provincial governments to make reforms at the provincial level. Regionalization was the primary means adopted in most provinces to enact these reforms. This was intended to achieve several health policy objectives, including improved health outcomes, flexibility in care delivery, better integration and coordination in delivery of services, and greater citizen participation in planning and service delivery. The goal was also to modify some structural features of medicare that entrenched medical dominance, cost increases, and a curative approach to health problems.

During the mid-1990s, new initiatives were taken to health care reform and renewal with the establishment of the National Forum on Health (NFH) in 1994. NFH was intended to involve the public in identifying common goals and innovative ways to improve the health care system and health status of the population. Dickinson addresses two specific areas in which NFH was influential: the development and use of expanded and improved health information systems as a way to improve the quality and safety of the health care system, and targeted funding. The Romanow Commission, established in 2001, was another step in the direction of reforming the health care system. The Romanow report (2002) confirmed and highlighted four objectives to guide health policy – sustainability, access, quality, and accountability. It also supported the principle of a single, public payer and rejected options that would move the system toward increased privatization.

Dickinson points out that by the turn of the century, First Minister Accords became an effective mechanism to achieve inter-governmental consensus on health reform priorities and their funding. Dickinson concludes that while these reforms may not have resolved all the contradictions, they may have created an atmosphere of increased cooperation and collaboration that has never before characterized Canadian health care politics.

While the focus of health care policy is mainly on treatment of illness and injury, public health policy and practice are concerned with preventing illness and injury. Both health care and public health policies have complementary objectives, that is, to improve the health status of the population. Quinlan and Dickinson, in Chapter 3, focus on public health issues and policy in Canada. They argue that the efforts to develop a new public health system are the result of the confluence of several forces, including globalization, climate change, and the inability of both the public health and health care systems to deal with existing and emerging health problems.

The early impetus for public health concerns arose because of the rise of British industrial capitalism, urbanization, and colonialism. The initial public health initiative took the form of Factory Acts and associated legislation to protect workers' health and regulate conditions of work, immunization, effective water treatment, sewerage and waste disposal systems, and quarantine regulations.

Some of the same factors also motivated the development of the Canadian public health system. Recent health crises in both domestic and international contexts highlighted the health risks faced by Canadians and the limitations of the current systems to respond effectively. On the domestic front, the concerns arose out of water contamination problems in several places, and the security of food safety. On the global level, the HIV/AIDS pandemic, Severe Acute Respiratory Syndrome (SARS), bird flu, and West Nile virus highlighted the increasing interrelationships of the world's populations. Some changes have also been prompted by epidemiological transition and realization that the health care system is unable to manage most of the current health problems.

These developments have led to the realization that more resources are required for the public health system and that both the public health system and the health care system must be better coordinated in order to respond effectively to existing and emergency health problems. The creation of the Public Health Agency of Canada (PHAC) is a step in that direction. Quinlan and Dickinson argue that a further move toward developing a more integrated and coordinated public health system involves identifying the structural components of the present system. They identify and discuss five components based upon the work of Frank. These are Health Surveillance, Disease and Injury Prevention, Health Protection, Population Health Assessment, and Health Promotion. Another dimension which has recently gained considerable attention is Emergency Preparedness. All aspects of public health are represented within the structural dimensions of the present-day public health system in Canada.

Quinlan and Dickinson conclude that it is necessary to strengthen the public health system through increased funding, legislative improvements, and improved coordination across jurisdictions and institutions if the system is to meet the challenges presented by current and emerging health problems.

Thomas-MacLean and Poudrier address the issue of population health status in Chapter 4. They provide an overview of several widely accepted population health status indicators, including life expectancy, infant mortality, child and maternal mortality rates, and causes of death. These indicators show that health status is unequally distributed within the population. These social variations in health status are the outcome of socio-economic disparities and differential life chances of individuals and sub-groups within the population. These health inequalities have been neglected because public health discourse has focused upon individual manifestations of inequality, along with the health behaviours of those with low incomes.

Thomas-MacLean and Poudrier conclude with a presentation of selective initiatives that expand the focus of health research in areas such as the role of racism and racialization in health and illness, factors associated with power and community in health and illness, and the impact of marginalization/empowerment on health and illness. These and other initiatives, if fully realized, they conclude, are likely to enhance our understanding of the complex relationship between health status, determinants of health, inequality, and empowerment.

1

Sociology, Medicine, Health, and Illness: An Overview

B. SINGH BOLARIA University of Saskatchewan, University of Victoria

INTRODUCTION

Medical sociology covers a wide range of substantive areas and encompasses a diversity of issues pertaining to health and illness, medical institutions, the structure and organization of the health care sector, and the political, economic, and social determinants of the nature and composition of the health care delivery systems. Medical sociologists and others interested in this area approach and examine these essential topics and issues from various theoretical perspectives and paradigms and use varying levels of analyses and methodologies (Bourgeault, 2006). Certain paradigms and orientations continue to be dominant in medicine and medical practice, which are implicated in the definition and etiology of health and illness and in public debates about health policy. Thus, it is instructive to examine topics such as the evolution of the dominant paradigm of scientific medicine, determinants of health and illness, and the focus of research and levels of analysis. Such an examination, however brief, is essential to our understanding of the current organization and delivery of health services, and ideological constraints and limitations within which the policy alternatives to "solve" the "health crises" are being debated.

EVOLUTION AND THE DOMINANT PARADIGM OF SCIENTIFIC MEDICINE

The knowledge of modern scientific medicine is founded on the work of Koch, Pasteur, and other bacteriologists. The germ theory of disease, which gained prominence in the late 19th century, had a profound impact on the practice of medicine. As Waitzkin (1979, p. 684) states: "The isolation of specific bacteria as the etiologic agents in several infectious diseases created a profound change in medicine's diagnostic and therapeutic assumptions. A unifactorial model of disease emerged. Medical scientists searched for organisms causing infections and single lesions in non-infectious disorders." Renaud (1977, p. 139) also makes the point that the current medical paradigm of the "specific etiology" of disease and specific therapies has its roots in the germ theory of disease developed by Pasteur and Koch. While the germ theory helped to develop the prevention of infectious diseases and improved medical practice, the paradigm of specific etiology and specific therapies gave rise to the essentially curative orientation of medicine and medical practice; that is, that people can be made healthy by medical technologies and technological fixes (Renault, 1977).

This paradigm basically adopted a "mechanistic model" of the human body. This approach has a long history. Philosophers like Descartes (1596–1650) established the philosophical base for a machine model of the human body; that is, that the human body is assumed to work in the same way as a machine. As McKeown (1965, p. 38) states:

> The approach to biology and medicine established during the seventeenth century was an engineering one, based on a physical model. Nature was perceived in mechanistic terms, which led in biology to the idea that a living organism could be regarded as a machine which might be taken apart and reassembled if its structure and function were fully understood. In medicine, the same concept led further to the belief that an understanding of disease processes and of the body's response to them would make it possible to intervene therapeutically, mainly by physical (surgery), chemical, or electrical methods.

Disease, then, is an alteration, a pathological change in the body machinery that must be "fixed" (Navarro, 1986, p. 166). Many diseases are viewed as mere technical defects; treatments are oriented toward restoring the "normal" functioning of the human machine. This approach basically ignores social causes of much ill health. The mechanistic-individualistic paradigm narrows and limits the medical task, primarily curative, individualistic, and interventionist (Doyal & Pennell, 1979).

This mechanistic conception brought about a shift from the consideration of illness as a breakdown of the total system to the notion that ill health could be caused by the malfunctioning of one particular part of the body machinery – in other words, localized pathology (Doyal & Pennell, 1979). This idea led to the medical fragmentation of the delivery of health care. Again, it is based on the premise that the human body is like a machine, and can, like any mechanical system, be broken down into different parts for repair. Many instruments were developed (thermometer, stethoscope) to examine the interior of the body machinery. This shift toward localized pathology had a profound impact on the division of labour (specialization) in medicine.

The specialization in medical knowledge and practice tends to focus on specific parts of the body machine, such as the nervous system, the cardiovascular system, the gastrointestinal system, and so forth (Navarro, 1986, p. 167).

The work of bacteriologists and other scientists undeniably had a positive impact on the control of infectious diseases and led to improvements in medical practice. However, several studies tend to cast doubt on the historical importance of these discoveries (Powles, 1973; Carlson, 1975). It is argued that the major decline in mortality and morbidity was due to better nutrition and sanitation and other environmental improvements, and that the decline in mortality and morbidity patterns, rather than following significant diagnostic and therapeutic discoveries, in fact preceded them (Waitzkin, 1979). Whatever the sequence of events, laboratory medicine with its emphasis on an individualistic, scientific, machine model of the human body achieved ascendancy. It should be noted that the dominant scientific paradigm is not mere linear evolution of scientific discoveries. As Navarro (1986, p. 167) and others have argued, the form and nature of medicine is determined by class and power relations in the society and not by scientific imperatives. The ascendancy of scientific laboratory-based medicine and the dominant position of **allopathic medicine** in North America at the beginning of this century were aided by the publication of the Flexner Report (Brown, 1979; Berliner, 1977; Kunitz, 1974; Waitzkin, 1979; Kelman, 1977).

Abraham Flexner visited medical schools both in the United States and Canada in 1904–05. The Flexner Report (1910) was critical of the medical schools that did not have the facilities to teach laboratory-based scientific medicine. It called for the reorganization or, failing that, closure of such institutions (Hewa, 2002). Ninety-two medical schools were closed (mainly in the United States) or reorganized between 1904 and 1915 (Waitzkin, 1979). Some of these institutions taught alternative forms of healing, such as homeopathy, midwifery, and herbalism. This report was highly critical of these alternative practices and helped to relegate them to subordinate status vis-à-vis the allopathic practice of medicine (Kelman, 1977; Berliner, 1975; Kunitz, 1974). The norm for medical education and practice became laboratory-based scientific medicine. The Flexner Report was hailed "as the document that helped change modern medicine from quackery to responsible practice" (Waitzkin, 1979, p. 685).

Before the report's recommendations were implemented, the allopathic physicians had faced stiff competition, which affected their incomes, from practitioners trained in a variety of alternative healing traditions. The costs of delivering premedical education, as well as the necessity for expensive laboratory facilities, led to high tuition fees in medical schools, making medical education all but inaccessible to working-class students. In addition to the changes in the class composition of the medical profession, these changes also led to reduced competition and higher incomes for the doctors (Waitzkin, 1979).

In Canada, the rise and social legitimacy of scientific medicine was also bolstered by the Flexner Report. A focus on scientific education, the formation of medical associations, a tightening of licensing standards, and the marginalization of alternative forms of healing all helped to establish the monopoly of scientific medicine and change the social profile, prestige, and income of physicians (Hewa, 2002; Bolaria, 2002). The Carnegie Foundation also helped support Flexner's tour and subsequent publication of the report. In addition, the General Education Board of the Rockefeller Foundation provided financial support to medical schools that implemented the report's recommendations (Nielsen, 1972). The philanthropic support of the Foundation was, according to Waitzkin (1979, pp. 686–687), based upon a number of considerations:

> The humanitarian image of this philanthropic work helped justify the exploitation of workers and the environment by which the parent industries accumulated high profits.... Secondly, the development of laboratory-based medical science diverted attention away from the illness-generating condition of capitalist production and class structure.... A third reason for support of scientific medicine by the capitalist class was the need for a workforce healthy enough to participate in the production process.

The Flexner Report, supported by the medical profession and by philanthropic foundations, helped to consolidate the dominance of the allopathic practitioners and to establish laboratory-based scientific medicine as the norm for medical education and practice. This mechanistic-individualistic conception is currently pervasive in medical practice and research. As Rodberg and Stevenson (1977, p. 113) point out: "Modern medicine operates according to an individualistic, scientistic, machine model. Humans receive medical treatment outside of, and abstracted from, their normal social and environmental context."

HEALTH AND ILLNESS

The mechanistic view of the human organism has dictated a similar vision of health and illness. For instance, the *Dorland Medical Dictionary* defines health as "a normal condition of body and mind, i.e., with all the parts functioning normally"; and disease is defined as "a definite morbid process having a characteristic strain of symptoms – it may affect the whole body or any of its parts, and its **etiology, pathology,** and prognosis may be known or unknown" (Inglefinger, 1982).

This mechanistic view of health and illness is of particular significance with regard to the etiology of health and illness as well as the treatment. As Doyal and Pennell (1979, p. 34) note: "Ill health is now defined primarily in terms of the malfunctioning of a mechanical system, and treatment consists of surgical, chemical or even electrical intervention to restore the machine to normal working order." Medical experts' advanced training permits them to recognize a "malfunction" and prescribe appropriate treatment to correct it and thus make the body "functional." In functional terms, health means "the state of optimum capacity of an individual for the effective performance of the roles and tasks for which he has been socialized" (Parsons, 1972, p. 117). In Parsons's definition, this "capacity to perform" appears to be the sole criterion of health. The experience of ill health in itself does not constitute illness.

Others have argued that health in capitalist society is tied to production and capital accumulation process. This means the individual's ability or capacity to engage in productive work contributes to accumulation (Kelman, 1977).

Viewed in this way, health has important implications in terms of the level of health care services. Employers want to keep workers in good working order. As Rodberg and Stevenson (1977, p. 112) indicate: "From the point of view of capital, the health care system does not have to satisfy workers and it is not important that they feel well, as long as they are able to work hard." The definition of health and illness in relation to the accumulation process is an important aspect of the capitalist value system, which regards workers primarily as producers: "they are machines, one dimensional contributors to the accumulation process" (Rodberg & Stevenson, 1977, p. 112).

Viewed in this context, the investments to maintain healthy and productive workers are considered in the same way as investments in other factors of production, and have to be balanced against returns. If workers are hard to replace or reproduction costs are high, employers are greatly concerned about the health of the workers and are interested in prolonging their productive life span. Conversely, if workers are easily replaceable, employers are less concerned about their health. Workers are kept healthy so long as the cost of health care is less than the cost of replacing them.

If workers are "owned" by the employers, such as occurs with slave labour, the employers are deeply interested in protecting their property. For instance, slaves in the

United States had more systematic access to health care and enjoyed somewhat better health status than the freed slaves and poor whites (Postell, 1961; Stampp, 1956). However, health expenditures were tempered with return on this investment. Slaves were kept healthy so long as the cost of health care was less than the cost of replacing them (Kelman, 1977, pp. 16–17). In addition to this instrumental view of the health and fitness of the workers, "under capitalism, health is also defined in an individualistic way. It is always individuals who become sick, rather than social, economic or environmental factors which cause them to be so" (Doyal & Pennell, 1979, p. 35). This individualistic and functional definition of health provides the basis for the essentially curative focus of medicine itself, which has important social and economic significance (Doyal & Pennell, 1979). For instance, the expansion of technologically curative medicine provides the base for a profitable health care industry.

This type of analysis would suggest the termination of health resources to the elderly and infirm who no longer work and who contribute little to the accumulation process because investment in their health will produce few, if any, returns (Kelman, 1977; Rodberg & Stevenson, 1977; Dreitzel, 1971). To be sure, such policies, strictly speaking, have not been politically and culturally feasible. Even in the United States, where there is no universal health care program as in Canada, the elderly, chronically unemployed, and poor receive certain health services, however limited, under the Medicare and Medicaid programs. A strictly functional definition of health and sickness purely in terms of the worker's ability to perform cannot always be operationalized because of political and cultural considerations. It is of no less significance to note that nursing homes and other health care institutions that provide services to the aged also provide opportunities for capital investments and profits, particularly for nursing homes that are privately owned and operated but subsidized by public funds.

REDUCTIONISM IN MEDICINE

The mechanistic-individualistic conception of disease, which attributes disease to a "malfunctioning" of the human body, absolves the economic and political environment from responsibility for disease. These reductionist tendencies in scientific medicine also "shifted the focus of research and action from societal problems – a topic that implied potential threats to the organization of capitalist production and class structure – to pathophysiological disturbance at the level of the individual patient – much less threatening subject matter" (Waitzkin, 1979, p. 686).

A similar reductionist approach emphasizes individual lifestyle. In Canada in 1974, the publication of Lalonde's paper "A New Perspective on the Health of Canadians," gave prominent attention to health risks associated with individual lifestyles and consumption patterns. Lifestyle was also one of the foci of another health policy, "Achieving Health for All: A Framework for Health Promotion" (Epp, 1986). While the clinical model attributes disease to the "malfunctioning" of the human body, the new reductionism introduces the idea that the causes of disease lie in individual lifestyles and behaviours. In the former case the normal functioning of the body can be restored through "technological fixes," while in the latter the solution lies primarily in changing individual behaviours and patterns of consumption. It is argued that since the major risk factors causing much of mortality are under the personal discretion of the individuals, there would be a considerable reduction in mortality if individuals would focus their attention on changing those aspects of their lifestyles that are injurious to their health. Both approaches obscure the social nature of disease and fail to recognize the important relationships between social and material conditions and health and sickness.

Studies from the historical materialistic epidemiological perspective focus on illness-generating conditions and social-structural determinants of health and illness (Bolaria & Bolaria, 2002; Raphael, 2004, 2006).

SOCIAL PRODUCTION OF ILLNESS

Social medicine is primarily concerned with the conditions in society that produce illness and death. While "traditional **epidemiology** has searched for causes of morbidity and mortality that are amenable to medical intervention, historical materialistic epidemiology [has] found causes of disease and death that derive from social conditions" (Waitzkin, 1983, p. 64). Social epidemiology and the environmental approach to health are in conflict with the biological and individual orientation of the predominant paradigm. The overarching theme of the social epidemiological approach is that health and illness cannot be understood by referring only to biological phenomena and medical knowledge. Rather, human health and illness are embedded in economic, social, and cultural contexts, and these factors play an important role in creating the social distribution of health and illness. Material and social conditions that produce illness and mortality include social class, economic cycles, socially produced stress, production processes, and working conditions (Waitzkin, 1983; Navarro, 1986; Smith, 1981; Lynch, 2000; Auger et al., 2004; Kawachi & Kennedy, 2002; Lynch et al., 2000; Wilkinson et al., 2002).

The realization that social and material conditions produce illness and mortality and social variability in health and illness patterns is not new. There is a long history of research and analysis with focus on social and material conditions, most notably in the work of 19th century scholars Friedrich Engels and Rudolf Virchow (Engels, 1973 [1845]; Virchow, 1957, 1958, 1960; cited in Waitzkin, 1983, pp. 65–75). Although their writings have received relatively little notice, their analysis is very relevant to the current debate. Engels's research was aimed at a broad description of working-class life as well as workers' health and safety. For Engels, the roots of illness and early mortality of working-class people were embedded in the process of industrial production and social environment. His analysis focused on the links between environmental toxins, poor housing conditions, poor nutrition, industrial production, working conditions in mining and the textile industry, various infectious diseases, pulmonary disorders, black lung disease, eye disorders, and other occupational diseases and injuries. Virchow focused on the social and economic deprivations of working-class life and linked working-class people's higher morbidity and mortality to inadequate housing, poor nutrition, and inadequate clothing. These deprivations increased working-class susceptibility to disease and illness. While Engels focused his analysis mainly on structural contradictions of production and contradictions between profit and safety, Virchow focused on class inequalities in social distribution and the consumption of resources (Waitzkin, 1983).

The link between social and material conditions and illness and disease is increasingly recognized (Waitzkin, 1983; Navarro, 1986). As Feldberg and Vipond (2006, p. 235) state: "The new diseases, often labeled lifestyle diseases, are actually diseases of circumstances.

They reflect living conditions, poverty, and access to housing and income." For instance, cancer and other chronic diseases are substantially related to environmental factors and the workplace. There is also evidence linking incidence of illness to economic cycles and levels of employment. Disruption of stable community relations has consistently led to an increase in hypertension rates. Rather than focusing on individual lifestyle and its relation to stress, "historical materialist epidemiology shifts the level of analysis to stressful forms of social organization connected to capitalist production and industrialization" (Waitzkin, 1983, p. 63). Studies in the area of occupational health and safety produce persuasive evidence that links work environment and the labour process to illness and disease and points to basic contradictions between profit and safety (see for example, Smith, 1981). Social variability in mortality rates and life expectancy among individuals and groups is produced by structurally produced inequalities, differential life chances, and qualitatively different experiences of social and economic determinants of health and illness (Raphael, 2004, 2006; Bolaria & Bolaria, 2002).

Epidemiological data in Canada and elsewhere show a persistent and pervasive association between socio-economic status and health status (Link & Phelan, 2000; Mirowsky, Ross & Reynolds, 2000; Syme & Yeu, 2000; Federal, Provincial and Territorial Advisory Committee on Population Health, 1999a, b; Wilkinson, 1996; Evans, Barer & Marmor 1994; Marmot et al., 1984, 1991). Those who are advantaged with respect to socio-economic status are also advantaged in health status. As Link and Phelan (2000, p. 43) remark: "People who are more advantaged with regard to resources of knowledge, money, power, prestige, and social connections enjoy a health advantage." Similar patterns of disease, illness, and mortality are prevalent for children (Canadian Institute of Child Health, 2000). Childhood disadvantages accumulate in later life. As Mirowsky, Ross, and Reynolds (2000, p. 60) state: "Relatively small social status differences in health established in childhood and adolescence accumulate and grow throughout most of adulthood." Socio-economic inequalities are also linked to stress (Evans, Barer & Marmor, 1994). Those of a lower socio-economic status are not only subject to more stress but also have fewer resources to cope with it. The Whitehall Study of British Civil Servants (Marmot et al., 1984, 1991) provides strong and consistent evidence of differences in mortality and social hierarchy (levels) in the civil service.

Gender and racial inequalities produce social variability in the health status of men and women and racial groups (Galabuzi, 2004; Pederson & Raphael, 2006; Shah, 2004; Bolaria & Bolaria, 1994a, b). These health status differences are related to varying life experiences and variance in social and material conditions experienced by various groups. Women's and men's life experiences are different and are shaped by socially structured gender roles. Different life circumstances and experiences in turn produce differences in health and illness patterns between men and women. Race and class intersect with gender to produce subgroup differences in health and illness patterns. Discrimination can affect the health status of racial minorities in a number of ways, including differential life chances, low socio-economic status, social exclusion, and unequal access to health care.

MODE AND TYPES OF ANALYSIS

A plethora of sociological and behavioural studies are devoted to analyzing the "medical behaviour" of individuals. These studies have produced a large body of theoretical and empirical literature. Much of this literature concerns the study of differential attitudes toward health and illness, differential health practices, variability of reactions to symptoms and illnesses, and variability in the use of health services.

Another kind of analysis focuses on the behaviour of the provider of services and health care institutions. The health sector, however, is integrally related to the larger society. It is therefore argued that to study the health care system without attention to its linkages to broad political, economic, and social forces is misleading. These studies try to transcend the individual level of analysis to find how these linkages determine the nature, composition, and function of the health care sector and the very definitions of health and illness.

A significant portion of early research in medical sociology has been about the "medical behaviour" of consumers of health care services and the social processes that influence the decisions of individuals to use medical services. A number of authors have identified sociopsychological, sociodemographic, and socio-economic variables to account for variability in health behaviour and illness behaviour. These authors focus on psychological, social, ethnic, cultural, and class factors, with various degrees of emphasis (for details, see Bolaria, 2002). The role of culture and ethnicity in patients' behaviour and their response to illness and in their use of health facilities is also noted. These studies show considerable variations along cultural and ethnic lines. The response to illness may also take the form of self-help or self-medication and consultation with relatives, friends, and neighbours. Some writers also relate the delay in seeking medical help to particular medical orientations and to socio-economic factors (for references and details see Bolaria, 2002).

However, sociopsychological models, with their emphasis on the characteristics of individuals, their value systems, perceptions, health beliefs, and orientations, are of limited use because they tend to overlook the importance of class inequalities (except indirectly, as they affect perceptions and values), the availability of and accessibility to medical services, the organization and delivery of health care services, and other structural factors.

Rather than studying the behaviour of the consumers, others have analyzed the behaviour of the providers of health services and the interaction among various interest groups within the health sector. Their focus is primarily on what "goes on" within the health sector without reference to the linkages between the health sector and the broader society. Studies in this area have focused on such topics as the organization and distribution of health care services, medical education, health care institutions (e.g., hospitals and nursing homes), the professional domination and medical division of labour, and racial inequality in the health sector.

Other analysts question the clinical effectiveness and technical claims of modern scientific medicine (McKinlay & McKinlay, 1987; Illich, 1976; Raphael, 2003). There is no doubt that profound improvements in health status have occurred in the past century, particularly in industrialized countries. But how much of this improvement is due to access and availability of improved health services? It is estimated that only 10–15 percent of the increased longevity since 1900 is due to improvements in the health care system (McKinlay & McKinlay, 1987; Raphael, 2003). The limitations of the existing system have also become apparent due to its inability to contend with the complexity of many contemporary chronic conditions. Chronic conditions such as cancer, cardiovascular problems, lung diseases, and diabetes have eclipsed infectious diseases as causes of illness and mortality. The primarily curative orientation of medicine also came under scrutiny because of some domestic and global health issues. The contaminated water problems, security of the food supply and HIV/AIDS, concerns about new infectious diseases such as Severe Acute Respiratory Syndrome (SARS), bird flu, and West Nile virus brought into sharp focus the limitations of the existing system and calls for the development of a broad public health strategy to deal with these diseases (Feldberg & Vipond, 2006; Rioux, 2006; Fidler, 2000).

Illich (1976) provides considerable evidence of the ineffectiveness of modern medicine in reducing morbidity and mortality and in improving the health of the population. He portrays medicine as a coercive institution and has taken the view that current medical practices generally do more harm than good. Illich's analysis centres on three categories (clinical, social, and structural) of **iatrogenesis** (the causing or inducing of a disease by a physician or medical treatment). He feels that iatrogenesis is clinical when "pain, sickness, and death result from the provision of medical care"; social when "health policies reinforce an industrial organization which generates dependency and ill health"; and structural when "medically sponsored behaviour and delusions restrict the vital autonomy of people by undermining their competency in growing up, caring for each other and aging" (Illich, 1976, p. 165).

According to Illich, clinical iatrogenesis includes "all clinical entities for which remedies, physicians or hospitals are the pathogens or 'sickening' agents." Medical domination has led to loss of autonomy and creation of dependency for patients. The responsibility for health is expropriated from individuals by the medical profession.

Illich attributes these iatrogenic effects to the industrialization, bureaucratization, and monopoly power of the medical profession, as well as the overmedicalization of life, which perpetuates an addictive dependency on medicine and medical institutions. The solution, therefore, lies in debureaucratization, deindustrialization, and demonopolization. He proposes demedicalization and the return of more autonomy and responsibility to individuals for their health and self-care (for a critique, see Starr, 1981; Navarro, 1977, pp. 38–58; Waitzkin, 1976). He confines the solutions to the health care system itself, without reference to structural tendencies and political, social, economic, and class forces in the broader society that perpetuate this system. As Waitzkin (1983, p. 5) notes: "Without attention to these connections, the health system falsely takes on the appearance of an autonomous, free-floating entity, whose defects purportedly can be corrected by limited reforms in the medical sphere."

A considerable volume of literature does focus on the linkages between the political, economic, and social systems and the health care sector (see, for example, Navarro, 1986; Waitzkin, 1983; Doyal & Pennell, 1979; Coburn, 2006; Bourgeault, 2006). This approach is predicated on the fact that the contradictions in medicine reflect the contradictions in society; that is, the health sector is so integral to the broader society that the attempt to study the one without attention to the other will be misleading. As Waitzkin (1983, p. 5) comments: "Difficulties in health and medical care emerged from social contradictions and rarely can be separated from those contradictions." For instance, one of the contradictions in this society is between profit and safety. If it interferes with profits, an improvement in occupational health and safety is not very likely to be implemented. Gender and other inequalities in the health sector are reflections of these inequalities in society (Hofnichter, 2003; Davey-Smith, 2003). While in the discussion of escalating health care costs the focus is generally on consumers and the health sector labour force, little attention is given to the corporate invasion of the medical sector, usually referred to as the "medical-industrial complex." A high-technology mentality has encouraged costly and expensive medicine.

Others have noted the role of the capitalist state, class contradictions, the ideology of medicine, medicalization, and illness related to the capitalist production process (for example, see Berliner, 1977; Fee, 1983; Salmon, 1977; Swartz, 1977; Walters, 1982; Kelman, 1971, 1975, 1977; Navarro, 1976, 1977, 1986; Turshen, 1977; McKinlay, 1984; Waitzkin, 1983; Waitzkin & Waterman, 1974; Minkler, 1983; Crawford, 1980; Smith, 1981; Coburn, 2006; Bourgeault, 2006).

It is increasingly recognized that the sociopsychological models of consumer behaviour and studies that focus exclusively on the health sector and its contradictions do not provide an adequate and comprehensive analysis of the current health crisis, which is characterized by escalating costs and diminishing returns. By focusing on individuals and the health sector, these analyses tend to portray individuals and the health sector as though they existed in a vacuum. They tend to decontextualize the individuals and the health sector. The health care policies that flow from these analyses would further increase the disparities in health status and health care utilization in the populace. For instance, those who depend upon public-sponsored health services would be adversely affected by any rationing of services or promotion of self-care. It is argued that because of the close linkages between medicine and the social, economic, political, and class forces in the broader society, attempts to reform and transform medicine must be tied to wider strategies of change in the societal structure. The contradictions in medicine reflect contradictions of larger society, and they cannot be resolved by focusing on the health sector alone or on individual clinicians (Waitzkin, 1983, p. 8).

FROM HEALTH TO WELL-BEING AND HEALTH PROMOTION

The traditional definition of health as the absence of disease and sickness has come under increasing scrutiny. It is argued that this conceptualization of health individualizes the problem and hampers a broader consideration of the meaning of health and the societal causes of collective health and illness. A broader reconceptualization of the meaning of health encompasses a state of complete physical, mental, emotional, and social well-being – not merely the absence of disease (World Health Organization, 1946, p. 3). This extended concept places issues of health, illness, and health care in a broader social context and highlights conditions that need to be considered in any health policy initiatives.

Effective health promotion policy and practice need to consider the social determinants of health, such as the social, economic, and physical environment; health services, personal resources and coping, health knowledge, and lifestyle behaviours (Federal, Provincial and Territorial Advisory Committee on Population Health, 1999a). The health promotion framework proposes both strategies and mechanisms to eliminate barriers to achieving health for all. The strategies involve fostering public participation, strengthening community health services, and coordinating healthy public policy. The mechanisms to realize these strategies involve self-care, mutual aid, and a healthy environment

(Dickinson, 2002). Thus, health education seems to be one of the central foci in achieving health for all.

Concomitant with these developments, there has been a shift in sociological inquiry away from the study of illness at the individual level to a macro level that focuses on large-scale structural factors, including political and economic forces, the medical profession, and health-related institutions and agencies (Brown, 1996). Segall and Chappell (2000, pp. 2–20) characterize the shift in the scope and theme of sociological inquiry as a transformation of medical sociology into a sociology of health, which has a broader focus on health-related topics including population health, health behaviour, and health promotion.

RESEARCH AND PRACTICE

Jake Epp, the then Minister of Health and Welfare observed in 1986:

> The first challenge we face is to find ways of reducing inequities in the health of low- versus high-income groups in Canada.
>
> There is disturbing evidence which shows that despite Canada's superior system, people's health remains directly related to their economic status. For example, it has been reported that men in the upper income group live six years longer than men with a low income. The difference is a few years less for women. With respect to disabilities, the evidence is even more startling. Men in upper income groups can expect 14 more disability-free years than men with a low income; in the case of women, the difference is eight years.
>
> Among low-income groups, people are more likely to die as a result of accidental falls, chronic respiratory disease, pneumonia, tuberculosis and cirrhosis of the liver. Also, certain conditions are more prevalent among Canadians in low-income groups; they include mental health disorders, high blood pressure and disorders of the joints and limbs.
>
> Within the low-income bracket, certain groups have a higher chance of experiencing poor health than others. Older people, the unemployed, welfare recipients, single women supporting children and minorities such as natives and immigrants all fall into this category. More than one million children in Canada are poor. Poverty affects over half of single parent families, the overwhelming majority of them headed by women. These are the groups for whom "longer life but worsening health" is a stark reality. (Epp, 1986, p. 398)

The above statement by the then Minister of Welfare was made two decades ago. As noted before, many more empirical studies have recognized the impact of economic and social determinants on the health status of individuals, groups, and populations. The significance of social determinants of health was also emphasized in many submissions to the Romanow Commission on the Future of Health Care in Canada (Romanow, 2002). In spite of this evidence, the social determinants have received little attention in Canadian health policy debates and remain marginalized in developing public policy (Lavis, 2002). Behavioural and lifestyle changes to health promotion continue to predominate (Raphael, 2003). This is primarily due to the dominant paradigms of scientific medicine with their focus on biomedical health and individual lifestyle and behavioural determinants of health. The focus on individual lifestyles and self-imposed risks tends to downgrade the importance of social, economic, and environmental factors in production of illness and is consistent with the ideology of individualism, individual choices, individual responsibility, and currently neo-liberal ideology in the context of globalization and conservative political environment (Bolaria, 2000; Raphael, 2003; Coburn, 2006; Teeple, 2000; Bryant, 2006). As Raphael (2003, p. 37) states:

> Political pressure on federal, provincial, and local governments to conform to these shifting ideological sands blend well with the persistent bias of health workers in favour of individualistic, biomedical and lifestyle approaches to health. The media also prefers easy-to-understand biomedical and lifestyle headlines. The social-determinants-of-health approach is lost among such ideological imperatives.

Public policy plays an important role in determining the level of funding, organization, and delivery of health services. Public policy is also crucial in determining the quality of social determinants of health (Bryant, 2006; Bryant, Raphael & Rioux, 2006). Recent economic policies and decline in the welfare state have contributed to the decline in the quality of primary social determinants of health such as levels and distribution of income (Teeple, 2000). Continuation of these policies is bound to have negative health outcomes for individuals, groups, and populations. The understanding of the public policy processes, and links between public policy and quality of social determinants of health, are crucial to our understanding of the health care system and population health. Bryant (2006, pp. 210–211) states:

> There is need to move away from biomedical and epidemiological models to consider the influence of political ideology, social organization, and economic infrastructure to understand how economic and social inequalities lead to health inequalities. Directing the health sector's gaze to broader political and economic factors may be the most effective means of improving population health and reducing inequalities in health.

CONCLUSION

The mechanistic view of the human organism is still the prevalent and dominant paradigm in scientific medicine. This is significant with regard to the etiology as well as the treatment of health and illness. Ill health in this context means the breakdown and malfunctioning of the machine (the human body), and treatment consists of surgical or chemical interventions to restore normal functioning. In functional terms, the sole criterion of health is the capacity of the individual to perform as he or she has been socialized to perform. The experience of ill health in itself does not constitute illness.

Others have argued that health in capitalist society is tied to production and the capital accumulation process. Viewed in this way, health has important implications in terms of health services. Employers want to keep workers in good working order and "it is not important that they feel well as long as they are able to work hard." Viewed in this context, investments to maintain healthy and productive workers are considered the same way as investments in other factors of production, and they must be balanced against returns.

While the clinical model attributes disease to the "malfunctioning" of the human body, the new reductionism introduces the idea that disease lies in individual lifestyle and behaviour. In the former case, the normal functioning of the body can be restored through "technological fixes," while in the latter, the solution lies primarily in changing individual behaviours and patterns of consumption. Both approaches obscure the social nature of disease, which is the subject matter of historical materialistic epidemiology, which identifies social conditions in society that produce illness, disease, and mortality. A number of recent studies underline the persistent association between socio-economic status and health status.

Research studies cover a wide area ranging from the medical behaviour of consumers to analysis of the health sector and its contradictions, and the linkages between the political, economic, social, and class forces in the broader society and the health care system. In a similar vein, the conventional definition of health as the absence of disease is increasingly replaced with a broader understanding of health as complete physical, mental, emotional, and social well-being.

While there is increasing recognition of the link between political, economic, and social forces, and the organization and funding of health services, and the quality of social determinants of health, these considerations remain mostly marginalized in Canadian health policy debates and discussions. It is precisely a knowledge of those links which is crucial to our understanding of population health and health inequalities. The essays in this volume address some of the issues previously discussed and endeavour to provide an understanding of medicine, health, illness, and health care in Canada.

GLOSSARY

allopathic medicine the treatment of disease by conventional means; for example, by using drugs that have opposite effects to the symptoms.

epidemiology the study of the incidence and distribution of diseases and of the control and prevention of diseases.

etiology the study of the causation of diseases and disorders, especially of a specific disease.

iatrogenesis the causing or inducing of a disease by a physician or by medical treatment.

pathology the science of bodily diseases; the symptoms of a disease.

REFERENCES

Auger, N, Raynault, M-F., Lasard, R., & Choiniere, R. (2004). Income and health in Canada. In D. Raphael (Ed.), *Social determinants of health* (pp. 39–52). Toronto: Canadian Scholars' Press.

Berliner, H.S. (1975). A larger perspective on the Flexner Report. *International Journal of Health Services, 5*, 573–592.

Berliner, H.S. (1977). Emerging ideologies in medicine. *Review of Radical Political Economics, 9*(1), 116–124.

Bolaria, B.S. (2000). An introduction to Social issues and contradictions: Sociological perspectives. In B.S. Bolaria (Ed.), *Social issues and contradictions: Sociological perspectives* (pp. 1–21). Toronto: Thomson Nelson.

Bolaria, B.S. (2002). Sociology, medicine, health, and illness: An overview. In B.S. Bolaria & H.D. Dickinson (Eds.), *Health, illness, and health care in Canada* (3rd ed., pp. 1–18), Toronto: Thomson Nelson.

Bolaria, B.S., & Bolaria, R. (Eds.). (1994a). *Women, medicine and health.* Halifax and Saskatoon: Fernwood Publishing and Social Research Unit.

Bolaria, B.S., & Bolaria, R. (Eds.). (1994b). *Racial minorities and health.* Halifax and Saskatoon: Fernwood Publishing and Social Research Unit.

Bolaria, B.S., & Bolaria, R. (Eds.). (2002). Personal and structural determinants of health and Illness. In B.S. Bolaria & H.D. Dickinson (Eds.), *Health, illness, and health care in Canada* (3rd ed., pp. 445–459). Toronto: Thomson Nelson.

Bourgeault, I.L. (2006). Sociological perspectives on health and health care. In D. Raphael, T. Bryant, & M. Rioux (Eds.), *Staying alive* (pp. 35–58). Toronto: Canadian Scholars' Press.

Brown, E.R. (1979). *Rockefeller medicine men: Medicine and capitalism in the progressive era.* Berkeley: University of California Press.

Brown, P. (Ed.). (1996). *Perspectives in medical sociology.* Prospect Heights, IL: Waveland Press.

Bryant, T. (2006). Politics, public policy, and population health. In D. Raphael, T. Bryant, & M. Rioux (Eds.), *Staying alive* (pp. 193–220). Toronto: Canadian Scholars' Press.

Bryant, T., Raphael, D., & Rioux, M. (2006). Toward the future: Current themes in health research and practice in Canada. In D. Raphael, T. Bryant, & M. Rioux (Eds., pp. 373–382), *Staying alive.* Toronto: Canadian Scholars' Press.

Canadian Institute of Child Health (CICH). (2000). *The health of Canada's children.* Ottawa: Canadian Institute of Child Health.

Carlson, R. (1975). *The end of medicine.* New York: Wiley Interscience.

Coburn, D. (2006). Health and health care: A political economy perspective. In D. Raphael, T. Bryant, & M. Rioux (Eds.), *Staying alive* (pp. 59–84). Toronto: Canadian Scholars' Press.

Crawford, R. (1980). Healthism and the medicalization of everyday life. *International Journal of Health Services, 10*(3), 365–388.

Davey-Smith, G. (2003). *Health inequalities: Life-course approaches.* Bristol: Policy Press.

Dickinson, H.D. (2002). Health care, health promotion, and health reforms. In B.S. Bolaria & H.D. Dickinson (Eds.), *Health, illness, and health care in Canada* (3rd ed., pp. 351–371). Toronto: Thomson Nelson.

Doyal, L., & Pennell, I. (1979). *The political economy of health.* London: Pluto Press.

Dreitzel, H.P. (Ed.). (1971). *The social organization of health.* New York: Macmillan.

Engels, F. (1973 [1845]). *The conditions of the working class in England in 1844.* Moscow: Progress.

Epp, J. (1986, November-December). Achieving health for all: A framework for health promotion. *Canadian Journal of Public Health, 77*(6), 393–407.

Evans, R.G., Barer, M.L., & Marmor, T.R. (Eds.). (1994). *Why are some people healthy and others not? The determinants of the health of the population.* New York: Aldine DeGruyter.

Eyer, J. (1984). Capitalism, health, and illness. In J.B. McKinlay (Ed.), *Issues in the Political Economy of Health Care* (pp. 23–59). New York: Tavistock.

Federal, Provincial and Territorial Advisory Committee on Population Health. (1999a). *Statistical report on the health of Canadians.* Ottawa: Minister of Public Works and Government Services.

Federal, Provincial and Territorial Advisory Committee on Population Health. (1999b). *Toward a healthy future: Second report on the health of Canadians.* Ottawa: Minister of Public Works and Government Services.

Feldberg, G. & Vipond, R. (2006). Cracks in the foundation: The origins and development of the Canadian and American health care systems. In D. Raphael, T. Bryant, & M. Rioux (Eds.), *Staying alive* (pp. 221–240). Toronto: Canadian Scholars' Press.

Fidler, D.P. (2000). The globalization of public health. In D.P. Fidler (Ed.), *International law and public health: Materials on an analysis of global health jurisprudence* (pp. 16–23). Ardsley: Transnational Publishers.

Galabuzi, G.E. (2004). Social exclusion. In D. Raphael (Ed.), *Social determinants of health* (pp. 235–252). Toronto: Canadian Scholars' Press.

Galabuzi, G.E. (2006). *Canada's economic apartheid.* Toronto: Canadian Scholars' Press.

Hewa, S. (2002). Physicians, the medical profession, and medical practice. In B.S. Bolaria & H.D. Dickinson (Eds.), *Health, illness, and health care in Canada* (3rd ed., pp. 55–81). Toronto: Thomson Nelson.

Hofnichter, R. (Ed.). (2003). *Health and social justice: Politics, ideology, and inequality in the distribution of disease.* San Francisco: Jossey-Bass.

Illich, I. (1976). *Medical nemesis: The expropriation of health.* New York: Pantheon.

Inglefinger, F.J. (Ed.). (1982). *Dorland medical dictionary.* New York: Holt, Rinehart and Winston.

Kawachi, I. & Kennedy, B. (2002). *The health of nations: Why inequality is harmful to your health.* New York: New Press.

Kelman, S. (1971). Toward the political economy of medical care. *Inquiry, 8*(3), 30–38.

Kelman, S. (1975). The social nature of the definition problem in health. *International Journal of Health Services, 5*(4), 625–642.

Kelman, S. (1977). The social nature of the definition of health. In V. Navarro (Ed.), *Health and medical care in the U.S.: A critical analysis* (pp. 3–20). Farmingdale, NY: Baywood.

Kunitz, S.J. (1974). Professionalism and social control in the progressive era: The case of the Flexner Report. *Social Problems, 22,* 16–27.

Lalonde, M. (1974). *A new perspective on the health of Canadians.* Ottawa: Information Canada.

Lavis, J. (2002). Ideas at the margin or marginalized ideas? Nonmedical determinants of health in Canada. *Health Affairs, 21*(2), 107–112.

Link, B.G., & Phelan, J.C. (2000). Evaluating the fundamental cause explanation for social disparities in health. In C.E. Bird, P. Conrad, & A.M. Fremont (Eds.), *Handbook of medical sociology* (5th ed., pp. 33–46). Upper Saddle River, NJ: Prentice Hall.

Lynch, J. (2000). Income inequality and health: Expanding the debate. *Social Science and Medicine, 51,* 1001–1005.

Lynch, J.W., Davey-Smith, G., Kaplan, G.A., & House, J.S. (2000). Income inequality and mortality: Importance to health of individual income, psychosocial environment, or material conditions. *British Medical Journal, 320,* 1220–1224.

Marmot, M.G., Shipley, M.J., & Rose, G. (1984). Inequalities in death-specific explanations of a general pattern. *Lancet, 83,* 1003–1006.

Marmot, M.G., Smith, G.D., Stanfeld, S., & Patel, C. (1991). Health inequalities among British civil servants: The Whitehall II study. *Lancet, 337,* 1387–1392.

McKeown, T. (1965). *Medicine in modern society.* London: Allen and Unwin.

McKinlay, J.B. (Ed.). (1984). *Issues in the political economy of health care.* London: Tavistock.

McKinlay, J. & McKinlay, S.M. (1987). Medical measures and the decline of mortality. In H.D. Schwartz (Ed.), *Dominant issues in medical sociology* (pp. 691–702). New York: Random House.

Minkler, M. (1983). Blaming the aged victim: The politics of scapegoating in times of fiscal conservatism. *International Journal of Health Services, 13*(1), 155–168.

Mirowsky, J., Ross, C.E., & Reynolds, J. (2000). Links between social status and health status. In C.E. Bird, P. Conrad, & A.M. Fremont (Eds.), *Handbook of medical sociology* (5th ed., pp. 47–67). Upper Saddle River, NJ: Prentice Hall.

Navarro, V. (1976). *Medicine under capitalism.* New York: Prodist.

Navarro, V. (Ed.). (1977). *Health and medical care in the U.S.: A critical analysis.* Farmingdale, NY: Baywood.

Navarro, V. (1986). *Crisis, health, and medicine.* New York: Tavistock.

Navarro, V. (2002). *The political economy of social inequalities: Consequences for health and quality of life.* Amityville: Baywood Press.

Nielsen, W.A. (1972). *The big foundations.* New York: Columbia University Press.

Parsons, T. (1972). Definitions of health and illness in the light of the American values and social structure. In E.G. Jaco (Ed.), *Patients, physicians, and illness* (2nd ed., pp. 107–127). New York: Free Press.

Pederson, A. & Raphael, D. (2006). Gender, race, and health inequalities. In D. Raphael, T. Bryant, & M. Rioux (Eds.), *Staying alive* (pp. 159–192). Toronto: Canadian Scholars' Press.

Postell, W.D. (1961). *The health of slaves on southern plantations.* Baton Rouge: Louisiana State University Press.

Powles, J. (1973). On the limitation of modern medicine. In *Science, Medicine and Man* (Vol. 1, no. 1, pp. 1–30). London: Pergamon.

Raphael, D. (2003). Addressing the social determinants of health in Canada: Bridging the gap between research findings and public policy. *Policy Options, 24*(3), 35–40.

Raphael, D. (2004). Introduction to *Social determinants of health.* In D. Raphael (Ed.), *Social determinants of health* (pp. 1–18). Toronto: Canadian Scholars' Press.

Raphael, D. (2006). Social determinants of health: An overview of concepts and issues. In D. Raphael, T. Bryant, & M. Rioux (Eds.), *Staying alive* (pp. 115–138). Toronto: Canadian Scholars' Press.

Renaud, M. (1977). On the structural constraints to state intervention in health. In V. Navarro (Ed.), *Health and medical care in the U.S.: A critical analysis* (pp. 135–136). Farmingdale, NY: Baywood.

Rioux, M. (2006). The right to health: human rights approach to health. In D. Raphael, T. Bryant, & M. Rioux (Eds.), *Staying alive* (pp. 85–110). Toronto: Canadian Scholars' Press.

Rodberg, L., & Stevenson, C. (1977). The health care industry in advanced capitalism. *Review of Radical Political Economics, 9*(1), 104–115.

Romanow, R.J. (2002). *Building on values: The future of health care in Canada.* Saskatoon: Commission on the Future of Health Care in Canada.

Salmon, J. (1977). Monopoly capital and the reorganization of the health sector. *Review of Radical Political Economics, 9*(1), 125–133.

Segall, A., & Chappell, N.L. (2000). *Health and health care in Canada.* Toronto: Prentice Hall.

Shah, C.P. (2004). The health of aboriginal peoples. In D. Raphael (Ed.), *Social determinants of health* (pp. 267–280). Toronto: Canadian Scholars' Press.

Smith, B.E. (1981). Black lung: The social production of disease. *International Journal of Health Services, 11*(3), 343–359.

Stampp, K.M. (1956). *The peculiar institution.* New York: Knopf.

Starr, P. (1981). The politics of therapeutic nihilism. In P. Conrad & R. Kern (Eds.), *The sociology of health and illness: Critical perspectives* (pp. 434–448). New York: St. Martin's Press.

Swartz, D. (1977). The politics of reform: Conflict and accommodation in Canadian health policy. In L. Panitch (Ed.), *The Canadian state: Political economy and political power* (pp. 311–343). Toronto: University of Toronto Press.

Syme, S.L., & Yeu, I.H. (2000). Social epidemiology and medical sociology: Different approaches to the same problem. In C.E. Bird, P. Conrad, & A.M. Fremont (Eds.), *Handbook of medical sociology* (5th ed., pp. 365–376). Upper Saddle River, NJ: Prentice Hall.

Teeple, G. (2000). *Globalization and the decline of social reform into the twenty-first century.* Aurora: Garamond Press.

Turshen, M. (1977). The political ecology of disease. *Review of Radical Political Economics, 9*(1), 45–60.

Virchow, R. (1957). *Werk und werkung.* Berlin: Rutten & Loeng.

Virchow, R. (1958). *Disease, life and man.* Translated by L.J. Rather. Stanford University Press.

Virchow, R. (1960). *Cellular pathology.* New York: DeWitt.

Waitzkin, H. (1976). Recent studies in medical sociology: The new reductionism. *Contemporary Sociology, 5,* 401–405.

Waitzkin, H. (1979). The Marxist paradigm in medicine. *International Journal of Health Services, 9*(4), 683–698.

Waitzkin, H. (1983). *The second sickness: Contradictions of capitalist health care.* New York: Free Press.

Waitzkin, H., & Waterman, B. (1974). *The exploitation of illness in capitalist society.* Indianapolis: Bobbs-Merrill.

Walters, V. (1982). State, capital and labour: The introduction of federal-provincial insurance for physician care in Canada. *Canadian Review of Sociology and Anthropology, 19,* 157–172.

Wilkins, R., Berthelot, J.-M., & Ng, E. (2002). Trends in mortality by neighbourhood income in urban Canada from 1971–1996. *Health Reports. Supplement 13,* 1–28.

Wilkinson, R.G. (1996). *Unhealthy societies: The afflictions of inequality.* London: Routledge.

World Health Organization (WHO). (1946). *Constitution of the World Health Organization.* New York: World Health Organization Interim Commission.

2

HEALTH CARE AND HEALTH REFORMS: TRENDS AND ISSUES

HARLEY D. DICKINSON University of Saskatchewan

INTRODUCTION

Canadians have access to a wide range of physician and hospital services without any direct out-of-pocket costs. This system of **universal**, **accessible**, **comprehensive** and **portable** medical and hospital care insurance, **publicly administered** on a non-profit basis, is called **medicare**. Medicare is consistently identified on public opinion polls as one of the country's most popular government programs, and it is a source of great national pride. Yet, at the same time, it is a source of perpetual public concern.

As a source of national pride it is widely seen as a central element of our national identity and as something that makes us different from, and more caring and compassionate than, Americans. As taxpayers, however, we worry about the cost of medicare and whether it is financially sustainable. We also worry about whether it is draining public resources away from other areas of public policy, such as post-secondary education, social services, national defense and security, etc.

For at least the past twenty years, these concerns have been expressed in a public discourse about the medicare crisis. Numerous cost containment and various cost transfer measures have been implemented as possible solutions to the crisis. Paradoxically, in many cases, these cost containment and cost transfer measures are seen as part of the problem, rather than part of the solution.

Cost transfer initiatives are of two main types. The first involves directly transferring costs from the public sector to the private sector. This can be referred to as **marketization**. The second, indirect cost transfer strategy, involves having family, friends, and community organizations providing uncompensated care to individuals in need. This is often referred to as **downloading**.

The other main dimension of the perpetual crisis in health care involves concerns about whether medicare has the capacity to satisfy the existing and emerging health care needs of Canadians in a timely and effective fashion. This concern is partially rooted in the epidemiological shift that is taking place in many societies, including Canada. The changing pattern of illness is related to several factors, including the aging of the population (the so-called demographic transition), changing lifestyles, climate change, and the changing types and patterns of illness associated with these developments. The response to the epidemiological shift has given rise to various efforts to expand the scope, increase access, and improve the quality of health care services, including government commitments to introduce publicly financed and administered home care and pharmacare programs.

The other main dimension of the health care crisis is the lack of transparency and accountability of health care policy-makers, system managers, and service providers. In recent years, there have been several reforms introduced that are intended to increase transparency and accountability in health care.

This chapter describes historical and contemporary issues and trends associated with the development and reform of medicare in particular and the Canadian health care system more generally. It consists of two main sections. In the first section, I provide a brief account of the introduction of medicare and some of its structural and fiscal problems. In the second section, I provide a brief overview of issues and trends in health care since the mid-1990s. Here I identify a new inter-governmental decision-making process, and the emergence of a consensus on four general priorities – Sustainability, Access, Quality, and Accountability. I also discuss numerous specific reforms related to health care financing, health information systems, primary health care reform, patient safety, and wait times, among others. The chapter ends with a brief conclusion.

MEDICARE: ORIGINS AND CONTRADICTIONS

A brief look at the development of medical care and hospitalization insurance in Canada reveals a system in constant transition. Throughout the first decades of the twentieth century, hospital and medical care insurance was on and off national and provincial political agendas. By the 1940s, failure of the market to ensure adequate access to necessary medical and hospital care, combined with limitations of various locally developed collectivist solutions, had generated renewed interest in a system of public insurance. This was given added impetus because wartime military and industrial recruitment efforts revealed that an alarmingly high proportion of recruits were too sickly for military or industrial service (Fuller, 1998, p. 27). As a result, and faced with other evidence of the poor health of the Canadian population, health insurance was firmly established as a key component in government plans for the reconstruction of Canadian society following the Second World War (Smiley, 1963).

Thus, in 1945, the federal government put forward a plan for itself and provincial governments to share the costs of a universal medical care and hospital services insurance program. It was believed that improving access to medical and hospital services by removing financial barriers would result in improved population health status. In turn, this was thought to translate directly into increased productivity and national prosperity. A more particular motivation for proposing a state financed universal and comprehensive health insurance program was concern that the proposed private sector alternatives were inadequate (Taylor, 1978).

Thus, by the end of the Second World War, there was a political consensus that health care could not be left entirely to the market. Beyond that, however, there was little agreement. The medical profession, for example, favoured a hospital and medical care insurance system that was based on voluntary participation in physician-sponsored or for-profit insurance plans where government was limited to means-testing patients and covering the costs of care for those who could not pay for it themselves (Fuller, 1998). The private insurance industry was in favour of a similar arrangement. Business organizations in general, as well as several provincial governments, also favoured such an arrangement because of concerns about creeping socialism (Fuller, 1998). Even the trade union movement was ambivalent about universal, compulsory tax financed and publicly administered medical care and hospitalization insurance because, in many cases, they had negotiated collective agreements that provided insurance coverage for their membership through voluntary, private plans and were concerned that a universal public plan would undermine member loyalty (Walters, 1982). Western Canadian farmer organizations and left wing political parties were among the strongest supporters of state insurance (Dickinson, 1993).

Despite these differing views, in 1945, the federal government introduced draft legislation for a universal, comprehensive, publicly financed and administered hospital and doctor services plan. Key features of that legislation were the establishment of health regions, patient registration with physicians, a capitation mode of payment, financial incentives for physicians to adopt preventative approaches, and the administration of the system by commissions of physicians and consumers (Taylor, 1978; Vayda and Deber, 1992, p. 126).

The proposed legislation was not enacted because the federal and provincial governments could not agree on taxation issues relative to the plan and because of provincial government concerns about federal incursion into areas of provincial jurisdiction (Taylor, 1960). As federal-provincial discussions bogged down, and the prospects of implementation receded into the future, a new consensus emerged around the adoption of an incremental approach to the introduction of government financed medical care and hospital services insurance.

The province of Saskatchewan took the lead in this regard. In 1946, it introduced the first province-wide publicly financed and administered hospitalization insurance program. In 1962, the Saskatchewan government again pioneered the development of medicare when it introduced the country's first publicly financed and administered medical care insurance system (Taylor, 1978).

The first step taken by the federal government occurred in 1948 with the introduction of the Hospital Construction grants program. This program provided provinces with money to build acute care hospitals. In 1958, the federal government introduced the Hospitalization Insurance and Diagnostic Services Act and thereby took a second giant step toward medicare. Under this Act, the federal and provincial and territorial governments shared the costs of a national system of hospitalization insurance. The next step was passage of the 1966 Medical Care Services Act. This Act enabled the federal and provincial and territorial governments to share the costs of all medically necessary physician services. By 1972, all the provinces had signed on and medicare was a reality.

It must be noted, however, that there really is not a single Canadian health care insurance system. Rather, there are thirteen provincial and territorial medical care and hospitalization insurance systems all of which receive federal government resources and all of which are loosely structured by the framework of medicare principles that are currently expressed in the 1984 Canada Health Act.

The main contradictions of medicare were related to the cost sharing formula. Under the terms of the 1966 arrangement, federal government contributions were directly tied to, and determined by, provincial expenditures on hospital and medical care services. As a result, the federal government had no control over its health care expenditures. Naturally, from the federal government's perspective, that was an undesirable situation.

Provincial governments also came to be dissatisfied with that arrangement because it discouraged innovation and experimentation with alternative forms of non-physician and non-hospital community-based health care because community-based forms of health care and treatment were ineligible for federal funds.

The original cost-sharing agreement also discouraged provincial governments from attempting to improve the efficiency of hospital and medical care services because every dollar saved by the provinces resulted in a corresponding decrease in the amount of money transferred to them by the federal government. Thus, the federal and provincial and territorial governments were interested in changing the terms and conditions of the original cost sharing arrangement (Soderstrom, 1978).

The 1977 Federal-Provincial Arrangements and Established Programs Financing Act (EPF) was the first substantial revision of health insurance cost sharing arrangements. The EPF had a number of effects:

- it reduced the federal government's share of the cost of medicare from about 50 to approximately 25 percent
- it uncoupled federal costs from provincial expenditures
- it limited the growth in direct federal government increases to the rate of growth of the gross national product (GNP)
- it provided a $20 per capita incentive for provinces to put more resources into community care (Vayda, Evans & Mindell, 1979).

The transfer of tax points from the federal to the provincial and territorial governments made this financially attractive because it enabled them to increase their levels of income taxation to make up for reduced federal cash transfer payments.

Further cost control incentives were provided to the provinces by the federal government in the mid-1980s. Revisions to the cost sharing arrangements at that time limited federal transfers to the provinces to an annual rate of growth that was two percentage points *below* the rate of increase in the GNP. Following that, the federal government further reduced the level of transfer payments to the provinces by freezing them for two years at the 1989–90 levels. In 1992–93, federal transfers were allowed to increase at the rate of growth in GNP *less* three percent.

These reforms of funding formula helped create a political will among provincial governments to reform the nature and organization of medicare at the provincial level. Regionalization was the primary means adopted in most provinces to enact these reforms.

Regionalization is intended to accomplish several health policy objectives including cost control, increased responsiveness to health care needs, improved health outcomes, flexibility in care delivery, better integration and coordination within and between elements of the health care system, and greater citizen awareness of, and participation in, health care planning and service delivery (Angus, 1991; Angus, Auer, Cloutier & Albert,

1995; Crichton et al., 1997; Dorland & Davis, 1996; Lomas, 1996; Lomas, Woods & Veenstra, 1997; Lomas, 1997; Lewis, 1997; Mahtre & Deber, 1998). This is an ambitious agenda, and a daunting array of goals to pursue. Not surprisingly, the success of regionalization in achieving these goals is uneven.

It is generally agreed that regionalization marked an important shift in health care governance from a system of government or physician control toward some form of democratic control or managerial control (Blishen, 1991; Crichton et al., 1997; Lomas, 1997; Bickerton, 1999). In fact, different provinces adopted different models in this regard. Some provinces opted for a democratic strategy of governance based on elected boards and others opted for a managerial model wherein the boards played an advisory role to a CEO. Currently, most provinces have moved toward a managerial model.

Regardless of the governance model adopted the goal was the same, namely, to modify or remove the structural features of medicare that entrenched medical dominance, inflationary cost increases, and a curative, medical and hospital-based approach to health problems. It is fair to say that some progress toward achieving all these goals has been made, although all the problematic features mentioned here remain more or less problematic.

Despite this progress, all levels of government were being publicly criticized for their handling of medicare, in part, because of their own acrimonious public attacks against each other concerning which level of government was responsible for the crisis in health care. These inter-governmental squabbles eroded public confidence in government and in its capacity and commitment to a sustainable public health care system. As a result, by the mid-1990s, governments were looking for a new way forward.

A NEW APPROACH TO HEALTH CARE REFORM AND RENEWAL

The cutbacks and cost control strategies of the previous decade had forced and/or accelerated significant reforms to the structure and governance of provincial and territorial health care systems. With regionalization, provincial and territorial governments moved some distance toward developing more integrated and coordinated community-based health care systems.

By the mid-1990s, however, the federal government was looking for ways to assume a more positive leadership role than it had throughout the 1980s and early 1990s. Thus, in 1994, then Prime Minister, the Right Honourable Jean Chrétien, established the National Forum on Health (NFH) in an attempt to provide this leadership. The NFH, which the Prime Minister chaired, was intended to inform and involve the public in identifying common goals and innovative ways to improve the health care system and to improve the health status of the Canadian population. The fact that the Prime Minister chaired the NFH increased its status and sent the message that the federal government was taking health care issues seriously.

In terms of setting goals and suggesting innovative ways to achieve them, the NFH was influential in at least two respects that are relevant to this chapter. First, it called for governments to develop and use expanded and improved health information and health information systems as a way to improve the quality and safety of the health care system. Second, it proposed that federal government cash transfers to the provinces be targeted to goals agreed to through inter-governmental negotiations.

The Canadian Health Information Roadmap Initiative was launched in 1999 as a result of the call for expanded and improved health information and health information systems coming from the NFH and other sources, including the Advisory Council on Health Infostructure of the federal Minister of Health. The Roadmap Initiative is a collaborative effort involving the Canadian Institute of Health Information (CIHI), Statistics Canada, Health Canada, and many other national, regional, and local groups.

The main aim of this initiative is to help health care decision-makers answer two questions: "How healthy are Canadians?" and "How healthy is the Canadian health care system?" To answer these questions, existing health databases are being expanded and improved, and new databases are being created (CIHI, 2006a).

The Canadian Community Health Survey (CCHS) is a good example of new databases being created to support improved health status and improved regional health care systems. The CCHS was begun in 2000 with the aim "to provide timely cross-sectional estimates of health determinants, health status and health system utilization at a subprovincial level (health region or combination of health regions)" (Statistics Canada, 2006). More information on this survey can be found on the website.

The Canadian Population Health Initiative (CPHI) was another new initiative at the national level intended to create new knowledge on the social determinants of health; to contribute to the establishment of a national population health information system; to report on the health status of Canadians and contribute to public debate through the publication of reports and other means of informing the public; and to support analysis of policy options in the public, private, and voluntary sector (PHAC, 2006).

The Canadian Institute for Health Information (CIHI) website has several population health reports on a variety of topics, including the health of rural Canadians, young Canadians, women, and the overweight (CIHI, 2006b).

The CPHI is an integral part of the effort to establish the renewed and expanded public health system discussed in the next chapter. By producing new knowledge and transferring it to health care decision-makers, the CPHI contributes to the culture and practice of evidence-based decision-making. In addition, by making this information available to the public, it also contributes to enhanced accountability among health care providers, including governments.

The Canadian Health Infoway is another element of the Canadian Health Information Roadmap Initiative. Its main objective is to facilitate and support the adoption of electronic health records (EHR) across Canada. EHRs are secure and confidential electronic records of individuals' health status and health care use that is available to the individual and appropriate health care providers anywhere, anytime, and in this way it facilitates "the sharing of data – across the continuum of care, across health care delivery organizations and across geographies" (CHI and HCC, 2006, p. 2).

Another important initiative related to developing and using good quality health and health care information occurred with the establishment of the Canadian Institutes for Health Research (CIHR). The CIHR were created in 2000 with the following mandate:

> To excel, according to internationally accepted standards of scientific excellence, in the creation of new knowledge and its translation into improved health for Canadians, more effective health services and products and a strengthened Canadian health care system (CIHR, 2006a).

When the CIHR was established it absorbed the biomedical and clinical research funding functions of the Medical Research Council (MRC) and expanded them to include research on health services and systems, and population and public health. Combined, these four domains frame the research agenda of the thirteen constitutive institutes that make up the CIHR.

Most CIHR funded health research projects focus on issues determined by the applying researchers; about 30 percent of the funds, however, are allocated toward strategic areas of research identified by the CIHR (CIHR, 2006a). These strategic areas reflect some of the government's policy priorities and include research on wait times, chronic disease, aboriginal peoples' health, obesity, and mental health in the workplace.

The CIHR is more than an agency that funds research, however, although it certainly is that. In addition, it is charged with ensuring that the knowledge produced through its research grants is translated into improved health care systems and improved population health status. This requirement has generated tremendous interest in the factors that determine the effective knowledge translation and application. An indicator of this interest is the recent inauguration of a new journal – *Implementation Science* – devoted to the study of these processes (*Implementation Science*, 2006).

The translation and application of research knowledge in medical practice is referred to as evidence-based medicine (Sackett et al., 1997). This concept was developed in the early 1990s and quickly extended beyond the clinical domain to all levels of health care decision-making in the form of evidence-based decision-making (Dickinson, 1998).

On the surface, the use of the best available scientific research for health care services is unproblematic. Evidence-based decision-making, however, is seen by some to be an effort to increase managerial control over the functioning and costs of the health care system and, therefore, over the discretionary decision-making powers of health care service providers. This is most commonly achieved by establishing research-based best practices guidelines that service providers are expected to adopt. From the point of view of some service providers this entails a loss of professional autonomy and freedom. For this reason, some physicians have been vocal critics of evidence-based decision-making (Charlton, 1997), but they are not the only critics of this practice (Dickinson, 1998; Armstrong, 2001).

Nor are concerns with reducing decision-making to a narrowly conceived scientific basis entirely new. Similar concerns were expressed in the 1960s and 1970s in relation to efforts to ground various social services, corrections and educational policy, and practice decisions in social science research knowledge (Dickinson, 2003). Despite these concerns, evidence-based decision-making in a public health care system is consistently identified as a goal, and it is one important form that the emphasis on knowledge translation has assumed.

Another form of knowledge translation is the commercialization of research knowledge and technologies. This interest in, and support of, commercialization of health research knowledge is a component of Canada's Innovation Agenda (NCE, 2006). Health care is a lucrative investment and source of economic growth both in Canada and worldwide. Also, because it is among the most information and knowledge intensive industries, it is seen as a core element of the new knowledge economy.

Targeted funding is another of the new principles guiding health care reform that emerged from the report of the National Forum on Health. The Health Transition Fund

(HTF) is a good example of this principle. The HTF was a $150 million dollar fund established by the federal government that was in operation from 1997 to 2001. Its purpose was to support innovative programming and service delivery in four strategic areas: Home Care; Pharmacare/Pharmaceutical Issues; Primary Care/Primary Health Care; and Integrated Service Delivery.

These four areas were agreed upon because they reflected priorities of all levels of government and corresponded to a number of initiatives that already were taking place (Health Canada, 2006a). An important additional feature of the operation of the HTF was a new spirit of inter-governmental cooperation that characterized its administration. Although the federal government contributed the funds for the HTF, their allocation was a collaborative effort involving representatives from federal, provincial, and territorial governments.

The First Ministers' Health Accords demonstrate this same spirit of collaboration. The introduction of First Ministers' Accords was an important step toward increased intergovernmental cooperation and coordination of health care policy-making and implementation. By involving the Prime Minister and the provincial and territorial premiers directly in health policy-making, implementation, and evaluation, it also introduced a higher level of political responsibility and accountability into efforts to coordinate the actions of all levels of government. Before discussing these Accords further, I present a brief overview of selected elements of the Romanow Commission and the contributions it made to health care reform in the 21st century.

THE ROMANOW COMMISSION

The Romanow Commission on the Future of Health Care in Canada was another step in the direction of reforming both the public health care system and the character of intergovernmental relations around the development, implementation, and evaluation of health care policy and practice. The Romanow Commission was established in 2001 by then Prime Minister the Right Honourable Jean Chrétien. Its mandate was to review the health care system, engage the public in a national dialogue on the future of health care in Canada, and to make recommendations to the federal government. The final report was released under the title *Building on Values: The Future of Health Care in Canada* (Romanow, 2002).

The report confirmed and highlighted four objectives to guide health policy, practice, and reform that the First Ministers had already agreed on – sustainability, access, quality, and accountability. These goals were also highlighted in the *Kirby Senate Committee Report on the State of the Health Care System in Canada*, as well as in a number of provincial government reports, including the 2000 *Fyke Report* (Saskatchewan), the 2001 *Clair Commission Report* (Quebec), the 2002 *Mazankowski Report* (Alberta) and, more recently, the 2005 *Menard Report* (Quebec). Arguably, the Romanow Commission report has been the most influential in reaffirming the goals of contemporary health reform and, perhaps, even more importantly, in suggesting the means to achieving them.

The Romanow Commission report unambiguously endorsed a set of goals and means intended to ensure the sustainability of an expanded and improved *public* health care insurance system in Canada. It clearly rejects options that would move the system toward increased privatization. At the time the Romanow Commission report was released, it was estimated that 40 percent of expenditures on health care were wholly public, 25 percent were mixed public/private, and 30 percent were wholly private. Wholly public expenditures mostly are for physician and hospital services, mixed expenditures are mainly on things like drugs, and wholly private expenditures include services such as vision and dental care.

Thus, it is clear that Canada already has a mixed public-private health care system. The real struggle is over the balance of public-private. Some want to move the system more toward private expenditures and for-profit-services, and others want to maintain the *status quo*. It should be noted, however, that the previously mentioned figures refer to the proportion of public and private health care *expenditures*. The public-private balance would be dramatically shifted toward the private side of the equation if we looked at who provided services, rather than at who paid for them. Most physician services, for example, are provided by doctors in private practices that, in effect, are small businesses (Naylor, 1986). The debate over public or private health care is often confused over whether the issue is private versus public *payment* or private versus public service *provision*.

The Romanow Commission recommendations are explicitly intended to support the principle of a single, public payer, and to counter pressures to move the Canadian health care insurance system toward greater private expenditures. Strong and consistent evidence shows the costs of administering single payer systems are very much lower than the costs of administering systems characterized by multiple payers (Woolhandler & Himmelstein, 2004).

From the mid-1990s to 2004, public health care expenditures grew at a faster pace than private health care expenditures. In 2004 and 2005, respectively, public expenditures increased by 6.7 and 7.3 percent. In those same two years, however, private expenditures increased by 8.2 and 8.7 percent, respectively, reaching, in 2005, an all time high of $43.2 billion (Health Edition, 2005). That year, total health expenditures in Canada exceeded $142 billion. Whether this higher rate of growth in private expenditures is a long-term trend remains to be seen.

Despite the constantly growing burden of health care costs, the greatest threats to the sustainability of the *public* health care system currently are related to issues of access, quality, and accountability. In order to improve access, quality, and accountability, Romanow recommended additional federal government funding. The First Ministers' Health Accords have become the most important means for setting health care priorities and allocating resources to them.

FIRST MINISTERS' HEALTH ACCORDS

To date, there have been three First Ministers' Accords – in 2000, 2003, and 2004. The first Health Accord identified a number of general objectives and priority areas for health care funding. These included improved access to diagnostic and treatment services and improved quality of care. To these ends the federal government contributed an additional $21.1 billion over five years to the Canada Health and Social Transfer (CHST) fund. This included $800 million to support reform of primary health care services in the provinces and territories. It also included $1 billion over two years to assist provincial and territorial governments to purchase medical diagnostic and treatment equipment. In addition, $500 million was provided to develop further the Canada Health Infoway and specifically to encourage adoption of EHRs (Department of Finance, 2006).

The 2003 accord built on the 2000 accord and on the recommendations of the Romanow Commission report. As a result of the 2003 accord, the federal government provided $36.8 billion over five years. Most of this money ($31.5 billion) was provided to the provinces and territories in the form of cash transfers. This $31.5 billion dollars included $16 billion over five years in the form of the Health Reform Transfer fund targeted to support primary health care reform, home care, and development of a national pharmacare program to cover catastrophic drug costs. Also included was another $1.5 billion paid out over three years to be used by provincial and territorial governments to purchase diagnostic equipment and to train personnel to use it. Fourteen billion dollars over five years was also added in the form of cash transfers to the provinces and territories through the Canadian Health and Social Transfer (CHST) fund. Expenditures of CHST funds are not targeted in the same way as the other increases just mentioned, although it is expected that they will be spent on health care, post-secondary education, and social services (Department of Finance, 2006).

Another important component of the 2003 First Ministers' Accord was the agreement to restructure the CHST in order to improve transparency of, and accountability for, public health care expenditures. The CHST fund was discontinued and two new funds created – the Canada Heath Transfer (CHT) and the Canada Social Transfer (CST). The CHT are funds targeted for health care, and the CST consists of funds intended for post-secondary education, social assistance, and social services (Department of Finance, 2006).

The 2003 accord included a commitment by all governments to develop comparable indicators of population health status, health outcomes, and quality of health care services, and to publicly report these on a regular basis. This is a core element of the agreement to increase transparency and accountability related to health care.

The 2003 First Ministers' Accord included a commitment to establishing the Canadian Patient Safety Institute (CPSI). Consequently, the federal government made available $50 million over five years to support patient safety initiatives. The CPSI was formally established December 2003 as an independent, non-profit organization with an arm's length relationship to governments, regulatory bodies, and other system stakeholders. It conducts its own research and also acts as a clearing house for information and techniques for improving patient safety (CPSI, 2006). Thus, its role is mainly educational.

Concern over patient safety reflects the fact that adverse events (AE), the "unintended injuries or complications resulting in death, disability or prolonged hospital stay that arise from health care management" (Baker et al., 2004, p. 1678), are a significant problem in many societies, including Canada. Although AEs can occur anywhere, the main focus of research and remedial action to date has been hospitals.

A recent Canadian study, the first to provide a national estimate of AEs among patients in Canadian acute care hospitals, showed that about 7.5 percent of the 2.5 million annual hospital admissions in Canada was associated with an AE. This is about 185 thousand AEs – seventy thousand of which were potentially preventable (Baker et al., 2004, p. 1678), including between 9,259 and 23,750 preventable deaths (Baker et al., 2004, p. 1684).

This problem is not unique to Canada, or to public health care systems like Canada's. International comparisons show similar rates of AEs in several countries. A survey of recent hospital patients from six countries, for example, showed that 34 percent of

U.S. hospital patients reported one or more of four types of AE. Canadian patients were next with 30 percent reporting an AE, followed by patients from Australia (27 percent), New Zealand (25 percent), Germany (23 percent), and the UK (22 percent) (Kermode-Scott, 2005, p. 1100). Davis (2004, p. 1689) helps put the magnitude of this problem into perspective with his report that of the leading twenty causes of death in New Zealand, in-hospital AEs are 11th, coming ahead of air pollution, alcohol and drugs, and traffic accidents, among others.

Several heath care organizations and provider groups are aware of the problem and committed to its management. These include the Canadian Patient Safety Institute (CPSI) and the Canadian Medication Incident Reporting and Prevention System (CMIRPS).

The Canadian Patient Safety Institute emerged from recommendations of the National Steering Committee on Patient Safety (NSCPS) established in 2001 as a result of a one-day forum held at the annual meeting of the Royal College of Physicians and Surgeons (CPSI, 2006). In 2002, the NSCPS released a report recommending a coordinated national strategy for improving the safety of the Canadian health care system. Central to this strategy was a Canadian Patient Safety Institute.

The Canadian Medication Incident Reporting and Prevention System (CMIRPS) is aligned closely with the objectives of the Canadian Patient Safety Institute. CMIRPS is a response to research showing that medication errors are the most common form of AEs (Wilson, 2001). CMIRPS is a made-in-Canada patient safety initiative that is the collaborative result of a coalition of health and consumer groups (Health Canada, 2006b). It is funded by Health Canada but operates independently of it.

Underpinning these patient safety initiatives is the assumption that AEs are mainly the result of systems failings, not individual errors or incompetence. It is hoped that this approach will encourage health care service providers to be forthcoming when adverse events occur. Establishing a "no fault" mechanism to compensate patients or their families is also seen as an important incentive in this regard insofar as it removes the need for victims or their families to sue for compensation.

Furthermore, all governments (except Quebec and Alberta) agreed to the establishment of the Health Council of Canada (HCC) and to participate in its reporting activities. Establishing the HCC was a core recommendation of the Romanow Commission. The HCC monitors and reports publicly on the progress made toward achieving the agreed to goals of the First Ministers' accords. In addition to the HCC, several provinces have established their own equivalents to the health quality council, including Alberta, New Brunswick, Newfoundland and Labrador, Ontario, and Saskatchewan.

The 2004 accord built on the previous two and increased federal government cash transfers to the provinces by another $41.3 billion over ten years. Under the terms of this accord, $35.3 billion was allocated to establish a new CHT base of $19 billion in 2005–06 and to fund an annual 6 percent increase commencing 2006–07.

The new CHT base closed the so-called Romanow gap by bringing federal government expenditures up to 25 percent of total public expenditures on health care – the same proportion the federal government contributed in 1977 following introduction of the Established Programs Financing Act. This level of federal government spending was unanimously agreed by the provincial and territorial premiers to be necessary to ensure the sustainability of the Canadian public health insurance system.

The 2004 accord provided an additional $500 million for investment in medical and diagnostic equipment, and a $5.5 billion Wait Times Reduction transfer fund over five years to assist provincial and territorial governments implement their respective wait time reduction strategies. There also are assessments of progress toward realizing the goals of this accord planned for 2008 and 2011 (Department of Finance, 2006).

Figure 2.1 shows that since the year 2000, all increases in federal transfers to provincial/territorial governments for health care have taken place through the targeted funding strategy underpinning the First Ministers' Health Accords.

Timely access to appropriate and safe diagnostic and treatment services is the central and most urgent problem confronting the Canadian health care system. The problem of access is experienced and expressed as frustration over wait times. As we have just seen, under the 2004 accord, the federal government committed $5.5 billion to augment provincial and territorial governments' wait time reduction strategies. Under the terms of the 2004 accord, an agreement was made to reduce waiting times to evidence-based medically acceptable times for cancer and heart surgery, diagnostic imaging, joint replacement, and cataract removal (Health Canada, 2006c). In 2005, the Wait Time Alliance of Canada released a series of wait times for several high priority conditions: "routine hip and knee replacements should be done in nine months (three months for consultations and a further six months for surgery); routine cataract surgery, four months; radiation therapy for cancer patients, ten working days; non-urgent heart by-pass surgery, under six months; CT scans, MRIs and nuclear medicine diagnostic

FIGURE 2.1
Federal Cash Transfers to Provinces and Territories for Health and Social Programs

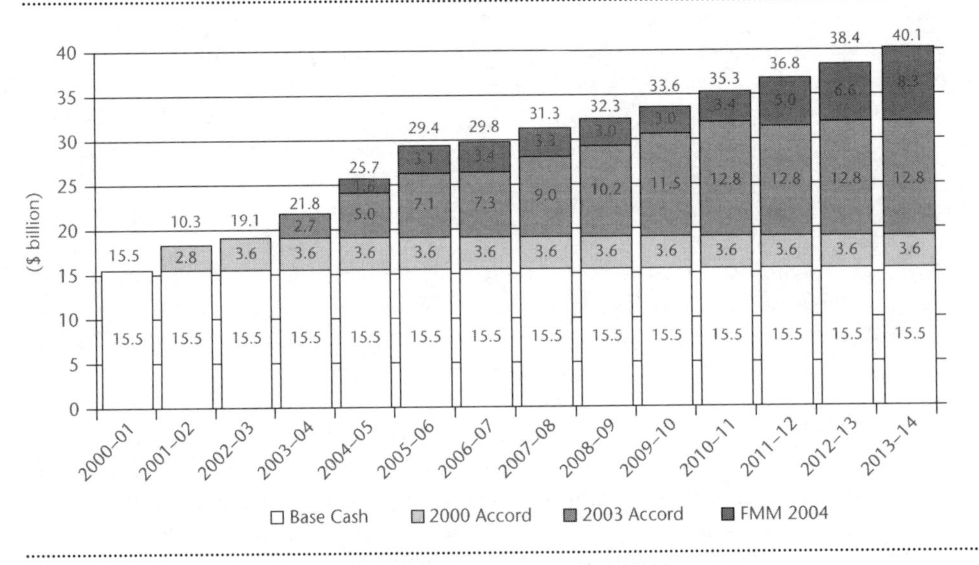

Source: Federal Transfers in Support of the 2000/2003/2004 First Ministers' Accords. http://www.fin.gc.ca/FEDPROV/fmAcce.html. Accessed October 13, 2006.

imaging, within seven days" (Hartt, 2006, p. 48). Recently, the Federal Minister of Health called for the inclusion of pediatric care services within the wait times guarantee initiative (Health Edition, 2005).

The current federal government Minister of Health is also a strong advocate for health care guarantees. Health care guarantees set precise timelines for receiving diagnostic and treatment services within the publicly funded health care system. If these times are exceeded, the governments, and possibly direct service providers, are responsible to provide it.

The 2002 Kirby Commission Final Report supported introduction of care guarantees, but the Romanow Commission report of the same year opposed them. Those opposed to care guarantees argue they will increase pressure on policy-makers to move away from the principle of a single public payer toward more private purchases of health care services. Thus, opponents argue that care guarantees not only guarantee individuals access to timely care but they also guarantee Canadians a two-tiered health care system in which those who can afford to pay for their health care will get it privately and others will have to wait in lengthening public system queues, especially in relation to non-priority health care services.

Most provinces discourage private payment for physician and hospital services by requiring doctors to be either fully in medicare or fully outside of it. Thus, physicians can choose to charge patients and/or their insurance companies for care, or they can bill medicare, but they cannot do both.

In six provinces private health care insurance is prohibited. In 2005, the Supreme Court of Canada ruled in a 4 to 3 decision that the Quebec government's general ban on private insurance for medicare services violated sections of the Quebec Charter of Rights and Freedoms in a situation where the waiting times for services were unreasonably long. This is known as the Chaoulli decision, named after Dr. Jacques Chaoulli, an opted-out Montreal physician who along with his patient George Zeliotas who had been waiting for knee replacement surgery sued the Quebec government and finally took the case all the way to the Supreme Court of Canada (Marchildon, 2006).

In post-Chaoulli Canada, governments committed to the single-payer medicare system are scrambling to figure out how to prevent the entry of two-tier medicine through the back door of care guarantees. Part of the response has included efforts to increase the number of health care providers, particularly physicians and nurses, so as to increase capacity in the public system. The Health Human Resources (HHR) strategy, first introduced in the 2003 First Ministers' Accord, is one major initiative in this regard. This strategy has three main dimensions – the development of a pan-Canadian HHR planning capacity, a recruitment and retention strategy, and a strategy to transform training and education programs and processes (Health Canada, 2006d).

Simply stated, the goal of the pan-Canadian HHR planning initiative is to develop a framework and capacity for addressing HHR needs on a national basis. This is a formidable task given the size and diversity of provincial health care systems and the wide variation in economic circumstances between provinces and territories (Health Canada, 2006e).

Recruitment and retention activities include efforts to increase diversity within the health care workforce so as to better reflect the changing composition of the Canadian population, to increase the supply and geographical and specialty distribution of health care workers, and to improve their working conditions (Health Canada, 2006f).

The third dimension of the HHR strategy is to shift the nature of primary health care towards inter-professional collaborative care teams that include patients, their families, friends, and informal caregivers in planning and providing care. Institutionalizing the collaborative care model requires substantial reforms to existing health profession curriculum and training. The Inter-professional Education for Collaborative Patient-Centered Practice (IECPCP) program is a federal government program to support innovative education and training initiatives based on the model of inter-professional, patient-centered, collaborative practice (Health Canada, 2006g).

The electronic health record (EHR) is also seen as essential to advancing the goal of well functioning and effective inter-professional teams of primary health care providers. As important as the EHR is seen to be for advancing health care in the 21st century, at this stage it is more of a dream than a reality. To the extent that it exists at all, it exists in the context of large institutional settings, mainly large acute care hospitals. This is not surprising. The creation and operation of a pan-Canadian health information system, including the EHR, is a task of overwhelming proportions and cost. And while there are various pilot projects that clearly demonstrate the value of moving toward more effective use of information and communication technologies for better informed decision-making at all levels of the health care system, the resources required for a comprehensive EHR, let alone an electronic health information system, are staggering. Of course, as we all know, information and computer technologies have a limited shelf life, and constantly need to be upgraded and replaced, so conversion to such systems always entails rearranged and increased resource allocation requirements.

When we move out of the institutional sector, the promise and magnitude of the conversion becomes even greater. The 2002 Canadian Medical Association (CMA) Physician Resources Questionnaire, for example, revealed only 3 percent of Canadian physicians exclusively used electronic patient records, 24 percent used a combination of electronic and paper records, and 69 percent used only paper records. Currently, 94 percent of physician visits in Canada involve paper records and most prescriptions are handwritten (CHI and HCC, 2006, p. 2).

For most physician practices, either solo or group, there are not only benefits associated with adopting EHRs, there are also costs. The benefits identified by physicians on the 2002 Physician Resources Questionnaire included an improved ability to share records among health care providers (76 percent). This includes, of course, other physicians and medical specialists, as well as a range of non-physician health care providers. This is extremely important given the commitment of all levels of Canadian government to provide 50 percent of Canadians with access to multi-disciplinary primary health care teams by 2009.

In addition to this benefit, physicians also see EHRs contributing to improved continuity of care (68.3 percent); improved clinical processes or workflow (68 percent); improved quality of care (59.3 percent); facilitated clinical decision-making (58.4 percent); improved patient safety (55.4 percent); and improved patient satisfaction (37 percent) (CMAJ, 2002).

Despite these anticipated benefits, physicians in small, private practices will require substantial financial, and innovative technical and training support to make the transition to EHRs (Baron et al., 2005).

CONCLUSION

In this chapter I provided a descriptive overview of the development and reform of medicare, that complex system of medical and hospital care insurance that, at the same time, is a source of great national pride and concern. Since its inception, medicare has been undergoing constant reform. Driving these reforms were structural characteristics of medicare itself. These include the scope of medicare and the initial intergovernmental funding arrangements.

Medicare is a tax-financed, publicly administered medical care and hospital service insurance system. At the time of its development, it was generally thought that access to medical and hospital services would dramatically improve the health status of the population. And while it certainly is true that good quality medical and hospital care provided on a timely basis does help restore people's health, it also is true that other non-medical determinants of health make greater contributions to this.

This fact, combined with the demographic and epidemiologic transitions taking place, has resulted in changed health care needs. In the contemporary context, incurable chronic conditions account for an increasing proportion of health care services. The proportion of preventable and curable infectious disease has been declining, although it is true that globalization, climate change, and other factors are contributing to resurgences of both old and new infectious diseases. Despite this, the demand for non-medical and non-hospital care services has been increasing, but the terms and conditions of medicare agreements hindered governments' capacity to shift health care resources out of the medical and hospital sectors. Although these constraints are still present, there is an emerging consensus among policy-makers and the public to find a way to expand medicare to include homecare services and a pharmaceutical insurance plan.

The compromises governments had to make to introduce medicare, and the concessions that both levels of government made to the medical profession, resulted in an inflationary system with little or no capacity for external management (Badgley & Wolfe, 1967). This resulted in a strategy of cutbacks by the federal government throughout the late 1970s and into the 1990s. These cutbacks shifted an increasing proportion of health care costs to provincial governments. Most provincial governments responded to this and other factors by regionalizing health care service delivery. Despite this positive response, deep and repeated cuts to public health care expenditures contributed to the growing sense that our health care system was in a perpetual state of increasing crisis. This generated increased pressure on governments to find a way to work together to resolve the crisis. By the turn of the century, First Ministers' accords were proving to be an effective means to achieve inter-governmental consensus on health reform priorities and their funding.

This is not to say that the contradictions of medicare have been resolved, but there is currently a spirit of increased cooperation and collaboration that has never before characterized Canadian health care politics. At least for the time being, this is cause for confidence that our prized health care system will be healthy enough to survive and respond to the new needs confronting it.

STUDY QUESTIONS

1. *Outline and discuss the strengths and weaknesses of the cost control strategies applied to medicare in the 1980s and 1990s.*
2. *What are some of the ways in which electronic health records (EHRs) are thought to improve the efficiency and effectiveness of the health care system? What are some of the limits and concerns associated with them?*
3. *What are the pros and cons associated with the idea of care guarantees?*
4. *Compare the strengths and weaknesses of the current health care financing strategy with the original approach.*
5. *The achievement of health and the containment of costs cannot be achieved without first limiting the power and autonomy of the medical profession. Discuss.*

GLOSSARY

comprehensive coverage a core principle of medicare related to the fact that all services deemed medically necessary are covered.

downloading the transfer of care from the publicly financed services sector to the voluntary sector where uncompensated care is provided by family (often women), friends, and various community associations.

evidence-based decision-making this idea was first introduced as evidence-based medicine (EBM) and it was defined as "the conscientious, explicit and judicious use of current best evidence...(that integrates the best external evidence with individual clinical expertise and patient choice)...in making decisions about individual patients" (Sackett et al., 1997). The principles of EBM were subsequently extended to include both management and policy level decision-making in health care and came to be known as evidence-based health care, or more commonly evidence-based decision-making (EBDM).

knowledge translation The CIHR (2006b) defines KT as "the exchange, synthesis, and ethically-sound application of knowledge – within a complex set of interactions among researchers and users – to accelerate the capture of the benefits of research for Canadians through improved health, more effective services and products, and a strengthened health care system." Many different terms, such as knowledge transfer, knowledge utilization, and knowledge exchange, currently are being used as synonyms.

marketization the direct transfer of costs from the public sector to the private sector.

medicare a system of universal, comprehensive, tax financed, portable hospitalization and medical care insurance publicly administered on a non-profit basis.

portable coverage this refers to the fact that Canadian citizens eligible for coverage under medicare are covered regardless of the province in which they receive treatment.

regionalization a system of health system governance designed to increase local citizen involvement in health care planning and service delivery, to facilitate greater integration and coordination of the health care system, and to increase the efficiency and effectiveness of the health care system.

universal coverage one of the core principles of medicare related to the fact that all citizens are entitled to coverage by medicare as a right of citizenship.

REFERENCES

Angus, D.E. (1991). *Review of significant health care commissions and task forces in Canada since 1983–84.* Ottawa: Canadian Hospital Association/Canadian Medical Association/Canadian Nurses Association.

Angus, D.E., Auer, L., Cloutier, J.E., & Albert, T. (1995). *Sustainable health care for Canada.* Ottawa: University of Ottawa Press.

Armstrong, P. (2001). Evidence-Based Health Care Reform: Women's Issues. In P. Armstrong, H. Armstrong, & D. Coburn (Eds.), *Unhealthy times: Political economy perspectives on health and care in Canada* (pp. 121–145). Toronto: Oxford University Press.

Badgley, R.F., & S. Wolfe. (1967). *Doctors' strike: Medical care and conflict in Saskatchewan.* Toronto: MacMillan.

Baker, G.R., Norton, P.G., Flintoff, V., Blais, R., Brown, A., Cox, J., Etchells, E., Ghali, W.A., Hebert, P., Majumdar, S.R., O'Beirne, M., Palacios-Derflingher, L., Reid, R.J., Sheps, S., & Tamblyn, R. (2004). The Canadian Adverse Effects Study: The incidence of adverse effects among hospital patients in Canada. *Canadian Medical Association Journal, 170*(11), 1678–1686.

Baron, R.J., Fabens, E.L., Schiffman, M., & Wolf, E. (2005). Electronic Health Records: Just around the Corner? Or over the Cliff? *Annals of Internal Medicine, 143*(3), 222–226.

Bickerton, J. (1999). Reforming health care governance: The case of Nova Scotia. *Journal of Canadian Studies, 34*(2), 159–190.

Blishen, B.R. (1991). *Doctors in Canada: The changing world of medical practice.* Toronto: University of Toronto Press in association with Statistics Canada.

Charlton, B.G. (1997). Restoring the balance: Evidence-based medicine put in its place. *Journal of Evaluative Clinical Practice, 3*(2), 87–98.

CHI (Canada Health Infoway) & HCC (Health Council Canada). (2006). Beyond good intentions: Accelerating the electronic health record in Canada. Report of a Conference, June 11–13, 2006, Montebello, QC.

CIHI (Canadian Institute for Health Information). (2006a). Retrieved October 6, 2006 from http://www.cihi.ca/cihiweb/dispPage.jsp?cw_page=profile_roadmap_launch_e.

CIHI (Canadian Institute for Health Information). (2006b). Retrieved October 29, 2006 from http://www.cihi.ca/cihiweb/dispPage.jsp?cw_page=cphi_e.

CIHR (Canadian Institutes for Health Research). (2006a). Retrieved October 28, 2006 from http://www.cihr-irsc.gc.ca/e/30240.html#slide1_e.

CIHR (Canadian Institutes for Health Research). (2006b). CIHR Knowledge Translation Award. Retrieved November 1, 2006 from http://www.cihr-irsc.gc.ca/e/27904.html.

CMAJ (Canadian Medical Association Journal). (2002). What paperless office? *Canadian Medical Association Journal, 167*(2), 182.

CPSI (Canadian Patient Safety Institute). (2006). Retrieved October 15, 2006 from http://www.patientsafetyinstitute.ca/index.html.

Crichton, A., Robertson, A., Gordon, C., & Farant, W. (1997). *Health care a community concern? Developments in the organization of Canadian health services.* Calgary: University of Calgary Press.

Davis, P. (2004). Health care as a risk factor. *Canadian Medical Association Journal, 170*(11), 1688–1689.

Department of Finance, Government of Canada. (2006). Retrieved October 13, 2006 from Federal Transfers in Support of the 2000/2003/2004 First Ministers' Accords, http://www.fin.gc.ca/FEDPROV/fmAcce.html.

Dickinson, H.D. (1993). The struggle for state health insurance: Reconsidering the role of Saskatchewan farmers. *Studies in Political Economy, 41*, 133–156.

Dickinson, H.D. (1998). Evidence-based decision-making: An argumentative approach. *International Journal of Medical Informatics, 51*, 71–81.

Dickinson, H.D. (2003). A sociological perspective on the transfer and utilization of social scientific knowledge for policy-making. In F. Champagne & L. Lemieux-Charles (Eds.), *Multidisciplinary perspectives on evidence-based decision-making in health care* (pp. 41–69). Toronto: University of Toronto Press.

Dorland, J.L., & Davis, S.M. (1996). Regionalization as health care reform. In J.L. Dorland & S.M. Davis (Eds.), *How many roads...? Regionalization and decentralization in health care* (pp. 3–7). Kingston, ON: Queen's University School of Policy Studies.

Fuller, C. (1998). *Caring for profit: How corporations are taking over Canada's health care system.* Vancouver: New Star/Canadian Centre for Policy Alternatives.

Hartt, S. (2006, February). What the Chaoulli decision said about health care rhetoric versus health care reality. *Policy Options*, 44–48.

Health Canada. (2006a). Retrieved October 10, 2006 from http://www.hc-sc.gc.ca/hcs-sss/finance/htf-fass/index_e.html.

Health Canada. (2006b). Retrieved October 10, 2006 from http://www.hc-sc.gc.ca/dhp-mps/medeff/advers-react-neg/fs-if/cmirps-scdpim_e.html.

Health Canada. (2006c). Retrieved October 29, 2006 from http://www.hc-sc.gc.ca/hcs-sss/qual/acces/wait-attente/index_e.html.

Health Canada. (2006d). Retrieved October 29, 2006 from http://www.hc-sc.gc.ca/hcs-sss/hhr-rhs/strateg/index_e.html.

Health Canada. (2006e). Retrieved October 29, 2006 from http://www.hc-sc.gc.ca/hcs-sss/hhr-rhs/strateg/plan/index_e.html.

Health Canada. (2006f). Retrieved October 29, 2006 from http://www.hc-sc.gc.ca/hcs-sss/hhr-rhs/strateg/recru/index_e.html.

Health Canada. (2006g). Retrieved October 29, 2006 from http://www.hc-sc.gc.ca/hcs-sss/hhr-rhs/strateg/interprof/index_e.html.

Health Edition. (2005). Total health expenditure reaches $142 billion. *Health Edition, 9*(35), 1.

Health Edition. (2006). Pediatric services seen as new priority area. *Health Edition, 10*(41), 1.

Health Edition. (2006). Retrieved November 1, 2006 from http://www.implementation-science.com/home/.

Kermode-Scott, B. (2005, November 12). US has most reports of medical error. *British Medical Journal,* (331). Retrieved November 14, 2005 from http://www.bjm.com.

Lewis, S. (1997). *Regionalization and devolution: Transforming health, reshaping politics?* HEALNet Regional Health Planning Theme, Occasional Paper No. 2. Saskatoon.

Lomas, J. (1996). Devolved authorities in Canada: The new site of health-care system conflict. In J.L. Dorland, & S.M. Davis (Eds.), *How many roads....?: Regionalization and decentralizaition in health care* (pp. 26–34). Kingston: Queen's University School of Policy Studies.

Lomas, J. (1997). Devolving authority for health care in Canada's provinces: 4. Emerging issues and prospects. *Canadian Medical Association Journal, 156*(6), 817–823.

Lomas, J., Woods, J., & Venstra, G. (1997). Devolving authority for health care in Canada's provinces: 1. An introduction to the issues. *Canadian Medical Association Journal, 156*(3), 371–377.

Marchildon, G.P. (2006). Health reform after Chaoulli. *Policy Dialogue, The SIPP Newsletter, 12*, 12–13.

Mhatre, S.L., & Deber, R.B. (1998). From equal access to health care to equitable access to health: A review of Canadian health commissions and reports. In D. Coburn, C. D'Arcy, & G. Torrance (Eds.), *Health and Canadian society: Critical perspectives* (3rd ed., pp. 459–484). Toronto: University of Toronto Press.

Naylor, C.D. (1986). *Private practice, public payment: Canadian medicine and the politics of health insurance, 1911–1966*. Kingston & Montreal: McGill-Queen's University Press.

NCE (Networks of Centres of Excellence). (2006). Canada's innovation agenda: The process through which new economic and social benefits are extracted from knowledge. Presentation.

PHAC (Public Health Agency of Canada). (2006). Retrieved October 9, 2006 from http://www.phac-aspc.gc.ca/ph-sp/phdd/determinants/determinants2.html.

Romanow, R.J. (2002). *Building on values: The future of health care in Canada*. Retrieved October 31, 2006 from http://www.hc-sc.gc.ca/english/care/romanow/hcc0086.html.

Sackett, D.L., Richardson, W.S., Rosenberg, W., & Haynes, R.B. (1997). *Evidence-based medicine: How to practice and teach EBM*. New York: Churchill Livingstone.

Smiley, D.V. (Ed.). (1963). The Rowell-Sirois report: An abridgement of book 1 of the Royal Commission on Dominion-Provincial Relations. Toronto: McClelland and Stewart.

Soderstrom, L. (1978). *The Canadian health system*. London: Croom Helm.

Statistics Canada (2006). Retrieved October 30, 2006 from http://www.statcan.ca/english/concepts/health/cchsinfo.htm.

Taylor, M.G. (1960). The role of the medical profession in the formation and execution of public policy. *Canadian Journal of Economics and Political Studies, 25*(1), 108–127.

Taylor, M.G. (1978). *Health insurance and Canadian public policy: The seven decisions that created the Canadian health insurance system*. Montreal: McGill-Queen's University Press.

Vayda, E., & Deber, R.B. (1992). The Canadian health care system: A developmental overview. In C.D. Naylor (Ed.), *Canadian Health Care and the State: A Century of Evolution* (pp. 125–140). Montreal & Kingston: McGill-Queen's University Press.

Vayda, E., Evans, R.G., & Mindell, W.R. (1979). Universal health insurance in Canada: History, problems, trends. *Journal of Community Health, 4*, 217–231.

Walters, V. (1982). State, capital and labour: The introduction of federal-provincial insurance for physician care in Canada. *Canadian Review of Sociology and Anthropology, 19*(2), 157–172.

Wilson R. (2001, Spring). Quality improvement will require a major commitment. *Hospital Quarterly*, 20–24.

Woolhandler, S., & Himmelstein, D.U. (2004). The high costs of for-profit care. *Canadian Medical Association Journal, 170*(2). On-line journal. Retrieved October 30, 2006 from http://www.cmaj.ca/cgi/content/full/170/12/1814.

3

THE EMERGING PUBLIC HEALTH SYSTEM IN CANADA

ELIZABETH QUINLAN University of Saskatchewan

HARLEY D. DICKINSON University of Saskatchewan

INTRODUCTION

Public health policy and practice are concerned with preventing injury and illness within a population. These are major concerns in all societies, and are increasingly becoming issues of international significance. However laudable the goal of public health policy, it is not possible to prevent all injuries and illnesses. The provision of health care services, therefore, is also a major policy concern in all societies. In principle, preventing injury and illness and providing health care services for those who are injured and ill are complementary objectives. In practice, however, they often are in competition for scarce resources. As a result, the priority given to public health policy with its focus on prevention versus health care policy with its focus on treatment varies over time and with different social, economic, and political circumstances.

Public health issues, for example, were of paramount concern to policy makers in Western societies from the late 18th century until the early part of the 20th century. During this period, health care services generally were left to the market where a large number of mostly unregulated service providers competed for customers. In most countries, it was not until the early part of the 20th century that significant public policy efforts were made to develop and regulate heath care providers and to develop and manage a more or less integrated and coordinated health care system. For most of the last century, health care policy focused mainly on medical and hospital care. It was only during the last two or three decades of the 20th century that substantial efforts were made to reform the Canadian *medical* care system and turn it into a *health* care system.

Recently, **health promotion** has become a goal of health policy. Complementing the dual focus on prevention and treatment, which traditionally has characterized health policy, health promotion encourages and empowers individuals to make healthy choices and discourages them from making unhealthy choices. The health promotion framework draws attention to a wide range of **social determinants of health and illness** that differentially affect the **health status** of the population as a whole, as well as the health status of various sub-groups in society. The growing emphasis on health promotion, combined with more traditional concerns about illness prevention, is referred to as the *"new public health"* paradigm. Our main focus in this chapter is the new public health and the emergence of a new public health system in Canada. We argue that the efforts to develop a new public health system are the result of the confluence of several forces, including globalization, the emergence of a new balance of socio-political forces, climate change, and the inability of both the public health systems and health care systems to deal with existing and emerging health problems.

BACKGROUND

All societies have been and are concerned with the health and well-being of their members (Awofeso, 2004). By the 18th century, several Western European societies were undergoing revolutionary transformations associated with societal modernization. Modernization involves a number of major structural and institutional transformations to societies. The transition from a pre-modern to a modern society is characterized by the following transformations: from an agricultural, non-market economy with little division of labour and family-based production to an industrial, money-based market economy with extensive division of labour and mass production; from rural to urban geographies; from decentralized political structures to a centralized state; from communalism and personal (affective) ties to individualism and impersonal, instrumental relations; and from a predominance of mysticism and religious knowledge to rationalism and scientific knowledge.

The development of modern, science-based public health and health care systems is generally seen as one indicator of the modernization process. However, there is not a full consensus regarding whether the transition actually occurred. Francis (1987), for example, argues that many features of modern societies are present in pre-modern societies. Others, who agree that significant societal changes did take place, argue they cannot be properly understood in evolutionary terms. It is possible, for example, for societies that have modern characteristics to transform in such a way as to take on characteristics identified as pre-modern. The resurgence of religious fundamentalisms can be understood as an example of the non-evolutionary or non-teleological nature of social change.

The historically unprecedented production of wealth associated with societal modernization and the rise of capitalist industrialization were achieved, in part, at the expense of the health and safety of the growing class of waged workers. Indeed, the ruthless exploitation of men, women, and children in the pursuit of profit so undermined the health of the working population that the survival of capitalism itself was threatened. Unregulated capitalism was unsustainable. It was in this context that initial public health efforts aimed at regulating the terms and conditions of work for the capitalist working class were first developed. In England, a society at the leading edge of capitalist development in the 18th and 19th centuries, these initial public health initiatives took the form of the Factory Acts and associated legislation that limited the employment of children as well as hours and conditions of work.

The rise of capitalism was accompanied by rapid urbanization, that is, the widespread movement of people from rural areas to cities to take up jobs in the new factories. The rapid and uncontrolled growth of cities resulted in extremely unsanitary and unhealthy living conditions. Unsafe water supplies and inadequate sewerage and waste disposal systems created an environment where infectious diseases such as typhoid, cholera, small pox, and tuberculosis thrived. Thus, in addition to efforts to regulate the terms and conditions of factory work, early public health efforts consisted of introducing immunization and public education campaigns, effective water treatment and food safety mechanisms, and new sewerage and waste disposal systems. These are still central elements of all public health systems.

Colonialism was another motor and consequence of capitalist growth and it too contributed to the need to develop public health systems. On the one hand, colonialism provided a source of cheap raw materials and labour for the voracious capitalist systems of Europe and North America. On the other hand, it provided a worldwide market for the vast quantities of commodities that the industrial mode of production made possible. The incorporation of colonies into the world capitalist system resulted in the establishment of new trade, travel, and residential patterns for indigenous and migrant workforces as well as for colonial administrators, merchants, and soldiers. These, in turn, created new disease vectors. It is in this context that quarantine regulations came to be a first small step toward the development of a global public health system.

Given that Canada was part of the emerging world capitalist system, these factors also motivated development of the Canadian public health system. The development of the Canadian public health system, however, was, and continues to be, impeded by a number of structural features of Canadian society and geography. Constitutional jurisdiction over public health issues, for example, is split between federal, provincial/territorial, and municipal levels of government. This makes it difficult to plan and implement integrated and standardized approaches to public health, in the same way that it has made it difficult to develop and reform the health care system. Compounding difficulties is the fact that Canada's relatively small and geographically dispersed population makes it difficult for municipal and provincial governments independently to raise the tax revenues necessary to develop public health systems. It also is the case that provision of health care services usually trumps political support for public health systems.

Despite these challenges, for most of the 20th century, the Canadian public health system functioned reasonably well. The limitations of the existing system, however, increasingly became apparent toward the end of the last century. Some of the resultant public health crises were the result of domestic factors, but many of the most dramatic developments were the result of the current phase of globalization.

On the domestic front, for example, contaminated water problems became increasingly apparent starting in the 1990s. Walkerton, Ontario; North Battleford, Saskatchewan; and more recently the Kashechewan Reserve, Ontario, reminded us of the serious impact inadequate or failed public health protection systems can have on the health of communities. In addition to crises such as these, which garnered national and international media attention, it has become commonplace for local news media to announce "boil water" advisories for more and more communities.

The security of the food safety system also has been challenged by the appearance of new diseases such as "mad cow disease," or Bovine Spongiform Encephalopathy (BSE). Mad cow disease is a fatal brain-wasting disease of cattle. It first appeared in Britain in 1986. It appears to be caused by changes in the feeding patterns of market-oriented beef production. In particular, it is thought that the relatively recent practice of including animal offal in cattle feed created a new pathway for the disease to enter cattle populations (Center for Disease Control, 2007a). This practice has generated so much concern as a human public health problem because it appears that it can be transmitted from cattle to humans in the form of variant Creutzfeldt-Jakob disease (vCJD), also called new variant Creutzfeldt-Jakob disease (nvCJD) (Center for Disease Control, 2007b).

On the global level, the HIV/AIDS pandemic and outbreaks of other new infectious diseases such as Severe Acute Respiratory Syndrome (SARS), bird flu, and West Nile virus have highlighted the increasing interrelationship of the world's population, global climate change, and the importance of well-functioning public health and health care systems. The AIDS pandemic began in the summer of 1981, and since then it has caused the deaths of an estimated 25 million people, making it one of the most lethal epidemics in human history. In 2006, it is estimated to have infected about 39.5 million people and to have killed between 2.5 and 3.5 million people worldwide, including about 570,000 children (UNAIDS, 2006). Like all other diseases, AIDS is unequally distributed among populations. Most AIDS cases currently are in sub-Saharan Africa. There, and in all other geographical locations, it is more prevalent among the poor. Compounding this unequal incidence of AIDS is the fact that the antiretroviral drugs that can help manage its symptoms and delay death are not affordable by the poor – those who are most affected by the disease.

There were three global outbreaks (pandemics) of influenza during the 20th century. The Spanish Flu epidemic of 1918 was the most severe and worldwide it killed between 20 and 50 million people. The Asian Flu pandemic in 1957–58 and the Hong Kong Flu in 1968–69 were the other major flu pandemics, although there were, of course, other less serious influenzas through the 20th century. In the last few years, a new bird flu virus (H5N1) has emerged that is lethal for birds and at least some humans who have been in contact with them. There is increasing concern among public health professionals and policy makers that this virus may mutate into a strain that will cause the next great flu pandemic by becoming easily transmitted from human to human (Mayo Clinic, 2005).

Despite differences between these pandemics and those that occurred historically, they share in common the fact that, by and large, they are unintended consequences of various social and natural forces. Public health and health care systems are currently faced with a new challenge in the form of global terrorism and the intentional inflicting of large-scale injury and illness on civilian populations.

Some changes to public health have also been prompted by a relatively recent shift in the nature of illness and our recognition that the health care system is unable to manage most of the current health problems. Chronic conditions have eclipsed infections and accidents as reasons for illness and death. Two-thirds of total deaths in Canada are due to four chronic conditions: cardiovascular disease, cancer, lung disease, and diabetes (Secretariat for the Intersectoral Healthy Living Network, 2005). Taken together, these chronic diseases account for over 20 percent of the total direct and indirect costs of illnesses in Canada (Frank, 2003). Cancer alone is responsible for 29 percent of all deaths each year. Diabetes is the leading cause of blindness and leg amputations. Among Aboriginal peoples, the prevalence of diabetes is three times higher than it is among other Canadians. Chronic mental illnesses, such as depression, are a leading cause of disability worldwide. In a comparison of the economic burden of disease in countries with established market economies, depression ranks second only to ischemic heart disease (National Institute of Mental Health, 2001). Yet, mental health has been identified as the "orphan child" of Canada's health care system (Romanow, 2002).

In the main, the health care system has been unsuccessful in contending with the complexity of most chronic conditions. Some have estimated that only 10–15 percent of the increased longevity over the past century is due to the improvements in the health care system (Raphael, 2003). The greatest proportion of increased health status and life expectancy is the result of successful public health measures and the more equitable distribution of social wealth made possible by the development of the welfare state in the post-World War II period. Subsequent rollbacks of welfare state programs have many concerned that the trends toward increased population health status and longevity may be reversed.

The shift in the nature of health problems from accidents and injuries to chronic diseases, which are increasingly being conceptualized as public as well as personal health problems, has created a new focus for public health planning and policy-making and it has necessitated the development of innovative public health. New communication technologies, for example, have increased access to the information necessary to achieve improved population health; genomic and other kinds of scientific research also are changing the way we view and treat disease. Many feel that biotechnology will eventually enable prevention interventions to be targeted at genetic factors, not just environmental and educational factors associated with illness prevention. These changes in public health are reverberating in the schools and training programs for public health providers, including the formation of new interdisciplinary public health programs (Clark & Weist, 2000).

THE NEW PUBLIC HEALTH SYSTEM IN CANADA

As we have seen, profound changes to modern societies have produced equally profound changes to the nature and distribution of health problems; these, in turn, have challenged our understanding of the nature of the new public health problems and how we, as a society, can best to respond to them. There is no obvious consensus concerning either the nature of the problems confronting us, or regarding how we should respond to them. An obvious point of disagreement remains the relative balance of resources that should be put into the health care system to deal with existing injury and illness compared to what we put into the public health system in an effort to prevent injury and illness and to promote health. This is a highly charged political issue in Canadian society and around the world.

Public and private resources devoted to health care services in Canada are enormous and growing. It is estimated, for example, that in 2005 total expenditures on health care reached $142 billion. This expenditure represents more than 10 percent of the Canadian gross domestic product (CIHI, 2005). In comparison, it was estimated that total expenditures on public health would be about $7 billion in 2005, up from just over $1 billion in 1975 (CIHI, 2005). These figures include provincial/territorial level expenditures on a variety of programs including food and drug safety programs; health inspections; health promotion activities; community mental health programs; public health nursing; measures to prevent the spread of infectious diseases; and promotional activities to improve workplace health and safety (CIHI, 2005). These figures must be cautiously interpreted because of what the CIHI describes as "notable differences in the amount of detail" provincial/territorial governments are able to provide (CIHI, 2005).

There is no consensus concerning the correct balance, although there does appear to be emerging agreement that more resources are required for the public health system. There also is agreement that both the public health systems and the health care systems must be better coordinated and integrated if we are to develop a more comprehensive and effective response to existing and emerging public health problems. An indicator of the growing emphasis on improving coordination and integration is the recent creation of the Public Health Agency of Canada (PHAC) and the 2004 appointment of Dr. David Butler-Jones as the country's first Chief Public Health Officer. Table 3.1 lists the branches of the PHAC.

In addition to the PHAC, the federal government created the Pan-Canadian Health Network and six National Collaborating Centres for Public Health. These new organizations are designed to support Canada's public health strategies by improving the coordination and collaboration of governments, academia, researchers, and non-governmental organizations within Canada. The PHAC will also be the focal point for international collaborations involving sharing Canada's research and expertise with a number of global partners, including the World Health Organization, the U.S. Centers for Disease Control and Prevention, the new European Centre for Disease Prevention and Control, as well as other public health agencies (PHAC, 2004b).

TABLE 3.1 *Branches of the Public Health Agency of Canada*

Infectious Disease and Emergency Preparedness (IDEP) Branch

- Centre for Infectious Disease Prevention and Control (CIDPC)
- Centre for Emergency Preparedness and Response (CEPR)
- National Microbiology Laboratory (NML)
- Laboratory for Foodborne Zoonoses (LFZ)
- Pandemic Preparedness Secretariat (PPS)

Health Promotion and Chronic Disease Prevention (HPCDP) Branch

- Centre for Chronic Disease Prevention and Control (CCDPC)
- Centre for Health Promotion (CHP)
- Transfer Payment Services and Accountability Division

Public Health Practice and Regional Operations (PHPRO) Branch

- Office of Public Health Practice (OPHP)
- Regions

Strategic Policy, Communications and Corporate Services (SPCCS) Branch

- Strategic Policy Directorate
- Communications Directorate
- Finance and Administration Directorate
- Human Resources Directorate
- Information Management and Information Technology Directorate
- Audit Services Division

Source: Public Health Agency of Canada, 2004.

Despite the existence of the PHAC, inter-jurisdictional coordination and cooperation among government departments remains a persistent problem, in part because health issues are not priority concerns in many policy areas, in part because provincial governments often create their own coordinating agencies, and because of the inherent difficulty in prioritizing health concerns in government departments primarily responsible for non-health issues. However, it is clear that considerable effort and resources have recently been committed to improving and managing a substantially expanded new public health system.

A further move toward developing a more integrated and coordinated public health system involves identifying the structural components of the present system. Frank (2003) has made an important contribution in this regard by identifying five main components of the Canadian public health system. The Frank model provides a way to systemize data collecting and reporting and to provide a common framework for public health planning and service delivery. These components are: Health Surveillance; Disease and Injury Prevention; Health Protection; Population Health Assessment; and Health Promotion (Frank, 2003).

Health surveillance is defined as "the tracking and forecasting of any health event or health determinant through the continuous collection of high-quality data, the integration, analysis and interpretation of those data into reports, advisories, alerts, and warnings, and their dissemination to those who need to know" (Kirby Commission, 2003, p. 26). Many of these reports are distributed to health care practitioners with specific information regarding appropriate interventions. The Internet and other electronic forms of communication are becoming important features of national and international health surveillance practices. With their capacity to communicate across great distances almost instantaneously, these technologies are being harnessed to improve the detection, reporting of, and response to, outbreaks of transmittable diseases.

The emergence of BSE, West Nile, SARS, bird flu, and other "zoonoses" (diseases that spread to humans from other animals, insects, and birds) has provoked new-found concern about global transmission of infectious diseases. During the first outbreak of West Nile in 2001, for example, the public health system response included surveillance of dead birds, mosquitoes, and human cases, and the withdrawal of blood products that were collected during the peak period of the outbreak.

These recent outbreaks have brought to light some of the complex social and ethical issues that arise in health surveillance. The dissemination of information, including the identities of affected individuals, might be important for controlling epidemics; yet, making those identifies public can fuel prevailing views that immigrants, or other minority groups, are threats to national security and health. In a public health crisis, people often revert to division. Conceptualizing the crisis as emanating from a particular group of people is a way of regaining a sense of control that is lost in the face of threats to life and safety. For instance, over the course of the SARS outbreak, Asians were often associated with the virus. As a result, members of Asian communities felt stigmatized and many experienced harassment and discrimination and were ostracized by landlords, employers, retailers, and the public (Leung, 2004).

Disease and injury prevention involve a range of interventions, including vaccination programs, infectious disease investigation and outbreak control, workplace health and safety regulations, cancer screening, and programs to encourage healthy behaviours such as anti-smoking campaigns, physical activity, and bicycle helmet use.

The direct and indirect economic costs of injuries in Canada are estimated to be $12.7 billion annually (Health Canada, 2002). A major cause of injury-related death and disability is motor vehicle crashes and public health initiatives include seat belt use, better road design, speed limits, and educational and enforcement efforts to reduce drinking and driving. In recent years, disability and death due to chronic illnesses, such as cardiovascular disease, cancer, and other "lifestyle diseases" have surpassed communicable diseases as the main source of mortality. As a result, the disease prevention dimension of public heath has shifted focus. The Kirby Report (2003) recommended the creation of a national chronic disease prevention strategy to implement this new focus. The "Integrated Pan-Canadian Healthy Living Strategy" was announced in October 2005 with the goal of achieving a 20 percent increase in the proportion of Canadians who are physically active, eat healthfully, and are at healthy body weights. A "social marketing" approach, in combination with establishing and mobilizing a network of partner organizations, was adopted as the means to implement this strategy. The social marketing dimension of the implementation process includes a website and a toll-free number to appeal to various population subgroups (parents aged 25–45 with children 2–12 years old with special emphasis on women and Aboriginal peoples). The network component involves relevant intermediaries including non-governmental organizations, private sector, and other community partners (Secretariat for the Intersectoral Healthy Living Network, 2005).

Disease and injury prevention in the workplace are addressed by provincial regulations, such as occupational health and safety and labour standards, collective agreements if the workplace is unionized, or policies in workplaces where such policies have been developed. Most of these regulatory instruments were conceived, enacted, and implemented in order to address workers' physical health, yet increasingly, work-related health problems tend to be psychological rather than physical injuries and fatalities. Moreover, traditional public health programming in the workplace has largely been directed to employees to change their individual behaviours, despite the fact that research is demonstrating the importance of organizational culture and managerial practices with respect to work-related health, particularly psychological health (Shannon, Robson & Sale, 2001). Thus, the concept of "healthy workplaces" has attracted greater interest in the last few years. "Healthy workplaces" are more than the absence of "job stressors," they are sites where employees are self-actualized through their productivity, and organizational knowledge is harnessed to further their healthy responses to known risk factors (Kelloway & Day, 2005). Quebec is the first jurisdiction in North America to introduce legislation to address employees' mental health by providing protection from psychological harassment in the workplace (Quebec Labour Standards, 2004).

Health protection involves inspections of restaurants, child care centres, nursing homes, and other public facilities, as well as the monitoring and enforcing of water and air quality standards. In its early days, the public health system in Canada focused on these health protection measures. The 1872 federal Quarantine Act, for example, is one of the earliest and longest standing pieces of public health legislation. This Act empowers the federal government to establish quarantine facilities at any location in Canada, divert airplanes and/or cargo ships to alternative landing sites, and to screen, inspect, and detain passengers. The Food and Drug Act and the Tobacco Act are more recent examples of federal government public health legislation. Both Acts govern the marketing and availability of various products, including natural health products, cosmetics, and tobacco, and to specify labeling requirements. The most recent health protection legislation is the 1999 Environmental Protection Act. This Act establishes government powers to evaluate potential risks of environmental pollutants and toxic substances to address pollution prevention and the protection of the environment.

Population health assessment includes efforts to develop theories, methods, and measures of population health status and quality of life indicators. This dimension of the public health system is charged with evaluating and comparing overall trends and changes in population health status. Evaluations are used to develop new, and review existing, health policies and programs. The examination of existing public health programs for their effectiveness, to determine what works in which contexts, makes use of "naturally occurring experiments" to inform and guide future policy and program decision-making.

Conventional research that assesses the health status of populations has been criticized for under-estimating the effects of social inequalities on health status. Gender, race, class, and other dimensions of social inequality are included as "controllable" variables and it is often ignored that these are only simplistic representations of very complex social relations (Polanyi, McIntosh & Kosny, 2005). How these structural inequalities combine with individual and collective actions to affect health status has yet to be fully incorporated into population health assessment. The use of "lay" knowledge, the knowledge that is rooted in the everyday experiences of peoples' lives, has been proposed as a means of understanding how individual and collective actions arise from the meanings that people attach to their health-related experiences (Popay, Williams, Thomas & Gatrell, 2003). The pressing challenge for population health assessment, then, is to develop more sophisticated models that incorporate the aggregate patterns of social inequalities, health outcomes, and the meanings that people attach to their health-related experiences.

Health promotion involves strengthening community health services, establishing joint partnerships between governments and communities to solve pressing health problems, and to advocate for healthy public policies, including those that address the social determinants of health: income, education, housing, affordable and safe food, and safe communities. This is defined as "the process of enabling people to increase control over, and to improve, their health" (Frank, 2003, p. 49).

Health promotion is founded on the recognition that health status cannot be wholly explained by individual lifestyle choices such as smoking, diet, and physical activity. In addition to these risk factors, socio-economic factors are important predictors of health status. Studies done in the late 1970s of British civil servants in Whitehall drew attention to the link between social class and health (e.g., Marmot, Rose, Shipley & Hamilton, 1978). Recent research indicates that relative material deprivation (the gap between the rich and the poor) appears to be more important than absolute deprivation in determining health status (Kawachi & Kennedy, 2002; Wilkinson, 1994). At the individual level, psychosocial effects of one's perceived position in the hierarchy produces stress and often leads to actions and behaviours that undermine health. At the community level, an increased hierarchy reduces overall social cohesion and social support networks, and this weakens individuals' health. Examples of initiatives undertaken in other countries, such as India and Japan, confirm that improvements to health status can be achieved through structural reforms that reduce economic disparities (Poland, Coburn, Robertson & Eakin, 1998).

Several international public health policy documents are notable for their articulated aim of addressing the social determinants of health through the integration of public health systems with government welfare programs and coordination with the health-relevant activities of non-governmental organizations. In particular, the World Health Organization's Ottawa Charter (1986) and companion document The Healthy Cities Project (1987) explicitly focus on reducing economic and social inequities through inter-sectoral collaborations. The Ottawa Charter identifies peace, shelter, education, food, income, a stable economic system, sustainable resources, social justice, and equity as prerequisites for health. The Charter proposes various coordinated income and social policies and programs, such as legislative changes, fiscal measures, and inter-sectoral collaboration; the main premise is policies and programs need to be adapted to the local needs of individual countries so that communities themselves can exercise more control over their own health, endeavours, and destinies. The World Health Organization's Healthy Cities Project began in 1987 with eleven cities that had initiated various collaborations between community groups and now involves several hundred cities around the world. The notion that communities are favourably placed to identify problems, assume leadership, and take action on the factors that determine health has been endorsed by the Canadian National Forum on Health (Health Canada, 1997) and by the Romanow Commission (Commission on the Future of Health Care in Canada, 2002). Set against this background, health promotion policy and practice in Canada are based on three interrelated strategies: 1) increasing the role of the public in policy-making, 2) increasing community control over their health and environments, and 3) inter-sectoral coordination of public policy.

An underlying premise of health promotion is that public health should facilitate a more equitable distribution of society's resources that are inequitably apportioned by the "market." Along with unemployment insurance, pensions, and other redistributive programs of the welfare system, public health is part of "the price we pay to some people for bearing part of the cost of other people's progress" (Titmuss, 1968, p. 119). Of all the dimensions of the public health system, health promotion most clearly expresses the "new" public health concepts of community development, civic engagement, and collaborative action. It is also the dimension that fuels the greatest debate. Health promotion strategies that aim to empower communities and encourage collective action and public participation often face vigorous opposition, in part because of the difficulty in demonstrating the effectiveness of empowerment, public participation, and community development on the health status of the population in concrete terms, and in part because of the prevailing social norm of rugged individualism that is so firmly entrenched in North American culture (O'Neill, Pederson & Rootman, 2000; Hayes, 1999).

In addition to the structural dimensions of public health outlined above, another has recently emerged and gained considerable attention through the various institutions of public health. "Emergency Preparedness" involves measures taken to safeguard against politically motivated threats to health: nuclear, biological, or chemical agents, or terrorist attacks. Canada might not be a primary target; however, the health effects from these threats are not necessarily limited by political boundaries.

Frank (2003) does not identify emergency preparedness as a distinct dimension of the emerging new public health system in Canada, although the federal government does identify it as part of the newly emerging Canadian public health system. In the post-9/11 period, it is increasingly agreed upon that emergency preparedness is necessary for the public health system to be able to quickly detect and respond to both intentional and natural disasters and emergencies. The scale and speed with which potential pandemics and terrorist attacks can occur also make it necessary for countries to collaborate in the collection and sharing of relevant information in a timely fashion. Thus, Canada is a signatory to WHO's International Health Regulations and, as such, has agreed to monitor, report, and contain communicable diseases.

Following the September 11, 2001, attacks on New York and Washington, the then United States Secretary of Health and Human Services initiated a meeting among countries fighting bioterrorism to discuss plans to share information and better coordinate their efforts to protect global health security. The first formal meeting of this Global Health Security Initiative (GHSI) was held in Ottawa on November 7, 2001. In addition to the Canadian Minister of Health who hosted it, that meeting involved the Ministers/Secretaries/Commissioners of Health from the European Commission, France, Germany, Italy, Japan, Mexico, the United Kingdom, the United States, and the World Health Organization. Since then, the group has met at least once a year. They have agreed to cooperate on a number of fronts in order to develop and improve public health capacity to respond effectively to the threat of international biological, chemical, and radio-nuclear terrorism (GHSI, n.d.). Perhaps more than any others, these initiatives underscore the new and unique challenges faced by those charged with developing and implementing the new public health systems.

CONCLUSION

Over the course of its long history, public health has been imbued with a social justice ethic. In its early days, during the 18th and 19th centuries, the formal public health system addressed the terms and conditions of work and unsanitary living conditions, and introduced public education campaigns to reduce the spread of infectious diseases. More recently, the system has focused on the contribution of individual "lifestyle" factors to chronic, non-communicable diseases. The "new" public health concentrates on the effect of collective lifestyles of modern societies and the social environments on the health of populations. All of these aspects of public health are represented within the structural dimensions of the present-day public health system in Canada. These dimensions, described in this chapter, although presented as if they were separate, are in fact, interlocking components of an emerging system. Population health assessments, for example, inform health promotion strategies, and disease and injury prevention policies assume well-functioning health protection programs. The dimensions of surveillance, disease and injury prevention, and emergency preparedness could reasonably be considered under one broad functional category, "health promotion and protection."

The public health system is plagued by "crisis management." A perennial problem is sustained, system-level investment. A related problem for the public health system is the lack of legislation that identifies roles and responsibilities of the various levels of government or terms of inter-jurisdictional cooperation. Both Frank (2003) and the Kirby Commission Report (2003) call for strengthening the public health system through increased funding, legislative improvements, and improved coordination across jurisdictions and institutions. These recommendations are necessary if the system is to meet the imminent challenges presented by the aging population, the increase in urbanization and mental health problems, and environmental concerns, including the depletion of ozone in the stratosphere, global climate change, and the threats of international terrorism, all of which have demonstrated adverse health effects.

STUDY QUESTIONS

1. *What is the "new" public health?*
2. *List and describe the main structural dimensions of the public health system in Canada.*
3. *What are some of the imminent public health challenges?*
4. *Describe the barriers to the full realization of a strengthened public health system.*
5. *Well-designed public health policies are effective social welfare policies. Discuss.*

GLOSSARY

disease and injury prevention a range of initiatives in various domains of social life, including vaccination programs, investigation and outbreak control, workplace health and safety regulations, cancer screening, and programs to encourage healthy behaviours, such as anti-smoking campaigns, physical activity, and bicycle helmet use.

health promotion measures that enable people to improve and increase their control over their health. Of all the dimensions of the public health system, health promotion most clearly articulates the philosophy of the "new" public health. Health promotion involves strengthening community health services, joint partnerships between government and community to solve pressing health problems, and advocacy for healthy public policies, including policies that address the social determinants of health: income, education, housing, affordable food, and safe communities.

health protection a long-standing core dimension of public health. Health protection includes inspections of restaurants, child care centres, nursing homes, and other public facilities, and the monitoring and enforcement of water treatment and air quality standards.

health status a description and/or measurement of the health of an individual or population at a particular point in time against a prescribed set of standards.

health surveillance the collection, interpretation, and communication of health data. Health surveillance covers not only disease, but also health risk factors, health determinants, and other social conditions that facilitate real time notification and response to occurrence of a public health threat.

population health assessment the evaluation of the health of the population, overall trends and changes in health, and comparisons of health within subgroups of the population. Population health also involves the development of theories, methods, and measures of population health status and quality of life indicators.

public health the science and art of promoting health, preventing disease, prolonging life, and improving quality of life through the organized efforts of society.

social determinants of health the set of social and economic factors that influence the health status of individuals, communities, and populations. These factors, which include income, food, housing, employment, social exclusion, and access to health services, enable people to improve and increase their control over their health.

REFERENCES

Awofeso, N. (2004). What's new about the "new public health"? *American Journal of Public Health, 94*(5), 705–709.

Canadian Institute for Health Information (CIHI). (2005). *Fact sheet.* Retrieved September 26, 2006, from http://secure.cihi.ca/cihiweb/en/downloads/NHEX_Dec7_factsheet_e.pdf.

Center for Disease Control. (2007a). BSE (Bovine Spongiform Encephalopathy, or Mad Cow Disease). Retrieved August 21, 2007 from http://www.cdc.gov/ncidod/dvrd/bse.

Center for Disease Control. (2007b). vCJD (variant Creutzfeld-Jakob Disease). Retrieved August 21, 2007 from http://www.cdc.gov/ncidod/dvrd/vcjd/index.htm.

Clark, N., & Weist, E. (2000). Mastering the new public health. *American Journal of Public Health, 90*(8), 1208–1211.

Francis, D. (1987). The great transition. In R. Anderson, J. Hughes, & W. Sharrock (Eds.), *Classic disputes in sociology* (pp. 1–35). London: Allen and Unwin.

Frank, J. (2003). *The future of public health in Canada: Developing a public health system for the 21st century.* Ottawa: Canadian Institutes of Health Research: Institute of Population and Public Health.

GHSI (n.d.) Introducing the Global Health Security Initiative. Retrieved September 12, 2006, from http://www.ghsi.ca/english/index.asp.

Hayes, M. (1999). Population health promotion: Responsible sharing of future directions. *Canadian Journal of Public Health, 90,* S15–S17.

Health Canada. (1997). *National forum on health, 1994 to 1997.* Retrieved July 23, 2006, from http://www.hc-sc.gc.ca/hcs-sss/com/nfh-fns/index_e.html.

Health Canada. (2002). *Economic burden of illness in Canada, 1998.* Ottawa: Health Canada.

Kawachi, I., & Kennedy, B. (2002). *The health of nations: Why inequality is harmful to your health.* New York: New York Press.

Kelloway, E., & Day, A. (2005). Building healthy workplaces: What we know so far. *Canadian Journal of Behavioural Science, 37,* 223–235.

Kickbusch, I. (2003). The contribution of the WHO to a new public health and health promotion. *American Journal of Public Health, 93*(3), 383–388.

Kirby, M. (2003). *Reforming health protection and promotion in Canada: Time to act.* 14th Report of the Standing Senate Committee on Social Affairs, Science, and Technology.

Leung, C. (2004). *Yellow peril revisited: Impact of SARS on the Chinese and southeastern Asian Canadian communities.* The Chinese Canadian National Council-National Office.

Marmot, M., Rose, G., Shipley, M., & Hamilton, P. (1978). Employment grade and coronary heart disease in British civil servants. *Journal of Epidemiology and Community Health, 32,* 244–249.

Mayo Clinic (2005). *Bird flu vaccines: Challenges of preventing a pandemic.* Retrieved September 16, 2006 from http://www.mayoclinic.com/health/bird-flu-vaccine/ID00035.

National Institute of Mental Health. (2001). *The impact of mental illness on society*. 01–4586. Maryland: US Department of Health and Human Services.

O'Neill, M., Pederson, A., & Rootman, I. (2000). Health promotion in Canada: Declining or transforming? *Health Promotion International, 15*(2), 135–141.

Parkes, D. (2004). Targeting workplace harassment in Quebec: On exporting a new legislative agenda. *Employee Rights and Employment Policy, 8*, 423–455.

PHAC (2004a). Welcome to the Public Health Agency's website. Retrieved September 18, 2006 from http://www.phac-aspc.gc.ca/about_apropos/index.html#org.

PHAC (2004b). Information September 2004 backgrounder: Public Health Agency of Canada. Retrieved September 18, 2006, from http://www.phac-aspc.gc.ca/media/nr-rp/2004/phac_e.html.

Poland, B., Coburn, D., Robertson, A., & Eakin, J. (1998). Wealth, equity and health care: A critique of a "population health" perspective on the determinants of health. *Social Science and Medicine, 46*(7), 785–798.

Polanyi, M., McIntosh, T., & Kosny, A. (2005). Understanding and improving the health of workers in the new economy: A call for a participatory dialogue-based approach to work-health research. *Critical Public Health, 15*(2), 103–119.

Popay, J., Williams, G., Thomas, C., & Gatrell, A. (2003). Theorizing inequalities in health: The place of lay knowledge. In R. Hofricher (Ed.), *Health and social justice: Politics, ideology, and inequity in the distribution of disease* (pp. 385–409). San Francisco: Jossey-Bass.

Québec Commission des Normes du Travail. (2004). *Labour Standards Act and Regulations.* Section 81.18. Retrieved July 4, 2006, from http://www.cnt.gouv.qc.ca/en/normes/harcelement.asp.

Raphael, D. (2003). Addressing the social determinants of health in Canada: Bridging the gap between research findings and public policy. *Policy Options*, 35–40.

Romanow, R. (2002). *Building on values: The future of health care in Canada.* Ottawa: Commission on the Future of Health Care in Canada.

Secretariat for the Intersectoral Healthy Living Network. (2005). *The Integrated pan-Canadian healthy living strategy.* Ottawa: Ministry of Health.

Shannon, H., Robson, L., & Sale, J. (2001). Creating safer and healthier workplaces: Role of organizational factors and job characteristics. *American Journal of Industrial Medicine, 40*, 319–334.

Titmuss, R. (1968). *Commitment to Welfare.* London: Allen and Unwin.

UNAIDS (2006). *Global Report: Overview of the global AIDS epidemic.* Retrieved September 16, 2006, from http://data.unaids.org/pub/GlobalReport/2006/2006_GR_CH02_en.pdf.

Wikipedia, (n.d.a). Bovine spongiform encephalopathy. Retrieved September 4, 2006, from http://en.wikipedia.org/wiki/Bovine_spongiform_encephalopathy.

Wikipedia, (n.d.b). AIDS. Retrieved September 4, 2006, from http://en.wikipedia.org/wiki/AIDS.

Wilkinson, R. (1994). The epidemiological transition: From material scarcity to social disadvantage? *Daedalus: Journal of the American Academy of the Arts and Sciences, 123*(4), 1–78.

World Health Organization (1986). *Ottawa charter for health promotion: The move towards a new public health.* First International Conference on Health Promotion. Ottawa, November 21, 1986. Geneva: World Health Organization.

World Health Organization (1987). *Healthy cities: Health for all targets.* Copenhagen: World Health Organization.

4

Health Status in Canada

ROANNE THOMAS-MACLEAN University of Saskatchewan

JENNIFER POUDRIER University of Saskatchewan

INTRODUCTION

What are the factors which influence health and illness? Researchers concerned with health status seek to understand some of the reasons why people become ill. The forces that shape health and illness are known as determinants of health. The state of knowledge surrounding determinants of health is continually evolving as researchers increasingly engage with various understandings of what forces shape health and illness.

Health status refers to determinants of health such as: health conditions, human function, and deaths (Canadian Institute for Health Information (CIHI), 2003, p. 3). Traditionally, the overall health of a population has been measured through key **indicators of health status**. These include: life expectancy, mortality rates, and causes of death.

Influenced by sociology, expanding conceptualizations of health have more recently resulted in some recognition of the social factors which influence health status. For instance, the Canadian Institute for Health Information (CIHI) distinguishes between health status and non-medical determinants of health. Table 4.1 provides details of health indicators related to both health status and non-medical determinants of health used by Statistics Canada.

The latter (non-medical determinants) can also be described as **social determinants of health** and include: health behaviours, living and working conditions, personal resources, and environmental factors (CIHI, 2003, p. 3). Other researchers consider additional social determinants of health including "peace, social support and family violence" (Public Health Agency of Canada (PHAC), 2002, p. 1). More commonly, specific social determinants of health include: income, employment, education, child care, and housing (PHAC, p. 1). Each of the social determinants of health influences health status in Canada.

Along with broad conceptualizations of health, researchers and policy-makers have become interested in factors which influence groups differentially, and have worked toward developing new understandings of health and illness which better reflect the

TABLE 4.1 *Health Indicators*

Health Status			
Well-Being	**Health Conditions**	**Human Function**	**Deaths**
Self-rated health	Body mass index (BMI), Canadian standard	Functional health	Infant mortality
Changes over time in self-rated health	Body mass index (BMI), International standard	Two-week disability days	Perinatal mortality
Self-esteem	Arthritis/ rheumatism	Activity limitation	Life expectancy
	Diabetes	Conditions causing activity limitation	Mortality crude counts/rates, age-standardized rates:
	Asthma	Disability-free life expectancy	Total mortality
	High blood pressure	Disability-adjusted life expectancy	Circulatory disease deaths
	Chronic pain – affects activities	Disability-adjusted life years	Cancer deaths
	Chronic pain – severity	Health expectancy	Respiratory disease deaths
	Depression		Suicide
	Low birth weight		Unintentional injury deaths
	Cancer incidence, age-standardized rates:		AIDS deaths
	All cancer incidence		Potential years of life lost (PYLL):
	Lung cancer incidence		Total PYLL
	Colorectal cancer incidence		Cancer PYLL
	Breast-female cancer incidence		Circulatory PYLL
	Prostate cancer incidence		Respiratory PYLL
	Injury hospitalizations		Unintentional injuries PYLL
	Food and water-borne diseases		Suicide PYLL
	Injuries		AIDS PYLL

Non-Medical Determinants of Health

Health Behaviours	Living and Working Conditions	Personal Resources	Environmental Factors
Smoking status	High school graduates	School readiness	Exposure to second-hand smoke
Smoking initiation	Post-secondary graduates	Social support	
Changes over time in smoking behaviour	Average number of years of schooling	Life stress	
Frequency of heavy drinking	Unemployment rate		
Leisure-time physical activity	Long-term unemployment rate		
Breastfeeding practices	Low income rate		
Dietary practices	Children in low income families		
	Average personal income		
	Housing affordability		
	Decision latitude at work		
	Median share of income		
	Government transfer income		
	Owner-occupied dwellings		
	Crime rate and youth crime rate		

Source: Health Indicators, November 2003. Statistics Canada, catalogue no. 82–221-XIE.

complexity of health disparities and inequality. Sociological critiques of risk factors have illuminated new directions for understanding the reasons people become ill. This chapter begins with a discussion of health status which is followed by consideration of social determinants of health. The chapter concludes with a discussion of emerging trends in the area of inequality and health which suggests that a more robust conceptualization of health status is emerging.

SELECTED INDICATORS OF HEALTH STATUS

Life Expectancy

The overall health of a population may be determined through several indicators. One important indicator is **life expectancy** which has increased in Canada over the last century. Table 4.2 depicts changes in life expectancy (years) over a 70-year period for males and females in Canada, showing an increase in life expectancy for both males and females between 1931 and 2001. For females in 1931, the average life expectancy at birth was 62.1 years, while for males it was 60.0. Between 1931 and 2001, the average life expectancy at birth for females increased by 20 years, from 62.1–82.1. The increase for males, in the same time period, was 17 years, from 60.0–77.0. Table 4.2 also illustrates a life expectancy gap between females and males, with females living, on average, approximately five to six years longer than males between 1991 and 2001. The gap between females and males increased during a 60-year period (1931–91), from 2.1–6.3 years. However, the gap is narrowing as the difference in average life expectancy between females and males has declined steadily from 6.3–5.1 years between the years 1991 and 2001.

Further variations in life expectancy can be explored through provincial comparisons. Table 4.3 shows the average life expectancy at birth for males and females for each of the ten provinces in 2005. Life expectancy is highest for males in Ontario, Manitoba, Saskatchewan, Alberta, and British Columbia. In these provinces, life expectancy for males is 75 years. Life expectancy for females is highest in Saskatchewan. In this province, life expectancy for females is 82 years. Life expectancy for females is lowest in Nova Scotia and Newfoundland and Labrador at 80 years, while the lowest life expectancy for males is in Prince Edward Island at 73 years.

Mortality Rates

Infant mortality rates are also considered a solid indicator of the overall health of a society. A dramatic decrease in infant mortality rates accounts for much of the increase in life expectancy in Canada within the last century. **Maternal death rates** have also

TABLE 4.2 *Life Expectancy at Birth in Canada, by Sex, Selected Years, 1931–2001*

Year	Female	Gain	Male	Gain	Female-Male Difference in Life Expectancy
1931	62.1	—	60.0	—	2.1
1961	74.3	12.2	68.4	8.4	5.9
1991	80.9	6.6	74.6	6.2	6.3
1999	81.7	0.8	76.3	1.7	5.4
2000	82.0	0.3	76.7	0.4	5.3
2001	82.1	0.1	77.0	0.3	5.1

Source: Adapted from Statistics Canada. (2005). Canada at a Glance, 2005. Retrieved Feb. 2006, from http://www.statcan.ca/english/freepub/12-581-XIE/12-581-XIE2005001.pdf.

TABLE 4.3 *Life Expectancy at Birth in Canada, by Sex and by Provinces, 2005*

Province	Female	Male
Newfoundland and Labrador	80	74
Prince Edward Island	81	73
Nova Scotia	80	74
New Brunswick	81	74
Quebec	81	74
Ontario	81	75
Manitoba	81	75
Saskatchewan	82	75
Alberta	81	75
British Columbia	81	75

Source: Adapted from Statistics Canada. (2005). Life Expectancy at Birth, by Sex, by Provinces. Retrieved Feb. 2006, from http://www40.statcan.ca/l01/cst01/health26.htm.

declined significantly. Figure 4.1 shows the decline in both maternal and infant death rates. The decline can be attributed to improvements in the standard of living over time, as well as medical advances and better access to health care (PHAC, 2005). In 2002, the infant mortality rate was 5.4 infant deaths per 1,000 live births. The leading causes of death in infants (children under 1 year of age) are perinatal conditions, which include factors related to gestation and respiratory distress, congenital anomalies, and Sudden Infant Death Syndrome (SIDS). While congenital anomalies account for one of the leading causes of death in children who are 1–4 years of age, the causes of death in children do vary markedly from the causes of death in infants.

Child mortality rates have decreased over time. In 2002, Canada's child mortality rate was 6.6 deaths per 1,000 births. The leading cause of death in this age group is injury, with the leading cause being transport injuries. Congenital anomalies represent the second leading cause of death for children who are between 1–4 years of age, while cancer is the third leading cause of death in this age group.

FIGURE 4.1

Causes of Death, Children < 5 Years, Worldwide, 2000–03

*One-third of neonatal causes are infectious diseases.

Source: World Heath Day Toolkit, World Heath Organization 2005.

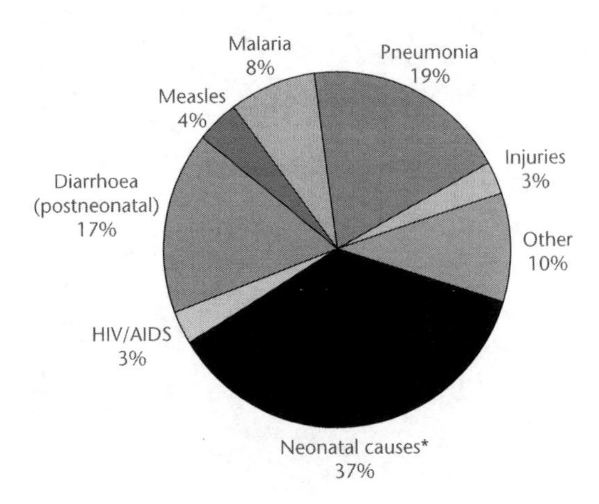

Socio-economic status affects maternal health, infant mortality rates, and child mortality rates. Women with lower socioeconomic status have higher rates of maternal death. Variations in socio-economic status are also connected to variations in childhood injuries. Further, Aboriginal Canadians experience higher infant death rates than non-Aboriginal Canadians and Aboriginal children are more likely to experience injuries than non-Aboriginal children (PHAC, 2005)

For adults, the leading cause of death in 1995 was heart disease. Within the country, cardiovascular disease rates vary, with the Atlantic provinces having higher rates than the western provinces. There is a relationship between risk factors for cardiovascular disease and the variation between the provinces. Risk factors for cardiovascular disease include smoking, high blood pressure, and obesity. Rates for these risk factors are all higher in Atlantic Canada as compared to western provinces, such as British Columbia.

The variations in health status described in this section suggest that health and illness are strongly influenced by social context. In other words, health is shaped through complex patterns of interaction between individuals and their social environment. For this reason, it is important to develop an understanding of additional factors shaping health status.

SOCIAL DETERMINANTS OF HEALTH

Health researchers recognize that the social determinants of health are as influential on health status as behaviour and medical care (PHAC, 2002, p. 2). It has been shown that the magnitude of inequality in socioeconomic status between members of a population affects health status. Increased disparities in the social determinants of health have been noted over the last 15–20 years (PHAC, p. 2).

For example, housing and food security crises, a lack of regulated child care, and job insecurity are all factors that may result in a decline of health status. Canadians with low incomes are less likely to rate their health as excellent in comparison to those with high incomes as Figure 4.2 shows (Canadian Public Health Association (CPHA), 1999, p. 8).

FIGURE 4.2

Self-rated Health Status of Canadians by Income Levels

Source: Canadian Public Health Association. (1999). Building a Healthy Future. Retrieved Feb. 2006, from http://www.phac-aspc.gc.ca/ph-sp/ phdd/pdf/ resources/Building_e.pdf.

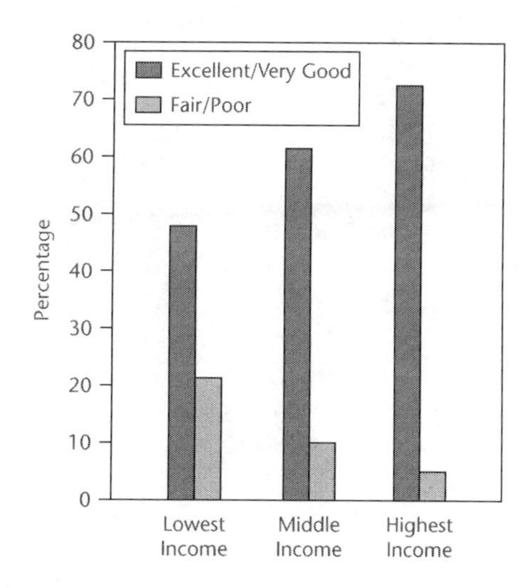

Approximately 50 percent of Canadians with low incomes report their health as very good to excellent as compared to 70 percent of those in the highest income bracket. People with low incomes have shorter life expectancies and are more likely to be ill than those with higher incomes. It should be noted that the gap between those who are wealthy and those with low incomes is considered more problematic than the income of a population, with a larger gap or more inequality connected to poorer health (CPHA, p. 8).

Emerging data regarding the link between inequality and poor health has led to changes in the ways in which health researchers identify risk factors connected to health status. A great deal of health research, particularly in epidemiology, has focused on identifying individualized risk factors for illness. These models of research assert that illness is caused by a complex "web" of influences ranging from the individual to the societal (Shim, 2002, p. 131). More recently, researchers have suggested that there is a need for "epidemiologic theory" (Krieger, 1994, p. 887). Such theory seeks to examine at a macrological level what makes societies healthy or ill through consideration of such factors as time, place, and environment (Krieger, p. 887). Further, it has been argued that while inequalities connected to race, class, and gender have been explored, the social construction of these categories has been neglected (Shim, p. 130).

Those critical of epidemiological research state that while it purports to examine social inequality, the reality is that epidemiological research transforms complex concepts, such as gender, into individual risk factors (Krieger, 1994; Shim, 2002). Shim cites the example of sedentary lifestyles as a way of illustrating how the shift from complexity to individuality occurs. Physical activity has been shown to vary by race and gender. Such research implies that it is up to the individual to address their lifestyle, without exploring the ways in which race and gender are constructed and "with little discussion or explicit study of the complex social contexts and causes leading to sedentary lifestyle" (Shim, 2002, p. 133). This means that:

> Epidemiological approaches to managing race, class and sex/gender distill the effects of *social* and *relational* ideologies, structures and practices organised around such differences into characteristics of discrete and self-contained individuals...[which] thereby renders invisible the very social relations of power structuring material and psychic conditions and life chances that contribute to the stratification of health and illness. (Shim, p. 134)

Williams (2003) concurs and states that: "risk factor epidemiology tends to assume a freedom to make health choices that is out of line with what many lay people experience as real possibilities in their everyday lives" (p. 147).

Raphael (2000) cites a number of Canadian studies which demonstrate the connections between inequality and health status in this country. For example, one study (Wilkins et al. in Raphael, p. 196) showed that people living in the poorest 20 percent of neighbourhoods were more likely to die of common diseases such as cancer, heart disease, and diabetes than those in wealthier neighbourhoods. Raphael also directs attention to *The Health of Canada's Children Report* which showed that children living in low income families had higher incidence rates of illness, hospital stays, and injuries (p. 196). While Raphael states that the emphasis of Canadian research into health and inequality has tended to document the relationship between poor health status and low incomes, he also asserts that there is evidence of a national decline in health which corresponds with growing economic inequality (p. 197). Despite emerging knowledge surrounding health and inequality in Canada, Raphael states that additional research is needed. Like Williams and Shim, Raphael argues that health inequalities have been neglected because public health discourse has focused upon individual manifestations of inequality, along with the health behaviours of those with low incomes.

Alleviating the concerns raised by health researchers regarding the construction of social categories at the micrological or individual level may mean acknowledging the politics of health and illness, as well as beginning from a research orientation concerned with "social justice" (Shim, 2002, p. 144). Williams (2003) argues that sociology may draw upon epidemiology, but he also states that sociology has carved a niche for itself with respect to health and illness. Sociological perspectives on health status may then explore "the connections between structures, ideologies, policies, contexts, lifecourses or lifecycles and their impact on health and wellbeing" (Williams, p. 135).

Williams expands Shim's thinking about epidemiological sociology to suggest that the discipline must move beyond individualized conceptualizations of social categories in order to address inequality and power (p. 135). In his robust description of the potential of sociology for understanding health and illness, Williams also asserts that subjective understandings of experience are also in need of development. Thus, Williams argues for the development of a more complex understanding of the relationships between social structure, forms of inequality, and individual behaviour. The challenge is to guard against explanations for health and illness that do not individualize social factors and to understand the relationship between experience and social structure. Explanations that underscore the complexity of health and illness and the role of power among marginalized groups are also important. The next section of this chapter explores a variety of ways in which these challenges might be addressed.

NEW DIRECTIONS AND FUTURE STRATEGIES IN SOCIAL INEQUALITY AND HEALTH

One key development in social inequality in health is a fresh attention to understanding the complex role of racism and **racialization** in health and illness. The role of racism in morbidity rates, for example, has been very difficult to capture methodologically. For instance, research shows that African Americans are more likely to suffer from heart disease that those in other categorical groups (Ding et al., 2003). This could be explained by addressing intervening variables such as environmental factors (such as housing), lifestyle factors (such as individual diet), and biological factors (such as genetic predisposition). It has been argued that new explanatory models should be considered to capture the potentially profound and intricate role of racism or racialization on health status. For example, the Access Alliance Multicultural Community Health Centre (AAM-CHC) and its partners produced a review of Canadian research associated with health and racialized groups in Toronto, entitled "Racialised Groups and Health Status: A Literature Review Exploring Poverty, Housing, Race-Based Discrimination and Access to Health Care as Determinants of Health for Racialised Groups." In their review of the literature, they found that empirical research has not explored the complex relationships between racism, income, and health in the Canadian context. Race-based discrimination has been explored extensively vis-à-vis individual mental health at the micro-level and currently more attention is being paid to the ways in which racism, inequality, and health interact at structural levels (AAMCHC, 2005). The AAMCHC suggests that one direction for future research is to draw more extensively on the lived experience (knowledge) of specific racialized groups in order to define "racism," and to contribute to the research process more broadly.

In other innovative directions, new strategies for understanding the broader and contextual factors associated with power and community in health and illness have emerged. In a strategy geared toward self-determination in the First Nations, the National Aboriginal Health Organization (NAHO) has developed the Regional Longitudinal Health Survey (RHS). According to NAHO, the objectives of the RHS are to:

> Collect information about the health of First Nations peoples as a means of improving their own health and living conditions. In the past, researchers sometimes collected information on First Nations with little or no explanation to the people they were examining, for reasons often unknown or unexplained and with results that were not shared with First Nations. (NAHO, 2004, p. 3)

Accordingly, the RHS is about empowering First Nations communities to collect and share information that is relevant and credible for First Nations governance and policy making. The guiding principle of the RHS is Ownership, Control, Access, and Possession (OCAP). OCAP means that First Nations control data collection processes in their communities. First Nations own, protect, and control how information is used. The right of First Nations communities to Own, Control, Access, and Possess information about their peoples is fundamentally tied to self-determination and to the preservation and development of their culture. OCAP allows a community to make decisions regarding why, how, and by whom information is collected, used, and shared for research, evaluation, and planning purposes (NAHO, 2005; Shnarch, 2004).

The guiding principles for understanding health indicators in this context begin from the point of view that "a system so complex as the natural world and the human connections to these environments includes many different levels of understanding" (NAHO, 2005, p. 7). Figure 4.3 provides an example of the ways in which all levels of wellness are interconnected and based on balance.

Likewise, the approach to coordinating the vast array of information collected and shared through the RHS falls in line with principles of holism and complexity. Figures 4.3 and 4.4 visually describe the approach to the research process whereby health concerns have been filtered through the seven levels of understanding, then grouped into four quadrants.

The RHS includes information regarding traditional and comparative health indicators, such as exercise, nutrition, and dental care. However, the RHS also includes "a type of data not available from the usual sources, such as information on the health practices, beliefs and knowledge, perceptions and past histories of First Nations peoples. Thus, the survey paints a more holistic portrait of First Nations health" (NAHO, 2004, p. 3). Figure 4.4 shows the range of health indicators addressed in the RHS, including more complex and contextual issues, such as the use of traditional medicines or healers, the role of community development, and the perceptions about the impact of residential schooling. An illustration of the integration of complex health indicators is presented

FIGURE 4.3
Visual Model of Health from a First Nations Perspective

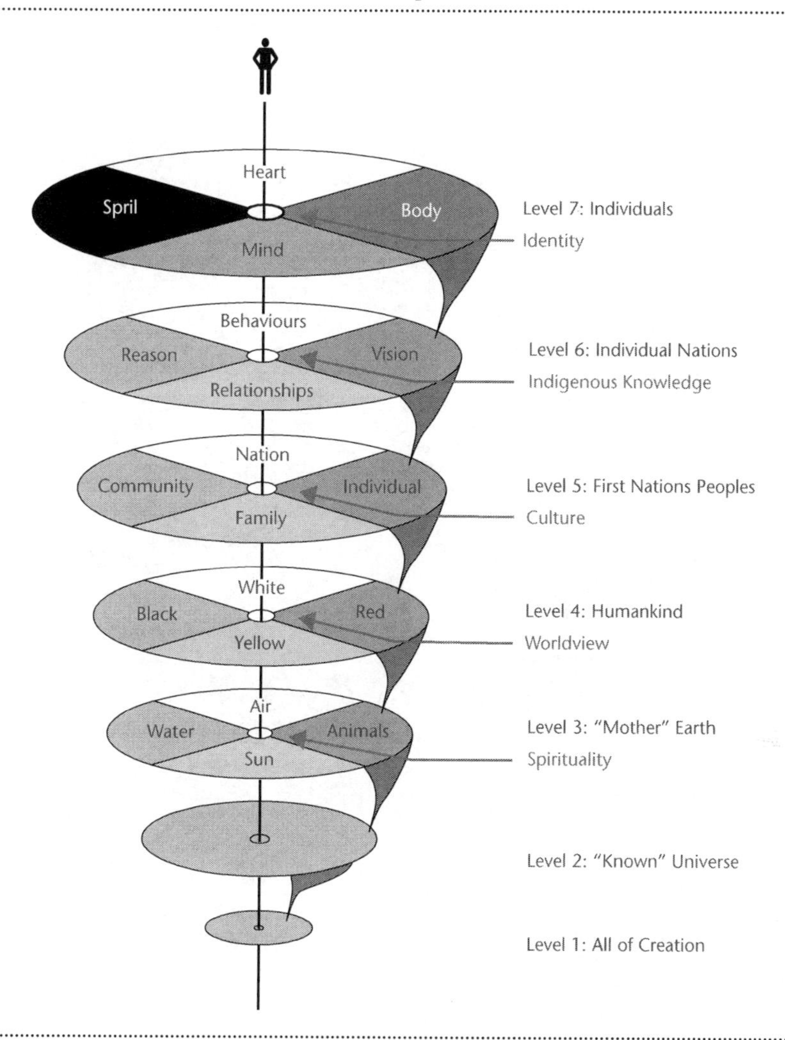

Source: First Nations Regional Longitudinal Health Survey (RHS) 2002/03.

in Table 4.4 where the findings on residential schooling are reported (NAHO, 2005, p. 2). This model illustrates how principles of holism and context, alongside social and individual experience, can play an important role in understanding health and illness.

The RHS has taken a compelling new direction in terms of addressing the complexity of health and illness in context. It has also addressed the role of empowerment and self-determination through the guiding principles of OCAP.

In the international context and drawing upon the same types of themes and principles, a recent publication produced by the Health Evidence Network (HEN) published

FIGURE 4.4
First Nations Regional Health Survey Topics

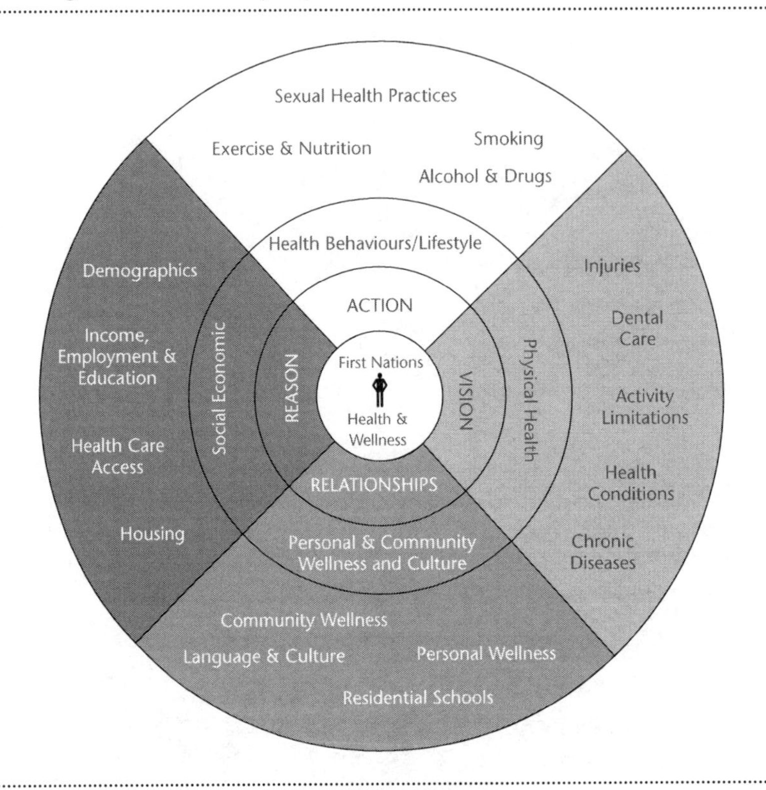

Source: First Nations Regional Longitudinal Health Survey (RHS) 2002/03.

by the World Health Organization (WHO), argues that empowerment is a viable strategy to improve health status and to reduce health disparities. While difficult to define specifically because successful empowering health strategies are created in specific contexts and based upon the needs of those in local contexts, "empowerment" is generally understood as a paradigm of research, practice, outcome, or tool with a focus on bottom-up community participation. At the same time, empowerment is "recognized both as an outcome by itself, and as an intermediate step to long health status and disparity outcomes" (Wallerstein, 2006, p. 4). HEN has found that interventions and research that have been focused on the process of empowering communities or groups has improved the lives of people. In particular, "women's empowering interventions, integrated with the economic, educational, and political sectors have shown the greatest impact on women's quality of life, autonomy and authority and on policy changes, and on improved child and family health" (Wallerstein, 2006, p. 4). In order to be effective in improving quality of life, participatory empowering health strategies need to be combined with practices geared toward building community capacity and autonomy. Based

TABLE 4.4 *Highlights of First Nations Regional Health Survey*

Residential Schools	About one in five (20%) attended residential school. Among those aged 18–29 years, the proportion is only 6% compared to 47% and 43% for those aged 50–59 and 60–69 years; Nearly half (47%) of those who attended residential school reported that it had negatively affected their overall health and well-being; A number of things were identified as contributing to the negative impacts of attending residential school: Isolation from family (81%) Verbal or emotional abuse (79%) Harsh discipline (78%) Loss of cultural identity (77%) Separation from First Nation community (74%) Witnessing abuse (72%) Loss of language (71%) Physical abuse (69%) Loss of traditional religion or spirituality (67%) Bullying from other children (62%) Poor education (45.4%) Harsh living conditions (43.7%) Lack of food (43%) Lack of proper clothing (41%) Sexual abuse (33%)
Active Living	Walking is the reported physical activity (90% reported it), followed by fishing (43%), berry-picking or other food gathering (38%), swimming (38%), bicycling (35%), and hunting or trapping (32%). Overall, one in five (21%) have "sufficient" physical activity (at least 30 minutes of physical activity resulting in increased heart rate and breathing for 4 or more days of the week). The proportion is higher for men than women (27% vs. 15%). About one-third (35%) of respondents always or almost always eat a nutritious and balanced diet compared with more than half (53%) who only sometimes do. The remaining 12% either rarely (9%) or never (3%) eat a balanced and nutritious diet. Three out of five (59%) adults often consume traditional protein-based foods, such as game and fish. The proportion was higher (71%) in small communities. There are no gender, age, income, or education related differences found in the consumption patterns for traditional foods. Nearly three-quarters (73%) are considered either overweight (37%), obese (31%), or morbidly obese (5%). Most adults with diabetes are classified as obese.

Alcohol, Tobacco, Drugs	Nearly three in five (59%) smoke either daily (46%) or occasionally (13%). The rate is slightly (but probably not significantly) lower than in 1997 and is about triple the rate for Canadians in general. Smoking rates decrease rapidly with age, from 70% among those 18–29 years old to 28% among those 60 and over. Alcohol abstinence is more common among First Nations but so is heavy drinking. About two-thirds (66%) consumed alcohol, compared to 79% of the general Canadian population. Meanwhile, one in six (16%) First Nations consume five or more drinks on an occasion on a weekly basis compared to only 6% of Canadians overall. Alcohol consumption was lowest among those 60 years and older (36.3%) and was more common among men (69%) than women (62%). Those in remote isolated communities were more likely to drink than those in non-isolated communities (76% vs. 85%). More than one-quarter (27%) used marijuana in the past year, about double the Canadian rate (14%).

Source: First Nations Regional Longitudinal Health Survey (RHS) 2002/03.

on the literature, HEN has summarized several areas of policy around empowerment to be considered:

- Successful empowering interventions cannot be fully shared or "standardized across multiple populations, but must be created within or adapted to local contexts" (e.g. culture and gender appropriateness).
- Specific population programs to overcome the larger political, social, racial, and economic forces that produce and maintain inequities need to be developed and further evaluated.
- Structural barriers and facilitators to empowerment interventions need to be identified locally.
- Empowerment strategies, including community-wide participation, seem worthwhile to be integrated into local, regional, and national policies, and economic, legal, and human rights initiatives.
- Health promotion should address effective empowerment strategies, such as:
  - increasing citizens' skills, control over resources, and access to information relevant to public health development;
  - using small group efforts, which enhance critical consciousness on public health issues, to build supportive environments and a deeper sense of community;
  - promoting community action through collective involvement in decision-making and participation in all phases of public health planning, implementation and evaluation, use of lay helpers and leaders, advocacy and leadership training, and organization capacity development;
  - strengthening healthy public policy by organization and inter-organizational actions, transfer of power and decision-making authority to participants of

interventions, promotion of governmental and institutional accountability and transparency, and being sensitive to the health care needs defined by community members.

Overall, there are compelling new directions for future research that continue to take into account the significant role of context, community power, and empowerment in explanatory models associated with the social context of health and illness.

CONCLUSION

This chapter has explored the factors which shape health and illness in Canada, beginning with an overview of the concept of health status and non-medical (social) determinants of health. A variety of health status indicators was presented, demonstrating changes over time as well as disparities between the provinces of Canada.

A discussion of the social determinants of health illustrated the connections between inequality and poor health. This discussion suggests that prior, individualistic emphases in research are being enriched with more sophisticated knowledge about the complex interplay of health, inequality, and society.

The chapter ends with a presentation of selected initiatives which expand the focus of research in the area of health status in Canada. If fully realized, these initiatives promise to add another layer of complexity to understanding the relationship between health status, determinants of health, inequality, and empowerment.

STUDY QUESTIONS

1. *What are some of the indicators of health status and non-medical determinants of health discussed in this chapter? How do they help to explain health and illness in our society?*
2. *What are some of the reasons sociologists are critical of epidemiological approaches to health status?*
3. *In what ways are racism and racialization associated with health and illness? What strategies could researchers employ in order to explore the role of race in research on health and illness?*
4. *How do empowerment strategies seek to improve health status in Canada?*

GLOSSARY

child mortality rates the number of deaths of children between one and four years of age divided by the number of live births. It is usually expressed as a rate per 1,000 live births.

indicators of health status measurements of health conditions and death.

infant mortality rates the number of deaths of live-born children under one year of age divided by the number of live births. It is usually expressed as a rate per 1,000 live births.

life expectancy the number of years a person is expected to live, from their year of birth.

maternal death rates the number of deaths of women while pregnant or within one year of the termination of pregnancy divided by the number of live births. It is usually expressed as a rate per 100,000 live births.

racialization the process by which racial categories are constructed as different and unequal in ways that lead to health inequalities, and social, economic, and political impacts (Galabuzi, 2001).

social determinants of health a constellation of a variety of social factors which may include behaviour, economic and financial concerns, as well as issues associated with the broader context of a society.

REFERENCES

Access Alliance Multicultural Community Health Centre. (2005). *Racialised groups and health status*. Retrieved Feb. 2006, from http://atwork.settlement.org/downloads/atwork/Racialised_Groups_Health_Status_Literature_Review.pdf.

Canadian Institute for Health Information. (2003). *Health indicators*, 2003(2): November 2003. Statistics Canada, Catalogue no. 82–221-XIE.

Canadian Public Health Association. (1999). *Building a healthy future*. Retrieved Feb. 2006, from http://www.phac-aspc.gc.ca/ph-sp/phdd/pdf/resources/Building_e.pdf.

Ding, J., Diez Roux, A.V., Nieto, F. J., McNamara, R.L., Hetmanski, J.B., Taylor, H.A., Jr, & Tyroler, H.A. (2003). Racial disparity in long-term mortality rate after hospitalization for myocardial infarction: The atherosclerosis risk in communities study. *American Heart Journal, 146*(3), 459–464.

Krieger, N. (1994). Epidemiology and the web of causation: Has anyone seen the spider? *Social Science and Medicine, 39*(7), 887–903.

National Aboriginal Health Organization. (2004). *Backgrounder, First Nations regional longitudinal health survey*. Retrieved Feb. 2006, from http://www.health-sciences.ubc.ca/iah/acadre/site_files/resources/RHS_backgrounder_sept_9_04.pdf.

National Aboriginal Health Organization. (2005). *First Nations regional longitudinal health survey: The people's report, 2002/2003*. Retrieved Feb. 2006, from http://www.rhs-ers.ca/english/pdf/rhs2002–03reports/rhs2002–03-the_peoples_report_afn.pdf.

National Aboriginal Health Organization. (2005). *RHS at a glance: Selected findings from the First Nations regional longitudinal health survey, 2002/2003*. Retrieved Feb. 2006, from http://www.rhs-ers.ca/english/pdf/rhs2002–03reports/rhs_at_a_glance.pdf.

National Aboriginal Health Organization. (2005). *RHS 2002/2003 adult survey highlights: The good, the bad and the ugly*. Retrieved Feb. 2006, from http://www.naho.ca/firstnations/english/documents/RHS_Adult_Highlights.pdf.

Public Health Agency of Canada. (2002). *The social determinants of health: An overview of the implications for policy and the role of the health sector*. Retrieved Feb. 2006, from http://www.phac-aspc.gc.ca/ph-sp/phdd/pdf/overview_implications/01_overview_e.pdf.

Public Health Agency of Canada. (2005). *Make every mother and child count: Report on maternal and child health in Canada*. Catalogue no. H124–13/2005.

Raphael, D. (2000). Health inequalities in Canada: Current discourses and implications for public health action. *Critical Public Health, 10*(2), 193–216.

Schnarch, B. (2004). Ownership, control, access and possession (OCAP) or self-determination applied to research: A critical analysis of contemporary First Nations communities. *Journal of Aboriginal Health, 1*(1), 80–95.
Shim, J.K. (2002). Understanding the routinised inclusion of race, socioeconomic status and sex in epidemiology: The utility of concepts from technoscience studies. *Sociology of Health & Illness, 24*(2), 129–150.
Statistics Canada. (2005). *Canada at a glance, 2005*. Retrieved Feb. 2006, from http://www.statcan.ca/english/freepub/12–581-XIE/12–581-XIE2005001.pdf.
Statistics Canada. (2005). Life expectancy at birth, by sex, by province. Retrieved Feb. 2006, from http://www40.statcan.ca/l01/cst01/health26.htm.
Wallerstein, N. (2006). *What is the evidence on effectiveness of empowerment to improve health?* Copenhagen, WHO Regional Office for Europe (Health Evidence Network report). Retrieved Feb. 2006, from http://www.euro.who.int/ Document /E88086.pdf.
Williams, G.H. (2003). The Determinants of Health: Structure, Context and Agency. *Sociology of Health & Illness, 25*(Silver Anniversary Issue), 131–154.

PART 2

THE HEALTH SECTOR AND HEALTH SERVICES

In recent years, the health sector and health services have expanded considerably beyond conventional Western medicine and conventional therapies. There has been an extensive interest in complementary and alternative medicine (CAM) in Canada, and an increase in utilization of CAM together with conventional medicine and therapies. The health sector encompasses a plethora of services and therapies, both conventional and alternative. Health care providers then include personnel working in both the conventional and alternative fields. These developments have important consequences for service providers and service recipients. Four readings in this section address an array of issues concerning conditions of work for service providers, the relation between conventional and alternative medicines and therapies, and their consequences for service recipients.

The basis of care in the health care system is the service provider. The first three chapters in this section examine an array of factors that affect the nature, organization, and conditions of work for doctors and nurses, and the consequences of these factors for service providers and recipients. These chapters focus on the two principal occupations in the health care system: doctor and nurse.

The first reading, by Bourgeault, examines the role of internationally educated physicians and nurses in the provision of health services in Canada in the context of international mobility of this labour force. The flow of physicians and nurses into and out of Canada, she argues, is influenced by factors such as health human resource policy, immigration policy, working conditions of health professionals, and various trade agreements. Bourgeault provides an extensive discussion of key immigration and emigration policy issues and programs to reduce barriers to integration of internationally trained health care providers, and argues for recruitment and retention strategies to reduce outflows of professionals thereby reducing the necessity to recruit internationally educated professionals. Internationally educated physicians and nurses are a crucial component of Canadian health human resources. As Canada is both importer and exporter of health care providers, it is important to examine both the flows into and out of Canada, and the policy and contextual factors that bear upon these flows.

Wotherspoon, in Chapter 6, focuses on the development of nursing education and its relationship to the development of nursing as an occupation. He argues that contradictions inherent in the provision and utility of nurses in Canada have limited nurses' position in the health care division of labour and ensured their subordination to the medical profession and hospital management. He argues further that medical dominance was partly facilitated and secured by the subordination of nursing.

Wotherspoon analyzes the nature and organization of contemporary nursing education and the contradictory consequences it has for the power and autonomy of nurses. Current educational and professionalization strategies are contributing to a significant fragmentation and differentiation of nursing work. The implications of this trend for professional development strategies are explored.

Varcoe and Rodney, in Chapter 7 focus on the nature and consequences of health care reforms, particularly hospital reforms, for nurses and patients. They argue that these reforms are a reflection of a corporate ideology that stresses the need to do more with less in the face of perpetual scarcity. The ideology of scarcity, combined with the biomedical model of health and illness, has given rise to a form of work organization in which only a limited range of health care needs are recognized as legitimate. As a result, only a few health care services are valued, while others are considered to be disposable. Thus nurses increasingly are discouraged, if not prohibited, from providing the emotional care required by many patients and their families.

The consequences of health care reforms and these management regimes for patients are a reduced quality and quantity of care. For nurses, the consequences are high levels of personal stress, distress, and disease. Many nurses respond to the distress by donating their private time to the job so that they can perform the essential functions of care that current corporate management regimes disallow. Some nurses have developed strategies of resistance to corporate imperatives and sabotage of management regimes in their attempts to provide care for patients and their families. Varcoe and Rodney conclude their chapter with the observation that an informed critique of current reforms is a prerequisite for real health care reform.

In the last reading, Northcott addresses the issue of complementary and alternative medicine (CAM) and its relationship to conventional medicine. Specifically, Northcott discusses the transformation of the relationship between conventional medicine and CAM from a discourse of division to a discourse of integration, presents a typology of CAM, and examines the utilization of CAM in Canada. Only a few decades ago, the proponents of conventional medicine described this orientation in terms such as scientific, rational, and legitimate, while at the same time dismissing alternative medicine with pejorative descriptors such as unscientific, illegitimate, and magical, and characterizing alternative practitioners as quacks and charlatans. This discourse of division also divided the users into those who had legitimate health concerns and those who were dupes, hypochondriacs, and fools. On the other hand, the proponents of alternative medicine described their orientation as personal, holistic, natural, and less invasive, and conventional medicine pejoratively as impersonal, disease-oriented, and invasive, and claimed that their patients were better served than those of conventional medicine.

Northcott shows that the discourse of division has been increasingly replaced with a discourse of integration. Alternative medicine is seen as complementary and compatible with conventional medicine. This merger of conventional and alternative medicine has been labeled as blended medicine, integrative medicine, and characterized as medical pluralism.

Northcott concludes with a discussion of the explanation of this accommodation and integration between conventional and alternative medicine. In response to increasing popularity and use of alternative medicine and the threat it posed to its domination, conventional scientific medicine embraced CAM as a strategy to preserve its dominant position in contemporary society and the medical market place. This blending and integration may also be seen as an attempt to commodify health care, to exploit and control existing medical markets, and to create new ones by an increasingly global and corporate health care industry.

5

On the Move: The Migration of Physicians and Nurses into and out of Canada

IVY LYNN BOURGEAULT McMaster University

INTRODUCTION

Health care workers have long been nationally and internationally mobile, but this has increased more recently both in terms of size and velocity. The labour market in health care, as in most domains, is becoming international in scope in part because labour mobility is often a requirement under international trade agreements. But this has not occurred without controversy. Concerns about the international migration of health care providers have become a more prominent and controversial feature of health sector analysis in recent years in light of severe staff and skill shortages in health systems of many countries.

Canada has not been immune to these trends. While some have lamented about Canada's health care "brain drain" (Hickey, 1995; Williams, 1997), it is important to note that we are not just an exporter of health labour, but a significant importer as well. Canada has historically relied extensively on foreign health labour to help solve shortages in rural and remote **under serviced areas** and in urban subspecialties (Barer & Stoddart, 1991; CIHI, 2001; OMA, 2002). For example, in the 1950s and 1960s, many nurses from Britain, particularly those with advanced training in midwifery, were recruited by Health Canada to serve in northern outposts (Mason, 1988). Today, immigrant doctors account for roughly one quarter of all physicians practicing in Canada; similarly, six to seven percent of all nurses have been trained in other jurisdictions. By way of contrast, between 16 and 20 percent of physicians emigrate from Canada, and although a smaller percentage of nurses emigrate, it has a critical impact on the delivery of health care.

Until very recently, some have argued that there was a lack of a coordinated effort between Canadian institutions with respect to the migration and regulation and registration of health care providers. For example, as Fooks (2003) points out, there are "[c]omplex and interdependent actors in multiple jurisdictions with unaligned accountabilities. Governments do one thing, educational institutions do another, and regulatory authorities do a third" (p. 7). Though we have moved in the direction of a nationally coordinated policy for health labour immigration, very little exists that addresses the issue of health labour emigration. The absence of such coordinated policy in Canada is notable in light of the associated problems of lost labour and potential solutions to human resource crises, and also because of the increasing salient ethical issues associated with the international migration of health care providers. These ethical issues have moved to the forefront not just of health policy, but also of foreign policy agendas.

In this paper, I will begin to map out:

- The flow of physicians and nurses into and out of Canada through available datasets and published documents.
- The policy, decision-making processes, and regulatory environments that influence the flow of physicians and nurses into and out of Canada.

THE DEMOGRAPHIC CONTEXT OF HEALTH LABOUR MIGRATION IN CANADA

International Medical Graduates in the Canadian Health Care System

Foreign *medical* labour is often referred to in the policy literature as **international medical graduates (IMGs)**. Though often considered a homogeneous group, IMGs are a varied group which include: 1) Canadians who pursue training elsewhere; 2) visa physicians who are recruited into Canada to meet particular needs; 3) graduates who enter Canada as refugees or who otherwise meet immigration requirements; and 4) visa trainees who enter Canada through postgraduate training positions (Barer & Stoddart, 1991). The probability of achieving full registration status with a provincial licensing authority varies dramatically across these categories, and across provinces and territories (see Figure 5.1). For example, the province of Quebec has the lowest percentage of IMGs in Canada, whereas Saskatchewan has the highest (CMA, 2001). Manitoba, for example, as well as Saskatchewan and Newfoundland, have recruited extensively in South Africa to meet the needs of their rural communities (Grant, 2004).

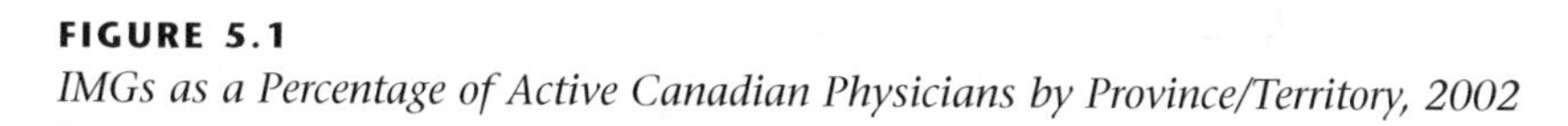

FIGURE 5.1

IMGs as a Percentage of Active Canadian Physicians by Province/Territory, 2002

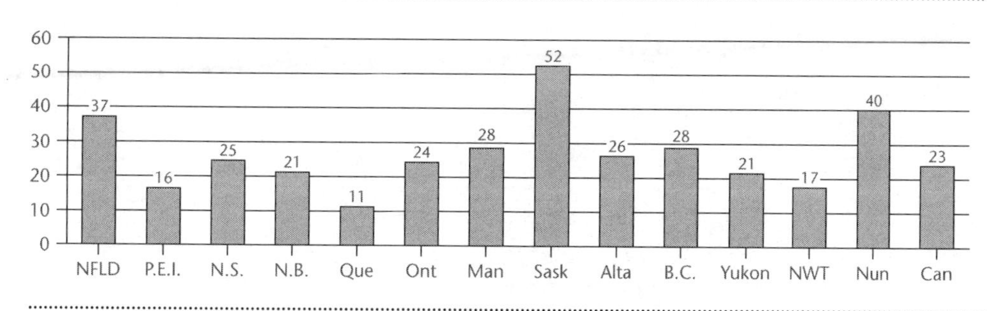

Source: Adapted from CIHI (2002) Supply, Distribution and Migration of Canadian Physicians, 2002.

Throughout most of the 1970s, roughly one third of our physicians were IMGs but this has most recently dropped to 23 percent (CIHI, 2003) (See Figure 5.2). This downward trend reflects limits on the number of post-graduate training spaces available as well as a number of other factors (CIHI, 2003). For example, prior to 1975, physicians were granted the maximum points for occupational demand; in 1975, however, incoming physicians were assigned no points, virtually disqualifying applicants who could not produce evidence of concrete job offers (Roos et al., 1976). This was consistent with the recommendations of the National Committee on Physician Manpower who wanted to focus on the goal of *self-reliance* for future physician needs (CMA, 1999). As a result, the number of immigrants claiming medicine as their intended occupation fell dramatically subsequent to these decisions in 1975.

More recently, according to the CMA (2001), the number of IMGs recruited has increased quite dramatically, from 388 in 1993 to 790 in 1997 (CMA, 2001). As Grant (2004) states,

> Part of the explanation for the recent increase in migration also rests with changes in Canada's supply of physician services. After years of seeking to curtail the number of physicians, and foreign-trained physicians in particular, practising in the country, there is growing support for the view of an impending shortage. (p. 7)

The proliferation of temporary medical licenses to IMGs is just one indication, as argued by CMA representatives, of the physician shortage in both family medicine and in particular specialties (Barer & Webber, 1999).

In terms of the sources of immigrant physicians who end up working within the health care system, they used to be graduates primarily of medical schools in the U.K. or Ireland. In 1985, 35 percent of graduates who began working in the Canadian health

FIGURE 5.2
IMGs as a Percentage of Active Canadian Physicians, 1969–99

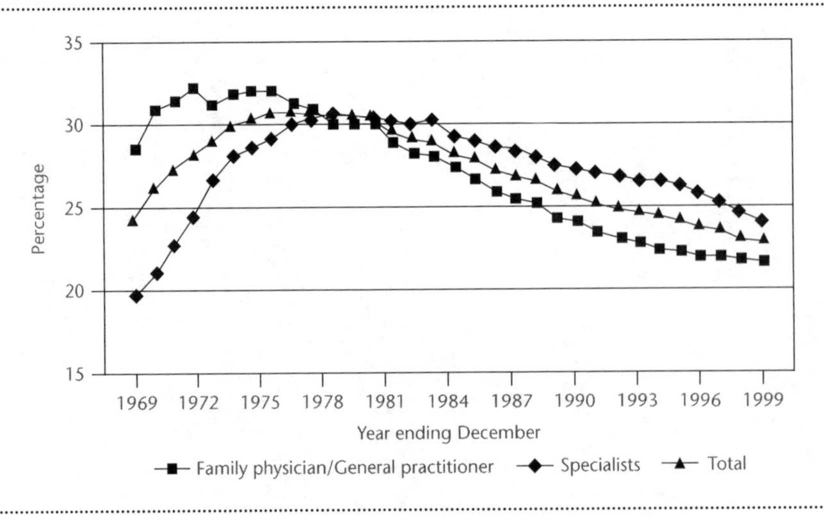

Source: Dr. M. Watanabe, *Canadian physician workforce: The role of IMGs,* International Medical Guidelines national symposium proceedings, 2002. Data from Southern Medical Database, Canadian Institute for Health Information.

care system were immigrants, but by 2000 the number of immigrants entering the system fell to just over five percent. Now, the majority of IMGs working within the health care system are from South Africa and India, with India being a notable source of specialists, and South Africa of general/family practitioners (many of whom are recruited into rural/remote areas), although this differs across provinces (Barer & Webber, 1999). For example, South African physicians account for 24 percent of those who entered in 2000, up from under nine percent in 1985 (CIHI, 2001). Interestingly, in 1998 only 3.3 percent of Canadian IMG physicians in active practice had been trained in the United States, of which one quarter had been trained in either California or New York. The relative importance of Eastern Europe as a source of IMGs has declined over this period, as Western European countries have become a more significant source. Demographically, IMGs tend to be older than Canadian-educated physicians (47 percent are age 55 or older, compared with 29 percent of all physicians) and a smaller proportion are female (22 percent versus 30 percent) (Hawley, 2004).

It is important to make some distinctions in the statistics presented here. First, there is a difference between the proportion of IMGs *in* the country (depicted in Figures 5.3 and 5.4) and those *entering* the country. Thus even though the number of physicians immigrating to Canada from the U.K. is in decline, they nevertheless still represent a sizeable proportion of IMGs in the country. Moreover, it is important to emphasize that it is not necessarily the case that those entering the *country* enter the *health care system*. Indeed, this difference is what has been highlighted by many as one of the key policy problems in this sector (see the following discussion).

FIGURE 5.3

Distribution of Active Civilian IMG Physicians by Place of Graduation and Type

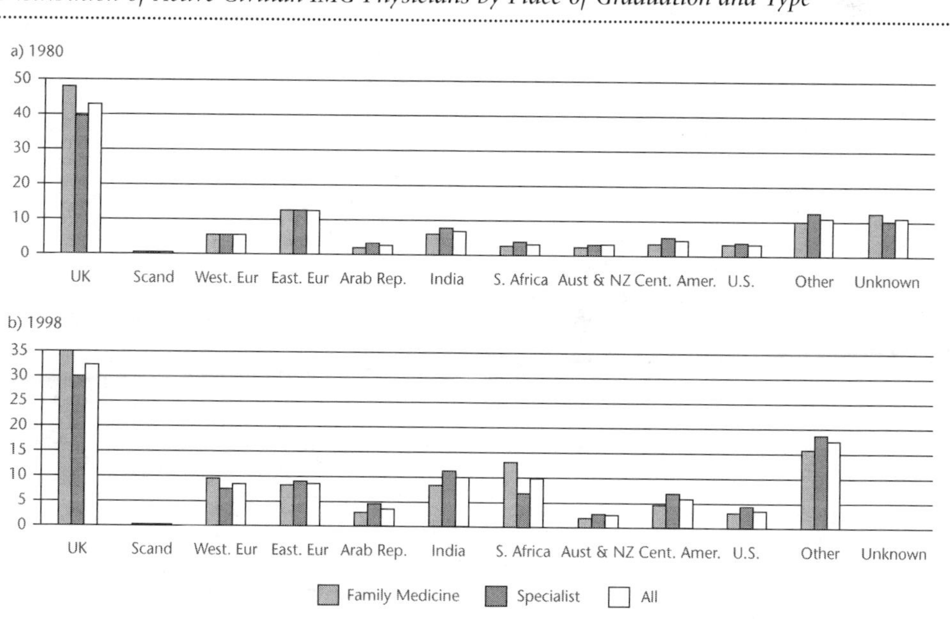

Source: Barer, Morris L., & Webber, William A. (1999). *Immigration and emigration of physicians to/from Canada*. Centre for Health Services and Policy Research University of British Columbia.

FIGURE 5.4

Percentage of IENs by Country of Graduation, Canada, 2003

Source: CIHI (Canadian Institute for Health Information). (2004). *Supply and distribution of registered nurses in Canada, 2003.*

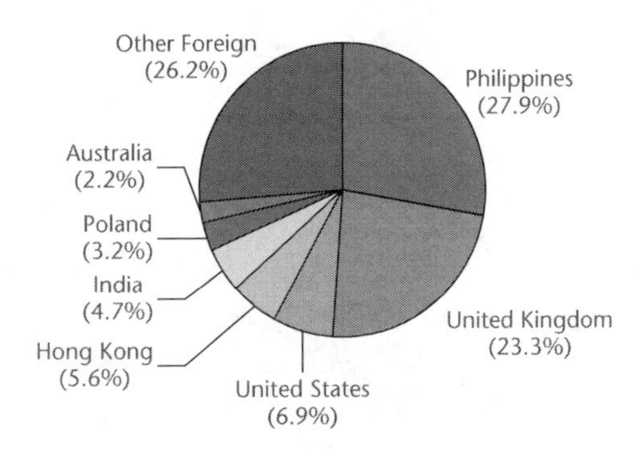

Internationally Educated Nurses in the Canadian Health Care System

The overall percentage of **internationally educated nurses (IENs)** has remained relatively steady over the last five to ten years (see Table 5.1). Specifically, in 2003, 7.3 percent of all nurses working in Canada were internationally trained, up from 6.8 percent in 1999 (CIHI, 2000). There has, however, been a slight increase in the recruitment of foreign trained nurses in some provinces and territories – notably British Columbia (15.0%), Ontario (11.4%), Saskatchewan, and the Northwest Territories – in the face of impending shortages (see Table 5.2).

The Philippines have been one of the primary sources for immigrant nursing labour in Canada (up to 26 percent of all IENs in 2003 from 23.5 percent in 1999) as it is elsewhere (Joyce & Hunt, 1982), but nurses from the U.K. represent an equal proportion (albeit down to 26 percent in 2003 from 30.5 percent in 1999); nurses from the United States (7 percent in 2003 down from 9.4 percent in 1999), Hong Kong (6 percent in both 2003 and 1999), and India (4.7 percent in 2003 and 4.3 percent in 1999) represent smaller groups of IENs (see Figure 5.5). In 2003, nurses from the Philippines, the U.K., and the United States represented 2.1 percent, 1.7 percent, and 0.5 percent, respectively, of all RNs employed in nursing in Canada (CIHI, 2004).

TABLE 5.1 *Number and Percentage of IENs in Canada, 1990–2003*

Year	# of IENs in Canada	# of RN Population
1990	19,144	8.6%
1999	15,564	6.8%
2000	14,177	6.1%
2001	15,659	6.8%
2002	15,847	6.9%
2003	17,633	7.3%

Source: Based on Little, L. (2005). The Canadian case. Presentation to Bellagio Institute Conference on the International Migration of Nurses. July. http://www.academyhealth.org/international/nursemigration/little.ppt and CIHI (Canadian Institute for Health Information). (2000). *Supply and distribution of registered nurses in Canada, 1999.*

TABLE 5.2 *RN Workforce by Location of Graduation and Province/Territory of Registration, Canada, 2003*

	N.L.	P.E.I.	N.S.	N.B.	Que.	Ont.	Man.	Sask.	Alt.	B.C.	Y.T.	N.W.T.	Nu.	CAN.
							(percentage distribution)							
Canadian Trained	97.8	97.9	97.7	98.8	97.5	88.5	94.1	95.5	88.9	84.5	93.1	89.1	85.7	91.8
Retained Graduates	93.0	69.0	77.6	85.9	95.7	80.8	83.8	81.4	61.6	55.6	0.0	11.1	0.0	80.0
Interprovincial Graduates	4.9	28.9	20.1	12.9	1.9	7.7	10.4	14.1	27.3	28.9	93.1	78.1	85.7	1.9
Canadian-trained	0.0	0.0	0.0	0.0	0.0	0.0	0.0	0.0	0.0	0.0	0.0	0.0	0.0	0
Foreign-trained	1.7	1.8	2.3	1.2	2.5	11.4	5.9	3.1	3.9	15.0	6.9	10.4	13.6	7.3
Philippines	0.3	0.0	0.2	*	0.6	2.9	2.6	0.6	1.9	4.7	*	2.2	*	2.0
United Kingdom	1.0	**	0.9	**	0.3	2.8	1.1	0.7	0.3	4.1	2.1	5.8	5.4	1.7
United States	0.2	1.0	0.6	0.5	0.1	0.9	0.7	0.5	0.0	0.7	*	*	*	0.5
India	*	0.0	*	0.0	0.1	0.7	0.1	**	0.4	0.4	0.0	0.0	0.0	0.3
Hong Kong	0.0	0.0	*	0.0	0.1	0.6	**	*	0.1	1.5	0.0	0.0	0.0	0.4
Poland	0.0	0.0	0.0	0.0	0.1	0.5	**	0.0	0.1	0.2	*	0.0	0.0	0.2
Australia	*	0.0	0.1	*	0.1	0.1	0.1	0.2	0.3	0.6	1.7	*	3.1	0.2
Other Foreign	0.2	*	0.5	0.2	1.4	2.9	0.9	1.1	0.8	2.8	*	*	3.5	1.9
Not Stated	0.5	0.3	0.0	0.1	0.1	0.1	0.0	1.3	7.2	0.5	0.0	0.5	0.8	0.9
Total RN Workforce	100	100	100	100	100	100	100	100	100	100	100	100	100	100

* Value suppressed In accordance with CIHI privacy policy
** Value suppressed to ensure confidentiality

Source: Adapted from CIHI, (2004). Supply and Distribution of Registered Nurses in Canada, 2003.

FIGURE 5.5
Physicians Who Moved Abroad or Returned From Abroad, Canada, 1969–2005

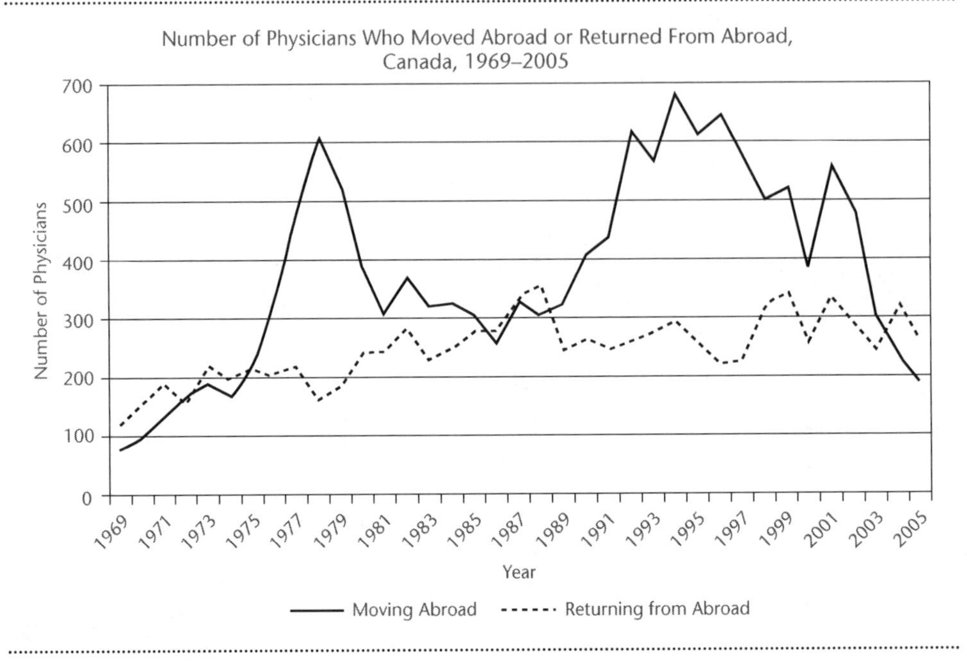

Source: SMDB, CIHI. Supply, distribution and migration of Canadian physicians 2005.

In addition to being disproportionately distributed across provinces, IENs from particular jurisdictions also tend to "cluster" in one province or region of the country. This is also likely to be the case for physicians. Further, similar to what we found in the case of physicians, the percentage of IENs as per the population of active nurses may mask some of the recent changes that are best captured by statistics on new entrants. For example, in Ontario, we find that from 1999–2003, on average 34 percent of the new registrants have been IENs. How long these new foreign trained applicants stay in the country is difficult to track. Indeed, many key informants noted how Canada may act as a sort of "weigh station" with the ultimate destination being the United States. Demographically, it has been found that IENs in the current workforce are, on average, more than five years older than Canadian-trained nurses (49.4 years to 44.1 years in 2003) (CIHI, 2004). We also know that immigrant nurses, particularly those of colour, occupy the lowest echelons of the profession if they do manage to make it in (Calliste, 1996). Indeed, it is common to find deskilling occurring simultaneously with immigration and this trend is not unique to Canada (IRPP, 2005).

Summary

In sum, what is clear in undertaking this comparative analysis of the demographic data available on internationally educated physicians and nurses is that

- We can state with some certainty that internationally educated physicians and nurses are a crucial component of Canadian health human resources.

- The source countries for internationally educated physicians and nurses have not only shifted over time, but they also differ across these cases.
- What is also clear from these demographic trends is that various health care and health human resource policy have an important influence.

Just as we have found fluctuations in the volume and demographics of health care providers who migrate to Canada, we find similar fluctuations in the number of providers leaving the country. Across all professions, the primary destination is our neighbour to the south – the United States – for a variety of reasons.

THE MEDICAL BRAIN DRAIN

Most of the ink spilled on the health care brain drain has been regarding the **out migration** of physicians from Canada; this drain was particularly heightened in the mid 1990s for reasons which will become clear. According to an article in the Vancouver Sun,

> Doctors are leaving Canada in near-record numbers and there are fears of a national shortage if the hemorrhage continues ... The numbers are even larger if they include medical students who left immediately after getting their degrees but before being licensed to practise. (Bueckert, 1995)

Bueckert quoted Bruno l'Heureux, then president of the Canadian Medical Association, in this article:

> "For 1994 the total approaches 800.... If you take into consideration the students who left immediately on receipt of their MD, the number (of departures) is just under 1000.... This... constitutes a loss of $750 million per year in tax-financed human capital, primarily to the United States." (Bueckert, 1995)

A study of physicians conducted by Ryten, Thurber, and Buske (1998) also found that the 1989 graduation cohort was diminished by 16 percent, the majority of which diminishment was caused by migration to other countries. The trend continued with a peak in 1995 with 85 percent of health graduates moving to the United States. This peak is widely attributed to the outflow of family physician graduates resulting from Ontario's decision to introduce geographic billing restriction legislation (Ma et al., 1997). Physicians left Canada at a rate about 10 times higher than all other Canadian emigrant workers but this still only represented less than one percent of physicians in Canada per year. These researchers concluded that "the yield of the Class of 1989 for Canada's physician workforce is insufficient to meet annual physician inflows from Canadian sources to serve population growth and to replace retiring or emigrating physicians" (Ryten et al., 1998, p. 9). Earlier, McKendry et al. (1996) found that 22 percent of Canadian physicians said they were likely to move to the United States whereas only four percent of the U.S.-based respondents indicated a willingness to move back to Canada. This was, however, at the peak of the migration of physicians away from Canada.

In 2004, a dramatic shift was noted in that for the first time since 1969 (the period for which data are available) more physicians returned to Canada than moved abroad (see Figure 5.6). Specifically, CIHI reported that in 2004, 317 physicians returned to Canada, and 262 moved abroad. In the period between 2000 and 2004, the number of physicians who left Canada declined by 38 percent. In 2004, 262 physicians left Canada, down from 420 physicians who left in 2000. It was also found that roughly 25 percent of the physicians who moved abroad in 2004 were IMGs, and 44 percent received their degree within the last 10 years. Of the physicians who left Canada, the majority were male (69%). Also, more male (74%) than female doctors returned from abroad (CIHI, 2005).

The Nursing Brain Drain

With respect to nurses, a recent CIHI (2004) report noted that over 5,000 nurses maintained their Canadian licence while working outside of Canada in 2003.[1] Over 80 percent were employed in the United States; indeed, Canadian nurses are one of the main sources of IENs in the United States (22 percent versus 32.6 percent for the Philippines) (Buchan, Parkin, and Sochalski, 2003). As stated by Aiken et al. (2004):

> Canada has long been a source of nurses for the United States, especially in Border States, where Canadian nurses' credentials are generally accepted by endorsement because of the comparability in educational and licensure requirements. (pp. 72–73)

Other countries that attract Canadian nurses are Saudi Arabia, the United Kingdom, and Hong Kong (see Figure 5.7). These totals, however, only include nurses maintaining their Canadian licenses while working abroad, thus these data are at best incomplete. To date, no study has investigated whether or not RNs that maintain their registration in Canada while abroad are more likely to return to Canada than those ceasing registration. Moreover, this snapshot in time also masks the trends over time that indicate a net loss in the 1990s of 5,000–16,000 RNs (Little, 2005).

FIGURE 5.6

Percentage of RNs with Secondary Registrations by Location of Employment, 2003

Source: CIHI (Canadian Institute for Health Information). (2004). *Supply and Distribution of Registered Nurses in Canada, 2003.*

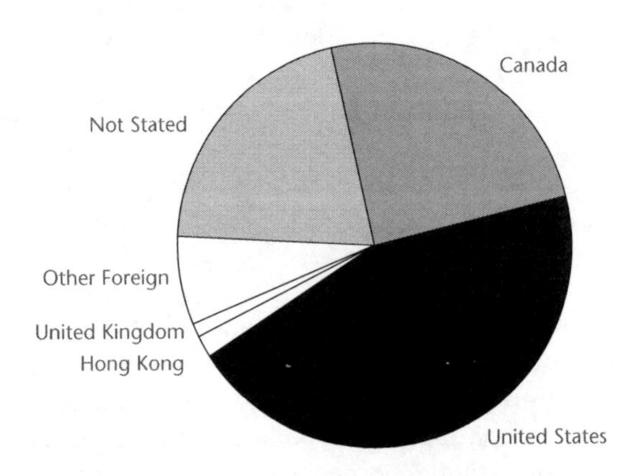

Summary

In sum, we have better data on the inflow of health care providers into Canada than we do of the outflow. Similar to the case for immigration, what is also clear from these demographic trends is that various health care and health human resource policies have an important influence and indeed the issues of immigration and emigration are linked, as will be discussed more fully next.

THE POLICY CONTEXT OF HEALTH LABOUR MIGRATION IN CANADA

The ebb and flow of health care providers into and out of Canada is due in large part to policy decisions and the broader policy context of health human resources. In this section I address the following key immigration policy issues:

- Barriers to the process of gaining entry and programs to help streamline this process;
- The relationship between immigration and the crisis of underserved areas; and
- The ethical issues involved in the migration of health care providers to Canada.

I also address the following key emigration policy issues:

- The impact of local remuneration and working conditions;
- Trade agreements; and
- Factors affecting return migration.

Barriers to Gaining Entry for Internationally Educated Physicians and Nurses

The process of being integrated into the Canadian health care system if you are trained internationally as either a physician or a nurse is incredibly complex. One visual depiction of the complexity of this situation highlights the various federal and provincial government agencies – professional bodies surrounded by social, ethical, political, and geographic contextual factors (see Figure 5.7). This "web" situates the internationally trained professional at the centre from which position they must mediate these various layers of influences in order to become integrated and practice in the health care system.

In this process, internationally trained health care providers must overcome some barriers to integration, many of which have been noted in the literature; for example,[2]

- Poor information available to prospective immigrants overseas, especially with regards to what they must do in order to legally practice their profession in Canada.
- Information available in Canada about professional standards and registration is often not clear, transparent, or understandable for a newcomer.
- Difficulty in having educational credentials recognized due to, for example, difficulties in getting official transcripts sent by institutions outside of Canada.
- Difficulty in having professional experience gained outside of Canada recognized.

FIGURE 5.7

Web of Federal/Provincial Government, Professional Bodies, and Contextual Factors involved in the Recognition of Internationally Trained Health Care Providers

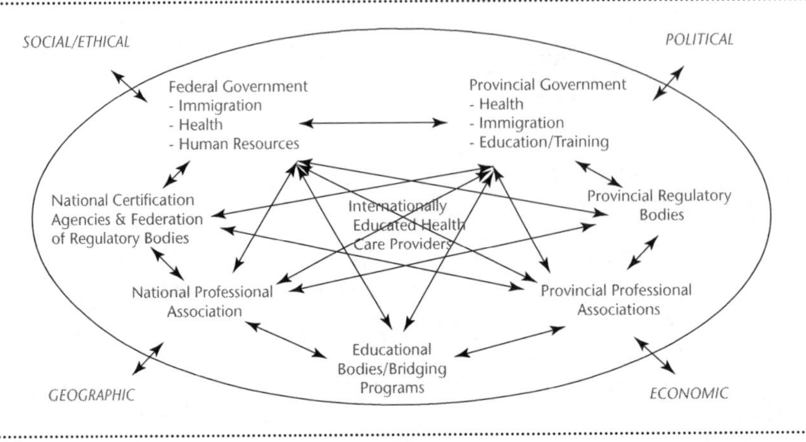

Source: Inspired by the "Web of stakeholders involved in the recognition of internationally trained professionals in Ontario" © 2000 Centre for Research and Education in Human Services.

- Absence of sufficient upgrading/bridging programs to assist newcomers to fill gaps in knowledge or experience vis-à-vis professional expectations in Canada.
- Need for improved orientation to Canadian workplace culture.
- Lack of occupation-specific language training, especially at high levels.
- Absence of, or difficulty in, accessing appeal processes.
- Direct and indirect costs of assessment processes can be prohibitive.

Specific barriers experienced by IMGs noted in several documents include limitations in the number of residency training positions. In 2002, for example, only 16.7 percent of the graduates of foreign medical schools who applied to CaRMS were successful in obtaining a postgraduate medical position.

The recently released report, *Navigating To Become A Nurse In Canada* (2005), summarized the barriers to integration of IENs as follows;

> Canada has 25 regulatory bodies for some 300,000 nurses. While each of these bodies has a similar general approach to assessment, there are some discrepancies and their assessment may differ. The assessment process can be protracted and take months, even years, to complete.... Moreover, IENs may apply to more than one jurisdiction and/or to more than one nursing regulatory body, resulting in duplication of effort.... Some provinces offer specific bridging programs for IENs but they are not all similar in content, length or cost and only some incorporate language and communication training. (p. 6)

Moreover, as noted by Lisa Little, Chair of the Steering Committee of the IEN-DP,

> There is widespread recognition that correcting the problems confronting IENs will require the co-operation of governments at all levels, regulatory bodies, unions, employers, government

> and community agencies and that addressing these particular issues must be part of an overall strategy.

The barriers to timely and effective integration of internationally educated physicians and nurses have associated costs for all involved. It is not surprising, therefore, that several programs have recently been mobilized to attend to these difficulties.

Programs to Reduce Barriers to Integration of Internationally Trained Health Care Providers

One of the key issues preventing efficient integration of internationally trained health care providers has been the many layers of organizations involved in the integration process; there can also often be insufficient communication between these key stakeholders. In response to these concerns, one of the key partnerships that have emerged in the new programs to reduce barriers has been between government and professional bodies at both the national and provincial levels. At the same time, however, there are synergies that are also possible within professions, again at both the national and provincial levels. I briefly mention here some of the key national initiatives.

ADVISORY COMMITTEE ON HEALTH DELIVERY AND HUMAN RESOURCES

The Advisory Committee on Health Delivery and Human Resources (ACHDHR) is a federal/provincial/territorial committee reporting to the Conference of Deputy Ministers of Health (CDM). One of the initiatives undertaken by the ADHDHR with respect to the integration of internationally educated health providers was to identify foreign credential recognition as a priority and as an initial step; it established a task force in June 2002 to address the integration of IMGs into the Canadian health care system. This followed on the heels of a National Symposium on IMGs held in Calgary in April 2002, which included representation from governments and key stakeholders in the medical community.

THE IMG TASK FORCE

The goals of the IMG Task Force (2004) were to

> develop strategies to aid in the integration of qualified internationally trained physicians to the Canadian physician workforce. The Task Force was asked to submit recommendations to the Advisory Committee by September 2003 with a goal of reporting the recommendations to the Conference of Deputy Ministers of Health in December 2003. (p. 6)

The key recommendations of the Task Force include:

1. Increase the capacity to assess and prepare IMGs for licensure.
2. Work toward standardization of licensure requirements.
3. Expand or develop supports/programs to assist IMGs with the licensure process and requirements in Canada.
4. Develop orientation programs to support faculty and physicians working with IMGs.
5. Develop capacity to track and recruit IMGs.

6. Develop a national research agenda, including evaluation of the IMG strategy. It would include the evaluation of the IMG licensure recommendations and the impact of the strategy on physician supply. (pp. 1–2)

Most of these are in the process of being addressed largely through the recently announced funds from Health Canada. Specifically, the 2005 budget earmarked $75 million (through Health Canada in follow-up to the Health Accord the previous fall) to be spent over the next five years to accelerate and expand the assessment and integration of internationally trained health professionals. So far, these groups include Pharmacy, Physiotherapy, Occupational Therapy, Medical Laboratory Technology, and Medical Radiation Technology (in addition to Medicine and Nursing).

Moreover, the ACHDHR viewed the work of the Task Force as a "successful template" that could be used to address the integration of other internationally trained health care providers. For example, the ACHDHR held an inaugural Task Force meeting on the recognition of IENs in February 2004. Similar to the case in medicine, this was in response to an environmental scan of current practices and policies with respect to IENs undertaken by the Canadian Nurses Association with funds from Human Resources and Skills Development Canada (HRSDC) Foreign Credential Recognition (FCR) program.

NATIONAL ASSESSMENT OF IENS

In March 2004, HRSDC announced funds for a Diagnostic for the National Assessment of International Nurse Applicants project by the Canadian Nurses Association (CNA). This diagnostic project (IEN-DP) was aimed at "identifying and assessing the current practices and policies with respect to the licensing of international applicants for each of the three regulated nursing groups (Registered Nurses (RNs), Registered Psychiatric Nurses (RPNs) and Licensed Practical Nurses (LPNs)) and providing draft recommendations for further action." This was seen as a critical first step in the process of understanding where systemic changes needed to be made to better integrate IENs into the Canadian health care system.

The report of this project, *Navigating to Become a Nurse in Canada*, was released May 12, 2005, which according to its press release "paints a disquieting picture of the experience internationally educated nurses (IENs) face in integrating into the Canadian health system. The report shows that language and culture remain two of the largest issues for IENs and makes several recommendations that will make the process more efficient, coordinated and responsive to today's realities." Some of the key recommendations included in the IEN-DP report are:

- The establishment of a national assessment service to create an evidence-based standardized approach to the assessment of IENs.
- The establishment of nationally standardized and flexible bridging programs to ensure IENs have the competencies required to meet Canadian nursing standards.
- The development of strategies to address the financial challenges incurred by IENs who enrol in bridging programs.
- The development of a central source of information such as a Web site specific to IENs to access complete, clear, and easily understood information related to immigration and nursing licensure/registration.

Summary

In sum, there have been numerous task forces, working groups, and joint government-profession committees that have been established to examine the barriers to the integration of internationally educated health care providers and an almost equal number of programs established to address these barriers. One of the key recommendations across both professions is the importance of a single portal of information made available to internationally trained health care providers wishing to immigrate to Canada. To date, some action has been taken toward this kind of centralization thus easing the integration process; a great deal of public funding has also contributed to the simplification of the integration process. The trick may be in ensuring that local human resource needs are also met.

DOES MIGRATION HELP SOLVE THE PROBLEM OF UNDERSERVED AREAS?

One of the questions that arise from the policies directed toward the integration of internationally trained health care providers is whether or not they actually help solve the problem of underserved areas. With respect to physicians, the use of IMGs as a long-term policy solution to the shortages of physicians in particular areas is considered by many to be questionable. Indeed, there is evidence to show that IMGs are no more likely to practice in rural or remote regions of Canada than Canadian graduates (Canada's Physician Workforce, 2005). For example, Barer and Webber (1999) argue that,

> While it is commonly assumed that a large proportion of physicians practicing in non-urban areas of the country are IMGs, in fact in 1998 only about 26 percent of those practicing outside census metropolitan areas were IMGs. This was not appreciably different than the overall ratio of IMGs to all practicing physicians in Canada. [Personal communication, Lynda Buske, Canadian Medical Association, April 1999].

Those IMGs that do work in rural areas usually only remain under some form of coercive intervention, after which they often "leak" into the larger geographically unrestricted Canadian physician supply (Barer & Stoddart, 1991). As Grant (2004) states,

> The difficulty arises from the tendency of many immigrant physicians, originally recruited by one province to address a shortage of physician services in remote and rural communities, to relocate to larger urban centres in another province. For some Canadian provinces, struggling to keep the burgeoning cost of their public health system in check, more physicians, from South Africa or elsewhere, in already over served areas is an unwelcome prospect. (p. 2)

Evidence also shows that the likelihood of IMGs immigrating to the United States is comparable to Canadian graduates (Canada's Physician Workforce, 2005).

The proportion of IENs in rural areas has also been found to be relatively low:

> Only 5.6% of the foreign-trained RNs in Canada work in rural and small town areas of the country compared with 18.7% of Canadian-trained RNs; only 1.9% of rural RNs in Canada are international nursing graduates. These numbers likely reflect overall immigrant settlement

> patterns or trends for Canada as a whole. If so, recruitment of foreign-trained nurses would probably have little impact on the numbers of RNs in rural Canada. (CIHI, 2002)

It is not readily apparent from the review of documents regarding the integration of IENs whether the issue of rural, underserved areas is salient.

Ethical Issues: International Migration or Self-Sufficiency?

One of the key ethical questions that arises from this research – and one that has become increasingly salient to all stakeholders involved – is whether or not we should be viewing immigration as a solution to our skilled worker shortages or whether we should be attempting to achieve self-sufficiency insofar as the number of health care providers in this country are concerned:

> The contributions of IMGs to healthcare in Canada have been great. Canada remains an appealing, safe place in which to live and work. Canada will continue to be attractive for healthcare professionals trained overseas. While focused recruitment from abroad will continue, such recruitment is not without important ethical constraints as there is a worldwide shortage of healthcare professionals, including physicians. It is wrong for Canada to actively recruit, or "poach" physicians from developing nations. Any active solicitation of physicians from countries that have a great need for physicians is troubling. Improving Canada's lot, at the expense of healthcare delivery in countries who are less fortunate is not a Canadian healthcare policy goal. (Final Report of Task Force on IMGs, 2004, p. 4)

International migration is commonly viewed as exacerbating shortages in source countries, particularly in African countries where the WHO has stated that the "shortage and migration of nurses and midwives continues to threaten the performance of health systems" (WHO, 2003, p. 2). Indeed, international recruitment began to generate increasing controversy in 2001, when South African Ambassador André Jaquet asked Canada's health ministers to stop the "targeted recruiting that leaves us even less able to grapple with the serious HIV/AIDS pandemic" (Sullivan, 2005a). Just one example noted in the literature details how when two South African anaesthetists were recruited by a Canadian institution to open a new Spinal Injuries Unit, the same day the Centre for Spinal Injuries in Boxburg, near Johannesburg, South Africa – the referral centre for the whole region – was closed and has not been open since (Martineau et al., 2002).

This has not gone unnoticed by the CMA. Its current president, Albert Schumacher, stated before a House of Commons committee in March 2005: "To continue to rely on and recruit IMGs in this way is both unsustainable and unethical, and we must overcome our reliance on them, particularly the active poaching from countries that can least afford it" (Sullivan, 2005a). Schumacher argued instead for a "made in Canada solution" by being self-sufficient in meeting its need for physicians. Echoing these sentiments, CMA past President Peter Barrett stated at the most recent CMA annual meeting in Edmonton (2005),

> "In the face of a global shortage of health care workers," he asked, "can a country in which 24% of practising doctors were educated outside its own borders continue to rely on physicians from countries that can least afford to lose them?" (Sullivan, 2005b)

As aptly summarized in the Final Report of the Task Force on IMGs:

> To date, there has been no national consensus on the merits or meaning of physician self-sufficiency for Canada. This lack of consensus has contributed to a national physician workforce planning process that remains challenged to comprehensively address the health professional needs of the Canadian public. (p. 3)

The self-sufficiency issue has also been raised in the case of nursing. For example, in a recent presentation for an international conference on the global migration of nurses, IEN-DP Chair, Lisa Little argued that we need more domestic production of nurses; better retention strategies to improve the quality of work life for nurses, such as increasing their autonomy and decision-making powers, reducing violence expressed toward nurses, and employing appropriate workloads (Little, 2005).

But this is not simply an issue on the Canadian radar. The World Medical Association's *Statement on Ethical Guidelines for the International Recruitment of Physicians* recommends that: "Every country should do its utmost to educate an adequate number of physicians, taking into account its needs and resources. A country should not rely on immigration from other countries to meet its need for physicians" (Sullivan, 2005a). Moreover, because of the ethical dilemmas of recruiting nurses from poorer nations, Commonwealth countries signed a Code of Practice agreeing not to recruit health care providers from developing countries known to be experiencing shortages (Cesa, 2004). Canada, along with Australia and the U.K. (two other top destination countries), failed, however, to endorse the phrase demanding some form of compensation for source countries.

Moreover, if we direct our attention and our policies toward, international migration – as it seems we are determined to do – a related concern is whether or not we should actively recruit internationally trained health care providers (as has been the case[3]), or simply focus on better integrating those providers who are already here. This latter group is "a source of untapped skilled workers and if not integrated into the Canadian labour force, represents a loss of human capital" (Cesa, 2004, p. 30) both to Canada and the country from which the provider came. As Linda Silas, President of the Canadian Federation of Nurses Unions (CFNU) states,

> There are foreign-trained nurses in Canada who with help (some of it very minimal) could be successfully integrated into our health care system. While CFNU believes that it is immoral to cherry-pick nurses and other health care professionals from the needy citizens of less developed nations, we believe that we have a practical and moral obligation to provide help to those who are in Canada now. (Silas, 2004, p. 7)

Similarly, Dale Dauphinee (2005), Executive Director of the MCC highlighted in a recent article the following key lessons:

- Raiding the physician resources of developing countries by developed countries is unacceptable.
- It is unacceptable to promote the human capital model but fail to provide the flexibility of educational and training opportunities for international medical graduates (IMGs) to learn needed skills and to become acculturated.

- The ethics of physician recruitment extend beyond the policy failures that lead to raiding to include issues of resource management within each recruiting country.
- Physician migration to and from Canada is influenced by variables such as loss of physicians to the United States, physician practice preferences with Canada, and the application of workforce policies and health plan administrative practices within Canada.
- Planners need to consider more carefully both sides of the issues: the intended results but also the unintended consequences of such plans and policies. (p. 22)

It is for these reasons that the programs detailed here are so important.

Some attention has been devoted to the problem of the emigration of nurses and of physicians but again, we find little coordinated policies evident.

Remuneration and Working Conditions

Many have linked anger over health care cuts to the emigration of physicians and nurses in the mid 1990s (Kasperski, 2000; Harper, 1998). For example, Dr. Lorne Tyrrell, dean of medicine and dentistry at the University of Alberta, said "This came home to me the other day when I spoke to a young ENT surgeon who is moving to North Dakota. When I asked him why he would leave Canada when we have such an acute need for specialists like him, he told me those opportunities to do surgery here were too restricted. His waiting room is always full here, but he only has access to an operating room in his Edmonton hospital for 2 hours every 2 weeks. In North Dakota, he gets 2 afternoons a week in the OR" (In Gray, 1999, p. 1028). Over time, these cuts took their toll.

Another reason for the outflow to the United States was directly related to the reduction in residency positions – a trend which not only affected IMGs, but also left few options for graduates to find residencies elsewhere (Gray, 1999). The departure of Canadian physicians to the United States was also facilitated by the rapid expansion of Health Management Organizations (HMOs) there which found Canadian trained family physicians ideal gatekeepers. Some of the key reasons our informants mentioned for emigrating from Canada included better remuneration, more operating time, and better equipment. Together, these influences help to explain the peak in physician outflow that is displayed in Figure 5.7 (above).

For nurses, the southward "brain drain" was particularly dramatic in the mid-1990s, when country-wide cuts in the hospital sector put many nurses out of work, to the delight of eager U.S. recruiters who lured Canadian nurses with signing bonuses of up to US$30,000 (Gray, 1999; Sibbald, 2002). A Registered Nurses Association of Ontario study of Ontario RNs who left Canada between 1991 and 2000 found that most (69.5 percent) said that job opportunities were the main reason they left Canada (specifically, the lack of full-time employment here). Family or personal reasons were cited next (25.5 percent), followed by pay and benefits (12.9 percent), and travel/weather 5.5 percent) (RNAO, 2001). A report by the CNA states that

> nurses here want full-time employment, appropriate workloads, involvement in decision-making and educational opportunities. During the cutbacks of the 1990s, many nurses were forced into part-time or casual jobs, and by the late 1990s 48% of nursing positions provided

TABLE 5.3 *Push and Pull Factors Influencing the International Migration of Health Care Providers*

Push Factors	Pull Factors
Low pay (absolute and/or relative)	Higher pay (and opportunities for remittances)
Poor working conditions	Better working conditions
Lack of resources to work effectively	Better resourced health systems
Limited career opportunities	Career opportunities
Limited educational opportunities	Provision of post-basic education
Impact of HIV/AIDS	Political stability
Unstable/dangerous work environment	Travel opportunities
Economic instability	Aid work

Source: Buchan, J., Parkin, T., & Sochalski, J. (2003). International Nurse Mobility: Trends and Policy Implications: WHORCNICN.

only part-time work. Desperate for stable employment, up to 15% of new Canadian graduates now move directly to the US; the CNA, which represents 115 000 nurses, wants to reduce this to 5%. (Sibbald, 2002, p. 535)

These reasons are not dissimilar to those found for nurses internationally (see Table 5.3) (Buchan, Parkin & Sochalski, 2003).

Trade Agreements

Some analysts stress the importance of looking beyond the particular policy contexts of nation states to understand the broader impact of trade agreements, such as the North American Free Trade Agreement (NAFTA), the World Trade Organization (WTO), and the GATS on the flow of health labour (Orzack, 1998; Bach, 2003). These trade agreements urge national governments to reduce or eliminate requirements and regulatory devices that impede or block the movement of goods and services. NAFTA, for example, allows for the following:

Nurses who are citizens of Canada and Mexico may work in the United States under the NAFTA ("TN") status. Canadian nurses must demonstrate the following:

1. They have a written offer of employment from a U.S. employer for a period not exceeding one year;
2. They are licensed in Canada and in the state of intended employment. Eighteen U.S. states endorse Canadian licenses without the exam;
3. They have proof of Canadian citizenship; and
4. They pay a US $56.00 fee to enter the United States (payable at the U.S. border).

Although it has been found that as a consequence of NAFTA there has not been a massive migration of nurses from Mexico to the United States (Aiken et al., 2004), it has made it easier for Canadian nurses to find work in the United States. This difference is due in large part to the equivalency of education and training (Bach, 2003). The overarching GATS also facilitate increased labour migration because of its efforts toward aligning the competency and recognition requirements for health care providers between countries. So historically, where national boundaries separated licensing, regulatory, and credentialing systems, the facilitation of enhanced international trade in services may weaken the autonomy and authority of nationally-based professional regulatory systems (Orzack, 1998). Taken together, these trade agreements represent new challenges in understanding the migration of health care providers that remain to be fully explored.

Return Migration

Very little is known about the factors affecting return migration of health care providers who leave Canada, and often economic concerns overshadow personal factors in such decisions. In the case of physicians, Webb (1997) argues that "[m]any Canadian doctors have emigrated [to the United States] only to return within a year or two, frustrated with a market-driven health care system and a much more eclectic and individualistic society" (p. 1489). Anecdotal evidence suggests that HMOs in the United States are difficult to deal with, family is missed, and some doctors have said that they find it very difficult working in an environment where health care costs are not paid by the state. Another salient factor noted by more than one of our key informants may be that global unrest is a catalyst for the return of physicians to Canada. In the post-9/11, Iraq war era, it could well be that Canada is considered safer than Europe and certainly safer than the United States. This may be true across professions. Further, in the case of nurses, because the job market for nurses has opened up again, particularly in Ontario, the tide appears to have reversed (Gray, 1999). Very few dedicated "repatriation" programs exist.

In sum, a variety of human resource policy influences can impact upon the emigration of Canadian health care providers just as they can influence the immigration of internationally trained providers. The imperative, therefore, is to be able to use these policy levers in a direction of retaining as many of the Canadian trained providers as we can with the aforementioned goal of self-sufficiency.

CONCLUSION

As has been hinted throughout this chapter, the issues of immigration to and emigration from Canada are intricately linked despite the fact that the more salient issue around immigration at this time is integration. Because of Canada's unique position as an importer and exporter (some have referred to Canada as a "weigh station" for U.S. destinations), our policy decision-makers can be somewhat more hesitant to enter into financial reciprocation agreements with source countries. It is a truly complex issue to manage health human resources while at the same time acknowledging the free movement of labour.

We also have to be clear on the implications of some of the demographic data. For example, given that we have found that internationally educated health care providers tend to be older, they may not be the most effective solution to the human resource crisis we face. In light of such data, the report *Navigating to Become a Nurse in Canada* states,

> Given that one of the root causes of the shortage of nurses in Canada is an aging workforce, a large proportion of these IENs reflect the same age profile. They will not be in a position to fill

> the gap when thousands of Canadian nurses retire. On the other hand, a large number of these IENs have several years of experience, which is a great asset to Canadian employers. (p. 21)

That is, better integration of internationally educated health care providers should be undertaken not so much as a solution to shortages but as an equity issue in its own right. A multi-pronged approach must be taken of which more efficient integration of internationally providers is a part, but must also include attention to factors affecting recruitment and retention. This is why it was important to examine both the flows into and out of Canada and the policy and contextual factors influences these flows.

Further, because of Canada's unique position of being both an importer as well as an exporter of health care providers, it is imperative for us to use this position to become a world leader in attending to the issues that draw health care providers both to our country and away from it. In both cases, a strong argument can be made for better recruitment and retention strategies within Canada to stem the tide of those leaving the health professions – not just for other countries, but altogether – and reducing the necessity for us to go outside our borders to recruit.

STUDY QUESTIONS

1. *What is the difference between the migration of internationally educated physicians and nurses into Canada? Out of Canada?*
2. *How is the migration of health care providers into Canada linked to the migration of Canadian trained health care providers to other countries?*
3. *If you were the Minister of Health of a particular province/territory, how would you address the ethical issues of health care provider migration?*

GLOSSARY

internationally educated nurses (IENs) nurses educated outside of Canada and the United States, either at the registered nurse (RN) or registered practical nurse (RPN) level.

international medical graduates (IMGs) graduates of medical schools outside of Canada and the United States.

out migration the migration outside of a country or area.

self-sufficiency a policy of relying largely on locally educated health care providers for Canada's health human resource needs.

under serviced areas areas of a province, country, or territory that have shortages of one or a number of health care providers or services.

REFERENCES

Aiken, L.H. et al. (2004). Trends in international nurse migration. *Health Affairs, 23*(3), 69–77.

Bach, S. (2003, July). *International migration of health workers: Labour and social issues.* Paper prepared for the Sectoral Activities Department, International Labour Office.

Barer, M., & Stoddard, G. (1991). *Toward integrated medical resource policies for Canada.* Report of the Conf. of Dep. Ministers of Health, Department of Ministers of Health.

Barer, M.L., & Webber, W.A. (1999). *Immigration and emigration of physicians to/from Canada.* Centre for Health Services and Policy Research University of British Columbia.

Buchan, J., Parkin, T., & Sochalski, J. (2003). *International nurse mobility: Trends and policy implications*: WHORCNICN.

Bueckert, D. (1995, May 11). Doctor's exodus stirs shortage fear. *The Vancouver Sun,* p. A2.

Calliste, A. (1996). Antiracism organizing and resistance in nursing: African Canadian women. *The Canadian Review of Sociology and Anthropology, 33*(3), 361–390.

Cesa, F. (2004, May). International medical graduates: A case study. *Health Policy Research Bulletin, 8,* 28–31.

CIHI (Canadian Institute for Health Information). (2000). *Supply and distribution of registered nurses in Canada, 1999.*

CIHI. (Canadian Institute for Health Information). (2001). *Canada's health care providers.* Retrieved September 1, 2006, from http://secure.cihi.ca/cihiweb/dispPage.jsp?cw_page=AR_35_E.

CIHI. (Canadian Institute for Health Information). (2002). *Supply and distribution of registered nurses in rural and small town Canada, 2000.* Ottawa: Written by R. Pitblado, J. Medves, M. MacLeod, N. Stewart, & J. Kulig as part of the Nursing Practice in Rural and Remote Canada Study. Retrieved and excerpted September 1, 2006 from: http://cranhr.laurentian.ca/faq14.html.

CIHI (Canadian Institute for Health Information). (2003). *Supply, distribution and migration of Canadian physicians, 2002.* Ottawa.

CIHI (Canadian Institute for Health Information). (2004). *Supply and distribution of registered nurses in Canada, 2003.*

CIHI (Canadian Institute for Health Information). (2005). *Supply,distribution and migration of Canadian physicians, 2004.*

CMA (Canadian Medical Association). (1999). *Canadian medical forum task force on physician supply,* Retrieved September 1, 2006 from http://www.cma.ca/index.cfm/ci_id/19522/la_id/1.htm.

CMA (Canadian Medical Association) (2001). *CMA Masterfile.*

CMA (Canadian Medical Association). (2005). *Canadian physician workforce:* Executive summary. Feb. Retrieved September 1, 2006 from http://www.caper.ca/docs/articles_interest/pdf_executive_summary_task_force.pdf.

Dauphinee, W.D. (2005). Physician migration to and from Canada: The challenge of finding the ethical and political balance between the individual's right to mobility and recruitment to underserved communities. *Journal of Continuing Education in the Health Professions, 25*(1), 22–29.

Fooks, C. (2003). *Moving towards national resource planning in Canada: Still looking for a home,* Canadian Policy Research Networks Doc. No. 25336. Retrieved September 1, 2006 from http://www.cprn.com/en/doc.cfm?doc=490.

Grant, H. (2004). *From the Transvaal to the Prairies: The migration of South Africa physicians to Canada.* Prairie Centre of Excellence for Research on Immigration and Integration. Working Paper 02–04.

Gray, C. (1999, October 19). How bad is the brain drain? *Canadian Medical Association Journal, 161*(8), 1028–1029.

Harper, T. (1998, June 10). Ottawa blamed for doctor exodus – Cutbacks trigger a brain drain, CMA charges. *The Toronto Star,* p. A3.

Hawley, G. (2004, May). Canada's health care workers: A snapshot. *Health Policy Research* 8.

Hickey, J.P. (1995). Why don't I send you and your wife two plane tickets...? *Canadian Medical Association Journal, 152*(11), 1865–1866.

IMG Task Force (2004). *Report of the Canadian task force on licensure of international medical graduates*, p. 1–2.

IRPP (Institute for Research on Public Policy). (2005). NEWS RELEASE: *Study reveals low returns on immigrants' foreign education and experience.* Accessed 8 February 2005. www.irpp.org.

Joyce, R.E. & Hunt, C.L. (1982). Philippine nurses and the brain drain. *Social Science and Medicine, 16*(12), 1223–1233.

Kasperski, J. (2000). *Too many hours, too much stress, too little respect.* Ontario College of Family Physicians. 357 Bay Street, Suite 800, Toronto.

Little, L. (2005, July). The Canadian case. Presentation to Bellagio Institute Conference on the International Migration of Nurses. Retrieved September 1, 2006 from http://www.academyhealth.org/international/nursemigration/little.ppt.

Ma, P.C., et al. (1997). Intention to relocate to the United States. *Canadian Family Physician, 43*, 1533–1539.

Martineau, T., Decker, K., et al. (2002). *Briefing note on international migration of health professionals: Levelling the playing field for developing country health systems.* Liverpool, Liverpool School of Tropical Medicine. p. 10.

Mason, J. (1988). Midwifery in Canada. In S. Kitzinger (Ed.), *The midwife challenge* (pp. 99–133). London: Pandora.

McKendry, R., et al. (1996). Factors influencing the emigration of physicians from Canada to the United States. *Canadian Medical Association Journal, 154*(2), 171–181.

OMA (Ontario Medical Association) Human Resources Committee. (2002). *Position paper on physician workforce policy and planning.*April 4. Toronto: Ontario Medical Association

Orzack, L. (1998). Professions and world trade diplomacy: National systems and international authority. In V. Olgiati et al. (Eds.), *Professions, identity, and order in comparative perspective (pp. 13–37).* Onati: Institute for International Study of the Sociology of Law.

RNAO (Registered Nurses Association of Ontario). (2001). *Earning their return - When & why Ontario RN's left Canada, and what will bring them back.* Toronto: Registered Nurses Association of Ontario.

Ryten, E. et al. (1998). The class of 1989 and physician supply in Canada. *Canadian Medical Association Journal, 158*(6), 723–9.

Sibbald, B. (2002, September 3). The nursing crisis: "Physicians should ponder what this will mean." *Canadian Medical Association Journal, 167*(5), 535. http://www.cmaj.ca/cgi/reprint/167/5/535.pdf.

Silas, L. (2004). *Slow the exit speed the entry.* Pre-budget Submission, Standing Committee on Finance, Hon. Massimo Pacetti, MP, Chair House of Commons, Ottawa, ON, November 2004.

Sullivan, P. (2005a, March 11). CMA challenges IMG "facts" before Commons committee. http://www.cma.ca/index.cfm?ci_id=10018542&la_id=1.

Sullivan, P. (2005b). CMA's concern over HR issues growing, annual meeting proves. http://www.cma.ca/index.cfm?ci_id=10028212&la_id=1&topstory=1.

Webb, R.J. (1997). Shades of greener grass. *Canadian Family Physician, 43*, 1489.

WHO (World Health Organization). (2003). *Strengthening nursing and midwifery*, report by the Secretariat, 56th World Health Assembly, Geneva, Switzerland.

Williams, L.S. (1997). The Road to Wisconsin. *Canadian Medical Association Journal, 156*(6), 860–863.

ENDNOTES

1. It is also interesting to note that 75 percent of duplicate registrations are found in Ontario.
2. These examples were highlighted by Wendy Martin in the report of the Canadian Midwifery Regulator's Consortium (2004) *Research Plan for a National Midwifery Assessment Strategy* which included a review of the following documents: *ACCESS!* – the report of the Task Force on Access to Professions and Trades in Ontario (1990), *Immigrants Need Not Apply* (1999), *Initiatives Affecting the Labour Market Integration of Foreign-Trained Professionals and Trades Workers* (2000), *Fulfilling the Promise* (2002), and *Roundtable Proceedings: Improving Access to the Professions and Trades through Prior Learning Assessment & Qualifications Recognition for Immigrants in BC* (2002).
3. According to a *Canadian Medical Association Journal* (2002, 166(2), 232) article, "Salesman succeeds in bringing MD recruits to BC," "Maurice Leblanc has already brought pharmacists to British Columbia from his native South Africa, and now he's doing the same thing with physicians. LeBlanc, who has lived in Mackenzie, a town of 6000 in northern BC, for a decade, traveled to South Africa in 1999 to find pharmacists for his business. When 4 of the town's 5 family doctors left the town last winter, the former salesman approached Dr. Jennifer Rice, medical director of the Northern Interior Regional Health Board in Prince George, and offered to travel to South Africa to recruit FPs. He asked for $3000 to help defray his travel expenses; Rice, who was used to paying recruitment companies $7500 for each doctor they recruited readily agreed....He did his homework carefully, building up a list of contacts and pinpointing the cities where he was most likely to find potential recruits. During the three weeks he met with 72 doctors and returned to Canada with 20 resumes of well-qualified candidates. Rice was 'absolutely thrilled.' Six of the doctors are currently going through official procedures to immigrate and will be coming to the region, and Rice is directing the others elsewhere."

6

Transformations in Canadian Nursing and Nurse Education

TERRY WOTHERSPOON University of Saskatchewan

INTRODUCTION

The first Canadian training school for nurses opened in St. Catharines, Ontario, in 1874. According to "The First Annual Report of The St. Catharines Training School and Nurses' Home, July 1, 1875"; 6

> the skilled nurse, by minutely watching the temperature, conditions of skin, pulse, respiration, and the various functions of all the organs, and reporting faithfully to the attending physician, must increase the chances of recovery two-fold. (cited in Gibbon & Mathewson, 1947, p. 145)

Clearly, "nursing skill" meant "service" in a dual way, with both the patient and the physician being served. The emergence of the hospital system within the context of burgeoning industrial capitalism set the tone for a nursing force characterized by a unique blend of Christian dedication, Victorian femininity, medical faith, and labour discipline. In this context, nurse training was oriented to produce a cheap, subservient, readily available workforce armed with a basic knowledge of hospital and sanitary procedures.

By the beginning of the 21st century, discourses emphasizing faithful service have been supplanted by those that stress professionalism, technical knowledge, and health care advocacy. Nurse training, and even much nursing work, has moved out of the hospital system. Nursing education is now concentrated in universities and colleges, augmented with symposia on credentialing, specialization, nursing research, and advanced medical technology. Nurses have promoted their occupation, sometimes through militant action, as a profession with distinct skills and privileges based on their claims to a unique body of nursing knowledge.

This chapter is concerned with the development of nursing education in Canada. The transformation that has just been described is interpreted in conjunction with the observation that Davies (1980, 1995) makes that nursing education in Britain and the United States emerged as a compromise arising from inadequate resources, struggles for control, and the nature of nursing as women's work. In particular, this chapter emphasizes the ways in which contradictions in the provision and utility of the education of nurses in Canada have served to circumscribe nurses' position in the Canadian health care system. Since the 19th century, with the emergence of the well-known "Nightingale system," prescient nurses and nursing supervisors have recognized the potential value of training for the establishment of a distinct sphere of nursing activity within the overall health care system. However, the nature of that training and role has been subject to varying, often conflicting, conceptions of groups within nursing and interests outside of nursing. Ultimately, then, the development of nursing and nurse training must be understood as part of a wider network of social, political, and economic relations.

NURSES AND PROFESSIONALISM

Professionalism is the key concept in most recent analyses of nursing. Nurses are regarded either as constituting a profession, with their traditional low status a relic of the past, or as falling short in their drive to professionalism, in which case the reasons for their failure become the focus of analysis.

A typical expression of the first view is the statement that nursing has been involved in a "progressive development toward professionalism" (Elliott, 1977, p. 69; Schwirian, 1998, pp. 12–13). Three interrelated factors are commonly cited to highlight this apparent evolutionary progress: the specialization and bureaucratization of health care, increasingly sophisticated medical technology, and the growth of nurses' own professional awareness (Innis, 1970; Kelly, 1985). As health care has become a more comprehensive, sophisticated enterprise, new medical knowledge and health care functions have become unequally distributed among participants in the health care system. This has afforded nurses the opportunity to organize and push for increased status and responsibility; they have willingly emulated the medical profession with the assumption that full professionalism is an inevitable outcome. In this evolutionary mode, the role of education is clear – education is the vehicle for professional status. More education for more nurses, built around a distinct scientific core of nursing knowledge, would allow nurses simultaneously to adapt to a changing world and to occupy a position of enhanced importance in the division of labour in health care (Canadian Nurses Association, 1997; Rogers, 1978).

As desirable as this image is from a nursing perspective, it fails to analyze adequately the wider context within which nursing operates, and it ignores many of the major constrains that continue to act upon nursing. Arising from the blend of optimism and frustration that has marked nurses' ongoing struggles for status, this viewpoint has interpreted the substantive gains that nurses have made against a backdrop of influential individuals and interest groups which seem to have no enduring connection to other aspects of social structure. The real historical barriers to nursing status seemingly can be dissipated merely through hard work and upgrading of skills on the part of nurses.

The second viewpoint paints a less flattering image of nurses. It takes as its starting point the obstacles that nurses face in their quest for status, and concludes that nursing is at best either a semi- or para-profession, most likely doomed to eternal inferiority to the medical profession (Cockerham, 1986; Wolinsky, 1980). Probably the clearest manifestation of this perspective is the fact that nursing is either virtually ignored or given only passing consideration in much of the literature on the sociology of medicine.

Against the visible unity and autonomy of the (predominantly male) medical profession, the service orientation of the internally divided (predominantly female) nursing ranks seems highly appropriate. This patronizing and accusatory view is expressed clearly by Hall (1970, p. 12), to whom

> it seems clear that, to date, nurses have not tried to focus their work efforts in a scientific mould. While medical care has been specializing along new types of diagnosis and treatment at a bizarre speed, nursing has shown no such trend.

We are left with the impression that no matter how strongly nurses struggled in the past to establish their occupational status, they have not worked hard enough. Ironically, this view fits nicely with the first position on nurses' professionalism, differing primarily in the assessment of the likelihood of nurses' success in achieving professionalism.

Unfortunately, the debate over whether or not nursing is a profession tends to divert attention from questions of greater significance. Professionalism is assumed to be a desirable attribute, without any critical appraisal either of the conditions within which professionalization occurs or of the strategic importance of professionalism as an ideological position (see Johnson [1972] for an extended critique of this approach). Instead, the circumstances under which the health care system and the role of nursing within it have developed are attributed to grand, amorphous tendencies such as "progress," "technological change," and "interest-group politics" without any sustained analysis of social relations in which these processes are grounded. Therefore, occupational roles and training are treated as neutral phenomena, given shape by the whims and visions of individuals acting as part of a seemingly natural evolution of social forces.

An alternative explanation of the development of nursing and nurse education focuses on the social relations that give shape to and are influenced by nursing. Nurses are recognized as dependent wage earners who pose problems of cost and control to their employers (Armstrong, Choiniere & Day, 1993; Cannings & Lazonick, 1975; Rafferty, 1996; White, 1990). Nursing emerges from and acts upon distinct social structures and practices that are characterized by regular, often contradictory, patterns. Consequently, issues concerning the training and welfare of nurses, although important in their own right, are viewed as meaningful only when interpreted in the context of wider trends associated with health care organization, policy, and finance.

NURSES AS SALARIED EMPLOYEES

One clear indication of the status of nurses is expressed by the relative incomes of nurses and other health care workers. As the data in Figure 6.1 indicate, the incomes of nurses have increased steadily both in absolute terms and in comparison with the average income of the Canadian workforce as a whole. Of the three designated health occupational categories, nurses have made the greatest relative gains. However, nurses' salaries, on average, did not achieve the national average for all occupations until the 1980s, and remain at levels that are about one third of the average for physicians and surgeons.

FIGURE 6.1

Average Annual Income for Selected Health Occupations in Canada, Census Years 1931–2001

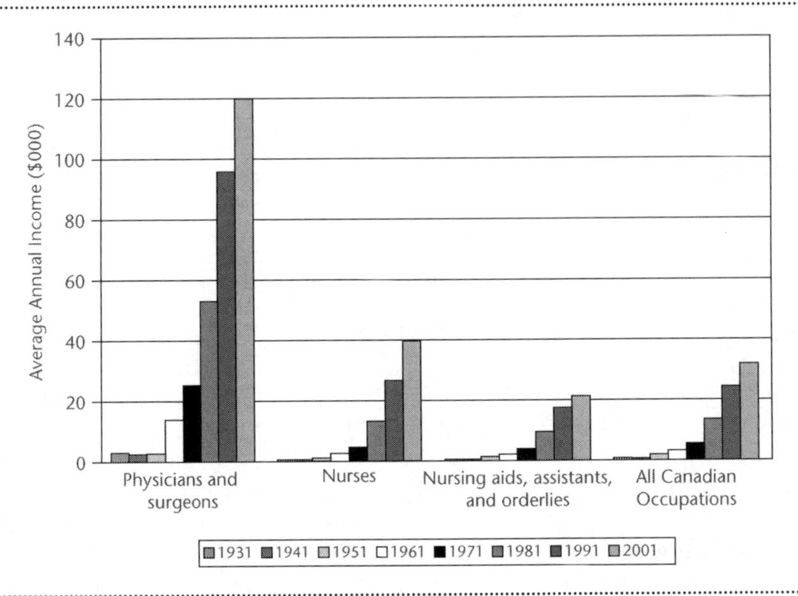

Source: Compiled and calculated from various Canadian census data.

The most common justification for the latter trend is that medical training is more arduous and is of much longer duration than nurse training. Therefore, in accordance with a functionalist analysis of stratification, the higher salaries of doctors are seen to represent a "payoff" for the years of training and sacrifice undertaken by the individual in order to fill the important medical positions (Davis & Moore, 1945). This correlation between years of training and occupational income is borne out, in broad terms, by general surveys of the labour force that reveal that workers with higher levels of education are likely to be found in higher income categories (see, for example, the monthly reports issued by Labour Canada under the title of The Labour Force). As such, it serves as a rallying point for nursing advocates who argue that more and better education is necessary for higher status. There are, though, some problems in this analysis. The income-education linkage is more likely to be a product of initial privilege, class power, and other social dynamics than an indicator of true market value (Livingstone, 2004). Moreover, the whole question of what constitutes recognized training must be considered. Historically, as will be discussed later, nurses have been trained on the job, providing cheap hospital labour in a prolonged apprenticeship period that is not regarded in the same way as is, for example, medical-ward experience and internship. At the same time, the fiscal returns and inducements for nurse training are not nearly as significant as a "reward for education" argument would have us believe.

A second argument for the relatively low wages that nurses receive is that nurses are much more poorly organized and less assertive than is the medical profession. Certainly doctors have benefited tremendously from the strength and ability of organizations like the Canadian and American Medical Associations to promote their own interests. In contrast, nursing leaders have chronically lamented the seeming inability of nurses to mobilize into a cohesive, powerful force. Unfortunately, advocates of these arguments tend to regard nurses and doctors as two independent rather than interdependent groups, and to confuse cause and consequence. While the medical and nursing professions each have their unique histories, the picture is incomplete without an analysis of how the medical profession has been able to advance in large part at the expense of nursing, through the subordination and guided development of nursing by doctors, health care policy-makers and managers, and the structure of health care systems.

This suggests the need for a relational analysis that can account for contradictions and constraints in nursing development. We can illustrate this type of analysis by returning to Figure 6.1 and taking note of the third category of health occupations, after doctors and nurses. The wage levels of nursing aides, assistants, and orderlies have remained relatively constant, at levels of about two-thirds of average occupational earnings. From a fiscal vantage point, this implies that nursing, as an intermediate health occupation, can both exert pressure on and be subject to pressure from at least two levels – doctors and managers from above, and auxiliary health care workers from below. Therefore, by way of example, health care administrators make decisions influenced by the fact that individual nurses are less costly than physicians but more costly than auxiliary health care workers. At the same time, nurses have reason to fear that they are potentially more dispensable to the health care system than are other health care workers under present circumstances. Registered nurses, for example, are typically excluded from legislation that enables physicians and surgeons to prescribe medication or perform surgery. These relations are intensified with the introduction of new medical technology and health care treatment models that serve to redefine the place and role of various health care workers. If the diagnosis of a cancer, for example, can be made by a laboratory technician with the aid of a sophisticated instrument, and if cancer can be treated with drugs prescribed by a physician, where does the nurse fit in? At another level, a greater integration of the health care system with other social educational services could provide opportunities for nurses to enhance their role in health care, or it could have the effect of making nursing a redundant occupation, as social workers, auxiliaries, nursing assistants, Nurse Practitioners with specialized qualifications, and other new occupations begin to provide nursing services.

So far, there is mixed evidence with regard to the future of nursing. There is a general tendency for licensed health care personnel, including registered nurses, to be replaced by unlicensed health care providers, but there are considerable variations among provinces in this regard (Saskatchewan Union of Nurses, 1998). As health care is restructured, full-time nurses are increasingly being replaced by part-time nurses, nursing is gradually shifting to non-institutional settings relative to hospitals and other long-term health care sites, and nurses are subject to new forms of surveillance and intensification of their work (Armstrong, Choiniere & Day, 1993, p. 46; Armstrong & Armstrong, 1996; Brannon, 1994).

Viewed in this context, nursing education is a significant variable in the development of the health care system. Education acts as a conduit for nursing knowledge, status, and credentials, but it also serves to stamp into place particular conceptions of nursing. More precisely, while the provision of educational opportunities is generally associated with the advancement of nursing, it is also a factor in the historical subordination of nurses.

WORK AND EDUCATION IN THE CANADIAN CONTEXT

Nursing education, like other forms of vocational training, began outside the formal system of public education in Canada. Mass public schooling emerged through the attempts by 19th-century school reformers to ensure the transformation of individuals into morally disciplined political subjects within a sphere of state rule (Corrigan, Curtis & Lanning, 1987; Wotherspoon, 2004). Vocational training was more strictly concerned with imbuing persons in specific jobs with the competencies and discipline that would make them productive workers. Once established in the throes of industrial development, however, the state public school system was subject to conscription by private capitalist interests concerned with obtaining at public expense a cheap, compliant, and differentiated labour force; schooling thus became penetrated by the logic of vocationalism (Bowles & Gintis, 1976; Schecter, 1977). However, a contradictory dynamic was generated by subordinate social groups that saw in public schooling a vehicle for upward social mobility and participation in hitherto closed political channels (Carnoy & Levin, 1985). A major consequence of the struggles that ensued over the nature and content of state schooling was the emergence in the 20th century of the education system as the primary channel of individual access to the job market.

The developing linkage between school and work provided a focal point for the energies of competing social interests. The educational credential provided a screening mechanism for employers, a "meal ticket" for individuals, and an instrument to guarantee status for certain prestigious occupational groups such as medical doctors. Little overt challenge was presented to the tacit consensus that formal schooling was a legitimate educational and selective enterprise. Instead, conflict centred on the amounts and content of formal education appropriate to particular occupations or positions in the labour force. As debate arose concerning how much and what kinds of education a person needed to enter, certain jobs began to dominate educational discourse; wider questions about the structures of education and work were no longer issues. The ground rules for work and schooling solidified, and only the details were open to contention (Wotherspoon, 2004).

Nurse training, which began in Canada within the hospital system, was absorbed into the state education system only through a protracted series of developments. The interconnection of such factors as the rising cost to hospitals of providing nurse training, corporate and state intervention in the health care system, and the organized efforts of nurses accompanied a transformation in nursing work away from a strictly supervised feminine servitude to a bureaucratically organized wage-labour force. The following sections outline the development of nurse training in Canada and discuss the nature of the Canadian nursing labour force.

THE DEVELOPMENT OF NURSING EDUCATION IN CANADA

The formal training of nurses in Canada began in the 1870s for the purpose of producing hospital personnel who could adequately carry out doctors' orders (Mussallem, 1965, pp. 5–6). In the mid-19th century, nursing was nearly unique as an occupation legitimately open to women. Nursing was established from the outset of the development of medical science as an auxiliary occupation, concerned primarily with "caring" rather than "curing," or hygiene rather than medical treatment (Gamarnikow, 1978; Corea, 1985;

Rafferty, 1996). The medical division of labour, reproducing the patriarchal structure of the bourgeois home and workplace, was clear - men were doctors and women were nurses.

Nursing, nonetheless, did present opportunities, however limited, for the career advancement of a select group of women. Early nursing promoters, such as Florence Nightingale in Britain and Isabel A. Hampton in North America, saw that an inexpensive, regimented nursing force could provide the necessary foothold to establish nursing in the health care process. The advantage of this strategy to solidify nursing status through the promotion of its ethos of service was that nursing could develop as a relatively autonomous enterprise, hierarchically organized around hygienic ideals under the supervision of women (Carpenter, 1977, pp. 166–167). However, the development of this autonomy was highly constrained.

Hospital administrators quickly came to appreciate the value of nurses for developing a clientele and providing inexpensive labour. With a nursing force at hand, public hospitals could shift their image and emphasis from providing a repository for the terminally ill to serving as a centre for treatment and recovery. The possibility that patients could be ministered back to health was crucial for an emerging industrial nation that required a continuous supply of able-bodied workers. Hospitals, in becoming important centres of health care, simultaneously began to train and contain nurses. Thus, generally following the pattern of industrialization in Canada, the number of hospital schools of nursing increased from one in 1874 (in St. Catharines) to 20 in 1900, 170 in 1909, and approximately 220 in 1930 (Canadian Nurses Association (CNA), 1968, p. 33; Duncanson, 1970, p. 112).

In this context, nurse training accomplished several contradictory functions. Extending over a 2–3-year period, training programs ensured that a supply of nurses was continually available for hospital service. The exploitation of the nurse trainee prevailed over educational aims so that lecture and study time was a "privilege" granted only in the interstices of up to 15 hours of daily ward duty (Duncanson, 1970, pp. 112–113; Mussallem, 1965, p. 6). Nurse training programs dampened the hostilities of doctors, who scorned nurses as unskilled and uneducated. At the same time, doctors who were suspicious that they might some day be displaced by trained nurses found that they could advance their own interests by their involvement in the nurse training program as lecturers and moral guardians. Discipline over nurse trainees was further maintained by a highly regimented supervisory structure, constant surveillance facilitated by the establishment of dormitories, inculcation of the virtues of obedience and commitment, and the absence for most trainees of any occupational alternatives.

The advantages in terms of costs and services that nurses offered to the hospital system were also used by nursing leaders in the early part of the 20th century as levers for gaining certain concessions, including reductions in the workday, specified educational time allocations, formalized instruction, and more standardized curricula (Duncanson, 1970, p. 113; Mussallem, 1965, p. 7). Trained nurses, working to enhance their own status in contrast with untrained nursing personnel, organized local, national, and international associations to provide a body for political lobbying. Nursing, as promoted by nursing administrators, was to be of service because it brought to the health care sector a cultivated worker who conformed to high standards of female gentility and passivity (Coburn, 1987, p. 448). In 1893, the American Society of Superintendents of Training Schools for Nurses of the United States and Canada was formed by 40 nursing-school superintendents in order to push for better-quality and more uniform nursing educational standards. This society laid the groundwork for a dominion-wide nursing organization, the Canadian National Association of Trained Nurses, established in 1908, which in 1924, with 52 affiliated member organizations, became the Canadian Nurses Association, or the CNA (CNA, 1968, pp. 36–38). These organizations focused the profession's energies on a drive for the establishment of registries of trained nurses, which received some degree of legislative recognition in all nine provinces between 1910 and 1922 (CNA, 1968, p. 38). They also began, especially with the aid of a 1914 Special Committee report on education, a lengthy campaign to have nursing education incorporated into the state education system (King, 1970, p. 69).

In the midst of these developments, the fundamental contradiction between state and private demands for low-cost but widespread health care services on the one hand, and nurses' demand for adequate training and remuneration on the other, intensified. In the early decades of the 20th century, health care services were becoming instituted as a regular social provision, in conjunction with the rise of a stable national workforce. Exacerbating this trend was the success of the medical profession in acquiring greater influence with the health care system. In this, the medical associations were aided by the large corporate foundations, especially the Carnegie Foundation, which sponsored the influential Flexner Report of 1910. In the wake of the report, major recommendations to reduce the number of North American medical schools and the supply of medical graduates, and to tighten control over medical education standards were quickly adopted (MacFarlane, 1965, pp. 19–21).

The data in Table 6.1 reveal the impact of these events on the medical and nursing labour forces. The supply of physicians was greatly moderated, especially in the period from 1911–21, when the population per physicians ratio actually increased, meaning that there were fewer physicians per capita in 1921 than in 1911. However, medical care was at that time highly labour-intensive so that, with fewer doctors, either patients received less medical attention, doctors worked harder, or other health care personnel filled the void. The rapid increase in the nursing labour force prior to the end of the 1980s (leading to a period of decline in the number of nurses before subsequent recovery by the end of the 20th century) suggests the importance of the latter possibility. The number of nurses increased by nearly four times between 1911 and 1921 and maintained an annual rate of increase of 55.1 percent, compared with a rate of 8.2 percent for doctors, between 1911 and 1986. Lower-cost nurses, trained for dedicated service and disciplined by social and labour market conditions, served, in effect, to subsidize the greater occupational rewards that doctors were in a position to enjoy.

With an expanded and diversified health care role, though, nurses were also able to assert more strongly their monetary and educational demands. However, as with doctors, nurses' progress in this regard was highly dependent on the intervention of external agencies. A university degree program in nursing, the first in Canada, was established at the University of British Columbia in 1919, and, with the efforts and financial assistance of the Canadian Red Cross Society, public health nursing programs were developed in six universities by 1920–21 (King, 1970, p. 70). However, as King indicates, there were serious inadequacies in the early university nursing programs in terms of both upgrading nursing skill and raising nursing status relative to other university-educated occupational groups: "In the teaching of nursing great emphasis was placed on technical skill,

TABLE 6.1 *Number of Physicians and Nurses, and Population per Physician and Nurse in Canada, 1901–2004*

	Physicians		Nurses	
Year	Number	Population per Physician*	Number†	Population per Nurse*
1901	5,441	978	280	19,014
1911	7,411	970	5,600	1,284
1921	8,706	1,008	21,385	410
1931	10,020	1,034	20,462	506
1941	11,873	968	25,826	441
1951	14,325	976	41,088	325
1961	21,290	857	70,647	258
1971	32,942	659	1,48,767	146
1981	45,542	538	2,06,184	119
1991	52,726	533	1,70,273	124
2001	58,133	533	2,31,512	135
2005	61,580	529	2,51,675	129

* Based on census data.

† Registered nurses for 1941–71; census figures for 1931 (graduate nurses) and earlier years (nurses). Excludes Newfoundland prior to 1961; excludes Yukon and Northwest Territories prior to 1941. The 1921 figure includes nurses-in-training. Figures for 1981 and later include only nurses registered during the first four months (three in Quebec) of the registration period and registered in the same province in which they work or reside.

Source: For 1901–71, Statistics Canada (1983). Historical Statistics of Canada (second edition). Ottawa: Minister of Supply and Services, Series B82–92. For 1981, Health Canada (1995). Health Personnel in Canada 1992. Ottawa: Minister of Supply and Services Canada. For 1990–2005, Canadian Institute for Health Information, Workforce Trends of Registered Nurses in Canada, 2005. Retrieved August 28, 2007, from http://secure.cihi.ca/cihiweb/dispPage.jsp?cw_page=AR_20_E&cw_topic=20; Canadian Institute for Health Information, Health Personnel in Canada, 1991 to 2000. Retrieved August 28, 2007, from http://secure.cihi.ca/cihiweb/dispPage.jsp?cw_page=PG_67_E&cw_topic=67&cw_rel=AR_21_E; and Canadian Medical Association, Statistical Information on Canadian Physicians Retrieved August 28, 2007, from http://www.cma.ca/index.cfm/ci_id/16959/la_id/1.htm.

following orders, and adhering to established practice; the intellectual component was subservient to the daily round" (1970, pp. 71–72).

There is evidence, too, of a strong occupational split in nursing between nursing supervisors and instructors, who had been trained in and had advanced through the hospital service system, and nurses who saw the need to develop the profession through university education and research (King, 1970, pp. 73–75). The latter group was given support by George Weir in the 1932 report Survey of Nursing Education in Canada, cosponsored by the CNA and the Canadian Medical Association. The report's primary recommendation was that nursing schools be removed from hospital control and placed under the auspices of the provincial education systems.

With the onset of the international economic crisis in the 1930s, the fate of this recommendation was suspended between conflicting interests. In the early part of the decade, expenditures on health services declined (Statistics Canada, 1983), placing increased pressure on the health care system and its labour force to operate more efficiently. At the same time, these conditions provoked intensified efforts from several quarters for an overall upgrading of the health care system. Potentially militant trade unions and the unemployed, subject to severe social and economic dislocation, posed a worrisome threat to state and corporate interests. Provincial and federal legislatures introduced a series of social reform measures, including health insurance schemes, as part of an attempt to pacify the working class and stabilize economic conditions (Swartz, 1977).

Corporate interests also played a more direct role, primarily through their charitable foundations, which provided financial assistance and funded research for selected health, education, and welfare projects, in order to secure social harmony, develop a stable work force, and promote a favourable investment climate. In the field of health care, the W.K. Kellogg Foundation has a history of prominence, having contributed over $263.5 million to various health care programs, mostly in the United States, Canada, and Latin America, between 1930 and 1980 (Kellogg, 1979, p. 112). Of that total, $822,000 was spent between 1944 and 1952 to provide staff, consultative services, and curricular and instructional resources for twelve university nursing schools (ten in the United States and two in Canada), and a grant of over $165,000 served to establish an experimental undergraduate nursing program, grounded in basic science training, at the University of Saskatchewan, beginning in 1952 (Kellogg, 1955, pp. 143–148). The advancement of more systematic training initiatives for nursing, combined with greater emphasis on scientific foundations within health care, offered nurses a chance to enhance their traditional status grounded in "romance, religion and femininity" with a new clinical role (Mansell, 2004, p. 163).

At the same time, other pressures were mounting to push the training of nurses out of the hospitals. Nurses, who in the 1930s often accepted board and lodging from their hospital employers in lieu of full salary payment, began in the 1940s to return to the community and, simultaneously, to demand higher wages (CNA, 1968, p. 34). A similar situation developed for nurses in training who exchanged fees and labour in return for training and services. The Department of National Health and Welfare estimates that by 1960, the average direct annual cost to the hospital per student was $1,000 (Mussallem, 1965, p. 40). Because hospitals compensated for this cost by underpaying nursing instructors and by extracting unpaid or underpaid labour from nursing students, a generally unsatisfactory situation prevailed. Moreover, low wages and low levels of government educational assistance made it economically unviable for most nurses and nursing teachers to extend their education beyond the minimal time period required for graduation from basic training, especially when the training program was prolonged excessively by the priority of work over training in the hospital system. Consequently, it is not surprising that Mussallem (1965), in a study prepared in the early 1960s for the Royal Commission on Health Services in Canada, indicts the nursing education system of the time as haphazard, outdated, educationally unsound, and inadequate for the needs of nurses and the health care system.

The Royal Commission's report itself recommended a reduction in the time span of the diploma program from three to two years and a separation of nurse training from hospital demands for nursing service, and stressed that the increasing need for qualified nurses required the coordinated development of nursing education programs integrated into the general system of higher education in Canada and the provinces (Duncanson, 1970, pp. 122–123). While the Royal Commission inquiry was being conducted, nurses' organizations, educational institutions, and the Ontario government cooperated in an initiative that led to the establishment in 1964 of a nursing diploma program at the Ryerson Polytechnical Institute. By 1968, in the wake of this precedent, 26 nursing diploma programs were offered in institutions other than hospital schools of nursing across Canada; by 1977, full-time enrolment in community college nursing diploma programs was 17,589, compared with 5,136 in hospital programs (CNA, 1981, p. 2; Statistics Canada, 1977). A similar expansion was underway in university degree nursing programs, with more programs, greater number of students, and the establishment of graduate degree programs.

RECENT TRENDS IN NURSING EDUCATION AND THE NURSING LABOUR FORCE

The move away from hospital-based nurse training has been associated with a general improvement in the overall status of nurses, but it has not solved several fundamental problems associated with training and maintaining an adequate supply of nurses required to address contemporary health care needs. Nurses continue to encounter serious obstacles in the quest to gain greater recognition for their role as a more highly qualified university-trained profession.

The provision of nursing education through the public education system has ensured that certain levels of funding, facilities, and standards will be maintained for nurse training, sheltered from the vagaries of hospital administration. At the same time, though, new sets of constraints emerge as nursing education is forced to compete for resources with other educational and state priorities. Insofar as the educational credentials of teachers, a major cost factor in postsecondary educational institutions, are linked to promotion and salary scales, nursing education is relatively inexpensive. In 1994, for example, only 27.7 percent of full-time university nursing teachers had completed doctorates, compared with an overall Canadian university teacher average of over 70 percent (Lortie, 1994, p. 32; Statistics Canada, 1995, p. 53). In addition, such low-cost, highly specific programs as computer-assisted instruction and self-directed learning modules are becoming prominent features of some university nurse education programs (Crawford, 1978; Hannah, 1978). These programs, besides reducing the costs of education relative to more open-ended discovery and analysis-based courses, prepare the student for work roles that are highly structured and involve few opportunities for the worker to exercise discretion on the job. Despite these constraints, significant changes in the organization and delivery of health care, along with the advancement of bodies of knowledge associated with medical, technological, and social dimensions of nursing, have prompted several initiatives to restructure education and practice.

For the past three decades, the two predominant educational streams for entry into nursing practice have been university degree programs (now normally four years in length), and nursing diploma programs, offered mainly through the community college system (typically three years in length). As the data charted in Figure 6.2 illustrate, until the end of the 20th century, diploma programs (and for much of the period prior to 1980 and briefly in the early 1990s, reliance on immigrant nurses trained in other nations) produced considerably more new entrants into nursing labour markets than did university degree programs.

FIGURE 6.2

Numbers of Nurses Graduating from Canadian Programs and Number of Immigrant Graduate Nurses Entering Canada, 1962–2004

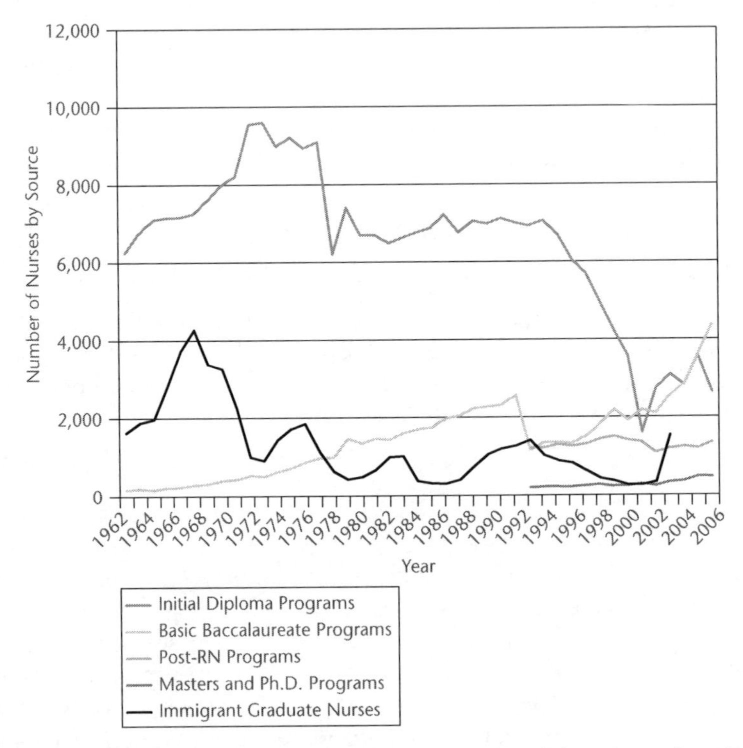

Note: Figures for graduates of basic baccalaureate programs from 1978–90 include graduates of post-RN baccalaureate programs; separate data for post-RN graduates and master's and doctoral graduates available starting in 1991. Figures for immigrant graduate nurses include immigrants who indicated that nursing is their intended occupation.

Source: Compiled with data from various sources: Health and Welfare Canada, Canada Health Manpower Inventory (Annual Series, 1969, 1976, 1985); Mussallem, H.K. (1965), Nursing Education in Canada, Ottawa: Queen's Printer; Health Canada (1995), Health Personnel in Canada 1992, Ottawa: Minister of Supply and Services Canada; Immigration Canada (Annual Series), Immigration Statistics, Ottawa: Minister of Public Works and Government Services Canada; Canadian Institute for Health Information (2000), Health Personnel in Canada, 1988–97, Ottawa: Canadian Institute for Health Information; Canadian Institute for Health Information (2001), Health Personnel in Canada, 1991–2000, Ottawa: Canadian Institute for Health Information; Canadian Nurses Association, The National Student and Faculty Survey of Canadian Schools of Nursing 2004–05. Report 3: Admissions, Enrolment and Graduates by Type of Nursing Program, 2000–04. Ottawa: Canadian Nurses Association Retrieved September 22, 2006, from http://www.cna-nurses.ca/CNA/documents/pdf/publications/Student_Faculty_2004_2005_Report_3_e.pdf.

The subsequent reversal of these trends represents, in part, the adoption of strategies for greater professional recognition of nursing through the CNA focus, reinforced through complementary positions advanced by several provincial nursing associations, on "entry into practice," which called for a minimum requirement of a complete baccalaureate degree as the standard for entry into nursing practice, initially targeted by the year 2000 (CNA, 1982, p. 1; Registered Nurses' Association of British Columbia, 1983). As the CNA itself admitted, such a goal seemed difficult to attain, given the slow rate of increase in the proportion of student admissions to degree nursing programs relative to diploma programs and the continuing lack of funds to expand degree nursing programs (1986, p. 5).

Initial efforts to achieve entry into practice objectives were frequently constrained by strong divisions within the nursing ranks and nurse organizations, including the promotion of divergent strategies by unions and professional associations, and tensions between staff nurses and nurse administrators (Mansell, 2004, pp. 197–198). The pace of nursing educational reform has also been slowed by limited commitments by governments and educational institutions to support nurse training programs, particularly at the university level. The state's hesitation to invest extensively in nursing education was revealed, for instance, in the heavy reliance on immigrant nursing labour, initially during the period in the late 1960s and early 1970s as nursing education was being transferred out of hospitals. By importing trained labourers (although not all workers will necessarily become employed in their intended occupations), Canada is able to transfer the cost of educating a substantial pool of workers to the countries of origin and gain in the process a cheap, often docile work force (Bolaria, 1987). Depending upon where the workers are placed in job situations, this may either ensure that lower-paid positions are constantly filled (as opposed to increasing wage levels), or reduce the overall costs of maintaining a trained work force. In 2004, graduates of foreign nursing programs, who accounted for 7.4 percent of the registered nurse workforce in Canada, were over-represented in hospital or institutional settings working in areas like geriatrics and long term care, maternity, and operating/recovery care where nurses with the lowest educational credentials were concentrated (data from Canadian Nurses Association, 2006).

The lack of government support for nursing education, especially at the university level, is also revealed in the problems that nurses have faced in upgrading their basic training. Nurses report being left out of decisions to introduce, and shut out from training to operate, new medical technology (Wallis, 1978). Absence of credit courses for upgrading training at work, lack of time off to attend classes that are offered, and lack of financial assistance are common problems for nurses working in Canadian hospitals and health care institutions, with nurse trainees in at least one institution reporting the need to hold bake sales and auctions to raise money for a tuition-assistance fund (Allen, 1985, p. 12).

Consequently, as revealed in Figure 6.2, diploma programs accounted for at least two-thirds of nursing graduates each year until the mid-1990s, with only gradual growth in the number and size of university programs. As late as 1994, for instance, there were 109 initial diploma programs and 26 basic and 32 post-R.N. baccalaureate programs in nursing in Canada (Statistics Canada, 1995, pp. 47–48), compared with 170 hospital schools and 16 university baccalaureate programs in 1963 (Mussallem, 1965, p. 11). In 1995–96, more than 20,000 students nationally were enrolled in diploma programs in nursing, compared with just under 9,400 in the longer degree programs (Statistics Canada, 1998, pp. 60, 68), and only 18.5 percent of all registered nurses employed in nursing in Canada had an academic degree (calculated from Statistics Canada, 1996, p. 16).

The transition to a university-based nursing education standard was accelerated by the end of the 1990s through extensive lobbying by the CNA and provincial nursing organizations; this, along with negotiations and agreements in conjunction with governments and nursing education institutions, was facilitated by more general needs and developments as adequate health care services loomed as a major policy priority. By 1998, the baccalaureate degree was required for nurse registration in the Atlantic provinces, and within the next five years, all provinces but Alberta and Quebec had completed agreements to adopt the degree standard (Canadian Nurses Association, 2003, p. 1). In the process, starting with an initiative in Alberta in 1995, colleges and universities across Canada engaged in a far-reaching series of collaborative agreements and arrangements to deliver joint nurse training programs (Kirkwood, 2005, p. 195; Canadian Nurses Association, 2003, p. 1). These included provisions for nurses who had initially graduated from diploma programs to upgrade their credentials to the degree standard, along with the introduction of increased options for nurse education continuing to both the master's and doctoral level (Dick & Cragg, 2006; Thorne, 2006). Consequently, just nearly two-thirds (88) of the 139 initial nurse education programs reported in 2004–05 by the Canadian Association of Schools of Nursing (CASN) offered bachelor's degrees, with the baccalaureate program accounting for nearly four out of five admissions and enrolments and three out of five graduates of initial nurse training programs the same year (calculated from data in CASN, 2006a, p. 1; CASN, 2006b, p. 1). Other indications of increased credentials across the nursing force are evident in the trends evident in Figure 6.2, with expanded numbers of nurses who initially graduated with diplomas completing post-RN degree programs and recent growth in the number of nurses completing graduate degrees (these are first reported separately from total baccalaureate data beginning in 1991). In 2004, there were 1,338 post-RN baccalaureate graduates, 427 graduates from master's programs in nursing, and 25 from doctoral programs (CASN, 2006a, p. 1). By 2004, nearly one-third of persons employed as Registered Nurses in Canada had baccalaureate degrees (close to half of these through initial training and slightly more than half upgrading to a degree after initial diploma certification) (Canadian Institute for Health Information, 2005, pp. 27–28). After long delays, nurses appear to be making significant advances toward their objective to be recognized as a professional university-trained nursing workforce.

However, while the attainment of a university degree is associated with professional gains for nursing, it does not guarantee that nurses will gain greater decision-making authority and autonomy. One of the major consequences of these trends is the tendency toward increased segmentation within nursing. While a longstanding division of labour that has often created differing career patterns and options for diploma and degree nurses may be disappearing, several factors are pushing the nursing workforce into diverse work pathways. As Picard (2000, p. 7) notes, the observation that, "There is no longer a 'typical' nurse," carries with it both advantages and serious limitations.

Hospitals remain the major workplace for Canadian nurses, but there is a gradual shift in the direction of greater community-based health care. Between 1992 and 2004, among registered nurses working in nursing, the proportion who worked in hospitals declined from 66.3–62.5 percent, while those who worked in community health settings increased from 7.1–13.4 percent (Canadian Institute for Health Information, 1998, p. 2; 2005, p. 95). Educational credentials have a bearing on the kinds of places and positions nurses are employed in. As the data in Table 6.2 and Figure 6.3 indicate, registered nurses with basic diploma training are overrepresented in general staff nursing positions, particularly in hospital and institutional settings, or they occupy intermediate and lower-level supervisory positions. By contrast, those with a university degree are more likely to be employed in senior management, educational, community health and home care, and more specialized clinical positions or settings associated with greater discretion or decision-making authority.

TABLE 6.2 *Registered Nurses Employed in Nursing in Canada by Position and Highest Level of Education in Nursing, 2001*

Highest level of education, expressed as percentage of nurses within each position

Position	Total Number	Diploma	Baccalaureate	Master's/ Doctorate
Chief Nursing Officer/CEO	2,013	50.5	39.8	9.7
Director/Assistant Director	2,244	55.1	34.9	10.0
Manager/Assistant Manager	12,540	58.4	37.6	4.0
Staff Nurse/Community Health Nurse	1,76,681	79.2	20.4	0.3
Nurse Practitioner	620	33.1	46.0	21.0
Clinical Specialist	2,321	52.5	26.7	20.9
Nurse Midwife	13	84.6	15.4	0.0
Instructor/Professor/Educator	5,658	28.7	53.3	18.0
Researcher	1,567	57.1	35.1	7.8
Consultant	6,076	49.8	45.5	4.7
Other	15,448	66.8	30.8	2.4
Not Stated	6,331	68.9	29.0	2.2
TOTAL – percent	100.0	74.0	24.3	1.8
– number	2,31,512	1,71,247	56,193	4,072

Source: Calculated from Canadian Institute for Health Information, Supply and Distribution of Registered Nurses in Canada, 2001. Ottawa: Canadian Institute for Health Information.

A related aspect of segmentation in nursing appears in the gender structure of the occupation. Nursing remains an overwhelmingly feminized occupation. Although the number and proportion of male nurses is gradually increasing, in 2004, men constituted only 5.4 percent of the registered nursing force in Canada, compared with 2.4 percent two decades earlier. Male nurses are slightly more likely than female nurses to have university degrees in nursing (in 2000, 24.2 percent of male registered nurses, compared to 22.9 percent of females, had university degrees), and are more likely to be employed in administrative, supervisory positions or more specialized clinical settings (Canadian Nurses Association, 2006; Statistics Canada, 2005b; Trudeau, 1996, pp. 23–24). Moreover, according to census data, in 2000, male nurses who worked on a full-time, full-year basis earned an average of $49,536, which was about $3,400 more than their female counterparts (Statistics Canada, 2005a).

Consequent to the growth of the health care system have been increasingly sustained legislative and managerial efforts to make the operation of the system more efficient and accountable. Initiatives such as community health centres, prescription drug assistance programs, hospital closures and health system consolidation, and the expansion of various private health care alternatives, regardless of their possible medical merits, have the clear effect of increasing the output of hospital workers while shifting some health care services from hospitals to less expensive and less labour-intensive in-home and community alternatives (Salmon, 1984; Armstrong & Armstrong, 2003). At the same time, institutional health care is being reorganized primarily through innovations in the supervision patterns of hospital and nursing-home employees in order to increase centralized

FIGURE 6.3

Distribution of Registered Nurses in Canada by Selected Fields and Positions, by Highest Level of Education in Nursing

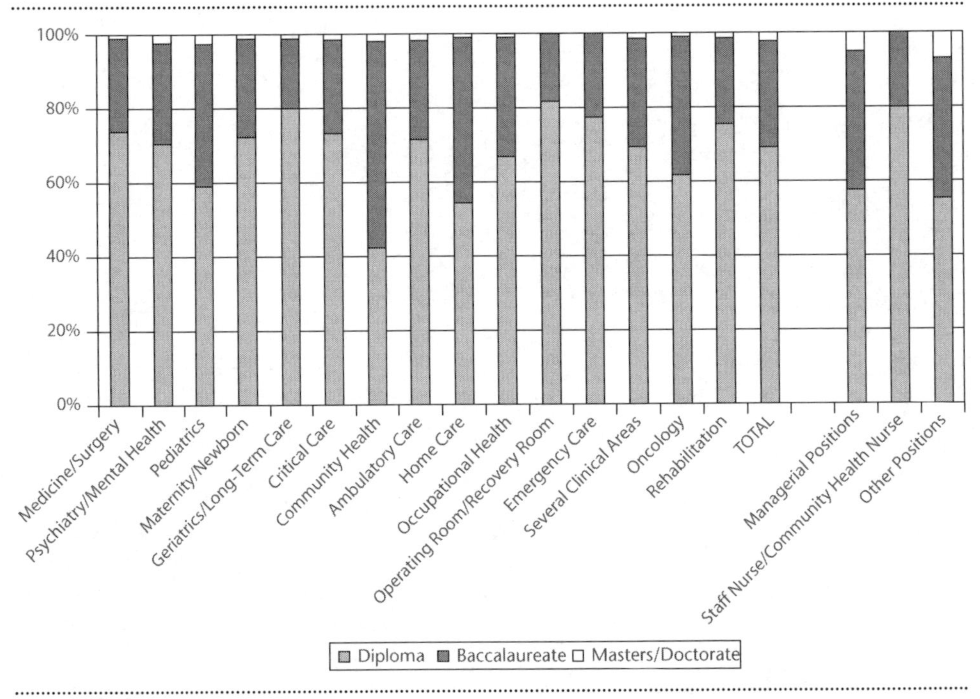

Source: Compiled from data from Canadian Nurses Association (2006). RN workforce profiles by area of responsibility year 2004. Ottawa: Canadian Nurses Association and Canadian Institute for Health Information (2002). Supply and Distribution of Registered Nurses in Canada, 2001. Ottawa: Canadian Institute for Health Information (June 18), p. 167.

managerial control and maximize employee productivity (Armstrong, 2001; Carpenter, 1977). Nurse training programs are being refocused not only to emphasize medical, technical, and knowledge-based advances in health care practice, but also issues related to workplace change and organization, cultural dimensions of health care, and social diversity among health care workers and service recipients (Dick & Cragg, 2006, pp. 201–205).

Nursing, as the largest single category of health care workers, remains central to the politics and structure of health care in Canada. The observed tendencies toward segmentation in nursing suggest that any benefits from a restructured organization of health care services will be distributed in a highly asymmetrical fashion. Within nursing, males and nurses with the highest educational credentials are moving into positions likely to serve as bases for further consolidation of authority and resources. This is evident in the expansion of specialization both within nursing and the rise of associated occupations, as illustrated, in part, in the range of areas represented in Figure 6.3. Many clinical specializations in nursing are developing unique credentialing and certification requirements, often leading to the formation of distinct occupational groups, notably licensed Nurse Practitioners distinguished by advanced education coupled with enhanced authority related to health assessment, diagnosis, care management, and prescription of medications.

While the resources that go into nursing education, as well as nursing initiatives in the direction of credentialing, the development of nursing knowledge and specialization may serve to upgrade the status of nursing as a whole, they are more likely to be channelled toward the minority of nurses who can use credentials and authority positions to their advantage. If these initiatives do enable nurses on the whole to legitimize their claims to greater proportions of health care resources, nursing administrators are liable to rely less upon nurses and more upon lower-paid auxiliaries to provide health care services (Armstrong & Armstrong, 2003, p. 107). The upper stream of credentialed nurses, with the assistance of agencies such as the Kellogg Foundation, which has funded major projects in nursing research, accreditation, and doctoral studies (CNA, 1983, pp. 29–30), may be able to insulate itself from the erosion of the profession as a whole by strengthening its own claims to essential health care skills and knowledge that it alone possesses.

Some of the fiscal and administrative support previously given to nursing diploma programs may be directed to promoting the expanded production of auxiliary health care workers, or to accelerating the training time required to meet pressing demands for more nurses. Concerns that Canada is entering a period of sustained and severe shortages of registered nurses induced in part by work pressures that motivate nurses to leave, or refuse to enter, the profession, will also influence the future of nursing and nurse training (CNA, 1997, pp. 14, 18; Ryten, 1997, pp. 43–44). The Canadian Nurses Association (2002), predicting a deficit of 113,000 registered nurses in Canada by 2016, estimates that the annual number of admissions to nursing schools would have to increase by three times in order to meet continuing demands for qualified nurses. Canadian health authorities and administrators, along with persons who have close contact with health care systems, have begun to pay closer attention to nurses' demands for improved working conditions, pay, and role in the delivery of health care services in a context in which ongoing nurse shortages can seriously undermine future attempts to ensure the provision and quality of primary health care. At the same time, however, strategies to contain health care costs and manage personnel shortages by reorganizing nursing work to focus on the most acute care needs, combined with realities that severely limits the extent to which university training programs are able to provide sufficient spaces, resources, and qualified nursing instructors to increase the supply of degree nursing graduates, suggest that nursing will continue to struggle in crucial respects (Armstrong, 2001, pp. 134–135; Dick & Cragg, 2006, pp. 204–205; Mansell, 2004, p. 201). Paradoxically, then, by advancing credentialing and research policies in the interest of the profession as a whole, nurses may be contributing to their own division into various segments based on highly skilled and educated nursing elites and masses of subordinate, lower-paid nursing support workers.

Nurses are increasingly cognizant of their uncertain status within a changing health care sector. In many cases, they have been able to use the realities of chronic shortages of health care workers to their advantage, gaining concessions in wages and improved professional working conditions from their employers. At the same time, however, they have had to rely upon collective action to make substantive gains or even to hold their ground against reductions in health care services and expenditures. As an indication of mounting tensions within the health care sector, nurses across Canada have not been hesitant to engage in strikes and other militant actions over the past two decades, and shifting more recently (particularly after being declared essential service workers in some jurisdictions) to public relations campaigns to advance their occupational interests (Hibbert, 1992; White, 1990; Ross-Kerr, 2003a, pp. 289-ff). In the process, nurses have been forced to rethink their status as workers and as professionals. While caring and service ethics remain important components of nurse training and work, nurses have shown through their struggles that the nature of that service can no longer be bound within restricted terms of docility.

CONCLUSION

This chapter has emphasized how the transformation of nursing from a subordinate service occupation into a more specialized and sophisticated profession has been rendered more apparent than real in many key respects through a series of external and internal constraining factors. Education has been a crucial channel for the occupational development of nursing, serving both to advance and to suppress its status. The pattern of nursing and nursing education in Canada has followed the interplay of nurses' organized efforts to establish their occupation with the development of a Canadian labour force in general and a health care labour force in particular. The frequent success of corporate, state, and medical interests in guiding the development of nursing has had a significant impact on the present status of nursing as a wage labour force divided by education and gender. Nurses, though, have come to recognize that their status as the largest single health care occupation is a potential power base (Armstrong, Choiniere & Day, 1993; Ross-Kerr, 2003b; Lerner, 1985; Mussallem, 1977). By promoting their ability to serve client needs and health care priorities rather than economic or systemic requisites, while simultaneously avoiding the trap of accepting a professional ideology as substitute for actual resources, nurses may yet succeed in their quest for status. To this end, nurses are beginning to align themselves with other groups of workers, including teachers and public services employees, who face similar threats and challenges. The consequences of nurses' development of a political strategy are significant, for without a clear analysis of their occupational situation, nurses are likely to suffer, as will the quality of the health services that they are able to provide.

STUDY QUESTIONS

1. *Which factors have facilitated the emergence of nursing as a prominent health care occupation? Which factors have served to constrain the development of nursing in Canada?*
2. *Nursing organizations have identified the attainment of a university degree by all persons seeking to become a registered nurse as a basic priority in their struggle to gain improved status and recognition in the health care field. Is this a useful and viable objective? Discuss key issues and problems associated with their efforts to achieve this goal.*
3. *Discuss the relationship between nursing and the development of the medical profession.*
4. *What implications have changes in medical technology and in the organization of health care services had for the development of nursing?*
5. *Discuss the ways in which the state education system is subject to pressures from various social interests, as illustrated by the example of nursing.*
6. *How does the development of nursing compare with trends in other related occupations, such as teaching and social work? Should nurses have the right to strike?*

GLOSSARY

degree program an education program, normally consisting of three to five years of formal education in an accredited university, leading to a degree.

diploma program an education program, normally consisting of two to three years of formal education in an accredited community college, leading to a diploma.

feminized occupation an occupation in which the majority, or increasing proportions, of workers are female; such work tends to be more highly structured and hierarchically organized, and less well paid, than other forms of work.

intensification a process in which workers are required to perform an increasing number of duties or tasks in a job; normally associated with increased external control over the work by people in managerial, administrative, or ownership positions.

professionalism an ideology that emphasizes the attainment of high levels of knowledge, skill, status, and control within a particular occupation.

registered nurse a nurse licensed to practise nursing as determined and registered by a professional certification body within Canadian jurisdictions on the basis of examinations following credentials received through accredited nursing diploma or degree programs.

segmentation the division of a body or object into two parts; in the case of nursing, a trend is evident in which different segments of the nursing force, with varying credentials and expertise, are engaged in diverse working situations reflected in unequal workloads, pay, and working conditions.

REFERENCES

Allen, M. (1985, May). Baccalaureate education remains an enigma for many nurses. *Canadian Nurse, 81*(5), 12.

Armstrong, P. (2001). Evidence-based health care reform: Women's issues. In P. Armstrong, H. Armstrong, & D. Coburn (Eds.), *Unhealthy times: Political economy perspectives on health and care* (pp. 120–145). Don Mills, ON: Oxford University Press.

Armstrong, P., & Armstrong, H. (2003). *Wasting away: The undermining of Canadian health care* (2nd ed.). Toronto: Oxford University Press.

Armstrong, P., Choiniere, J., & Day, E. (1993). *Vital signs: Nursing in transition*. Toronto: Garamond Press.

Bolaria, B.S. (1987). The brain drain to Canada: The externalization of the cost of education. In T. Wotherspoon (Ed.), *The political economy of Canadian schooling* (pp. 301–322). Toronto: Methuen.

Bowles, S., & Gintis, H. (1976). *Schooling in capitalist America*. New York: Basic Books.

Brannon, R.L. (1994). Professionalization and work intensification: Nursing in the cost containment era. *Work and Occupations, 21*(2), 157–178.

Canadian Hospital Association (1984). Canadian hospital directory statistical compendium. Toronto: Canadian Hospital Association.

Canadian Institute for Health Information. (1998). More registered nurses working part-time and in community-based health care: 1997 figures. Ottawa: Canadian Institute for Health Information, Canadian Nurses Association and Statistics Canada.

Canadian Institute for Health Information. (2005). Workforce trends of registered nurses in Canada, 2004. Ottawa: Canadian Institute for Health Information.

Canadian Nurses Association. (1968). The leaf and the lamp. Ottawa: Canadian Nurses Association.

Canadian Nurses Association. (1981). The seventh decade 1969–1980. Ottawa: Canadian Nurses Association.

Canadian Nurses Association. (1982). Entry to the practice of nursing: A background paper. Ottawa: Canadian Nurses Association .

Canadian Nurses Association. (1983). Nursing in Canada 1983. Ottawa: Statistics Canada and Canadian Nurses Association.

Canadian Nurses Association. (1986, October). Collaboration between nurse educators in the use of nursing education resources. *Entry to Practice Newsletter, 2*(5), 1–7.

Canadian Nurses Association. (1997). The future supply of registered nurses in Canada: A discussion paper. Ottawa: Canadian Nurses Association.

Canadian Nurses Association. (2002, June). Planning for the future: Nursing human resource projections. Ottawa: Canadian Nurses Association.

Canadian Nurses Association. (2003). Fact sheet: Nursing in Canada. Ottawa: Canadian Nurses Association.

Canadian Nurses Association. (2006). RN workforce profiles by area of responsibility year 2004. Ottawa: Canadian Nurses Association.

Cannings, K., & Lazonick, W. (1975). The development of the nursing labor force in the United States: A basic analysis. *International Journal of Health Services, 5*(2), 185–216.

Camoy, M., & Levin, H.M. (1985). *Schooling and work in the democratic state.* California: Stanford University Press.

Carpenter, M. (1977). The new managerialism and professionalism in nursing. In M. Stacey, M. Reid, C. Heath, & R. Dingwall (Eds.), *Health and the division of labour* (pp. 165–193). London: Croom Helm.

Citizenship and Immigration Canada. (annual series). Immigration statistics. Ottawa: Minister of Public Works and Government Services Canada/Citizenship and Immigration Canada.

Coburn, J. (1987). I see and am silent: A short history of nursing in Ontario, 1850–1930. In D. Coburn, C.D'Arcy, G.M. Torrance, & P.K. New (Eds.), *Health and Canadian society: Canadian perspectives* (pp. 441–462). Markham, ON: Fitzhenry & Whiteside.

Cockerham, W.E. (1986). *Medical sociology* (3rd ed.). Englewood Cliffs: Prentice-Hall.

Corea, G. (1985). *The hidden malpractice: How American medicine mistreats women.* New York: Harper & Row.

Corrigan, P., Curtis, B., & Lanning, R. (1987). The political space of schooling. In T. Wotherspoon (Ed.), *The political economy of Canadian schooling* (pp. 21–43). Toronto: Methuen.

Crawford, M.E. (1978, February). The curriculum revision process – Experienced at the college of nursing, the University of Saskatchewan. In *Perspectives: Nursing education, practice and research* (pp. 1–16). *Proceedings of the 1978 annual meeting of the western region – Canadian Association of University Schools of Nursing.* Calgary: University of Calgary.

Davies, C. (1980). A constant casualty: Nurse education in Britain and the USA to 1939. In C. Davis (Ed.), *Rewriting nursing history* (pp. 102–122). London: Croom Helm.

Davies, C. (1995). *Gender and the professional predicament in nursing.* Bristol, PA: Open University Press.

Davis, K., & Moore, W.E. (1945). Some principles of stratification. *American Sociological Review, 10,* 242–249.

Dick, D.D. & Cragg, B. (2006). Undergraduate education: Development and politics. In M. McIntyre, E. Thomlinson, & C. McDonald (Eds.), *Realities of Canadian nursing: Professional, practice, and power issues* (pp. 189–208). Philadelphia: Lippincott Williams & Wilkins.

Duncanson, B. (1970). The development of nursing education at the diploma level. In M.Q. Innis (Ed.), *Nursing education in a changing society* (pp. 109–129). Toronto: University of Toronto Press.

Elliott, M.R. (1977). Nursing and interdisciplinary practice. In B. LaSor & M.R. Elliott (Eds.), *Issues in Canadian nursing* (pp. 43–72). Scarborough: Prentice-Hall.

Gamarnikow, E. (1978). Sexual division of labour: The case of nursing. In A. Kuhn & M. Wolpe (Eds.), *Feminism and materialism – Women and modes of production* (pp. 96–123). London: Routledge & Kegan Paul.

Gibbon, J.M., & Mathewson, M.S. (1947). *Three centuries of Canadian nursing*. Toronto: Macmillan.

Hall, O. (1970). Social change, specialization, and science: Where does nursing stand? In M.Q. Innis (Ed.), *Nursing education in a changing society* (pp. 3–15). Toronto: University of Toronto Press.

Hannah, K.J. (1978, February). Overview of computer-assisted learning in nursing education at the University of Calgary. In *Perspectives: Nursing education, practice and research* (pp. 43–56). *Proceedings of the 1978 Annual Meeting of the Western Region – Canadian Association of University Schools of Nursing*. Calgary: University of Calgary.

Health Canada. (1995). Health Personnel in Canada 1992. Ottawa: Minister of Supply and Services Canada.

Health and Welfare Canada. (1985). Canada health manpower inventory 1985. Ottawa: Minister of National Health and Welfare.

Hibbert, J.M. (1992). Strikes by nurses. In AJ. Baumgart & J. Larsen (Eds.), *Canadian nursing faces the future* (pp. 575–595). St. Louis, MO: Mosby-Year Book.

Innis, M.Q. (Ed.). (1970). *Nursing education in a changing society*. Toronto: University of Toronto Press.

Johnson, T. (1972). *Professions and power*. London: Macmillan.

Kellogg, W.K., Foundation. (1955). *The first twenty-five years: The story of a foundation*. Battle Creek: W.K. Kellogg Foundation.

Kellogg, W.K., Foundation. (1979). *The first half-century 1930–1980: Private approaches to public needs*. Battle Creek: W.K. Kellogg Foundation.

Kelly, L.Y. (1985). *Dimensions of professional nursing* (5th ed.). New York: Macmillan.

King, M.K. (1970). The development of university nursing education. In M.Q. Innis (Ed.), *Nursing education in a changing society* (pp. 67–85). Toronto: University of Toronto Press.

Lerner, H.M. (1985). Educating nurses for power. In R.R. Wieczorek (Ed.), *Power, politics, and policy of nursing* (pp. 90–95). New York: Springer.

Livingstone, D.W. (2004). *The education-jobs gap: Underemployment or economic democracy*. Aurora, ON: Garamond Press.

Lortie, R. (1994, Fall). Part-time university teachers: A growing group. *Education Quarterly Review, 1*(3), 30–34.

MacFarlane, J.A. (1965). Medical education in Canada. *Royal Commission on Health Services Special Study* No. 13. Ottawa: Queen's Printer.

Mansell, D.J. (2004). *Forging the future: A history of nursing in Canada*. Ann Arbour, MI: Harbour Press.

Mussallem, H.K. (1965). Nursing education in Canada. *Royal Commission on Health Services Special Study* No. 16. Ottawa: Queen's Printer.

Mussallem, H.K. (1977). Nurses and political action. In B. LaSor & M.R. Elliott (Eds.), *Issues in Canadian nursing* (pp. 154–181). Scarborough: Prentice-Hall.

Picard, A. (2000). *Critical care: Canadian nurses speak for change.* Toronto: HarperCollins.

Rafferty, A.M. (1996). *The politics of nursing knowledge.* London: Routledge.

Registered Nurses' Association of British Columbia. (1983). Entry into the practice of nursing in the year 2000: Position statement of the registered nurses' association of British Columbia. Vancouver: Registered Nurses' Association of British Columbia.

Rogers, M.E. (1978). Emerging patterns in nursing education. In J.A. Williamson (Ed.), *Current perspectives in nursing education: The changing scene*, Vol. 2 (pp. 1–8). St. Louis, MO: C.V. Mosby.

Ross-Kerr, J.C. (2003a). Emergence of nursing unions as a social force in Canada. In J.C. Ross-Kerr & M.J. Wood (Eds.), *Canadian nursing: Issues and perspectives* (4th ed., pp. 280–300). Toronto: Mosby Canada.

Ross-Kerr, J.C. (2003b). Political awareness in nursing. In J.C. Ross-Kerr & M.J. Wood (Eds.), *Canadian nursing: Issues and perspectives* (4th ed., pp. 244–253). Toronto: Mosby Canada.

Ryten, E. (1997). A statistical picture of the past, present and future of registered nurses in Canada. Ottawa: Canadian Nurses Association.

Salmon, J.W. (1984). Organizing medical care for profit. In J.B. McKinlay (Ed.), *Issues in the political economy of health care* (pp. 143–186). New York: Tavistock.

Saskatchewan Union of Nurses. (1998, January). How rationalization of health services is effecting [sic] nursing in Saskatchewan/What's happening to nurses elsewhere? A look at the provinces. *Spectrum*, 5–20.

Schecter, S. (1977). Capitalism, class, and educational reform in Canada. In L. Panitch (Ed.), *The Canadian state: Political economy and political power* (pp. 373–416). Toronto: University of Toronto Press.

Schwirian, P.M. (1998). *Professionalization of nursing: Current issues and trends* (3rd ed.). Philadelphia: Lippincott.

Statistics Canada. (1983). Historical statistics of Canada (2nd ed.). Ottawa: Minister of Supply and Services Canada.

Statistics Canada. (1993). Employment incomes by occupation. Census of Canada. The nation. Ottawa: Minister of Industry, Science and Technology (cat. no. 93–332).

Statistics Canada. (1995). Nursing in Canada and nursing education programs, 1994. Ottawa: Minister of Industry (cat. no. 83–243).

Statistics Canada. (1996). Nursing in Canada, 1995. Registered nurses. Ottawa: Minister of Industry (cat. no. 83–243).

Statistics Canada. (1998). Education in Canada, 1997. Ottawa: Minister of Industry (cat. no. 81–229).

Statistics Canada (2005a). Occupation – 2001 National Occupational Classification for Statistics, Industry – 1997 North American Industry Classification System, Class of Worker, Sex and 2000 Employment Income for Population 15 Years and Over With Employment Income Who Worked Full Time, Full Year, for Canada, Provinces and Territories, 2001 Census – 20% Sample Data. Ottawa: Statistics Canada Cat. No. 97F0012XCB2001049. Retrieved September 21, 2006 from http://www12.statcan.ca/english/census01/Products/standard/themes/DataProducts.cfm.

Statistics Canada (2005b). Occupation – 2001 National Occupational Classification for Statistics, Selected Labour Force, Demographic, Cultural, Educational and Income

Characteristics and Sex for Population 15 Years and Over, for Canada, Provinces, Territories, Census Metropolitan Areas and Census Agglomerations, 2001 Census – 20% Sample Data. Ottawa: Statistics Canada Cat. No. 97F0012XCB2001050. Retrieved September 21, 2006 from http://www12.statcan.ca/english/census01/Products/standard/themes/DataProducts.cfm.

Swartz, D. (1977). The politics of reform: Conflict and accommodation in Canadian health policy. In L. Panitch (Ed.), *The Canadian state: Political economy and political power* (pp. 311–343). Toronto: University of Toronto Press.

Thorne, S. (2006). Graduate education. In M. McIntyre, E. Thomlinson, & C. McDonald (Eds.), *Realities of Canadian nursing: Professional, practice, and power issues* (pp. 209–226). Philadelphia: Lippincott Williams & Wilkins.

Trudeau, R. (1996, Autumn). Male registered nurses, 1995. *Health reports, 8*(2), 21–27.

Wallis, M. (1978, February). The technological society – its implications for nursing. In *Perspectives: Nursing education, practice and research* (pp. 81–91). *Proceedings of the 1978 Annual Meeting of the Western Region – Canadian Association of University Schools of Nursing*. Calgary: University of Calgary.

Weir, G.M. (1932). *Survey of nursing education in Canada*. Toronto: University of Toronto Press.

White, J. (1990). *Hospital strike: Women, unions, and public sector conflict*. Toronto: Thomson Educational Publications.

Wolinsky, E.D. (1980). *The sociology of health: Principles, professions, and issues*. Toronto: Little, Brown.

Wotherspoon, T. (2004). *The sociology of education in Canada: Critical perspectives* (2nd ed.). Don Mills, ON: Oxford University Press.

7

CONSTRAINED AGENCY: THE SOCIAL STRUCTURE OF NURSES' WORK

COLLEEN VARCOE University of British Columbia

PATRICIA RODNEY University of British Columbia

INTRODUCTION

Driven by neo-liberalism and corporatization as part of economic globalization, several decades of Canadian health care reform have worsened the conditions of nurses' work and thus the care nurses are able to provide. Yet, nurses are not mere pawns at the mercy of change. They have the capacity to critically analyze and influence their conditions of work – in other words, they have agency, albeit constrained. This chapter outlines key elements of the current sociopolitical context of health care, examines the consequences for nurses' work in the **culture** of health care characterized by a **corporate ideology**[1], and explores nurses' roles in shaping their work and work environments.

In this chapter we examine how corporate ideology operates in the everyday work of nurses and other health care providers, and in particular how the ideology of scarcity (Varcoe, 1997) – the pervasive assumption that resources are too scarce to provide adequate care – works with management technology in the control of work. We will consider how nurses' work is organized within scarcity and how nurses participate in corporate ideology. Patterns of practice foster a certain kind of "efficiency" by limiting and devaluing the body care and **emotional labour** of nursing. Nurses then donate unpaid time to limit the **moral distress**[2] they experience while working under such conditions. At the same time, nurses take multiple actions to limit the impact of their work environments on themselves and their patients, with some actions being more effective than others. In this chapter we consider both the moral distress and the health risks faced by nurses working in these conditions. We also examine both the impact on nurses and patients, and possibilities for improving such conditions.

This critical analysis of the culture of health care[3] is offered in the spirit of building on the strengths of the current system. Thus it will conclude by exploring how individuals and groups might develop a critical awareness of the culture of health care and the social structure of work, and how a greater nursing "voice" in policy might benefit all.

This chapter builds on our programs of research, which include:

1. A study of nurses' enactment of their moral agency, conducted in two acute medical units in two hospitals. The study included over 200 hours of participant observation and 22 interviews with eleven nurses from acute care and three from home care (Rodney, 1997).
2. A study of nurses' practice in relation to violence against women, conducted in the emergency units of two hospitals and their communities. The study involved over 200 hours of participant observation, and interviews with 45 participants, including nurses, social workers, physicians, clerks, and patients (Varcoe, 1997; 2001).
3. A study of the meaning of ethics and the enactment of ethical practice from the perspective of nurses (*The Ethics of Practice*). This study involved interviews with eighty-seven student, staff and advanced practice nurses from various practice settings in 19 focus groups (Rodney, Varcoe, Storch, McPherson, Mahoney, Brown, et al., 2002; Varcoe, Doane, Pauly, Rodney, Storch, Mahoney, et al. 2004).
4. A recent (2003–2006) participatory action research study of nursing practice (*Ethics in Action*) conducted in an Emergency Unit and a Medical Oncology Unit.[4] This study involved three years of participant observation, interviews, focus groups, meetings, workshops, and informal work within the two practice settings. At each site, the research team included staff nurses and academic investigators working in partnership. Along with qualitative data collection through focus groups and interviews, regular meetings with staff were conducted at each site to discuss, debrief, and to plan for change. The research process supported staff to initiate changes in their workplaces toward ethical practice.

Each of these studies used feminist and critical perspectives, and drew on the work of a number of diverse theorists. Following completion of the first two studies, the authors of this chapter drew on the work of Noblit and Hare (1988) to combine their findings (Varcoe, Rodney, & McCormick, 2003). Thus, this chapter draws on the four studies listed above as well as on meta-synthesis of the first two studies.

THE CORPORATE CONTEXT OF CONTEMPORARY HEALTH CARE

The Canadian health care system is increasingly shaped by globalization,[5] in which capital flows around the world to serve the interests of an economically dominant elite (Laxer, 1998). While the espoused intent of the health care reforms occurring in Canada and other Western countries is to improve the quality and accessibility of health care, the implementation of the reforms is fuelled by a powerful **corporate ideology** (Hiraki, 1998). Canadian health care reforms are being enacted in an era of escalating inequities in the distribution of human resources – and a corresponding acceptance that actions to save money in health care or other social services are inherently justifiable (Lynam et al., 2003; Bolaria, 1994; McQuaig, 1993, 1998; Saul,1997; Stephenson, 1999; Storch, 2003). This has resulted in a mechanistic, reductionist approach to health services that threaten the Canadian commitment to universal and equitable health care (Armstrong & Armstrong, 2003; Commission on the Future of Health Care in Canada,

2002; Pauly, 2004; Picard, 2000; Rachlis & Kushner, 1994). Cost constraint has, to a significant extent, trumped the quality and accessibility of health care.

Economic trends in Canada, including budget deficits and restrictions in the role of the federal government in maintaining the principles of medicare, put tremendous pressure on provincial and territorial governments to economize on health spending (Armstrong & Armstrong, 2003; Storch, 2003; Storch & Meilicke, 1994). Consequently, Canada has continued to experience "a climate for change in the organization and management of health services that transcend[s] anything since the foundation for the current system was completed in 1968" (Storch & Meilicke, p. 32). This climate has generated extensive cost constraint measures within health care.[6] Thus, in the 1990s, hospital units and entire hospitals were closed, community services shuffled, and health care staff moved around or dismissed at unprecedented rates. Only recently has Canadian research begun to evaluate the impact of these changes. Disparities in access to care increasingly are apparent in rural and remote settings, home care, mental health care, palliative care, elder care, and even acute care in large centres (Armstrong & Armstrong, 2003; Canadian Medical Association & Canadian Nurses Association, 2004; Commission on the Future of Health Care in Canada, 2002; Health Canada Secretariat on Palliative and End-of-Life Care, 2002; Lynam et al., 2003; National Advisory Committee, 2000; Penning, 2002; Stadjuhar, 2003).

Canadian data also portray increasing nursing workloads, with reductions in the quality of care and problems with trust, commitment, and morale (Canadian Health Services Research Foundation, 2001; Canadian Nurses' Association, 1998; Duncan et al., 2001; Dunleavy, Shamian, & Thomson, 2003; Estabrooks et al., 2002; Health Canada Office of Nursing Policy, 2001; Keddy et al., 1999; Laschinger et al., 2000; Shamian et al., 2002). Studies from the United States also illustrate serious erosion of the quality of care associated with similar cost constraint measures, particularly as workloads have increased for nurses and less qualified personnel have been used to replace nurses (Aiken, Clarke, & Sloane, 2000; Aiken et al., 2002; Barry-Walker, 2000; Estabrooks, 2005; Mohr, 1997; Stanton & Rutherford, 2004; Weiss et al., 2002).

Together, these studies warn that as the conditions of nurses' work deteriorate through casualization of the workforce, increased workload, loss of clinical leadership, and shortages of skilled health care providers, morbidity and mortality rises, and patient satisfaction is reduced. Nurse satisfaction is also reduced, and there are now serious problems with nurse illness, injury, and attrition.

The impact of corporatized health care reform is not uniform across all citizens. Rather, because such reforms are occurring at the nexus of multiple ideologies that are raced, classed, and gendered, the impact is greatest on those who are least privileged. As cost savings in health care reform are achieved primarily through lower wages, poorer care, and a shift of costs and responsibility to patients and their families (Armstrong, 2001; Björnsdóttir, 2001), women, racialized people, those with debilitating conditions, those who are impoverished, and those who are homeless are most effected (Anderson & Reimer Kirkham, 1998; Anderson, 2004; Franklin, Hwang, & Quantz, 2005; Lynam, 2005; Stephenson, 1999).

Why has a corporate ideology, with its aforementioned problems, taken such hold in Canada? An **ideology** is a set of ideas and images: "a shared set of fundamental beliefs, attitudes, and assumptions about the world that justify 'what is'" (Thomas, 1993, p. 8).

Ideologies are usually taken for granted because they are unconscious. They provide the conceptual machinery for questions, for the data gathered or ignored, and for the chosen interpretations (Thomas, 1993, p. 8). A corporate ideology has taken hold in Canada and is largely taken for granted. Noted cultural critic John Ralston Saul (1997) claims that Canada operates on myths (such as ideas that "we spend too much on social services," "current levels of care are no longer affordable") rather than memory and has lost sight of its commitment to the "**common good**"[7] that characterized the development of Canada as a nation. Operating on myth provides opportunities for unexamined ideas to exert their powerful influence. In health care, Canada has allowed its commitment to the common good to be replaced by corporatism. And, as Coburn points out, corporate ideologies are used "to make citizens powerless in their own countries...[with the] doctrine of 'we have no choice'" making adherence to corporate interests seem inevitable (2001, p. 60).

This chapter will therefore attempt to unmask what has been taken for granted. It will explore the consequences of corporate ideology for the everyday work of nurses and other health care providers, as well as for patients and their families. What has been taken for granted must be made visible if nurses and other health care providers are to work beyond constraints to their ability to provide good and ethical care (in other words, constraints to their **moral agency**), and if the nation is to move toward the more equitable health care system that most Canadians desire and all deserve.

CORPORATISM AT THE LEVEL OF PATIENT CARE

Both the ideologies and the practices of the corporate culture of health care are played out at the level of direct patient care (see also Rankin, 2003; Rodney & Street, 2004; Rodney & Varcoe, 2001). The research cited earlier indicates that each cost constraint measure has a direct impact on nursing practice, creating more work, more uncertainty, and less control over how nursing time is spent. Perhaps most importantly, "redesign" strategies, such as those aimed at reducing the length of hospital stay, have resulted in an increase in patient acuity and turnover, which in turn directly affect nursing workload. Nurses find themselves caring for more acute patients and processing more patients more quickly. Downsizing activities such as bed closures require nurses to organize those closures, move to new practice areas, and organize the reopening of beds and work areas. The consolidation of hospital boards and executive management, staff layoffs, and eliminating levels of management (and often the managers) create a climate of instability and uncertainty. Further, with less contact between direct care providers and management, nurses generally have less impact on decision making. Moving nurses to unfamiliar patient care areas and replacing registered nurses with practical nurses and/or care aides dilutes levels of skill, placing heavier responsibilities on the remaining staff.

AN IDEOLOGY OF SCARCITY

Our research indicates that nurses adjust their work to this evolving corporate context and make sense of the changing conditions of work in certain ways. Nurses participate in the corporate ideology and organize their work to maximize a certain kind of efficiency. One of the most profound ways that the ideas and images of corporatism are enacted at this level is through an **ideology of scarcity**. Ideas and images of resources as scarce and unattainable abound in the day-to-day world of nursing practice. And these ideas and images in turn drive practices that emphasize certain kinds of streamlining and efficiencies. So, for example, nurses might put diapers on competent adults because they do not have time to assist them to the toilet, justifying such practice as arising out of the necessity of scarce resources.

Corporate rhetoric and ideas dominate thinking both within the health care system and in the wider social context. Nurses receive messages about the state of the economy and health care from many sources, ranging from media messages, including local and health care specific media, to managers, coworkers, and patients. In the settings we have studied, messages about scarcity predominate. Along with increasing concern about "wait lists" and "wait times", news media continue to emphasize budget constraints in health care. Managers, responsible for implementing such budgets, promote ideas that resonate with the ideas of efficiency in a time of scarcity. In the words of one hospital manager, "To do the best job with the resources that you have, that is what exemplary is" (Varcoe, 1997, p. 125).

In our research on nursing work in these settings, this ideology of scarcity was primarily expressed in talk about time and enacted in nurses' work in the form of certain "efficiencies." In our early studies, nurses' talk revealed an acceptance of scarcity as the driving force in health care and as the driving force that organizes nursing practice. One nurse said, "It's money, it's management, it's things I can't really argue with" (Varcoe, 1997, p. 124). Another said:

> You'd like more staff and you'd like more participation but in reality there isn't the money, you aren't going to get the staff, so don't spend the time whining and sniveling, it's not going to be there. Just do the best you can with what you have. (Varcoe, 1997, p. 124)

In our more recent work, *Ethics in Action,* nurses continued to echo such sentiments, although to us the overall tone was at once both more defeated and angrier, with "frustration" being perhaps the most common descriptor of practice. One nurse recently said of her work:

> There are great people here and they're doing a great job under I think very stressful, high-pressure circumstances. I'm going to use a catch phrase: it's like its own war zone. (Staff Nurse Interview, *Ethics in Action*, 2005)

Another voiced other nurses' widespread concerns about not being able to practice according to their professional standards: "I don't feel like I have control over my practice and I'm not meeting [patient care] standards" (Staff Nurse Interview, *Ethics in Action*, 2005).

Despite the sense of acceptance of "fiscal realities," nurses' talk also conveyed a profound awareness of the discrepancies between the care they valued and the care they were able to provide. Much of this talk was couched in terms of time: time that nurses did not have to provide the care that their patients required. Time was described as "lacking," "inadequate," and "nonexistent," and the predominant impact of this scarcity was seen as inadequate attention to nonphysical care. In our more recent work, nurses' awareness of the influence of the wider context on their work seemed more acute, with expressions of frustration aimed not only at the impact on their work, but also at the immediate organizational conditions that gave rise to that impact – poor communication, lack of direction from managers, and unending change:

> Sometimes you get pulled like a piece of toffee. You know. People calling you names, the phones are ringing, you're having to put out a fire or you're having to start a fire under somebody, keep things moving, dealing with the administration, and that's the biggest problem is trying to get something going throughout the day so you can get your day done. (Staff Nurse Interview, *Ethics in Action*, 2005)

Nurses identified their attention to the nonphysical needs of patients as the aspect of care that suffered most, both during the provision of routine care and when patients experienced significant emotional crises. Nurses talked about the ways they routinely curtailed their conversation and attention to the emotional needs of patients, and as researchers we observed nurses letting patients know that they were busy so that patients did not expect to engage in conversation. Nurses routinely mentioned that they did not have time for "the psychosocial," meaning attention to patients' nonphysical needs. One nurse said that when patients request extra attention, "you think 'just don't bother me anymore, I want to do my work and get out of there'" (Staff Nurse Interview, *Ethics in Action*, 2005).

Even during devastating events, nurses felt they were unable to afford the time required for emotional care. Most who were interviewed told at least one story that exemplified such situations. Each nurse told a story about a patient who had experienced a profound loss, such as the death of a child or partner, or a terminal diagnosis, in which he or she was unable to provide the support the patient needed:

> It is really hard for a nurse to just sit there and do nothing at a bedside when she's got a gazillion things to do, but with some people that is almost what you need to do, just sit there for five minutes and not say anything, just be there and that builds the trust. Anyway that's a dream, we don't have the time to do that any more. (Varcoe, 1997, p. 165)

Note that this nurse refers to her emotional care as doing "nothing." Based on her analysis of nurses' talk about time in two studies, Stelling (1994a) concluded:

> This talk about time is not really about time at all....When nurses say they do not have time for interactional work with patients, the real problem is that they are unable to maintain its high priority when confronted with the demands and expectations of others. Thus time can be seen as a metaphor for autonomy and control; the emphasis on the shortage of time reflects the importance and pervasiveness of the lack of autonomy and control. (p. 210)

Consistent with Stelling's findings, nurses in our earlier studies saw the emphasis on corporate efficiency and physical "treatment" as being valued by other health care providers, especially those who have the most powerful influence on nursing practice – managers and physicians. Relationships between nurses and managers within the units were often characterized by a continuous struggle over resources, and nurses sometimes saw physicians as supportive of the corporate ideology.[8] One nurse said:

> The Emerg [sic] Physicians are there to make money, they are there to see the maximum number of patients in the minimum amount of time and they are somewhat reluctant to

deal with patients that are psychosocial or emotional because it takes longer and there is always that feeling of being inadequate when dealing with it, whether due to a lack of experience or lack of resources. (Varcoe, 1997, p. 167)

While such perspectives were still prevalent, in our more recent work nurses also often saw physicians as negatively impacted by health care reforms, and as allies toward better care. In the words of one nurse, "The politics are still there. The doctor/nurse thing is still there but you know that everybody is in it together" (Staff Nurse Interview, *Ethics in Action*, 2005).

Ideas of scarcity in health care are dominant in public spheres, at all levels of government, and among health care providers at various levels within the system and among patients. Nurses accepted these ideas to a large extent and shaped their practice to conform to corporate ideology and imperatives. Time, nurses' most valuable resource, was viewed as a scarce commodity and was often spent in the service of corporate goals rather than nursing or patient priorities. Thus, these ideas of scarcity supported cost constraint measures, and both the ideas and constraints structured nurses' work. As a result of corporate streamlining, nurses' work became structured as "efficient" practice (Rodney & Varcoe, 2001).

CORPORATE STREAMLINING AND "EFFICIENT" PRACTICES

In response to cost constraint measures and messages about the inevitability of scarcity in health care, and with at least a partial acceptance of those messages, nurses' work is organized to maximize their "efficiency." This efficiency is organized by what Smith (1987, 1990) calls "the relations of ruling" – structures, institutions, and regulations – that create understandings taken up by the nurses themselves (see also Stein, 2001). For example, in many organizations "patient care coordinators" have been re-labeled as "bed utilization managers" creating new understanding regarding what is important. The relations of ruling between management and nurses are mediated by various management technologies that organize nurses' efforts to efficiently process patients.

The introduction of management technology to manage nurses' labour shaped the relationship between fiscal restraint and nursing (Campbell, 1994). Based on her study of nurses' work, Campbell described how the introduction of patient classification and workload measurement systems in the 1970s and 1980s fundamentally altered control of nursing staffing decisions. The introduction of these technologies began the shift of decision making about patient "needs" and staffing from the site of "production" (i.e., where the work is done) to management.

These technologies, designed to improve the "efficiency" of nurses' labour, created "objective data" about patient "needs" and matched this data with the amount of nursing work required, thus transferring dominance from the professional judgment of nurses to that of managers who can claim to "know" based on data. Unfortunately, these formulas do not account for what Campbell (1994) calls "indeterminate work;" they calculate staffing based on minimized and standardized estimates of patient needs that do not account for individual or "real" patients.[9] Of course, a major component of nurses' "indeterminate work" is their emotional labour in support of patients. The consequences of these moves to manage nurses' labour include cutting the time allowed to complete care, speeding up of the pace of work, and adding more paper work. Campbell (1987) concluded:

> Recommended as a rational method of improving nurse productivity, I argue that objective needs assessment and staffing procedures result in decisions that are neither as rational as they seem nor more trustworthy than those made on nurses' judgment alone. The objective decisions do, however, mean that nursing-care time can be limited and nurses' work intensified. Such outcomes add stress to nurses' working conditions that, combined with reductions in the scope and level of services able to be offered under new time constraints, threaten the quality of care for hospital patients. (p. 463)

Today, with the introduction of sophisticated computerized information systems (at great expense to the health care system), management technologies have become less visible. When a nurse orders a laboratory test, sends a request to the pharmacy, or calls a porter to transport a patient, these acts are automatically counted and recorded and ultimately used in decision making about workload and staffing patterns. Printouts of varying levels of activity at different times of day are available. The problem of failing to capture the "indeterminate work" of nursing persists, but the data collection and decision making is invisible to nurses. Thus they participate unknowingly and are unable to contribute to a critical analysis of decision making. Whereas in the 1980s nurses critiqued patient classification and workload measurement systems as they filled in paper forms, as the technologies become more pervasive and less visible, such critique becomes impossible. There are no opportunities to object, "But that doesn't capture what we do!"

Over the past several decades, then, staffing patterns have been adjusted by using various management technologies to the point that the indeterminate work of nursing has been squeezed almost out of existence. Because only certain practices are "counted," because physiological care and medical treatment are valued over other forms of care, and because scarcity has been accepted, patterns of practice have developed to accommodate these values. Thus, the form of "efficiency" that has evolved is one that provides physiological care and medical treatment as quickly and as cheaply as possible.

In the units we studied initially, the patterns of practice reflected this sort of "efficiency," patterns that persist in units we studied more recently. In the emergency units, the predominant practice pattern was one of "efficient processing." In this pattern of practice, patients were: a) "stripped down" (literally and figuratively), to b) identify a manageable problem (such as a chest pain, laceration, or fever), and c) processed according to this manageable problem in order, to d) empty the stretcher. Various strategies were used to keep patients "on track." Assessments were routinized and circumscribed, and patients were encouraged to give only the information needed to identify the problem. Such strategies began with opening questions at triage such as, "What brings you to emergency today?" and continued with checklists and flow sheets tailored to identify physiological problems. These strategies were facilitated by behaviours that let patients know how busy the staff were and discouraged them from making demands for attention beyond what the nurse could meet.

Similarly, in the medical units, the actual running of departments was often seen to have priority over the needs of patients, including both physical and nonphysical needs. Patient needs were often subordinated to the needs of departments, so, for example, an unstable patient might be transported without adequate personnel and equipment (such as oxygen, a stretcher, and a nurse, rather than a wheelchair and a porter) in order to prevent delays in the X-ray department; home care patients with disabilities might be admitted to hospital and anesthetized repeatedly for small procedures because those procedures could not be coordinated.

In the various settings studied, nurses not only developed patterns of practice to maximize their own "efficiency" but also devised systems of working within the constraints of others. Nurses spent a good deal of effort accommodating the efficiencies of other health care providers and departments. In the emergency units, the nurses' first priority was usually to prepare patients for the physician's assessment; they would process the physician's orders immediately following the assessment, and often would interrupt their own work to allow others (for example, physicians, lab personnel) to complete theirs. Further, nurses devised other ways of facilitating the efficiency of others. For example, because physicians had limited time to spend on each patient and because nurses were often too busy to "catch" the physician, nurses devised systems to alert physicians to particular problems.

One of the ways in which these "efficient"[10] practices were maintained by nurses was the use of workplace sanctions. Nurses let one another know what was expected, rewarded one another for maintaining "efficiency," and penalized each other for not maintaining expectations. Nurses expressed regard for those who were "efficient" in terms of providing physical care and "getting the tasks done," and expressed derision for those who were "slow," were "bleeding hearts," spent "too much time talking," and so on:

> There are a few [nurses] in particular who deal with the emotional aspect first, unless of course [patients] are bleeding out or whatever. They meet the wrath of some of the other staff members quite significantly. "She's not pulling her load, she's doing that PR crap." (Varcoe, 1997, p. 173)

However, although we continued to observe such sanctions in our current work, we also observed active defiance of both workplace requirements and sanctions by colleagues that interfered with what individuals saw as "good care." For example, in our most recent study, one of the nurses with whom we worked closely vehemently declared that "I am NOT going to have a 52 year old patient die in the hall on my shift!" (Staff Nurse Interview, *Ethics in Action*, 2005) and defied rules to enact that declaration. We also witnessed the power of taking action collectively. For example, in the medical oncology unit, nurses banded together to block a policy of mixing men and women in the same rooms.

Paradoxically, accommodating the efficiencies of other health care providers and departments, and defying such constraints both sometimes threatened already thin nursing resources. The oncology nurses had to engage in multiple bed moves to prevent "co-ed" rooms, and the nurse with the critically ill patient had to add advocating for his care to her already impossible workload. Clearly, this is not the type of efficiency intended by a cost-benefit analysis that purportedly has health as the intended outcome.

Sanctions enacted by staff nurses were also evident at administrative levels. Administrators applied sanctions for "inefficiencies" such as an increased length of stay. A manager in an acute medical unit explained that her unit was held to a standard of a length of stay of seven days. That standard had been decreased from 11 days the year before, despite the fact that the population of patients that the unit served had changed to include more patients with complex health problems that required even more care. She went on to explain how the failure to comply with corporate edicts resulted in consequences that in turn created more problems:

> [T]here's no money so we ended up closing. Summertime last year we closed twelve beds to try and reap in the money so the outcome was...nursing lay off...if you can't shut down any more beds, then what we're going to do is [use] aides, not nurses. (Rodney, 1997, p. 241)

Failure to meet corporate goals, such as in this case decreasing the increased length of stay, often carried the risk of sanctions for managers, units, and staff, including staff layoffs, and/or the replacement of registered nurses with less prepared staff. This also demonstrates that cost constraint measures are not completely rational, as Campbell (1987) warned two decades ago. Units that are different in terms of patient population and patient needs are grouped together and expected to hold to the same standards in terms of markers such as length of stay, per capita costs, and so on. Thus, administrative sanctions work with sanctions applied by nurses to enforce practice in congruence with corporate goals.

CORPORATE CASUALTIES[11]

Thus far, we have argued that the corporate culture of health care is made manifest in an ideology of scarcity. We further argued that corporate streamlining and efficient processing shape direct patient care. But what is the impact on nurses as individuals and for nursing as a profession? What are the consequences for the patients, families, and communities that nurses serve? Overall, the social organization of "cost efficiency" exacts both a professional and personal toll when nurses are expected to accept responsibility for delivering a safe and sufficient level of care under conditions that become less and less capable of sustaining this work. The consequences are serious, not just because of the human costs to nurses, but because of the impact on the quality of care received by patients, families, and communities.

DISPOSABLE NURSES

Nurses providing direct care are treated as if they are disposable in at least four ways. Their intellectual and emotional labour, their personal time, and their well-being are too often sacrificed for the efficiency of the system. For example:

> [W]hen it gets busy, when it gets so busy you're so busy coping sometimes with just the actual immediate physical needs and their meds getting out and stuff like that that you often don't have the time to really think through the assessments...when I go home afterwards I think, "Wow, what about such and such?"...and you know, you hit yourself.... There's things that I forget too, like I go home and I think, "Now I wonder if..." (Rodney, 1997, p. 184)

First, let us look at the nurse's intellectual labour. This experienced medical nurse took pride in her ability to assess her patients and was acknowledged as a clinical resource by her colleagues. Yet in the interview cited above, she went on to tell a story of how she had missed picking up bladder distention on a patient who was showing many of the classic signs. Indeed, this nurse was what Benner and her colleagues (1996) would have recognized as an expert at clinical judgment. She knew "the particular patient, his typical pattern of responses, his (sic) story and the way in which illness has constituted his story. [She knew this] through advanced clinical knowledge...gained from experience with many persons in similar situations" (Benner, Tanner, & Chesla, 1996, p. 1). Yet she had little opportunity to employ that judgment in her work. In this sense, her intellectual labour was not valued.

Second, being busy with "just the actual immediate physical needs" means that nurses' emotional labour – the labour of dealing with emotional needs – is compromised (Staden, 1998; Varcoe, 1997; Yyelland, 1994).[12] For example, a nurse working in an emergency department said:

> There was a young fellow...diagnosed with leukemia down there, first thing in the morning they wheeled him in and told him what he had and he didn't want me to leave. Of course you are torn because you've got a lot of other things to do and in many respects he is a priority but the way we worked down there is ABC, life-threatening, limb-threatening, and he is neither of those....I waited for awhile and then I said, "Do you want to be alone or do you still want me to stay until your family comes...or can I get you a Social Worker or something?" I'm trying everything to get another body in there so I can get out and that's wrong, but what do you do? (Varcoe, 1997, p. 128)

And, as noted, nurses sometimes demeaned one another for attending to patients' emotional needs.

Thus, both intellectual and emotional labour are devalued by the way work is organized and by nurses themselves. Nurses in our studies did not have time to "think through" their care. Nor did they have time to "talk about it." Such concerns about excessive workloads – workloads that get in the way of nurses meeting the professional standards of their practice – are by no means new. At least five decades of empirical work in diverse studies from various practice contexts echo this concern (Rodney & Starzomski, 1993). What is new is the escalation of workloads and the concomitant reduction of professional resources. Nurses in our studies conveyed their distress, frustration, anger, and sometimes resignation, about this. For example, in our most recent study, the nurses in emergency routinely would begin each shift with what we called their "mantra" – "we're 5 [nurses] short, have 22 admits (admitted patients awaiting beds), one stretcher open, and the wait time [for patients] is over 4 hours" (Field Notes, *Ethics in Action*, 2004). We witnessed the consequences of this mantra almost every day that we did our observational fieldwork. Patients who were supposed to be admitted to hospital filled most of the emergency beds, patients were lined up in the halls in stretchers, and anxious (and often angry) patients and their family members spent long hours waiting to be seen. Nurses and other health care providers repeatedly expressed that they worried that they were going to "miss something."

Third, nurses' personal time was often treated as disposable. Not surprisingly, in order to complete their tasks, nurses routinely stayed past the end of their designated work shift but often did not claim overtime pay. In other words, they "donated" time to the health care system.[13] Nurses' "donations" often jeopardized their personal time. This was particularly apparent for nurses who faced concurrent child care demands, who frequently had to incur extra child care costs or arrangements in order to finish their work.

Again, nurses' donation of time is not a new empirical finding, appearing in a number of earlier studies of nurses' work (e.g., Stelling, 1994a, 1994b; Walters, 1994; Yyelland, 1994). For example, Stelling found that nurses often stayed past the end of their shifts but would only "claim" the overtime if it was a recognized medical emergency. She notes:

> There is an irony here. Women are supposed to give first priority to their families, and are consequently assumed or expected to have a lesser commitment to their careers. Somehow nurses' commitment to their patients, which is manifest in the way they talk about nursing and their work, in the overtime they work, and in their willingness to "pick up the slack," seems to be equated to women's "natural" commitment to their families and thereby deemed irrelevant to their professional commitment. Thus it becomes invisible and doesn't count as commitment. (1994a, p. 623)

Nurses' commitments to their patients and their own families, and their difficulty in meeting these commitments, exact significant personal costs. Therefore, the fourth "disposable" to be explored is nurses' well-being. Campbell (1994) noted that nurses working under excessive workloads suffer frustration, anxiety, and self-blame about the care they are able to give (p. 594). Nurses in our studies often experienced profound guilt and fatigue. One emergency nurse was embarrassed and apologetic about her work environment. After several hours of dashing from patient to patient, providing only urgent care and using techniques to forestall patient demands, she turned to one researcher, nearly in tears. "I'm sorry," she said, gesturing back to the unit, which was crowded, noisy, and crawling with people pushing various pieces of equipment about. "You should see it the way it should be, not like this" (Varcoe, 1997, p. 124).

Nurses from all practice settings units spoke of how tired they felt at the end of most shifts. The physical demands of providing basic nursing care to elderly and/or dependent patients were substantial, and there was almost always a sense that nurses were racing against the clock to complete the required tasks. Confounding the physical demands was the fatigue generated both by shift work and by the "second shift" that many nurses experienced in caring for their families. This finding has been well documented in previous studies: decades of research have explored the impact of nurses' work, the effects of shift work, and the impact on the quality of life for people (particularly women) in a variety of occupations who must balance responsibilities in the home and in the workplace (e.g., Aiken et al., 2002; Doyal, 1994; Long & Kahn, 1993; Lynn & Todoroff, 1995; Swanson-Kauffman, 1987). These impacts are exacerbated when, as was the case in the Emergency unit we most recently studied, nurses are denied vacation, required to work overtime, and frequently denied requests for shift changes.

As well as the guilt and fatigue that nurses in the studies experienced, there was an ever-present (but not often discussed) level of personal risk, both physical and psychological.

The physical risk was multidimensional. As she spoke of the risks posed by the complexity of the patients on her unit, one nurse manager warned:

> The other thing that we've got going on now is a lot more infectious diseases. You know with the AIDS patients, they're coming in with chicken pox and stuff....We're having a lot more dangerous [exposure to illnesses]...HIV, TB [tuberculosis], we've had a meningitis outbreak and...it's a personal threat to ourselves also...violence in patients....I think it contributes to the fatigue....And threat of injury. (Rodney, 1997, p. 201)

During fieldwork, we were told that a significant amount of "sick time" was taken by staff due to events such as back injuries, which had escalated with the increased acuteness and heavy care requirements of patients. In the emergency units, nurses told of often taking "mental health days" both informally and through stress leave programs. On the basis of our experiences in four research studies, and on the basis of related research studies (e.g., Clarke & Aiken, 2003; O'Brien-Pallas et al., 2006), it is clear that nurses routinely practice in environments that are not conducive to their well-being. Nor are such environments conducive to the care of either patients, families, or communities.

OVERLOOKED PATIENTS

In the corporate culture of health care today, nurses are all too often treated as disposable, while the well-being of patients, families, and communities is all too often overlooked.[14] Throughout our studies we observed situations in which, for example, elderly patients did not receive the basic physical care they required, patients with substance use problems were not treated appropriately for their withdrawal, and family members of dying patients were not adequately supported. Such situations arose at least partly because nurses and other members of the health care team (including physicians) were working under almost impossible structural constraints. Some administrators with whom we spoke also felt powerless to challenge or reverse these constraints. One nurse manager whose unit chronically functioned at 110 percent of the workload index (itself a poor estimate that under-measured nursing work) found that despite staff working "flat out," they were routinely unable to meet basic patient needs. Another manager noted that unless staff came to work with "100 percent energy, a clear mind, and an open heart," the demands of the workplace were impossible to meet.

In today's era of cost constraint nurses and other health care providers are often unable to meet patients' complex health care needs. Indeed, even basic physical needs are often not adequately met, particularly for the elderly. The "body care" inherent in nursing work – the work that addresses people's experiences of their embodied existence, especially when their bodies fail to function normally (Lawler, 1993, p. vi) – is overlooked. The nurse mentioned earlier elaborated on missing bladder distention:

> [A] lady...was in with neck pain, back pain and knee pain and they thought she possibly had some collagen disease, [she was] very stiff and all this kind of stuff. She had an IV [intravenous], she wanted to go on the [bed]pan constantly, she was on a slipper [small] pan because she couldn't get on a bigger one – she was too stiff – constantly [the urine] would back flow and get on the pad or she'd squirt over the front or something you know, and...I didn't really

> think about it, I just thought "It's the IV that's going," so the second night I capped [stopped] the IV, she was still going...something was going on in my mind you know, like she's not going [voiding] that much [quantity]...so I did an in and out catheter post void, eleven seventy-five [1,175 millilitres] I got, so it was all overflow [her bladder was full and overflowing]....But I didn't pick up on that the first night....I was just trying to...get everything together you know and...we had a couple of [patient] transfers in, a couple of admissions and things like that so you don't always pick up on those things. (Rodney, 1997, p. 188)

The woman had a serious and debilitating medical condition, yet it was extraordinarily difficult for the nurse – who was an expert – to assess even her basic physiological functions. Beside the immediate pain the woman might have experienced, a variety of complications, including infections might have arisen as a consequence. In another situation, an elderly woman immobilized with serious rheumatoid arthritis was to be discharged into the care of her daughter and son-in-law. The daughter was ill with cancer, and the son-in-law was in his sixties. Yet the body care involved in toileting the elderly woman, feeding her, washing her, and so on was not recognized or planned for in "the system." Nor was there the opportunity to devise a comprehensive interdisciplinary plan to help her with her pain and mobility. And there was certainly not the time to help her adjust to her altered level of independence or to listen to the concerns she might have for her daughter. Further, the needs of her family were not taken into account. In fact, we observed patients being discharged and returning to the emergency department in full-blown crisis. In our most recent study, one of our research colleagues relayed an account of a patient with cancer who, having been discharged from hospital and refused readmission to hospital, walked to the hospital barefoot in the middle of the night in her nightdress. She and her husband had been unable to obtain support for her escalating physical problems, so she returned to hospital alone and without identification so that hospital staff would be unable to return her home (Hartrick, Doane, & Varcoe, 2005, p. 251). Although the intent of health care reform has been to limit the costs of *treatment*, it has been *care* that has been limited.

Western health care systems have a long history of unresponsiveness to the needs of patients, families, and communities, particularly the needs of those marginalized because of age, race, gender, chronic illness, disability, and so forth (see, for example, Anderson, 2000; Browne & Fiske, 2001; Peternelj-Taylor, 2005; Stevens, 1992; Stephenson, 1999; Varcoe, 2001;Watson, 1994). As mentioned above, recent cost constraint measures have only made these dynamics worse, especially for those who are marginalized by other forms of oppression. Although nurses in our studies rationed their most valuable resource – their time – primarily based on patient acuteness, social judgments based on age, class, ethnicity, substance use, and so on, also figured into their allocation of resources. For example, the nurse who militated against the threat of her patient dying in the hallway had witnessed many elderly patients in similar circumstances, but the age of the patient seemed to add weight, not only to the nurse's concern but to the likelihood of others sharing that concern.

CONSTRAINED AGENCY

Clearly the well-being of nurses, patients, families, and communities is threatened in the corporate culture of health care. In closing this portrait of the social structure of nurses' work, we consider some of the implications for nurses as moral agents.[15] Moral agency can be understood as referring to how people, in this case nurses, fulfill their moral responsibility and accountability and deal with ethical problems (Rodney, 1997; Rodney, Brown, & Liaschenko, 2004).

Moral Distress

Nurses are often in situations which challenge their abilities to fulfill their moral responsibility and accountability, and they are too often overwhelmed by ethical problems; and they experience a great **moral distress** because of this. The ethical problems they face are sometimes dramatic questions of life and death decision-making – for instance, how to help a family decide whether or not to initiate tube feeding for a person who has suffered a stroke. More often, however, the ethical problems that nurses face are everyday questions, such as whether to restrain or "tie down" a confused patient. These questions are ethical because they revolve around "the good" in practice (Rodney, 1997; Rodney, Brown, & Liaschenko, 2004).[16]

Significantly, the ethical problems faced by nurses in our studies frequently emerged as a result of constraints and cutbacks in the workplace. For example, the need to physically restrain confused patients or to rapidly force-feed dependent elders was increased by inadequate staffing levels that precluded alternative approaches to care. Thus, the ethical problems with which nurses dealt were embedded in everyday practice in an era of health reform – problems that, as Liaschenko (1993) has warned, are frequently "discounted or trivialized or sentimentalized" in biomedical ethics (p. 9). Nurses felt badly about the abrogation of their professional responsibility and accountability, and about the difficulties they experienced in trying to deal with ethical problems in their practice. An emergency nurse cited earlier in this chapter was frustrated and tearful when she said, "You should see the way it should be, not like this" (Varcoe, 1997, p. 124). The nurse managers cited earlier were frustrated by their perceived inability to positively influence the conditions of nurses' work and patient care (see also Gaudine & Beaton, 2002). Almost every nurse we have encountered during our fieldwork in our four studies has expressed this kind of distress – distress that has been echoed by physicians, social workers, physiotherapists, patients, family members, and others involved (both directly and indirectly) in patient care.

The nurses' distress was not just fatigue. Their distress reflected the anguish and powerlessness inherent in moral distress. That is, nurses made moral choices, but situational constraints made it difficult to translate moral choices into moral actions (Hamric, 2000; Jameton, 1984; Rodney, Brown, & Liaschenko, 2004; Webster & Baylis, 2000). For example, we observed nurses working with social workers to set up support for a caregiver who had been physically abusive to an elderly parent, only to have the patient discharged (to make room for other patients) before those supports could be put in place. The moral distress that nurses experience is a reflection of their difficulty enacting their moral agency. As the enactment of moral agency is prerequisite to professional practice, the social structure of nurses' work (within current health care contexts dominated by corporatism and narrow definitions of efficiency) threatens the foundation of professional practice as well as the well-being of nurses.

Moral Resistance

Nurses in our studies did not passively acquiesce to the constraints inherent in the social structure of their work. They resisted in various overt and covert ways. Despite the constraints, nurses made efforts to "get to know" their patients, to work with others as a team, and to negotiate better care, particularly when they faced ethical problems. For example, in our most recent study, nurses in the acute medical oncology unit negotiated as a group with the hospital administration to prevent (or at least ameliorate) the implementation of co-ed rooms, which they thought would be contrary to dignity and choice (values from the CNA Code of Ethics, 2002) for many of their patients. In the Emergency setting, nurses worked against a policy that would permit narcotic administration in the hallway – advocating instead for strategies that would allow patients to receive more timely admission and pain management under conditions where the nurses could monitor the patients.

Nurses also attempted to enact their moral agency by bending the rules. In other words, they went outside of what was officially sanctioned in their attempts to provide good care. For instance, a nurse in a medical unit where there were no regular venues for communication with physicians (such as patient care rounds) explained how she requisitioned blood tests without waiting for a physician's order when worried about a patient's electrolyte status. She explained, "You always have to work a way around the system to make it work" (Field Notes, *Ethics in Action*, 2004). Similarly, nurses in emergency bent the rules, for example, by giving patients unordered pain medications to take home (see also Hutchinson, 1990).

The nurses we observed were usually motivated by what they saw as the best interests of the patients for whom they were caring, and they were caught in conflicts between institutional and medical rules (e.g., to monitor electrolytes only on a physician's order) and their own beliefs about what patients needed (e.g., to have electrolytes monitored during replacement therapy). Importantly, at least some of this subversion was a result of trying to "make up for" workplace constraints (e.g., the lack of patient care rounds and workloads that limited communication with physicians and others).

However, such actions, dubbed "responsible subversion" by Hutchinson (1990), may have negative as well as positive consequences. Nurses who bend the rules may experience sanctions if they are "caught," and rules may become more rigid once this happens. Moreover, if rules are not applied consistently, patients and families may become concerned about inconsistent (and possibly unjust) treatment. Further, there are a number of ethical questions about such subversion. These include questions about the rightness or wrongness of nurses practicing according to their own rules, about the ethical principles that underlie nurses' actions when they bend or break rules, about what would happen if everybody broke rules, about whether rule-breaking is the only course of action available to the nurse, and so on (Munhall, 1990). Thus, although this subversion often helped nurses to mediate the constraints inherent in the social structure of their work, it also had the potential to jeopardize their role and their care of patients and families. Further, in our studies we observed that rule-bending became so entrenched that practice problems were hidden and remained unexamined. Paradoxically, then, such subversion has the potential to jeopardize the nurses' enactment of their moral agency. In a sense, "responsible subversion" may be a "guerrilla tactic" that has the potential to backfire.

CONCLUSION

Beyond Guerrilla Tactics

At the same time as health care workers participate in corporatism, they engage in tactics that mitigate these dominant influences. However, most of these tactics are at the level of the individual and are not necessarily based on a critical awareness of dominance of corporate ideologies and practices. Thus, efforts to preserve quality in the health care system must become increasingly conscious, deliberate, and organized. In particular, nurses' work must be restructured to align with goals of health and the common good and in defiance of corporatism as the exclusive driving force in health care. The warnings we cited at the outset of this chapter about the danger to health and health care posed by corporatism must be heeded. Ideologies must be exposed and challenged, "efficiency" re-envisioned, and space for the intellectual, emotional, and body work of nursing must be carved out of the wasteland that corporatism has created in health care. Nurses must take active roles individually and collectively both in countering the erosion of health care and nursing practice, and in formulating policy. Collective action will require proactive work through professional nursing associations and unions. Through our *Ethics in Action* and other studies, we have learned that such collective action *must* systematically engage nurses at all levels – especially those in direct care roles, who often feel particularly powerless and disenfranchised.

Unmasking Ideology

This chapter has attempted to make visible some of the ways in which corporate ideologies are enacted within health care, within nursing practice, and by nurses themselves. It is hoped that this will be revealing for nurses and that they will be able to operate with a greater critical awareness of the ways in which ideologies are used to structure their work and of the ways in which they participate in undermining their own values. With this awareness, nurses might challenge the often taken for granted idea that "there is no more money," and recognize such ideas as tricks to hide the fact that money is simply being spent elsewhere (sometimes on expensive systems to keep track of their labour). Nurses might then refuse the corporate rhetoric (Hiraki, 1998) and challenge corporate ideologies. They might also then decide that accepting such ideas and sanctioning one another to work in compliance with corporatism is unacceptable, that it is neither in their own interests nor in the interests of their patients. Collective refusal to comply with corporatism would necessarily put patient needs and health outcomes ahead of corporate imperatives, would foreground alternate ideologies (perhaps ideologies of health, social justice, and the common good), and would require rethinking "efficiency."

Of course, individual nurses cannot do this work alone. There must be sufficient critical awareness of the issues and operating ideologies to make resistance the norm rather than simply the maverick behaviour of an individual. Shifting away from an environment of sanction and compliance would require and contribute to the creation of environments where relationships and trust flourish. Collective action within units, and in collaboration with existing groups such as professional organizations and unions, is necessary to move beyond guerrilla tactics to a full-scale assault on corporatism as the only or prevailing value in health care.

Re-imagining "Efficiencies"

This chapter has challenged the strategies currently employed in the name of cost efficiency. The form of efficiency that must be sought is one that takes into account effectiveness, impact on patient well-being, and long-term as well as short-term gains. Providing care that is at once efficient and effective would require that effectiveness be valued and understood (that is, that the goals of care be known), that strategies toward effective care not be thwarted by short-term "efficiencies," and that both be measured. Valuing effectiveness is predicated on an awareness of the dominance and impact of the current preoccupation with "cost constraint." Setting goals of care that aim for effectiveness and health outcomes requires valuing both, and it requires research evidence regarding the relationship between care and health outcomes; it requires as well the political will to implement care that has already been shown to be effective in terms of outcomes.

Health outcomes must be understood as more than individual responses to specific therapies and must be seen as including outcomes for groups and populations (Mitchell, 1993). Outcomes must be thought of beyond what can be achieved and measured within units (such as length of stay), organizations (such as bed numbers), and regions (numbers of staff). As was illustrated above, such measures are often used counterproductively. As Armstrong and Armstrong (1996) note, "effectiveness and efficiency cannot be measured primarily in terms of money spent and people processed" (p. 9). This suggests that measurement in health care must become much more complex, taking into account broader variables such as well-being, relief of suffering, and so on.

In terms of nursing work, the importance of attention to the emotional needs of patients has been illustrated in a variety of contexts (see, for example, Henderson, 2001). If nurses are to be more effective, as well as efficient, they must value effectiveness in terms of nonphysical care and have adequate control over their work to implement the care that will achieve meaningful health outcomes. Valuing effectiveness is again predicated on critical awareness of the dangers of an emphasis on efficiency regardless of effectiveness, and efficiency that overlooks difficult to quantify determinants of health such as social support, emotional support, and psychological well-being. Implementing effective nursing care requires, first, research that links care with broad health outcomes, and second, sufficient nursing control over practice to implement what has been shown to be effective (Nortvedt, 2001).

Creating Space for Intellectual and Emotional Work

Promoting the intellectual labour of nursing within the described context is challenging. As has been argued above, nurses do not have time to think, let alone practice health promotion, "innovate," lobby for changes in "rules" that are detrimental to care, introduce new or evidence-based practice, or evaluate care in terms of outcomes. And yet, these are the very strategies that are needed to develop a truly more efficient *and effective* health care system. There is beginning to be recognition at bureaucratic levels that the bottom has been reached in terms of the cuts that can be made in staffing. However, the damage will not be undone simply by reinstating numbers of positions. In words attributed to Albert Einstein, "The problems we have created cannot be solved at the level of thinking that created them."

Years of "reform" have eroded the culture of health care to one based predominantly on corporate values. Within this culture, the emphasis on efficiency has eroded the foundation for professional nursing practice. In addition to "righting" staffing to levels that can sustain safe care, space needs to be created for nurses to provide the emotional labour that patients require during illness and death experiences. Space needs to be created for nurses to provide reasoned care, based on evidence and research. Such space needs to be created for nurses who provide direct care, rather than allocating the thinking space only to those who practice in roles removed from direct care. This cannot be achieved simply by allocating reasonable staffing levels, but must also be supported by the continued development of clinical advanced nursing practice roles such as clinical nurse specialists, clinical practice leaders, clinical resource nurses, and clinical nurse researchers – roles that can contribute to and support direct care. Intellectual and emotional work must also be supported by greater attention being given, by researchers and educators who are not in direct care, to linking practice, especially body work and emotional and intellectual labour, to health and outcomes. Realistically capturing the indeterminate work of nursing, and supplementing the data captured by current technologies, will require voices from nursing to be heard in policy development from the unit to organizational to social levels.

This chapter was titled "**constrained agency**" to draw attention to the ideological and **structural constraints** to agency within nursing. However, nurses are never completely without agency. Whether it is an individual nurse offering an alternative to corporate images (perhaps we could see mentally ill patients as casualties of deinstitutionalization rather than as "repeaters" or "users"), or a group lobbying for change or participating in public policy formulation, the structure of nurses' work can be shaped by nurses to the extent that they are willing to take action. Questioning that which has been taken for granted is the first step. In the three years of our engagement with nursing colleagues in *Ethics in Action*, we have learned that nurses in direct care roles are more than ready – and capable – of taking that step.

ACKNOWLEDGEMENTS

The authors gratefully acknowledge all the research participants and the team of researchers with whom we work – especially Dr. Jan Storch and Dr. Gweneth Hartrick Doane. The research drawn upon in this chapter has been variously supported by the Canadian Nurses Foundation, National Health Research Development Program, Associated Medical Services, the Social Sciences and Humanities Research Council of Canada, and the University of Victoria.

STUDY QUESTIONS

1. *What are the relationships between the disvaluing of women and women's work in general and the disvaluing of the emotional labour of nursing?*
2. *What examples of responsible subversion have you observed? What were the consequences?*
3. *List the rhetoric currently in vogue in health care. What are the latest "buzz words" or popular areas of concern? What ideas, images, and assumptions underlie this language?*

4. *Imagine some situations in which you and the people you work with could constructively challenge the corporate ideology. Provide some examples of how you would achieve this.*

GLOSSARY

capping cost containment measures such as setting a predetermined level or number of activities to be performed within a specific program during a specified time frame; for example, a number of particular organ transplants or surgeries over a one-year period.

common good the well-being of aggregates (communities and society), not just individuals; some notion of the well-being of communities and society, if arrived at through participatory democratic processes, can provide a moral horizon for work in ethics and public policy.

constrained agency ideological and structural constraints to agency within nursing such that nurses are unable to act upon their professional responsibilities and accountability.

corporate ideology the taken for granted beliefs, attitudes, and assumptions that bring a business model to health care.

culture the processes that happen between people as individuals and as groups within organizations and society, and that confer meaning and significance; the health care system has its own culture(s).

downsizing cost containment measures such as bed closures, staff layoffs, and reductions in the length of hospital stay.

emotional labour the effort involved in dealing with other people's feelings and emotions and, in the case of nursing, dealing with the fears and worries of ill patients and their families and promoting the emotional well-being of patients.

globalization the economic, social, and political transformation of the world, such that capital flows around the world to serve the interests of an economically dominant elite.

ideology a set of beliefs, attitudes, and assumptions about the world that justify or explain "what is." Ideologies are not in and of themselves good or bad; when unexamined, however, they can lead to unanticipated consequences.

ideology of scarcity a perception about the state of the economy, fiscal realities, the availability of funds, and budgetary deficits, such that current levels of care are no longer affordable; a view popularized by the media, corporate elite, management elite, and others.

moral agency the actions through which people fulfill their moral responsibility and accountability and deal with ethical problems (Rodney, 1997; Rodney, Brown, & Liaschenko, 2004).

moral distress a situation that occurs when nurses (or other moral agents) are unable to translate their moral choices into moral action because of constraints in the organizational context; the aftermath can include anger, frustration, guilt, and powerlessness.

structural constraints administrative policies, procedures, and practices, such as allotted labour time and performance evaluation, that set the parameters within which labour is performed.

REFERENCES

Aiken, L.H., Clarke, S.P., & Sloane, D.M. (2000). Hospital restructuring: Does it adversely affect care and outcomes? *Journal of Nursing Administration, 30*(10), 457–465.

Anderson, J.M. (2000). Writing in subjugated knowledges: Towards a transformative agenda in nursing research and practice. *Nursing Inquiry, 7*, 145.

Anderson, J.M., Blue, C., & Lau, A. (1991). Women's perspectives on chronic illness: Ethnicity, ideology and restructuring of life. *Social Science and Medicine, 33*(2), 101–113.

Anderson, J.M., Dyck, I., & Lynam, J. (1997). Health care professionals and women speaking: Constraints in everyday life and the management of chronic illness. *Health, 1*(1), 57–80.

Anderson, J., & Reimer-Kirkham, S. (1998). Constructing nation: The gendering and racializing of the Canadian health care system. In V. Strong-Boag, S. Grace, A. Eisenberg, & J. Anderson (Eds.), *Painting the maple: Essays on race, gender, and the construction of Canada* (pp. 242–261). Vancouver: University of British Columbia Press.

Annas, G.J. (1995). Reframing the debate on health care reform by replacing our metaphors. *New England Journal of Medicine, 332*(11), 744–747.

Armstrong, P. (2001). The context for health care reform in Canada. In P. Armstrong, C. Amaratunga, J. Bernier, K. Grant, A. Pederson, A., & K. Wilson (Eds.), *Exposing Privatization: Women and health care reform in Canada* (pp.11–48). Aurora, ON: Garamond Press.

Armstrong, P., & Armstrong, H. (1996). *Wasting away: The undermining of Canadian health care*. Toronto: Oxford University Press.

Armstrong, P., & Armstrong, H. (2003). *Wasting away: The undermining of Canadian health care* (2nd ed.). Don Mills, ON: Oxford University Press.

Attridge, C., & Callahan, M. (1987). *Women in women's work: An exploratory study of nurses' perspective of quality work environments* (research report). Victoria, BC: University of Victoria, Faculty of Human and Social Development.

Barry-Walker, J. (2000). The impact of systems redesign on staff, patient, and financial outcomes. *Journal of Nursing Administration, 30*(2), 77–89.

Beeber, L.S., & Charlie, M.L. (1998). Depressive symptom reversal for women in a primary care setting: A pilot study. *Archives of Psychiatric Nursing, 12*, 247–254.

Bendix, R. (1993). Ideology. In W. Outhwaite & T. Bottomore (Eds.), *The Blackwell dictionary of twentieth-century social thought* (pp. 272–273). Oxford: Blackwell.

Benner, P.A., Tanner, C.A., & Chesla, C.A. (with contributions by Dreyfus, H.L., Dreyfus, S.E., & Rubin, J.) (1996). *Expertise in nursing practice: Caring, clinical judgment, and ethics*. New York: Springer.

Björnsdóttir, K. (2001). From the state to the family: Reconfiguring the responsibility for long-term nursing care at home. *Nursing Inquiry, 9*(1), 3–11.

Blue, A.W., Keyserlingk, E.W., Rodney, P., & Starzomski, R. (1999). A critical view of North American health policy. In H. Coward & P. Ratanakul (Eds.), *A cross-cultural dialogue on health care ethics* (pp. 215–225). Waterloo, ON: Wilfrid Laurier University Press.

Bolaria, B.S. (1994). Income inequality, poverty, food banks, and health. In B.S. Bolaria & H.D. Dickinson (Eds.), *Health, illness, and health care in Canada* (2nd ed., pp. 245–254). Toronto: Harcourt Brace.

Brown, M.C. (1996). Changes in Alberta's medicare financing arrangements: Features and problems. In M. Stingl & D. Wilson (Eds.), *Efficiency vs. equality: Health reform in Canada* (pp. 137–151). Halifax: Fernwood.

Browne, A. J., & Fiske, J. (2001). First Nations women's encounters with mainstream health care services. *Western Journal of Nursing Research, 23*(2), 126–147.

Burgess, M. (1996). Health care reform: Whitewashing a conflict between health promotion and treating illness? In M. Stingl & D. Wilson (Eds.), *Efficiency vs. equality: Health reform in Canada* (pp. 153–162). Halifax: Fernwood.

Campbell, M. (1994). The structure of stress in nurses' work. In B.S. Bolaria & H.D. Dickinson (Eds.), *Health, illness, and health care in Canada* (pp. 592–608). Toronto: Harcourt Brace.

Campbell, M.L. (1987). Productivity in Canadian nursing: Administering cuts. In D. Coburn, C. D'Arcy, G.M. Torrance, & P. New (Eds.), *Health and Canadian society: Sociological perspectives* (2nd ed., pp. 463–475). Toronto: Fitzhenry & Whiteside.

Canadian Health Services Research Foundation (2001). *Commitment and care: The benefits of a health workplace for nurses, their patients and the system.* Ottawa: Canadian Health Services Research Foundation.

Canadian Medical Association & Canadian Nurses Association (2004). *The taming of the queue: Toward a cure for health care wait times, (Discussion paper).* Ottawa: Canadian Medical Association & Canadian Nurses Association.

Canadian Nurses' Association. (1998). *The quiet crisis in health care.* Paper submitted to the House of Commons Standing Committee on Finance and the Minister of Finance. Ottawa: Canadian Nurses Association.

Carniol, B. (1995). *Case critical: Challenging social services in Canada* (3rd ed.). Toronto: Between the Lines.

Cassidy, B., Lord, R., & Mandell, N. (1995). Silenced and forgotten women: Race, poverty, and disability. In N. Mandell (Ed.), *Feminist issues: Race, class, and sexuality* (pp. 32–66). Scarborough, ON: Prentice-Hall.

Clarke, S.P., & Aiken, L.H. (2003). Registered nurse staffing and patient and nurse outcomes in hospitals: A commentary. *Policy, politics & nursing practice, 4*(2), 104.

Coburn, D. (2001). Health, health care, and neo-liberalism. In P. Armstrong, H. Armstrong, & D. Coburn (Eds.), *Unhealthy times: Political economy perspectives on health and care in Canada* (pp. 45–65). Don Mills, ON: Oxford University Press.

Collins, P.H. (1986). Learning from the outsider within: The social significance of black feminist thought. *Social Problems, 33*(6), 14–32.

Collins, P.H. (1989). The social construction of black feminist thought. *Signs: Journal of Women in Culture and Society, 14*, 745–773.

Collins, P.H. (1993). Toward a new vision: Race, class, and gender as categories of analysis and connection. *Race, sex & class, 1*(1), 25–45.

Commission on the Future of Health Care in Canada (2002). *Building on values: The future of health care in Canada. ["The Romanow Report"].* Ottawa: Commission on the Future of Health Care in Canada.

Corley, M.C., & Mauksch, H.O. (1988). Registered nurses, gender, and commitment. In A. Statham, E.M. Miller, & H.O. Mauksch (Eds.), *The worth of women's work: A qualitative synthesis* (pp. 135–149). Albany, NY: State University of New York Press.

Coward, H., & Ratanakul, P. (Eds.). (1999). *A cross cultural dialogue on health care ethics.* Waterloo, ON: Wilfrid Laurier University Press.

Curran, C.R., & Miller, N. (1990). The impact of corporate culture on nurse retention. *Nursing Clinics of North America, 25*(3), 537–549.

Dant, T. (1991). *Knowledge, ideology and discourse: A sociological perspective.* London: Routledge.

Dick, J., & Bruce, S. (1994). Cost containment: Doing more with less. In J.M. Hibberd & M.E. Kyle (Eds.), *Nursing management in Canada* (pp. 91–107). Toronto: W.B. Saunders.

Dickinson, H.D. (1994). Mental health policy in Canada: What's the problem? In B.S. Bolaria & H.D. Dickinson (Eds.), *Health, illness, and health care in Canada* (2nd ed., pp. 466–481). Toronto: Harcourt Brace.

Doyal, L. (1994). Waged work and well-being. In S. Wilkinson & C. Kitsinger, *Women and health: Feminist perspectives* (pp. 65–84). London: Taylor & Francis.

Duncan, S.M. (1992). Ethical challenges in community health nursing. *Journal of Advanced Nursing, 17*, 1035–1041.

Duncan, S.M., Hyndman, K., Estabrooks, C.A., Hesketh, K., Humphrey, C.K., Wong, J.S., et al. (2001). Nurses' experience of violence in Alberta and British Columbia hospitals. *Can. J. Nurs. Res., 32*, 57–78.

Dunleavy, J., Shamian, J., & Thomson, D. (2003). Workplace pressures: Handcuffed by cutbacks. *Canadian Nurse, 99*(3), 23–26.

Estabrooks, C. 2005. The impact of hospital nursing characteristics on 30-day mortality. *Nursing Research, 54*(2), 74–84.

Estabrooks, C.A., Tourangeau, A.E., Humphrey, C.K., Hesketh, K.L., Giovannetti, P., Thomson, D., Wong, J., Acorn, S., Clarke, H., & Shamian, J. (2002). Measuring the hospital practice environment: A Canadian context. *Research in Nursing and Health, 25*, 256–268.

Erlen, J.A., & Frost, B. (1991). Nurses' perceptions of powerlessness in influencing ethical decisions. *Western Journal of Nursing Research, 13*, 397–407.

Ferguson-Paré, M. (1997). *Leadership that supports autonomous professional practice of registered nurses.* Unpublished doctoral dissertation, The Fielding Institute.

Foucault, M. (1978). *The history of sexuality: An introduction.* (R. Hurley, Trans.). New York: Random House. (Original work published 1976).

Foucault, M. (1980). *Power/knowledge: Selected interviews and other writings (1972–1977).* C. Gordon, (Ed.). New York: Random House.

Freeman, T., & O'Brien-Pallas, L.L. (1998). Factors influencing job satisfaction on specialty nursing units. *Canadian Journal of Nursing Administration, 11*(3), 25–51.

Fuller, C. (1998). *Caring for profit: How corporations are taking over Canada's health care system.* Vancouver: New Star Books.

Gaudine, A.P., & Beaton, M.R. (2002). Employed to go against one's values: Nurse managers' accounts of ethical conflict within their organizations. *Canadian Journal of Nursing Research, 34*(2), 17–34.

Geertz, C. (1973). *The interpretation of cultures.* New York: Basic Books.

Gibb, H. (1998). Reform in public health: Where does it take nursing? *Nursing Inquiry, 5*, 258–267.

Growe, S.J. (1991). *Who cares? The crisis in Canadian nursing.* Toronto: McClelland & Stewart.

Hamric, A.B. (2000). Moral distress in everyday ethics. *Nursing Outlook, 48*, 199–201.

Hartrick-Doane, G., & Varcoe, C. (2005). *Family nursing as relational inquiry: Developing health promoting practice.* Philadelphia: Lippincott, Williams and Wilkins.

Health Canada Office of Nursing Policy. (2000). *Health Canada Office of Nursing Policy: Strategic priorities 2000–2001.* Ottawa: Health Canada Office of Nursing Policy.

Health Canada Office of Nursing Policy. (2001). *Healthy nurses, healthy workplaces.* Ottawa: Health Canada Office of Nursing Policy.

Health Canada Secretariat on Palliative and End-of-Life Care. (2002). *Discussion paper: National action planning workshop on end-of-life care.* Ottawa: Health Canada.

Hiraki, A. (1998). Corporate language and nursing practice. *Nursing Outlook, 46*, 115–119.

Hodnett, E., & Osborn, R.W. (1989). Effects of continuous intrapartum professionals support on childbirth outcomes. *Research in Nursing and Health, 12*(5), 289–297.

Hutchinson, S.A. (1990). Responsible subversion: A study of rule-bending among nurses. *Scholarly Inquiry for Nursing Practice, 4*(1), 3–17.

Jameton, A. (1984). *Nursing practice: The ethical issues*. Englewood Cliffs, NJ: Prentice-Hall.

Jennings, B., Callahan, D., & Wolf, S.M. (1987). The professions: Public interest and common good. *Hastings Center Report, 17*(1), 3–10.

Keddy, B., Gregor, F., Foster, S., & Denney, D. (1999). Theorizing about nurses' work lives: The personal and professional aftermath of living with healthcare "reform." *Nursing Inquiry, 6*, 58–64.

Ketefian, S., & Ormond, I. (1988). *Moral reasoning and ethical practice in nursing: An integrative review*. New York: National League for Nursing.

Kramer, M. (1974). *Reality shock: Why nurses leave nursing*. St. Louis, MO: C.V. Mosby.

Langer, A., Campero, L., Garcia, C., & Reynoso, S. (1998). Effects of psychosocial support during labour and childbirth on breastfeeding, medical interventions, and mothers' well-being in a Mexican public hospital: A randomized clinical trial. *British Journal of Obstetrics and Gynaecology, 105*, 1056–1063.

Laschinger, H.K., Finegan, J., Shamian, J., & Casier, S. (2000). Organizational trust and empowerment in restructured healthcare settings: Effects on staff nurse commitment. *Journal of Nursing Administration, 30*(9), 413–425.

Lawler, J. (1993). *Behind the screens: Nursing, somology, and the problem of the body*. Redwood City, CA: Benjamin/Cummings.

Laxer, J. (1996). *In search of a new left: Canadian politics after the neoconservative assault*. Toronto: Viking.

Laxer, J. (1998). *The undeclared war: Class conflict in the age of cyber capitalism*. Toronto: Penguin Books.

Liaschenko, J. (1993a). *Faithful to the good: Morality and philosophy in nursing practice*. Unpublished doctoral dissertation, University of California, San Francisco.

Liaschenko, J. (1993b). Feminist ethics and cultural ethos: Revisiting a nursing debate. *Advances in Nursing Science, 15*(4), 71–81.

Long, B.C., & Kahn, S.E. (Eds.). (1993). *Women, work, and coping: A multidisciplinary approach to workplace stress*. Montreal and Kingston, Canada: McGill-Queen's University Press.

Lynn, M., & Todoroff, M. (1995). Women's work and family lives. In N. Mandell (Ed.), *Feminist issues: Race, class, and sexuality* (pp. 244–271). Scarborough, ON: Prentice-Hall.

Lynam, M.J. (2005). Health as a socially mediated process: Theoretical and practice imperatives emerging from research on health inequalities. *Advances in Nursing Science, 28*(1), 25–37.

Lynam, M.J., Henderson, A., Browne, A., Smye, V., Semeniuk, P., Blue, C., Singh, S., & Anderson, J. (2003). Healthcare restructuring with a view to equity and efficiency: Reflections on unintended consequences. *Canadian Journal of Nursing Leadership, 16*(1), 112–140.

MacPhail, S.A. (1996). *Ethical issues in community nursing*. Unpublished master's thesis, University of Alberta, Edmonton.

McClure, M.L., Poulin, M.A., Sovie, M.D., & Wandelt, M.A. (1983). *Magnet hospitals: Attraction and retention of professional nurses*. Kansas City, MO: American Academy of Nursing.

McGowan, J. (1998). *Hannah Arendt: An introduction*. Minneapolis: University of Minnesota Press.

McQuaig, L. (1993). *The wealthy banker's wife: The assault on equality in Canada*. Toronto: Penguin Books.

McQuaig, L. (1998). *The cult of impotence: Selling the myth of powerlessness in the global economy*. Toronto: Penguin Books.

Millette, B.E. (1994). Using Gilligan's framework to analyze nurses' stories of moral choices. *Western Journal of Nursing Research, 16*(6), 660–674.

Mitchell, P. (1993). Perspectives on outcome-oriented care systems. *Nursing Administration Quarterly, 17*(3), 1–7.

Mohr, W.K. (1997). Outcomes of corporate greed. *Image: Journal of Nursing Scholarship, 29*(10), 39–45.

Mohr, W.K., & Mahon, M.M. (1996). Dirty hands: The underside of marketplace health care. *Advances in Nursing Science, 19*(1), 28–37.

Mouffe, C. (1993). *The return of the political*. London: Verso.

Munhall, P.L. (1990). Response to "Responsible subversion: A study of rule-bending among nurses." *Scholarly Inquiry for Nursing Practice, 4*(1), 19–22.

Nagle, L.M. (1999). A matter of extinction or distinction. *Western Journal of Nursing Research, 21*(1), 71–82.

Noblit, G.W., & Hare, R.D. (1988). *Meta-ethnography: Synthesizing qualitative studies*. Newbury Park, CA: Sage.

Northcott, H.C. (1994). The politics of austerity and threats to Medicare. In B.S. Bolaria & R. Bolaria, *Women, medicine and health* (pp. 7–24). Saskatoon: University of Saskatchewan.

Nortvedt, P. (2001). Clinical sensitivity: The inseparability of ethical perceptiveness and clinical knowledge. *Scholarly Inquiry for Nursing Practice, 15*(1), 25–43.

Oberle, K., & Grant, N. (1994). *Results of the AARN initiative regarding the impact of health care cuts* (unpublished research report). Edmonton: Alberta Association of Registered Nurses.

Oberle, K., & Tenove, S. (2000). Ethical issues in public health nursing. *Nursing Ethics, 7*(5), 425–438.

O'Brien-Pallas, L.L., Baumann, A.O., & Villeneuve, M.J. (1994). The quality of nursing work life. In J.M. Hibberd & M.E. Kyle (Eds.), *Nursing management in Canada* (pp. 391–409). Toronto: W.B. Saunders.

O'Brien-Pallas, L., Griffin, P., Shamian, J., Buchan, J., Duffield, C., Hughes, F., et al. (2006). The impact of nurse turnover on patient, nurse, and system outcomes: A pilot study and focus for a multicenter international study. *Policy, Politics & Nursing Practice, 7*(3), 169–179.

O'Neil, J.D. (1987). Health care in a central Canadian arctic community: Continuities and change. In D. Coburn, C. D'Arcy, G.M. Torrance, & P. New (Eds.), *Health and Canadian society: Sociological perspectives* (2nd ed., pp. 141–158). Toronto: Fitzhenry & Whiteside.

Pauly, B. (2004). Shifting the balance in the funding and delivery of health care in Canada. In J. Storch, P. Rodney, & R. Starzomski (Eds.), *Toward a moral horizon: Nursing ethics for leadership and practice* (pp. 181–208). Toronto: Pearson Prentice Hall.

Penning, M.J. (2002). The health of the elderly: From institutional care to home and community care. In B.S. Bolaria & H. Dickinson (Eds.), *Health, illness, and health care in Canada,* 3rd ed. (pp. 292–308). Toronto: Harcourt Brace.

Peter, E. (2004). Home health care and ethics. In J. Storch, P. Rodney, & R. Starzomski (Eds.), *Toward a moral horizon: Nursing ethics for leadership and practice* (pp. 248–261). Toronto: Pearson Prentice Hall.

Peternelj-Taylor, C. (2005). An exploration of othering in forensic psychiatric and correctional nursing. *Canadian Journal of Nursing Research, 36*(4), 130–147.

Phillips, S.S., & Benner, P. (1994). Preface. In S.S. Phillips & P. Benner (Eds.), *The crisis of care: Affirming and restoring caring practices in the helping professions* (pp. vii–xi). Washington, DC: Georgetown University Press.

Picard, A. (2000). *Critical care: Canadian nurses speak for change.* Toronto: HarperCollins.

Rachlis, M., & Kushner, C. (1989). *Second opinion: What's wrong with Canada's health care system and how to fix it?* Toronto: HarperCollins.

Rachlis, M., & Kushner, C. (1994). *Strong medicine: How to save Canada's health care system.* Toronto: HarperCollins.

Rankin, J.M. (2003). 'Patient satisfaction': Knowledge for ruling hospital reform—An institutional ethnography. *Nursing Inquiry 10* (1), 57–65.

Reinhardt, U.E. (1997). Spending more through "cost control": Our obsessive quest to gut the hospital. *Nursing Outlook, 45*, 156–160.

Rodney, P.A. (1997). *Towards connectedness and trust: Nurses' enactment of their moral agency within an organizational context.* Unpublished doctoral dissertation, University of British Columbia, Vancouver.

Rodney, P., Brown, H., & Liaschenko, J. (2004). Moral agency: Relational connections and trust. In J. Storch, P. Rodney, & R. Starzomski (Eds.), *Toward a moral horizon: Nursing ethics for leadership and practice* (pp. 154–177). Toronto: Pearson Prentice Hall.

Rodney, P., & Starzomski, R. (1993). Constraints on the moral agency of nurses. *Canadian Nurse, 89*(9), 23–26.

Rodney, P., & Street, A. (2004). The moral climate of nursing practice: Inquiry and action. In J. Storch, P. Rodney, & R. Starzomski (Eds.), *Toward a moral horizon: Nursing ethics for leadership and practice* (pp. 209–231). Toronto: Pearson Prentice Hall.

Rodney, P., & Varcoe, C. (2001). Toward ethical inquiry in the economic evaluation of nursing practice. *Canadian Journal of Nursing Research, 33*(1), 35–57.

Rodney, P., Varcoe, C., Storch, J., McPherson, G., Mahoney, K., Brown, H., et al. (2002). Navigating towards a moral horizon: A Multisite qualitative study of ethical practice in nursing. *Canadian Journal of Nursing Research, 34*(3), 75–102.

Saul, J.R. (1995). *The unconscious civilization.* Concord, ON: Anansi Press.

Saul, J.R. (1997). *Reflections of a Siamese twin: Canada at the end of the twentieth century.* Toronto: Penguin Books.

Scanlon, C. (1996–1997). Impact of cost containment on patient welfare concerns nurses. *American Nurses Association Center for Ethics and Human Rights Communique, 5*(2), 1–4.

Shamian, J., Kerr, M.S., Laschinger, H.K.S., & Thomson, D. (2002). A hospital analysis of the work environments and workforce health indicators for registered nurses in Ontario's acute-care hospitals. *Canadian Journal of Nursing Research, 33*(4), 35–50.

Sherwin, S. (1992). *No longer patient: Feminist ethics & health care.* Philadelphia: Temple University Press.

Sherwin, S. (1998). A relational approach to autonomy in health care. In S. Sherwin et al. (Eds.), *The politics of women's health* (pp. 19–47). Philadelphia: Temple University Press.

Shindul-Rothschild,J., Berry, D., & Long-Middleton, E. (1996). Where have all the nurses gone? Final results of our patient care survey. *American Journal of Nursing, 96*(11), 25–39.

Sibbald, B. (1997). Delegating away patient safety. *Canadian Nurse, 93*(2), 22–26.

Smith, C.E. (1993). Quality of life in long-term total parenteral nutrition: Patients and their family caregivers. *Journal of Parenteral and Enteral Nutrition, 17*, 501–506.

Smith, D.E. (1987). *The everyday world as problematic: A feminist sociology.* Toronto: University of Toronto Press.

Smith, D.E. (1990). *Conceptual practices of power: A feminist sociology of knowledge.* London: Routledge.

Smith, D.E. (1992). Sociology from women's experience: A reaffirmation. *Sociological Theory, 10*(1), 88–98.

Smith, D.M. (2000). *Moral geographies: Ethics in a world of difference.* Edinburgh: Edinburgh University Press.

Staden, H. (1998). Alertness to the needs of others: A study of the emotional labour of caring. *Journal of Advanced Nursing, 27,* 147–156.

Stanton, M.W., & Rutherford, M.K. (2004). Hospital nurse staffing and quality of care. *Agency for Healthcare Research and Quality: Research in Action Issue 14,* 1–9.

Stajduhar, K.I. (2003). Examining the perspectives of family members involved in the delivery of palliative care at home. *Journal of Palliative Care, 19*(1), 27–35.

Starzomski, R., & Rodney, P. (1997). Nursing inquiry for the common good. In S.E. Thorne & V.E. Hayes (Eds.), *Nursing praxis: Knowledge and action* (pp. 219–236). Thousand Oaks, CA: Sage.

Stein, J.G. (2001). *The cult of efficiency.* Toronto: Penguin.

Stelling, J. (1994a). Nursing metaphors: Reflections on the meaning of time. In B.S. Bolaria & R. Bolaria, *Women, medicine and health* (pp. 205–217). Saskatoon: University of Saskatchewan.

Stelling, J. (1994b). Staff nurses' perceptions of nursing: Issues in a woman's occupation. In B.S. Bolaria & H.D. Dickinson (Eds.), *Health, illness, and health care in Canada* (2nd ed., pp. 609–626). Toronto: Harcourt Brace.

Stephenson, P. (1999). Expanding notions of culture for cross-cultural ethics in health and medicine. In H. Coward & P. Ratanakul (Eds.), *A cross-cultural dialogue on health care ethics.* Waterloo, ON: Wilfrid Laurier University Press.

Storch, J.L. (1992). Ethical issues. In A.J. Baumgart & J. Larsen (Eds.), *Canadian nursing faces the future* (2nd ed., pp. 259–270). St. Louis, MO: Mosby Year Book.

Storch, J.L. (1996). Foundational values in Canadian health care. In M. Stingl & D. Wilson (Eds.), *Efficiency vs. equality: Health reform in Canada* (pp. 21–26). Halifax: Fernwood.

Storch, J.L., & Meilicke, C.A. (1994). Political, social, and economic forces shaping the health care system. In J.M. Hibberd & M.E. Kyle (Eds.), *Nursing management in Canada* (pp. 19–36). Toronto: W.B. Saunders.

Storch, J.L. (2003). The Canadian health care system and Canadian nurses. In M. McIntyre & E. Thomlinson (Eds). *Realities of Canadian nursing: Professional, practice, and power issues* (pp. 34–590). Philadelphia: Lippincott, Williams & Wilkins.

Swanson-Kauffman, K.M. (Ed.). (1987). *Women's work, families, and health: The balancing act.* New York: Hemisphere.

Taylor, C. (with Gutmann, A., Rockefeller, S.C., Walzer, M., & Wolf, S.) (1992). *Multiculturalism and "The politics of recognition."* Princeton, NJ: Princeton University Press.

Taylor, C. (1995). *Philosophical arguments.* Cambridge, MA: Harvard University Press.

Thomas, J. (1993). *Doing critical ethnography.* Newbury Park, CA: Sage.

Thorne, S. (1993). *Negotiating health care: The social context of chronic illness.* Newbury Park, CA: Sage.

Varcoe, C. (1997). *Untying our hands: The social context of nursing in relation to violence against women.* Unpublished doctoral dissertation. Vancouver: University of British Columbia.

Varcoe, C. (2001). Abuse obscured: An ethnographic account of emergency unit nursing practice in relation to violence against women. *Canadian Journal of Nursing Research, 32*(4), 95–115.

Varcoe, C., Doane, G., Pauly, B., Rodney, P., Storch, J. L., Mahoney, K., et al. (2004). Ethical Practice in Nursing - Working the In-betweens. *Journal of Advanced Nursing, 45*(3), 316–325.
Varcoe, C., Rodney, P., & McCormick, J. (2003). Health care relationships in context: An analysis of three ethnographies. *Qualitative Health Research, 13*(6), 957–973.
Walters, V. (1994). The social construction of risk in nursing: Nurses' responses to hazards in their work. In B.S. Bolaria & H.D. Dickinson (Eds.), *Health, illness, and health care in Canada* (2nd ed., pp. 627–643). Toronto: Harcourt Brace.
Watson, S.D. (1994). Minority access and health reform: A civil right to health care. *Journal of Law, Medicine & Ethics, 22*, 127–137.
Webster, G.C., & Baylis, F.E. (2000). Moral residue. In S.B. Rubin & L. Zoloth, (Eds.), *Margin of error: The ethics of mistakes in the practice of medicine* (pp. 217–230). Hagerstown, MD: University Publishing Group.
Weiss, S.M., Malone, R.E., Merighi, J.R., & Benner, P. (2002). Economism, efficiency, and the moral ecology of good nursing practice. *Canadian Journal of Nursing Research, 34*(2), 95–119.
Wilkinson, J.M. (1985). *Moral distress in nursing practice: Experience and effect*. Unpublished master's thesis, University of Missouri, Kansas City.
Wilkinson, J.M. (1989). Moral distress: A labor and delivery nurse's experience. *Journal of Obstetric, Gynecologic and Neonatal Nursing, 18*(6), 513–519.
Wolf, S.M. (1994). Health care reform and the future of physician ethics. *Hastings Center Report, 24*(2), 28–41.
Woodward, C., Shannon, H., Cunningham, C., McIntosh, J., Lendrum, B., Rosenbloom, D., & Brown, J. (1998). *Re-engineering in a large teaching hospital: A longitudinal study*. Working paper. Centre for Health Economic Policy Analysis, Hamilton, ON.
Yarling, R.R., & McElmurry, B.J. (1986). The moral foundation of nursing. *Advances in Nursing Science, 8*(2), 63–73.
Yates, B.C. (1995). The relationship among social support and short- and long-term recovery outcomes in men with coronary artery disease. *Research in Nursing and Health, 18*, 193–203.
Yeo, M., & Ford, A. (1996). Integrity. In M. Yeo & A. Moorhouse (Eds.), *Concepts and cases in nursing ethics* (2nd ed., pp. 267–306). Peterborough, ON: Broadview Press.
Yyelland, B. (1994). Structural constraints, emotional labour and nursing work. In B.S. Bolaria & R. Bolaria, *Women, medicine and health* (pp. 231–240). Saskatoon: University of Saskatchewan.

ENDNOTES

1. *Ideology* can be defined as "a shared set of fundamental beliefs, attitudes, and assumptions about the world that justify 'what is'" (Thomas, 1993, p. 8). Ideologies are usually taken for granted because they provide the conceptual basis for our theory and our research (Thomas, p. 8). Ideologies are not in and of themselves good or bad (Bendix, 1993; Dant, 1991; Thomas, 1993). However, making ideologies explicit can further critical inquiry in nursing and other disciplines (Hiraki, 1998; Rodney, 1997).

   By *corporate* ideology, we mean the beliefs, attitudes, and assumptions that bring a business model to health care. A corporate ideology takes direction from the operation of the marketplace and management and organizational theories (Hiraki, 1998, p. 117). As a consequence, health policy and health care delivery are "based upon economic and political values rather than values reflecting the broader social responsibilities of individuals in community" (Storch, 1996, p. 25).

2. *Moral distress* occurs when nurses (or other moral agents) are unable to translate their moral choices into moral action because of constraints in the organizational context. The aftermath can include anger, frustration, guilt, and powerlessness (Jameton, 1984; Rodney, Brown, & Liaschenko, 2004).
3. *Culture* is more than race or ethnicity. It includes the processes that occur between people as individuals and as groups within organizations and society, and that confer meaning and significance (Geertz, 1973; Rodney, 1997; Stephenson, 1999). Those of us in health care tend to see culture as residing in patients/clients and families. We need to understand that the health care system that we operate in has its own culture(s) (Coward & Ratanakul, 1999).
4. *Ethics in Action: Strengthening Nurses' Enactment of Their Moral Agency Within the Cultural Context of Health Care Delivery*. P. Rodney (Principal Investigator), G. Hartrick Doane, J. Storch, and C. Varcoe, funded by the Social Sciences and Humanities Research Council of Canada and the University of Victoria.
5. The global economy is part of *globalization*. Globalization "refers to the transformation – economic, social, and political – that has been underway since the 1970s....It refers not simply to the ways the world has been changing, but also to the ways the economically dominant want the world to change to serve their interests" (Laxer, 1996, pp. 21–22).

   The negative consequences of globalization include national and international insecurity caused by cuts to labour forces and social programs (Laxer, 1998; McQuaig, 1998; Smith, 2000). However, the consequences of globalization are not all necessarily negative. Cuts to labour forces and social programs do not have to be inevitable (McQuaig, 1998), and globalization can further international human rights initiatives (Smith, 2000). Economic globalization has led to the dominance of a corporate ideology in health care. And a corporate ideology has had a profound – and often negative – impact on the culture of health care delivery.
6. These cost constraints measures include **capping** (setting a predetermined level or number of activities to be done within a specific program, e.g., limiting the number of specific surgeries to be done over a year); **downsizing** (bed closures, staff layoffs, and redesign of the remaining activities, e.g., reducing the length of hospital stay); and **consolidation** of activities (e.g., merging hospital boards and executive management, which often includes a downgrading of the status and role of medicine and nursing in the new organizational structure). The measures further include restructuring and work redesign strategies such as reducing the levels of management, "cross training techniques" that allow staff to be moved between patient care areas, and changing the staff "mix," often by replacing registered nurse staff with practical nurses and/or care aides (Dick & Bruce, 1994, pp. 99–101).
7. The *common good* may be understood in terms of the well-being of aggregates (communities and society), not just individuals (Jennings, Callahan, & Wolf, 1987; Rodney & Starzomski, 1993). It should be noted that it is not unproblematic to try to define *the* common good. There is a danger that an autocratic (even totalitarian) process may be used to define it (Mouffe, 1993; Taylor, 1992). Nonetheless, some notion of the well-being of communities and society, if arrived at through participatory democratic processes, can provide a moral horizon for work in ethics and public policy (McGowan, 1998; Mouffe, 1993; Taylor, 1992).
8. This was the perception of many of the nurses in our studies. Whether physicians and/or managers *saw themselves as* embracing a corporate ideology is an empirical

question for other research. Indeed, nurses themselves often (unwittingly) embraced a corporate ideology by not questioning it.

9. Such indeterminate work is also unaccounted for when performed by nurses in managerial, educational, and advanced practice roles. And it is unaccounted for when it is performed by physicians, pastoral care workers, physiotherapists, social workers, and other members of the health care team.
10. The term "efficient" is placed in quotation marks to draw attention to the fact that the type of efficiency being referred to is only "efficient" in the sense of dealing with more patients in less time, and not in the sense of overall efficiency connected with health outcomes or immediate or long-term benefits for patients.
11. We are intentionally using mixed corporate and military metaphors here. Western biomedicine has been dominated by these two metaphors, which reflect "the quest for control that seems to define both modern medicine and modern politics" (Annas, 1995, p. 747). It is our contention that the quest for control is problematic for nurses, patients, families, and communities.
12. Yyelland (1994) distinguishes nurses' emotional labour from their technical labour. We are using the term "emotional labour" as one of many aspects of nurses' work, one that is concerned with promoting the emotional well-being of patients, and harmony among patients and health care professionals.
13. In British Columbia during 1998 and 1999, physicians were publicizing their "donations" of time by counting the number of days by which they claim to be subsidizing the health care system. While physicians can thus claim to be donating, for example, 52 days of unpaid work to the system, similar donations of nursing time are uncounted and unremarked.
14. Overlooking the well-being of patients, families, and communities is not the intention of a corporate focus on "outcomes." However, the authors' research and a growing number of other studies (e.g., Aiken, Clarke, & Sloane, 2000; Mohr, 1997) warn that it is the result.
15. Community care is also suffering. Nurses experience anguish when they try to support "high risk" families who are having difficulties with parenting (MacPhail, 1996; Oberle & Tenove, 2000). And home care nurses are deeply concerned about the difficulties they experience meeting their client/family needs because home care resources are so limited (Peter, 2004).
16. Traditional perspectives on moral agency reflect a notion of individuals engaging in self-determining or self-expressive choice (Sherwin, 1992; Taylor, 1992). In addition to this traditional view, there are perspectives that see moral agency as enacted through relationships in particular contexts (Rodney, 1997; Sherwin, 1992, 1998; Taylor, 1992).
17. As Benner, Tanner, and Chesla (1996) claim, "even in clinical situations, where the ends are not in question, there is an underlying moral dimension: the fundamental disposition of the nurse toward what is good and right and action toward what the nurse recognizes or believes to be the best good in a particular situation" (p. 6).

8

Complementary and Alternative Medicine in Canada: From Marginal to Mainstream

HERBERT C. NORTHCOTT University of Alberta

INTRODUCTION

Complementary and alternative medicine (CAM) refers to a wide range of therapies that have historically not been part of conventional Western medicine (Navarra, 2004). While complementary therapies are used together *with* conventional therapies and alternative therapies are used *in place of* conventional therapies, both complementary and alternative medicine may be integrated into conventional medicine (National Center for Complementary and Alternative Medicine, 2005). In recent decades, there has been an explosion in interest in complementary and alternative medicine in Canada and elsewhere (Fadlon, 2005; Health Canada, 2001; Kelner & Wellman, 2000). Indeed, the increasing utilization of CAM has been described as a widespread contemporary social movement (Crellin & Ania, 2002). Furthermore, it has been suggested that CAM has been "mainstreamed" (Tovey et al., 2004) and that 21st century medicine blends and integrates CAM with **conventional medicine** (Winnick, 2005; Lee et al., 2004; Tataryn & Verhoef, 2001). This emerging discourse of integration is a sharp contrast to the discourse of division that existed but a few decades ago (Winnick, 2005) when alternative therapies were frequently labeled and dismissed as quackery creating a rhetorical divide between conventional medicine and alternatives to conventional medicine. This chapter will review the transformation of the medical discourse of division into a discourse of integration, present a typology of CAM, and examine the utilization of CAM in Canada in the early 21st century.

FROM A DISCOURSE OF DIVISION TO A DISCOURSE OF INTEGRATION

The language used in the discussion of conventional medicine and CAM (see Northcott, 1994) has undergone a significant and rapid transformation. Only a few decades ago, the proponents of conventional medicine described their orientation using terms such as modern, scientific, rational, Western, dominant, orthodox, legitimate, official, and mainstream while at the same time dismissing alternative medicine with pejorative descriptors such as unscientific, irrational, mystical, unorthodox, heretical, cultic, illegitimate, marginal, and deviant. Similarly, alternative practitioners were characterized as quacks, charlatans and "snake-oil salespersons" misleading and defrauding the ignorant and the gullible. Note that the discourse of division not only divided the therapies and practitioners of conventional and alternative medicine, it also divided the users. Conventional medicine claimed that its users had legitimate health care concerns while characterizing the users of alternative medicine as deviant (Low, 2004, p. 95), socially marginal, fools, dupes, and hypochondriacs who often failed to have "real" health care needs.

On the other side of the rhetorical divide, the proponents of alternative medicine described their orientation as personal, natural, health-oriented, holistic, and less invasive while characterizing conventional medicine pejoratively as impersonal, unnatural, disease-oriented, fragmented, and invasive. Accordingly, the proponents of alternative medicine claimed that patients were badly served by conventional medicine and better served by alternative medicine.

The discourse of division has been increasingly replaced with a discourse of integration (Winnick, 2005; see Coulter, 2004 for a discussion of the various meanings and forms of integration). For example, alternative medicine is increasingly described as "complementary" medicine, the implication being that alternatives to conventional medicine are not necessarily the antithesis of conventional medicine but instead are compatible with, and, indeed, augment conventional approaches to health care. Note that the resulting merger of conventional and alternative medicine has been labeled **blended medicine** and increasingly **integrative medicine.** The blending and integration of CAM and conventional medicine suggest that **medical pluralism** has been increasingly accepted and legitimated (Kelner & Wellman, 2000; Sharma, 2000) or alternatively that there may be an ongoing process of convergence and "rapprochement" (Joudrey et al., 2004; Saks, 2003). The term medical pluralism suggests an integration and accommodation of alternative and conventional medicine into one broad health care delivery system with diverse and distinctive parts (Northcott, 1994). Alternatively, convergence implies that conventional and alternative medicine will incorporate elements from each other over time such that they become increasingly similar and indistinguishable from each other (Northcott, 2002).

I have argued previously that the discourse of division stemmed from a power struggle for social legitimacy, social resources, and control (Northcott, 1994). Ironically, these same goals that motivated the discourse of division several decades ago may be motivating the discourse of integration today. As CAM has become widely accepted and utilized among the general public, it can be argued that conventional medicine has responded by incorporating alternative medicine into conventional medicine in an effort to maintain its claims for social legitimacy and social resources and to gain and maintain control over the "competition" (Winnick, 2005). Fadlon refers to this process as the "domestication" of alternative medicine by conventional medicine. Fadlon (2005, p. 7) writes: "the exotic elements of non-conventional medicine have been downplayed and fused with scientific components, creating a hybrid form of medical treatment that is ultimately foreign enough to be fascinating, but also familiar enough not to be disconcerting." Fadlon claims that the process of domestication ultimately brings CAM under the control of conventional medicine. This domestication of CAM, she argues, explains the simultaneous use of conventional and non-conventional medicine that has become so common in recent years in industrialized countries around the world.

From the point of view of alternative medicine, this integration into conventional medicine has often been welcomed as it confers social legitimacy on practitioners who were previously marginalized (Health Canada, 1999). That is, integration may provide alternative practitioners with access to social resources such as fee-payment via public medicare, private health care insurance, or employee benefit programs and favourable legislation conferring state-sanctioned professional status, including licensure and self-regulation (Boon et al., 2004). Alternatively, it can be argued that the practitioners and users of alternative and conventional medicine have become increasingly aware of the limitations of both alternative and scientific medicine and have integrated alternative medicine with conventional medicine to compensate for apparent shortcomings.

Winnick (2005) examined editorials, feature articles, and scientific articles dealing with CAM published in five prestigious medical journals in the United States from 1965–99. She argued that in the last third of the 20th century, the dominance of mainstream allopathic scientific medicine was challenged by the increasing utilization of CAM by the general public. Winnick noted that mainstream medicine's response to CAM was caustic condemnation evident in published material up to the early 1970s. From the mid-1970s to the early 1990s, the tone of published articles became more introspective as authors reassessed the shortcomings of mainstream medicine and the attraction of CAM to the general public. Finally, material published in the 1990s emphasized the integration of CAM with mainstream medicine. In short, Winnick argues that alternatives to mainstream medicine were characterized as quackery in the mid-1960s and by the end of the 20th century had been recast as complementary medicine. She predicts that the next stage in this evolution of CAM will be its co-optation by mainstream medicine. Despite the changing stance of mainstream medicine to CAM, Winnick argues that the motivation of mainstream medicine remains unchanged, that is, the preservation of its dominant position in contemporary society.

The integration of CAM into mainstream medicine might imply a convergence whereby conventional and alternative medicine incorporate elements from each other over time such that they become increasingly similar and indistinguishable from each other. The recent emphasis on **evidence-based medicine (EBM)** uses scientific criteria (the gold standard is the double-blind **randomized controlled trial – RCT** – with random assignment of persons to treatment and control groups) to assess the efficacy of both mainstream medicine and CAM (Willis & White, 2004) and provides a basis for convergence. That is, therapies, regardless of their origins in mainstream or alternative medicine, and regardless of the explanations offered regarding how therapies might work, are accepted or rejected depending on the "evidence" of the effectiveness of therapeutic outcomes. This strategy maintains the dominance of scientific medicine. To this point, Willis and White (2004, p. 53) write: "it appears that it is hoped by some that EBM will provide a stick with which to beat CAM, thus providing a new tool for orthodoxy in the ongoing historical struggle to undermine and marginalize CAM at one level while, at another, selectively co-opting and incorporating aspects of CAM treatment into orthodox practice."

Some have argued that not all CAM therapies are amenable to scientific validation (especially in the form of the RCT) and instead require alternative criteria to assess their efficacy (Lee et al., 2004). Indeed, some CAM therapists argue that each individual and his/her disease are unique and therefore require a unique treatment rather than the standardized treatments offered by conventional medicine (Dew, 2004; Coulter, 2004). Even so, allowing for multiple criteria to assess effectiveness may still foster a convergence between CAM and mainstream medicine. For example, Willis and White (2004, p. 58) note that scientific legitimization is not the only form of legitimization for either CAM or conventional medicine. Either may be legitimized clinically, when consumers willingly purchase services from practitioners, and either may be legitimized through politico-legal criteria in the form of supportive and regulatory legislation, payment through state-funded health care insurance, and state-supported education programs. Indeed, Willis and White note that clinical and politico-legal legitimacy have often been more important than scientific legitimacy. In other words, the success of health care modalities has depended in the past and may continue to depend in the future more on consumer behaviour, the marketplace, and the politics of health care than on scientific evidence. Nevertheless, scientific criteria as sought in EBM will play a role, to some degree at least, in the convergence of CAM and conventional medicine.

The integration of CAM and conventional medicine has been variously characterized. Integration can be viewed as the convergence or accommodation of CAM and conventional medicine driven by an emerging consensus of what works and what does not work in terms of health care outcomes. Alternatively, integration has been described as the domestication, assimilation, co-optation, and incorporation of CAM *by* conventional medicine as conventional medicine attempts to preserve its dominance. In other words, some describe integrative medicine as monolithic and others as accommodative and pluralistic. Finally, some see the integration of CAM and conventional medicine as a result of forces external to both CAM and conventional medicine, for example, as a result of the commodification, marketization, corporatization, and globalization of health care.

It has been argued that the integration of CAM and conventional medicine has been primarily driven by consumer demand as exploited by corporate enterprise. CAM has been commodified, corporatized, and marketized successfully, and this marketing strategy has been facilitated and enhanced by integrating CAM with mainstream medicine. As Collyer (2004, p. 95) puts it: the "mainstreaming [of CAM] is primarily a market strategy." Similarly, given CAM's typically holistic orientation and its focus on lifestyles, illness prevention, and health promotion, it can be argued that the integration of CAM and conventional medicine is an aspect of the ongoing process of **medicalization** that is increasingly bringing virtually all aspects of human life to the attention of health care practitioners, health care consumers, and health care corporations. Further to this point, Goldstein (2000) argues that the contemporary fitness movement in Western societies has much in common with CAM and that the growing emphasis on fitness is likely to be a major "entry point" directing consumers to CAM. Goldstein further argues that health and fitness have been commodified and that the **commodification** of health, wellness, and fitness goes hand in hand with the commodification of CAM and of conventional health care more generally.

Goldstein (2000) observes that the fitness movement and CAM share a holistic orientation emphasizing body, mind, and spirit. It is notable that in a relatively secular time in human history, many CAM therapies have a spiritual component. In other words, CAM integrates physical health, mental health, lifestyle, and spirituality, reminiscent of an earlier time before the rise of science and the decline of religion, when religion, medicine, metaphysics, and magic were intertwined. 17th century Cartesian dualism claimed the body for science and left the mind and spirit to the church. The holistic health movement of the late 20th century and early 21st century, evident in both CAM and mainstream medicine, deconstructs the separation of mind and body and brings issues of the spirit back into the health care equation. Note, for example, that prayer is now often counted as a CAM therapy and spirituality is central to traditional Native American healing.

It is important to note that Canada's increasing cultural diversity and policy of multiculturalism suggest a social and cultural pluralism which may foster a medical pluralism in Canada which recognizes not only various complementary and alternative therapies but also entire **traditional systems of medicine** such as Ayurvedic medicine from India, traditional Chinese medicine, Mexican folk medicine, and Native American medicine. In other words, entire systems of medicine may increasingly coexist as parallel health care systems or in an integrated but plural health care system. Nevertheless, it seems more likely that elements of traditional medicine will be selectively incorporated into mainstream medicine and those elements least compatible with the biomedical model will be discarded (Fadlon, 2005). Just the same, while there is concern that selected indigenous botanical medicines are being "stolen" from indigenous peoples by corporations, there is also concern that indigenous cultural practices such as healing rituals and ceremonies are being commodified (National Aboriginal Health Organization, 2003), suggesting that traditional systems of medicine are being marketed as alternatives in an increasingly plural health care system.

The notion of an integrated medicine which incorporates CAM and conventional medicine may be problematic if it is assumed that conventional medicine on the one hand and traditional systems of medicine and various forms of CAM on the other hand are fundamentally different in terms of their underlying premises, philosophies, epistemologies, etc. about health and illness (Coulter, 2004). This argument, however, assumes that CAM and conventional medicine are each internally consistent, coherent, homogenous, monolithic, unitary, and unified, although diametrically opposed. However, the rhetoric of distinctiveness in epistemology and practice overstates reality. That is, the characterization of CAM and conventional medicine as distinct entities overlooks the diversity, inconsistencies, and divisions within both conventional medicine and CAM, as well as the overlaps and potentials for overlap, which often blur the distinctions between the two and which may allow for the integration of supposed opposites without considerable disruption. The notion of medical pluralism, for example, seems to allow for the loose integration of different modalities of health care based on fundamentally different beliefs about health and illness. As a further example, Adams and Tovey (2004) discuss the divisions between medicine and nursing as well as the divisions within nursing that foster an integration of nursing and CAM. Nevertheless, the nature of integration remains unclear. Coulter (2004) argues that the integration of CAM into mainstream medicine may involve the transformation (co-optation) of CAM without any substantial change to mainstream medicine, or alternatively, incorporating CAM may fundamentally transform mainstream medicine, later if not sooner.

A TYPOLOGY OF COMPLEMENTARY AND ALTERNATIVE MEDICINE

There are many different kinds of complementary and alternative therapies; indeed, the four-volume *Gale Encyclopedia of Alternative Medicine* (Longe, 2005) lists some 150 therapies and 300 herbs and other remedies. Complementary and alternative therapies can be grouped into the following categories (see National Center for Complementary and Alternative Medicine, 2005; Clarke, 2004; Roush, 2003; Skrabanek & McCormick, 1990), although some therapies combine aspects of several categories and so it is not always clear under which category a given therapy should be listed. Despite the ambiguities and some variation from one authoritative source to another, the following general typology is widely used at present.

1. **Biologically-based therapies**, including herbs, foods, vitamins, nutritional supplements, diets, and other biologically-based interventions with an emphasis on substances found in nature. Therapies include homeopathy, naturopathy, herbal remedies, flower remedies, megavitamin therapy, aromatherapy, apitherapy, detoxification, chelation therapy, and various diets (e.g., Atkins, Pritikin, macrobiotic, vegetarian);
2. **Manual therapies** which manipulate the body, including chiropractic, osteopathy, acupuncture, acupressure, massage, reflexology, Alexander technique, and hydrotherapy/aquatherapy/therapeutic baths;
3. **Energy therapies**, including bioelectromagnetic therapies using magnetism, electrical fields, light, or sound; and biofield therapies which manipulate energy fields in and around the body using therapeutic touch, Reiki, crystal healing, and aura imaging;
4. **Mind-body therapies** which emphasize the power of the mind to affect the body (and also the power of the body to affect the mind), including meditation, Yoga, Qi gong, Tai chi, biofeedback, progressive relaxation therapy, deep breathing, hypnosis, mental imaging/visualization/guided imagery, art therapy, music therapy, dance therapy, humour therapy, faith healing, Christian Science healing, prayer, and animal-assisted (pet) therapy;
5. **Supernatural (metaphysical) therapies** based on mysticism and including psychic surgery, psychic healing, voodoo, and magic (the supernatural category of alternative therapies is often excluded from discussions of CAM and will not be discussed further in this chapter);
6. **Diagnostic techniques**, for example, iridology that involves examination of the iris of the eye. Each area of the iris is used to diagnose the health of a different part of the body; and
7. **Traditional systems of medicine** (folk medicine), such as Ayurveda from India, traditional Chinese medicine, Mexican folk medicine (Curanderismo), and traditional Native American medicine. These systems typically "offer remedies in the context of spiritual and lifestyle guidance" (Cassileth, 1998, p. 8).

The following descriptions of CAM therapies are derived from several sources (see the National Center for Complementary and Alternative Medicine, U.S. National Institutes of Health's 2005 web site, as well as Low, 2004, pp. 127–138; Barnes et al., 2004; Northcott, 1994, 2002; Cassileth, 1998).

Biologically-Based Therapies

Homeopathy – Uses natural substances that are highly diluted to treat disease in the belief that substances that produce the same symptoms as disease, when highly diluted, stimulate the body's defenses.
Naturopathy – Uses natural healing therapies such as herbal remedies, nutritional supplements, and diets to enhance the natural healing powers of the body.
Herbal remedies – Long a main component of traditional systems of folk medicine, herbal remedies that have not been incorporated into mainstream medical pharmacology continue to be popular today.
Flower remedies – Essences prepared from flowers are ingested in the belief that specific flowers can modify specific emotions that are thought to underlie various diseases.
Megavitamin therapy – High (mega) doses of vitamins such as vitamin C, in excess of recommended daily allowances, are thought to be therapeutic.
Aromatherapy – Aromatic oils, which a person can smell and which are obtained from plants and trees, are absorbed into the body through the skin and/or inhaled into the lungs. Different aromatic oils are thought to be effective for treating specific conditions.
Apitherapy – Ingestion of bee products including bee venom, bee pollen, royal jelly, and honey, thought to be health promoting.
Detoxification – It is thought that the body may be purged of accumulated toxins by various methods such as fasting, ear candling (burning a candle with one end placed in the ear to draw out toxins), or colon therapy using enemas or laxatives or "colonic irrigation."
Chelation therapy – This is a form of detoxification therapy. A binding (chelating) agent is injected intravenously to remove toxic metals and wastes from the body.
Various diets – The Atkins diet is low in carbohydrates and high in protein. The Pritikin diet is low in fat and high in grains, beans, fruits and vegetables with an emphasis on fibre and water so as to yield low caloric density (i.e., relatively few calories per pound of food). The macrobiotic diet is also low in fat and high in whole grains and fresh vegetables. Vegetarian diets avoid meats and may also avoid other animal products such as milk, cheese, and eggs. The Ornish diet is a vegetarian diet that is high in fibre, low in fat, and includes skim milk and egg whites.

Manual Therapies

Osteopathy – Originally, osteopathy emphasized manipulation of skeletal joints and muscles to promote health through good circulation of the blood. Today, osteopathy in the United States and United Kingdom has converged with mainstream medicine.
Chiropractic – Chiropractic emphasizes manipulation of the spine to promote health by removing pressure on nerves.
Acupuncture – This ancient Chinese method uses needles inserted under the skin at selected points on the body to control pain and to stimulate healing. In traditional Chinese medicine it is thought that acupuncture helps to balance positive and negative energy in the body and promote the flow of vital energy. (Acupuncture could also be listed in the category of energy therapies.)
Acupressure – Acupressure is similar to acupuncture except that the practitioner's hands are used instead of needles. (One variation, Shiatsu, is a form of acupressure massage from Japan).

Massage – Massage involves the manual manipulation of muscle and other soft tissues. There are many different kinds of massage therapies, ranging from gentle massage to deep-tissue massage.
Reflexology – Focuses on pressure points located in the feet (or hands). Foot reflexology involves manipulation of the feet in the belief that points on the foot are connected to every part of the body and that manipulation of these points on the foot is therapeutic.
Hydrotherapy/aquatherapy/therapeutic baths – May be either hot-based or cold-based. Includes hot spring hydrotherapy – soaking in natural mineral hot springs, saunas, whirlpool baths, sitz baths, and cold water/ice compresses.
Alexander technique – Emphasizes health-promoting habits of posture and movement.

Energy Therapies

Electromagnetic therapies – Uses magnets and magnetism, electrical devices and electric current, for diagnosis and therapy.
Light therapy (phototherapy) – Uses natural or artificial light to treat various conditions such as depression and seasonal affective disorder.
Sound therapy – Variations include use of ultrasound, white noise, wind chimes, and tuning forks. It is believed that specific sound frequencies are therapeutic for specific organs of the body. Also known as vibrational therapy.
Therapeutic touch – A healer passes her/his hands over the patient's body, without touching the patient, to identify and correct energy imbalances thought to exist in the unhealthy body or to channel energy from the healer to the patient. Also known as healing touch.
Reiki – A form of therapeutic touch practiced in Japan. The Reiki practitioner is said to channel healing energy through his/her hands to restore energy flow and balance in the body.
Crystal Healing – Stones are used to provide positive energy and eliminate negative energy from the body. It is thought that different stones have different healing properties.
Aura imaging – Practitioners believe that the body produces a visible coloured aura that is thought to reflect the body's energy. Kirlian photography is said to make photographic images of the body's aura. The colours of the aura are said to have diagnostic utility.

Mind-Body (and Body-Mind) Therapies

Meditation – Involves relaxation and breathing techniques that promote mental and physical well-being.
Yoga – This ancient Indian practice combines stretching the body into various positions, meditation, and controlled breathing to balance body, mind, and spirit, and to control and balance bodily energy (prana). (Yoga combines elements of the energy and mind-body categories.)
Qi gong – An ancient Chinese therapy to promote harmony of body, mind, and spirit, and to stimulate the flow of energy (qi) in the body. Involves simple, repetitive movements, meditation, and deep breathing. (Qi gong can also be classified as an energy therapy.)
Tai chi – Chinese movement exercises usually performed slowly and deliberately. (Based on the same philosophy as Qi gong and therefore can also be classified as an energy therapy.)

Biofeedback – Teaches a person, through the use of electronic devices that measure bodily processes such as heart rate, blood pressure, and breathing, to control these bodily responses and to reduce stress and manage pain.
Progressive relaxation therapy – Involves tensing and relaxing muscles, moving in sequence from one part of the body to another.
Deep breathing – Involves repeated cycles of slow inhalation and exhalation while concentrating on breathing (and counting).
Hypnosis – A person in a hypnotic state is relaxed and more responsive to suggestion. Hypnosis is used to implant health-promoting suggestions in an individual's mind to influence behaviour and control symptoms such as pain.
Imagery and visualization techniques – These techniques emphasize the use of the mind and mental images to imagine the elimination of disease from the body, promote relaxation, and mobilize the body's natural resistance and strengths.
Art therapy – The patient engages in creative artistic activities to reveal health problems (both conscious and unconscious) and to promote catharsis, self-esteem, and healing.
Music therapy – Involves the use of music, both creating music and listening to music, as therapy.
Dance therapy – The patient engages in dance activities to promote healing and physical, emotional, mental, spiritual, and social well-being.
Humour therapy – Makes use of humour and laughter to alleviate symptoms such as pain, reduce stress, and promote a sense of well-being.
Faith healing – Emphasizes mental and spiritual practices such as prayer, religious rituals such as the "laying on of hands," etc. for healing purposes.
Christian Science Healing – Sickness is thought to be in the mind rather than the body and health is restored through prayer and divine intervention.
Prayer – Prayer is thought to be efficacious whether offered by the sick person or by others on behalf of the sick person. Some claim that prayer can be effective even when offered at a distance on behalf of a person who is unaware of the prayer (this latter kind of prayer could be classified in the category of energy therapy).
Animal-assisted (pet) therapy – Interaction with animals and/or responsibility for animals can be therapeutic and promote well-being. (A similar claim can be made for tending plants and gardens.)

Traditional Systems of Medicine

Western medicine and Western culture have been influenced by science with its naturalistic empirical orientation and by Cartesian dualism, which emphasized the separation of body and mind. In contrast, non-Western cultures and non-Western traditional systems of medicine have typically been holistic, emphasizing the interrelationships between body and mind, individual and community, and natural and supernatural (Segall & Chappell, 2000, p. 169). While Western medicine increasingly recognizes the interconnections of mind and body (consider, for example, the emerging field of psychoneuroimmunology and the holistic biopsychosocial model), traditional systems of medicine have long recognized these interconnections.

Ayurveda – Ayurveda is a traditional system of medicine from India. Ayurveda emphasizes harmony of body, mind, spirit, and environment, as well as the balance of vital energy (prana) and forces (doshas) in the body through the use of therapies such as Yoga, meditation, exercise, massage, diet, and herbal remedies.

Traditional Chinese medicine – Health is defined as the harmony of body, mind, and spirit, and the flow and balance of energy in the body (the flow of qi, the body's vital energy, is said to be disrupted when there is an imbalance between yin (negative energy) and yang (positive energy)). Health is promoted through the use of therapies such as herbal remedies, Qi gong, exercises, meditation, massage, and acupuncture.

Mexican folk medicine (Curanderismo) – Blends religion and folk medicine. Health is viewed as the equilibrium of the four bodily humours (blood, phlegm, black bile, and yellow bile), the balance of hot and cold conditions in the body, and harmony of the body, lifestyle, social relationships, natural environment, and the supernatural world. "Cold" therapies are used to treat "hot" illnesses and vice versa. Illnesses are said to have natural and/or supernatural causes. It is believed that some people cause illness in others through witchcraft and therefore social relationships are viewed as potential causes of illness. Treatments include prayer, ritual, religious counseling, herbal remedies, and folk drugs (see Cockerham, 2001).

Traditional Native American medicine – Aboriginal peoples in North America believe that health involves a balance of the mental, emotional, physical, and spiritual, as well as balance among individual, community, natural environment, and spiritual realm. Medicine men or women or shamans (spiritual healers) administer medicines and perform rituals designed to restore balance and promote healing (National Aboriginal Health Organization, 2003; Frideres, 2002).

Note that the list of therapies detailed above implies a corresponding list of therapists or practitioners. However, there is not necessarily a one-to-one correspondence between therapy and therapist. For example, herbal remedies are used by herbalists, homeopaths, naturopaths, chiropractors, practitioners of Traditional Chinese medicine, Native healers, some mainstream physicians, and may also be self-prescribed and purchased "over-the-counter" in pharmacies, health food stores, and grocery stores. Acupuncture might be offered by an acupuncturist, a practitioner of TCM, a naturopath, or a mainstream physician. Homeopathic remedies might be prescribed by a homeopath, naturopath, chiropractor, or mainstream physician. Not only can a given therapy be used by a variety of therapists, a given therapist may offer a variety of therapies. For example, an Ayurvedic practitioner might prescribe herbal remedies, diet, meditation, yoga, and massage. A Traditional Chinese practitioner might prescribe herbal remedies, diet, acupuncture, acupressure, massage (tui na), and Qi gong. Finally, a chiropractor might offer chiropractic therapy as well as naturopathic therapies.

Tataryn and Verhoef (2001) suggest that an integrated health care system combining CAM with conventional mainstream health care exists in Canada and discuss a typology of the components of this emerging and evolving integrated health care system. Their typology includes four categories: *body therapies* including substances such as vitamins, herbal remedies, diets, and chemotherapy, and also including physical manipulation of the body such as chiropractic, massage, exercise, and surgery; *body-mind therapies* such as meditation, psychotherapy, counseling, relaxation training, and support groups; *body-energy therapies* such as acupuncture, acupressure, therapeutic touch, Yoga, Qi gong, and Tai chi; and *body-spirit therapies*, including prayer, faith healing, ceremonial rituals, and First Nations traditional healing practices. Note that while mainstream medicine has concentrated on body therapies and CAM has focused more broadly on the range of body, body-mind, body-energy, and body-spirit therapies, mainstream medicine is not confined solely to body therapies. In other words, this typology highlights the overlaps and blurred boundaries that characterize CAM and mainstream medicine, and that continue to evolve in dynamic fashion.

THE UTILIZATION OF COMPLEMENTARY AND ALTERNATIVE MEDICINE IN CANADA

It has been argued that CAM has gone mainstream (Tovey et al., 2004). In other words, it is argued that CAM is now widely used by the general public who utilize both CAM and conventional medicine (Fadlon, 2005; Low, 2004; Northcott & Bachynsky, 1993). Furthermore, CAM has often been incorporated into the practices of conventional practitioners, and conventional and alternative practitioners increasingly refer patients to one another.

The use of CAM is estimated primarily by means of surveys of samples of the population. Surveys produce different statistics regarding utilization of CAM depending on whether the focus is on therapists visited or therapies utilized, and depending on the definition and range of CAM therapies/therapists used in the survey (e.g., some surveys of CAM use include chiropractors or prayer while others do not). Finally, statistics regarding CAM utilization depend on the time frame used in the survey (e.g., use in the last twelve months vs. lifetime utilization).

In the United States, Navarra (2004) notes that 69 percent of Americans have used CAM in recent years, 60 percent of physicians have referred patients to CAM practitioners, and 64 percent of medical schools offer training in CAM. A survey in 2002 (Barnes et al., 2004) of 31,000 adults in the United States found that 36 percent used at least one of 20 different CAM therapies during the past twelve months. When megavitamin therapy and prayer were added to the list of CAM, usage rose to 62 percent. The most commonly used forms of CAM were prayer (45%), herbal remedies (19%), deep breathing exercises (12%), meditation (8%), chiropractic (8%), Yoga (5%), and massage (5%). This survey found that while people of all backgrounds used CAM, women were more likely than men to use CAM as were people with higher education levels, people who were hospitalized in the past year, and former smokers. Most people were found to use CAM *with* conventional medicine rather than *in place of* conventional medicine.

In Canada, a survey in 2003 of 135,573 persons aged 12 or older found that 20 percent reported having visited with or talked to at least one type of alternative health care provider in the past twelve months (Park, 2005). Note that use of CAM does not necessarily depend on visits to a CAM practitioner and so overall usage of CAM will be higher than 20 percent. The alternative practitioners most commonly visited were chiropractors (11%) followed by massage therapists (8%), acupuncturists (2%), and homeopaths and naturopaths (2%). Excluding chiropractors, 12 percent of Canadians ages 12 and older had consulted at least one alternative practitioner in the past twelve months. Consultations were higher for women than for men, residents of western provinces, persons with higher incomes and higher education, persons with at least one chronic health condition, and persons aged 25–64 in comparison to younger ages 12–24 and ages 65 and older.

A survey of 1,500 adult Canadians in 1997 found that 73 percent had used at least one of 22 alternative therapies at some time in their lives, and 50 percent had used at least one alternative therapy in the past twelve months (Ramsay et al., 1999). This survey found that lifetime usage of alternative therapies was: chiropractic (36%), relaxation techniques (23%), massage (23%), prayer (21%), herbal remedies (17%), special diets (12%), folk remedies (12%), acupuncture (12%), Yoga (10%), and homeopathy (8%). In the previous twelve months, utilization was: prayer (18%), relaxation techniques (17%), chiropractic (13%), herbal remedies (12%), massage (12%), folk remedies (6%), aromatherapy (5%), homeopathy (4%), and Yoga (4%). Use of alternative therapies was higher in the western provinces, and for younger adults and persons with post-secondary education. Those persons who paid an alternative therapy provider for services in the past twelve months were most likely to be middle-aged (35–49), and have post-secondary education and higher incomes. Most (81%) of those persons using alternative therapies in the past twelve months did so to prevent future illness or to promote health and well-being.

It is notable that the 1997 survey found that Canadians sometimes obtain alternative therapies from their physicians: 100 percent of persons using high-dose megavitamins obtained them from their medical doctors, as was the case with 89 percent of lifestyle diets, 33 percent of special diets, relaxation techniques (35%), chiropractic (31%), acupuncture (24%), and herbal therapies (23%). For those respondents who indicated that they had at least one medical condition in the past twelve months, 45 percent said that they visited only a medical doctor, 6 percent visited only an alternative provider, 14 percent saw both a medical doctor and an alternative provider, and 35 percent saw neither. This study estimated that Canadians spent $3.8 billion on alternative medicine in twelve months in 1996/1997, including $1.8 billion on fees paid to alternative providers and $2.0 billion spent on alternative therapies including herbs, vitamins, books, classes, equipment, and diet programs.

An extensive literature has developed on the utility of CAM for a range of medical disciplines, diseases, and conditions including, for example, cardiovascular medicine (Stein & Oz, 2004), neurology (Oken, 2004; Weintraub, 2001), gynecology (Ostrzenski, 2002), psychiatry (Muskin, 2000), nursing (Snyder & Lindquist, 2002), rehabilitation (Leskowitz, 2003), physical therapy (Charman, 2000), pharmacy (Kayne, 2002), AIDS (Standish, Calabrese & Galantino, 2002), epilepsy (Devinsky, Schachter & Pacia, 2005), multiple sclerosis (Bowling, 2001), and old age (Cherniak & Cherniak, 2003).

Because CAM therapies tend to be holistic emphasizing the interconnectedness of body, mind, emotions, and spirit, as well as the interconnectedness of individual, community, and environment, they are particularly useful for treating health care problems that have a multi-factorial etiology and/or that respond to a multi-pronged treatment regimen. Mainstream medicine is most successful in treating problems that have a specific etiology and/or respond to a specific treatment (e.g., a disease caused by a bacterial infection and treated with an antibiotic medication). However, many health problems are more complex (e.g., alcoholism, depression, obesity, frailty in old age) and do not fit well into the bio-medical model. Indeed, these problems often have a better fit with CAM philosophies and modalities. Furthermore, interventions by mainstream medicine are often invasive and are not always effective. CAM offers less invasive, more natural therapies that claim to facilitate the natural healing powers of the body. Finally, mainstream medicine tends to diagnose, treat, and prescribe, and in the process disempowers the individual, while CAM tends to emphasize the empowerment of the individual and the role of the individual in her/his own health promotion and care. In short, CAM philosophies and modalities may appear more relevant for health promotion and for managing some of the conditions of life (such as stress or aging), as well as for treating chronic multi-factorial health problems. Nevertheless, it is easy to overstate the differences between mainstream medicine and CAM, reducing each to a simplistic caricature. There is considerable diversity in both mainstream medicine and CAM, and there appears to be an evolving convergence as mainstream medicine focuses more on health promotion, on complex chronic illnesses such as diabetes, and on the diseases and conditions of aging, for example. An emphasis on a healthy lifestyle including exercise, good nutrition, and stress reduction/management is good advice whether offered by CAM practitioners or the practitioners of mainstream medicine, and increasingly their voices are merging in an evolving and developing system of integrated health care.

CONCLUSION

A discourse of integration regarding CAM has emerged in the late 20th century and continues in the early 21st century. This discourse of integration has replaced the previous discourse of division and signals an accommodation between conventional medicine and alternative medicine. Contemporary conventional medicine, given this emerging and growing accommodation, has been variously characterized and labeled as blended, integrated, incorporative, accommodative, assimilative, pluralistic, convergent, hybridized, coopting, and neutralizing. In a similar vein, alternative medicine itself has been labeled as complementary, domesticated, and mainstreamed. While there are distinctions to be made among all of these terms, there is a common theme evident in these related processes and labels. The consensus is that scientific medicine, which reached a peak of hegemonic dominance and professional monopoly in the mid-20th century, has responded to the threat to its dominance evident in the growing popularity and consumerist demand for CAM by bringing CAM into its own orbit, incorporating CAM as its own, and shifting CAM into the scientific paradigm. As Fadlon (2005) argues, the strange, exotic, "other" has been made familiar, tame, and domestic. In a very sophisticated version of "if you can't beat them, join them," mainstream scientific medicine has responded to the threat of alternative medicine by redefining the adversary as complementary, and repositioning and redefining itself as integrated, blended, and pluralistic. By embracing CAM and bringing CAM into the mainstream, mainstream medicine attempts to preserve its dominant position in contemporary society and in the contemporary medical marketplace. What was once marginalized as irrelevant was made mainstream when its relevancy could no longer be trivialized.

Instead of viewing the integration of CAM into mainstream medicine as a strategy used only by mainstream medicine to preserve its medical dominance, the blending of CAM and conventional medicine may also be seen as a manifestation of a globalizing, corporatist, and capitalist agenda that attempts to commodify health care, to exploit existing markets, and to create new markets. That is, it may be argued that an increasingly global and corporate health care industry integrates mainstream and marginal medicine in order to respond to, create, and control markets. Turner (2004, p. xviii) writes that corporate health care in the 21st century, aided by the Internet and e-health, "will take a predatory interest in 'nativistic' or 'indigenous pharmacy,' will seek to commercialize alternative healthcare and to monopolize medical knowledge and research." Similarly, Collyer (2004) notes that CAM has become "big business" and writes about the marketization of health care. Goldstein (2000) observes that the fitness, wellness, health, and illness care are all being commodified. In other words, the 20th-century process of medicalization, which defines more and more aspects of our life as health care issues, continues in the early 21st century; specifically, this process involves extending the scope and control of health care practitioners in an increasingly integrated system that blends conventional, complementary, and alternative medicine, while expanding market opportunities for health care industries and corporations. In short, global, corporatist, capitalist, commercializing, commodifying, and consumerist movements in health care, along with mainstream medicine's attempts to preserve its dominance, are forces moving CAM from marginal to mainstream.

STUDY QUESTIONS

1. *Complementary and alternative medicine (CAM) is a term that refers to many diverse therapies that can be organized into distinct categories. Present a typology of CAM therapies and discuss the philosophical principles underlying each CAM category.*
2. *Compare and contrast CAM and conventional medicine.*
3. *Discuss the utilization of CAM by the general public.*
4. *Discuss the evolving relationship between CAM and conventional medicine.*

GLOSSARY

blended medicine refers to the blending of CAM and conventional medicine. See integrative medicine.

commodification the process of defining a thing as a commodity to be marketed, sold, and purchased.

complementary and alternative medicine (CAM) the wide range of therapies that have not historically been part of conventional Western scientific medicine.

conventional medicine the dominant system of scientific medicine in Western countries in the 20th and early 21st centuries.

evidence-based medicine (EBM) the use of scientific criteria to evaluate the efficacy of health care therapies.

integrative medicine the emerging system of health care that combines complementary, alternative, and conventional health care therapies and philosophies into one combined system.

medical pluralism the acceptance and legitimization of an integrated health care system characterized by diverse health care philosophies and practices.

medicalization the process of defining selected aspects of life as health care issues to be treated by health care practitioners.

randomized controlled trial (RCT) experimental research using random assignment of persons to treatment and control groups.

traditional systems of medicine systems of medicine that have existed for centuries in various parts of the world, for example, Traditional Chinese medicine in China, Ayurvedic medicine in India, and Native American medicine in the Americas.

REFERENCES

Adams, J., & Tovey, P. (2004). CAM and nursing. In P. Tovey, G. Easthope, & J. Adams (Eds.), *The mainstreaming of complementary and alternative medicine: Studies in social context* (pp. 158–174). London: Routledge.

Barnes, P., Powell-Griner, E., McFann, K., & Nahin, R. (2004). *CDC advance data report #343. Complementary and alternative medicine use among adults: United States, 2002.* Retrieved December 19, 2005 from http://nccam.nih.gov/news/camsurvey.htm.

Boon, H., Welsh, S., Kelner, M., & Wellman, B. (2004). CAM practitioners and the professionalization process: A Canadian comparative case study. In P. Tovey, G. Easthope, and J. Adams (Eds.), *The mainstreaming of complementary and alternative medicine: Studies in social context* (pp. 123–139). London: Routledge.

Bowling, A.C. (2001). *Alternative medicine and multiple sclerosis.* New York: Demos.

Cassileth, B.R. (1998). *The alternative medicine handbook.* New York: W.W. Norton.

Charman, R.A. (Ed.) (2000). *Complementary therapies for physical therapists.* Boston: Butterworth-Heinemann.

Cherniak, P., & Cherniak, N. (Eds.) (2003). *Alternative medicine for the elderly.* New York: Springer.

Clarke, J.N. (2004). *Health, illness, and medicine in Canada.* Don Mills, ON: Oxford University Press.

Cockerham, W.C. (2001). *Medical sociology* (8th ed.). Upper Saddle River, NJ: Prentice Hall.

Collyer, F. (2004). The corporatisation and commercialisation of CAM. In P. Tovey, G. Easthope, & J. Adams (Eds.), *The mainstreaming of complementary and alternative medicine: Studies in social context* (pp. 81–99). London: Routledge.

Coulter, I. (2004). Integration and paradigm clash: The practical difficulties of integrative medicine. In P. Tovey, G. Easthope, & J. Adams (Eds.), *The mainstreaming of complementary and alternative medicine: Studies in social context* (pp. 103–122). London: Routledge.

Crellin, J., & Ania, F. (2002). *Professionalism and ethics in complementary and alternative medicine.* New York: Haworth.

Devinsky, O., Schachter, S., & Pacia, S. (Eds.) (2005). *Complementary and alternative therapies for epilepsy.* New York: Demos.

Dew, K. (2004). The regulation of practice. In P. Tovey, G. Easthope, & J. Adams (Eds.), *The mainstreaming of complementary and alternative medicine: Studies in social context* (pp. 64–80). London: Routledge.

Fadlon, J. (2005). *Negotiating the holistic turn: The domestication of alternative medicine.* Albany, NY: State University of New York Press.

Frideres, J.S. (2002). Overcoming hurdles: Health care and aboriginal peoples. In B.S. Bolaria & H.D. Dickinson (Eds.), *Health, illness and health care in Canada* (3rd ed., pp. 144–166). Toronto: Harcourt Brace.

Goldstein, M.S. (2000). The culture of fitness and the growth of CAM. In M. Kelner, B. Wellman, B. Pescosolido, & M. Saks (Eds.), *Complementary and alternative medicine: Challenge and change* (pp. 27–38). Amsterdam: Harwood.

Health Canada (2001). *Perspectives on complementary and alternative health care: A collection of papers prepared for Health Canada.* Ottawa: Health Canada.

Health Canada (1999). *Practitioner perspectives on complementary therapy use among people living with HIV*. Ottawa: Health Canada.

Joudrey, R., McKay, S., & Gough, J. (2004). Student nurses' perceptions of alternative and allopathic medicine. *Western Journal of Nursing Research, 26*(3), 356–366.

Kayne, S.B. (2002). *Complementary therapies for pharmacists*. London: Pharmaceutical.

Kelner, M., & Wellman, B. (2000). Introduction. In M. Kelner, B. Wellman, B. Pescosolido, & M. Saks (Eds.), *Complementary and alternative medicine: Challenge and change* (pp. 1–24). Amsterdam: Harwood.

Lee, R., Kligler, B., & Shiflett, S. (2004). Integrative medicine: Basic principles. In B. Kligler & R. Lee (Eds.), *Integrative medicine: Principles for practice* (pp. 3–23). New York: McGraw-Hill.

Leskowitz, E.D. (2003). *Complementary and alternative medicine in rehabilitation*. New York: Churchill Livingstone.

Longe, J.L. (Ed.) (2005). *The Gale encyclopedia of alternative medicine*. Detroit: Thomson/Gale.

Low, J. (2004). *Using alternative therapies: A qualitative analysis*. Toronto: Canadian Scholars' Press.

Muskin, P.R. (Ed.) (2000). *Complementary and alternative medicine in psychiatry*. Washington, DC: American Psychiatric Press.

National Aboriginal Health Organization. (2003). *Traditional medicine in contemporary contexts*. Canada: National Aboriginal Health Organization. Retrieved December 5, 2005, from http://naho.ca.

National Center for Complementary and Alternative Medicine, National Institutes of Health. (2005). *Understanding complementary and alternative medicine*. Bethesda, MD: National Institutes of Health. Retrieved December 5, 2005 from http://nccam.nih.gov/health/.

Navarra, T. (2004). *The encyclopedia of complementary and alternative medicine*. New York, NY: Facts on File.

Northcott, H.C. (2002). Health care restructuring and alternative approaches to health and medicine. In B.S. Bolaria & H.D. Dickinson (Eds.), *Health, illness and health care in Canada* (3rd ed., pp. 460–474). Toronto: Harcourt Brace.

Northcott, H.C. (1994). Alternative health care in Canada. In B.S. Bolaria & H.D. Dickinson (Eds.), *Health, illness and health care in Canada* (2nd ed., pp. 487–503). Toronto: Harcourt Brace.

Northcott, H.C. & Bachynsky, J.A. (1993). Concurrent utilization of chiropractic, prescription medicines, nonprescription medicines and alternative health care. *Social Science and Medicine, 37*(3), 431–435.

Oken, B.S. (Ed.) (2004). *Complementary therapies in neurology: An evidence-based approach*. Boca Raton, FL: Parthenon.

Ostrzenski, A. (2002). *Gynecology: Integrating conventional, complementary, and natural alternative therapy*. Philadelphia: Lippincott, Williams & Wilkins.

Park, J. (2005). Use of alternative health care. *Health Reports, 16*(2), 39–42.

Ramsay, C., Walker, M., & Alexander, J. (1999). *Alternative medicine in Canada: Use and public attitudes*. Vancouver: Fraser Institute (also available on line as of January 11, 2006, at http://www.fraserinstitute.ca).

Roush, R.A. (2003). *Complementary and alternative medicine: Clinic design*. New York: Haworth Integrative Healing Press.

Saks, M. (2003). *Orthodox and alternative medicine: Politics, professionalization and health care*. London: Sage.

Segall, A., & Chappell, N.L. (2000). *Health and health care in Canada.* Toronto: Prentice Hall.

Sharma, U. (2000). Medical pluralism and the future of CAM. In M. Kelner, B. Wellman, B. Pescosolido, & M. Saks (Eds.), *Complementary and alternative medicine: Challenge and change* (pp. 211–222). Amsterdam: Harwood.

Skrabanek, P., & McCormick, J. (1990). *Follies and fallacies in medicine.* Buffalo: Prometheus.

Snyder, M., & Lindquist, R. (Eds.) (2002). *Complementary/alternative therapies in nursing* (4th ed.). New York: Springer.

Standish, L.J., Calabrese, C., & Galantino, M.L. (Eds.) (2002). *AIDS and complementary and alternative medicine: Current science and practice.* New York: Churchill Livingstone.

Stein, R.A., & Oz, M.C. (Eds.) (2004). *Complementary and alternative cardiovascular medicine.* Totowa, NJ: Humana.

Tataryn, D.J., & Verhoef, M.J. (2001). Combining conventional, complementary, and alternative health care: A vision of integration. Section VII in Health Canada, *Perspectives on complementary and alternative health care: A collection of papers prepared for Health Canada.* Ottawa: Health Canada.

Tovey, P., Easthope, G., & Adams, J. (Eds.) (2004). *The mainstreaming of complementary and alternative medicine: Studies in social context.* London: Routledge.

Turner, B.S. (2004). The end(s) of scientific medicine? Foreword. In P. Tovey, G. Easthope, & J. Adams (Eds.), *The mainstreaming of complementary and alternative medicine: Studies in social context* (pp. xiii–xx). London: Routledge.

Weintraub, M.I. (Ed.) (2001). *Alternative and complementary treatment in neurologic illness.* New York: Churchill Livingstone.

Willis, E., & White, K. (2004). Evidence-based medicine and CAM. In P. Tovey, G. Easthope, & J. Adams (Eds.), *The mainstreaming of complementary and alternative medicine: Studies in social context* (pp. 49–63). London: Routledge.

Winnick, T.A. (2005). From quackery to "complementary" medicine: The American medical profession confronts alternative therapies. *Social Problems, 52*(1), 38–61.

PART 3

INEQUALITY AND HEALTH CARE

It has long been known that social and economic inequalities are related to health status and the utilization of health care services. Not until the elucidation of the health field concept in the 1974 Lalonde Report did health care service planners begin to look seriously at the implications of this relationship for health care policy and service delivery. The health field concept entails the rather simple notion that health status is determined by a number of interacting factors: human biology and genetics, lifestyle choices and behaviours, the nature of the social and physical environments, and the nature and organization of the health care system.

Initially, policy-makers focused on altering lifestyle choices and behaviours as the most promising means to achieve health. Thus considerable efforts have gone into stop-smoking campaigns, reducing impaired driving, improving diets, and increasing exercise, among other things. More recently, attention has focused on the effects of social and economic inequality on health status. The policy consequences of this shift of focus have resulted in more attention being paid to how structural inequalities based on income, education, age, gender, and race can be reduced to improve overall population health status. This is a radical departure from the near exclusive focus on the health care system that dominated policy-making and public debate for the past several decades.

Despite strong evidence that economic inequalities result in reduced life chances and decreased health status, wide income disparities and poverty persist in Canada. For many people, poverty is a temporary condition. Some, including single-parent families, people of Aboriginal ancestry, members of visible minorities, and those with low levels of educational attainment, however, are at high risk for long-term poverty.

Bolaria and Bolaria draw our attention to the relationship between inequality, food insecurity, food banks, and health in Chapter 9. The issue of food insecurity came to prominence in Canada with the emergence of food banks in the 1980s. Since the first food bank opened in Edmonton in 1981, food banks and similar organizations have been established in many towns and cities across Canada. The continuing existence of food banks indicates that food insecurity and food dependency have become permanent features of Canadian society. Bolaria and Bolaria conclude that while material and social deprivations produce poor health status, food insecurity and compromised dietary intakes only exacerbate these conditions and further increase the health risks for the vulnerable populations.

The increasing ethical, religious, racial, and cultural diversity of the Canadian population has important implications for research and policy in population health and health care areas. The last reading in this section, by Kobayashi, focuses on some key issues concerning immigration, ethnicity, aging, and health. The first part presents a demographic profile of the changing Canadian population and increasing diversity in the Canadian mosaic. Kobayashi then provides a discussion of the health of immigrants, with a particular emphasis on what is commonly referred to as the "healthy immigrant effect." The literature indicates that while recent immigrants are healthier than their Canadian-born counterparts, over time this health status advantage decreases. The effect is stronger among new immigrants because they are often young and better educated and because of health requirements for entrance into Canada. The decline in health status over time is attributed to lifestyle changes and broader structural factors such as their location in the labour market, economic disadvantage, and social exclusion. Visible minority immigrants may face more disadvantages and poor health over time than non-visible minority immigrants. The chapter concludes with a discussion of ethnicity, aging, and social policy.

Social inequality and poverty are directly linked to lower health status. This is true regardless of the chosen indicators of health status: life expectancy at birth, infant mortality, psychomotor and growth retardation, or emotional disturbances. For the

Aboriginal population of Canada, the negative health consequences of social inequality and poverty are amplified. In Chapter 10, Frideres paints a grim picture of the life chances and health status of Canada's Aboriginal population. He attributes the plight of the Aboriginal peoples to several factors, including colonial and racist policies that contributed to the destruction of indigenous cultures and communities and their replacement with Western culture and institutions, including Western medicine, which emphasizes the individual causes and cures of illness. Failure to address the issues of low health status and life chances at the social policy level perpetuates the causes of the problem.

9

Inequality, Food Insecurity, Food Banks, and Health

B. SINGH BOLARIA University of Saskatchewan, University of Victoria

ROSEMARY BOLARIA Researcher and Medical Writer

INTRODUCTION

Poverty, malnutrition, hunger, and disease have come to be identified with underdeveloped Third World countries. While the significance and concentration of these problems in the Third World cannot be overstated, neither have the advanced capitalist countries eliminated economic inequalities and poverty. The inequalities of wealth and income produce differential **life chances** – chances for material and social rewards. Poverty translates into dependency on food banks, malnutrition and hunger, ill health, short life expectancy, and homelessness, to mention only a few of its effects (Bolaria & Wotherspoon, 2000; Bolaria, 2002).

Canada is a highly stratified society, which has widespread disparities in wealth, income, power, and prestige. These inequalities have important implications for people's lives. This chapter explores the linkages between income inequality, poverty, and life chances, with particular emphasis on food banks, food insecurity, and health.

INCOME INEQUALITY AND POVERTY

Income inequality is an important dimension of social stratification. An examination of income distribution data reveals wide income disparities among Canadians. These data also show that there has been very little change in the share of income held by Canadians in different income categories over time (National Council of Welfare, 2000a, b; Campaign 2000; Curry-Stevens, 2004). Income inequalities persist in Canada (National Council of Welfare, 2000a, b) and the inequality between the rich and poor has actually widened (Yalnizyan, 1998, 2000; Curry-Stevens, 2001). Data show that the share of total aftertax income in 2003 of the richest 20 percent of the family units was 43.7 percent and the poorest was five percent (National Council of Welfare, 2006a).

A significant number of Canadians live in poverty. The most common measure used to establish the poverty line is the low-income cut-offs used by Statistics Canada (National Council of Welfare, 2006a, b). There is no single cut-off line for all of Canada, because living costs vary by family size and place of residence. Most poor Canadians live on incomes that are substantially under the poverty line, that is, in the depth of poverty (National Council of Welfare, 2006a, b).

Table 9.1 shows national trends in poverty from 1980–2003. In 1980, the number of people living in poverty was a little over 3.8 million and the poverty rate was 16 percent. Both the number of people who lived in poverty and the poverty rate fluctuated throughout the 1980s. After some decline in the late eighties, there was substantial increase in the early and late nineties. For instance, in 1996 and 1997, the percent of persons living in poverty was a little over 20 percent. In 2003, the number of persons living in poverty was close to 5 million, nearly 16 percent.

As Table 9.2 shows, child poverty figures followed the same general pattern as statistics for the general population. Child poverty increased in the early part of the 1980s, declined during the next few years, and rose again in the 1990s. The stated commitment by the federal and provincial governments to eradicate child poverty has not been realized, and poverty rates for children have exceeded 20 percent in some years. Nearly one and a half million, or more than one in five, children are poor. In 2003, the number of children living in poverty was 1.2 million, or 17.6 percent.

TABLE 9.1 *Poverty, Trends, All Persons, 1980–2003*

	All Persons	Poor Persons	Poverty Rates
1980	24,107,000	3,852,000	16.0%
1981	24,389,000	3,872,000	15.9%
1982	24,654,000	4,251,000	17.2%
1983	24,890,000	4,631,000	18.6%
1984	25,128,000	4,704,000	18.7%
1985	25,358,000	4,447,000	17.5%
1986	25,612,000	4,202,000	16.4%
1987	25,921,000	4,145,000	16.0%
1988	26,253,000	3,953,000	15.1%
1989	26,620,000	3,719,000	14.0%
1990	27,014,000	4,369,000	16.2%
1991	27,367,000	4,781,000	17.5%
1992	27,715,000	5,062,000	18.3%
1993	28,031,000	5,416,000	19.3%
1994	28,351,000	5,271,000	18.6%
1995	28,662,000	5,530,000	19.3%
1996	28,967,000	5,970,000	20.6%
1997	29,227,000	5,867,000	20.1%
1998	29,443,000	5,466,000	18.6%
1999	29,694,000	5,151,000	17.3%
2000	29,988,000	4,917,000	16.4%
2001	30,321,000	4,711,000	15.5%
2002	30,611,000	4,963,000	16.2%
2003	30,893,000	4,917,000	15.9%

Source: National Council of Welfare, 2006. Poverty profile 2002–03, Table 1.1, p. 15.

TABLE 9.2 *Poverty Trends, Children Under 18, 1980–2003*

	All Children Under 18	Poor Children Under 18	Poverty Rates
1980	6,778,000	1,098,000	16.2%
1981	6,687,000	1,110,000	16.6%
1982	6,625,000	1,272,000	19.2%
1983	6,563,000	1,306,000	19.9%
1984	6,529,000	1,358,000	20.8%
1985	6,492,000	1,253,000	19.3%
1986	6,526,000	1,142,000	17.5%
1987	6,538,000	1,131,000	17.3%
1988	6,573,000	1,032,000	15.7%
1989	6,636,000	1,002,000	15.1%
1990	6,705,000	1,227,000	18.3%
1991	6,795,000	1,325,000	19.5%
1992	6,874,000	1,361,000	19.8%
1993	6,910,000	1,541,000	22.3%
1994	6,966,000	1,435,000	20.6%
1995	6,995,000	1,546,000	22.1%
1996	7,008,000	1,654,000	23.6%
1997	7,005,000	1,548,000	22.1%
1998	6,971,000	1,436,000	20.6%
1999	6,959,000	1,343,000	19.3%
2000	6,912,000	1,251,000	18.1%
2001	6,924,000	1,191,000	17.2%
2002	6,878,000	1,238,000	18.0%
2003	6,824,000	1,201,000	17.6%

Source: National Council of Welfare (2006, Poverty profile 2002–03, Table 1.2, p. 15).

Certain groups face a high risk of poverty. These include families headed by women, unattached or elderly women, the unemployed, those with irregular participation in the labour force, immigrant/racialized groups, and persons with low educational levels (National Council of Welfare, 2006a; Galabuzi, 2004, 2006). Women overall face a much higher risk of poverty than men, a phenomenon that has come to be known as the "**feminization of poverty**." For instance, the poverty rate for women in 2003 was 17.1 percent as compared to 14.7 percent for men, and the poverty rate for unattached women was 42.1 percent (National Council of Welfare, 2006a). Immigrants and their children, particularly recent immigrants, are at a high risk of poverty (Campaign 2000). The child poverty rate among all immigrants in 2001 was a little over 40 percent, the rate for immigrants who arrived since 1996 was 49 percent, and the rate for those with Aboriginal identity was 40 percent (Campaign 2000).

Because the vast majority of Canadians earn their income from wage employment, labour market characteristics that determine which jobs are well paid are particularly important in any discussion of poverty. For instance, those in managerial and professional occupations and their families are unlikely to live in poverty, compared with those in the service industries. Occupations with an above-average risk of poverty include farming, fishing, forestry, sales, clerical, and services (National Council of Welfare, 2006a, b).

Clearly, wide income disparities and poverty persist in Canada. Income inequality and poverty have an important influence on the lives of individuals. Income inequalities produce duality of consumption patterns between necessary subsistence goods by the poor and semi-luxury and luxury goods by the privileged groups (Chossudovsky, 1983; see also Kirkpatrick & Tarasuk, 2003). Economic and social inequalities produce inequality of opportunities and life chances, which are reflected in such measures as education, living standards, housing, health, and consumption patterns.

In addition to the differences in the goods they consume, persons with different income levels devote a different percentage of their money income to necessary subsistence goods. Low-income individuals and families spend a higher proportion of their incomes on necessities of life as compared to those with high incomes. Chossudovsky (1983, p. 76) notes that "food is by far the most important component of necessary consumption." Adequate production and supply of food in themselves do not assure adequate levels of food consumption and nutrition. Consumption levels are influenced by the social distribution of food to different groups in the population, which itself is a function of income distribution.

Income inequality and poverty produce food insecurity and food dependency. Since the early 1980s, it has become increasingly evident that a large number of Canadians depend on **food banks** (Bolaria, 2002; Bolaria & Wotherspoon, 2000). The very existence of food banks indicates that food insecurity and dependency have become permanent features of Canadian society.

FOOD INSECURITY AND FOOD BANKS

A commonly accepted definition of food insecurity is "the inability to acquire or consume an adequate diet quality or sufficient quantity of food in socially acceptable ways, or the uncertainty that one will be able to do so" (McIntyre, 2004, p. 174). Access to nutritionally adequate and sufficient quantity of food are influenced by social distribution of food among various groups in society, which as noted before, is in itself a function of income distribution. The poor and those in low-income groups face a high risk of food insecurity and even hunger.

A recent article based on the Canadian Community Health Survey (CCHS) reports that almost 15 percent of Canadians, or an estimated 3.7 million people, had experienced food insecurity at some point in 2000/01 (Ledrou & Gervais, 2005). Food insecurity was determined with three questions. If because of lack of money in the previous year they or someone in their household: had worried about not having enough to eat; had not eaten the quality or variety of food desired; and actually not had enough to eat. Respondents who replied affirmatively to at least one question were considered to have experienced food insecurity. Those who replied "never" to all three questions did not experience food insecurity.

The report also found that more than 40 percent of the individuals in low or lower-middle income households experienced food insecurity. The incidence of food insecurity was much less common in high-income households: four percent in high income and 11 percent in upper-middle income households. Even 25 percent of the middle-income households reported at least one dimension of the food insecurity (Ledrou & Gervais, 2005).

A higher proportion of women (16%) than men (13%) reported food insecurity. Among the women, the high-risk group was lone parents; 33 percent reported food insecurity. Food insecurity was also high among off-reserve Aboriginal populations where 31 percent reported food insecurity on at least one of the three dimensions. Residents of territories reported food insecurity well above the national average: Nunavut (56%); Northwest Territories (28%); and 21 percent in Yukon (Ledrou & Gervais, 2005).

These findings are consistent with other research on food insecurity and hunger. The National Longitudinal Survey of Children and Youth (NLSCY) in 1994 and 1996 provide further insight into the extent of food insecurity in Canadian households and child hunger. In response to the question "Has your child ever experienced hunger because there was no food in the house or money to buy food? If yes, how often?" hunger was reported in 57,000 families with children under age 11 and in 75,615 families with children under age 13 in the 1994 survey (McIntyre et al., 2000, 2001). The 1998–99 National Population Health Survey (NPHS), based upon different measures of food insecurity, revealed food insecurity in just over 10 percent of the households, which represented 3 million people (Che & Chen, 2001). Other studies which provide evidence of the extent and severity of food insecurity among low-income women with children come from Atlantic Canada and Metropolitan Toronto (McIntyre et al., 2002; Tarasuk & Beaton 1999). Almost all of the 141 families in the Atlantic Canada study reported food insecurity and over 90 percent of the women who used food banks reported some degree of food insecurity. In Figure 9.1, the Canadian Association of Food Banks' "HungerCounts" reveals the extent of food dependency in Canada.

While it is not possible to compare findings of different studies because of variations in measures used to assess food insecurity, the results of various studies provide persuasive evidence of the persistent link between inequality/poverty and food insecurity/hunger. As McIntyre (2004, p. 175) puts it: "A very brief social history of food insecurity in Canada would read simply: Poverty increased then it deepened. Food insecurity emerged then it increased in severity."

FIGURE 9.1

Monthly Canadian Food Bank Use, 1989–2006

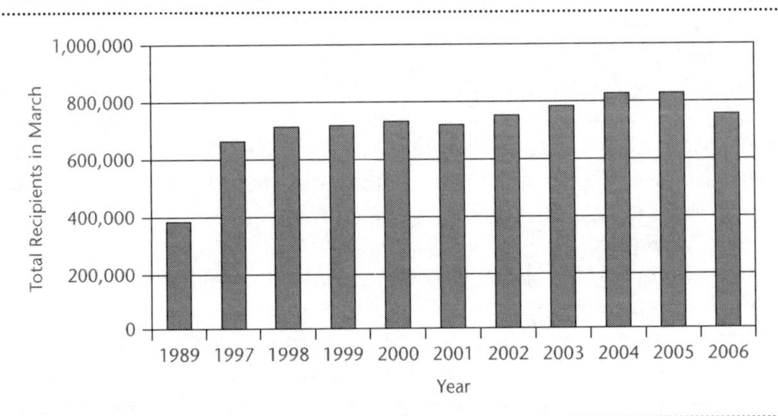

Source: Canadian Association of Food Banks (2006). Time for Action: Hunger Count 2006. Toronto. Figure 1, p. 12.

Inequality, poverty, food insecurity, and hunger are linked to inequalities in health status of the population. The issue of food insecurity came to prominence in Canada with the emergence of food banks in the 1980s. Since the first food bank opened in Edmonton in 1981, food banks and similar organizations have been established in many towns and cities across Canada. By 1984, there were 75 food banks in Canada, mostly in the western provinces. The number of food banks continued to increase through the 1980s. By 1991, there were 292 food banks in various parts of Canada; by 1997, 508 communities had one or more food banks (Bolaria, 2002). This growth continues. During the period 1997–2002, 1,800 new food banks opened in Canada (Canadian Association of Food Banks, 2002). The very existence of food banks and their proliferation indicate the extent to which poverty, food insecurity, and food dependency have become permanent features in Canada. The growing demand for their services has forced food banks to expand beyond their own distribution centres in order to distribute food through various affiliated agencies, and grocery and meal programs such as community kitchens, women's shelters, and other service organizations that feed specific client groups (Canadian Association of Food Banks, 2006; Bolaria, 2002).

The results of the Canadian Association of Food Banks, Hunger Count 2006 indicate that among the 753,458 people who received food assistance in a typical month, 41.0 percent were children under 18 years of age (Canadian Association of Food Banks, 2006). The data also show that there has been a progressive increase in food bank use over time. A slight decline began in 2005, and continued in 2006, compared to a record high of 841,640 in 2004.

INEQUALITY, FOOD INSECURITY, AND HEALTH

Despite remarkable improvement in the overall health of Canadians, health stats disparities among various groups continue to persist. These health differences result primarily from different life experiences and life chances among Canadians associated with differential opportunity structures. Differential opportunity structures produce different social and economic conditions, different social determinants of health, that produce different health outcomes for individuals, families, groups, and communities (Raphael, 2004; Bolaria & Bolaria, 2002). Social determinants of health such as income and income distribution, education, occupation, housing, food security, and social exclusion have a profound impact on the health status of the people (Raphael, 2004). Income remains the most important social determinant because of its link to other determinants such as housing and food security.

A number of studies have shown a link between income and health (Phipps, 2003; Wilkins et al., 2000; Davey-Smith, 2003; Auger et al., 2004; Ross et al., 2000). Those who are advantaged in socio-economic status are also advantaged in health status. Upper-income Canadians live longer, healthier, and more disability-free lives on average than poor Canadians. Groups with high incidence of low income and poverty, such as visible minorities, women, and Aboriginal people, have poor health status (Galabuzi, 2004; Shah, 2004; Pederson & Raphael, 2006; Health Canada, 2003). Studies also show the link between child health, birth outcomes, child mortality, and income levels (CICH, 1994, 2000; Statistics Canada, 2004, 2006; Phipps & Lethbridge, 2006).

The health status differences among Canadians are due to the differences in social determinants of health. Personal behaviour and lifestyles play a minor role in these differences

(Bolaria & Bolaria, 2002; Raphael, 2004). While considerable literature has now accumulated on socio-economic and health status, only recently a number of studies focused on the specific topic of food insecurity, hunger, and health-related consequences and outcomes (McIntyre, 2004; Tarasuk, 2004; McIntyre et al., 2003; Tarasuk, 2001; Vozoris, Davis, & Tarasuk, 2002; Vozoris & Tarasuk, 2003; Tarasuk & Beaton, 1999; Olson, 1999; Hamelin, Habicht & Beaudry, 1999). Studies in this area, with varying degrees of focus, highlight the nutritional and health implications of food insecurity for individuals and households. For instance, food insecurity is implicated in decreased consumption of nutritional food and fruit and vegetables, and overall reduction in food intake, and an increase in disordered eating patterns (Olson, 1999; Tarasuk, 2001). The Atlantic Canadian Study of Food Insecurity also examined the dietary intakes of mothers and their children. The study found that the mothers compromised their own nutritional intake to feed and preserve the adequacy of their children's dietary intake (McIntyre et al., 2003). Food insecurity is obviously implicated in the quantity and quality of food intakes among members in the household and is also implicated in alteration of body mass index (BMI) and obesity (Che & Chen, 2001; Olson, 1999). Other human development and social implications of food insecurity include physical impairment, loss of productivity for adult members, learning difficulties for children in school, decreased social participation, and feeling of powerlessness, stigmatization, and shame (Hamelin, Habicht & Beaudry; 1999; Hamelin, Beaudry & Habicht, 2002; McIntyre, Connors & Warren, 2000; Tarasuk & Beaton, 1999). While children's feeding programs may meet food needs, McIntyre, Connor, and Warren (2000) argue that these stigmatize the families, increase institutional control, continue dependency, and reproduce inequalities.

As the discussion of inequality, poverty, and food insecurity indicates, food insecurity and hunger arise in the context of financial insecurity; food insecurity and hunger arise in the context of financial insecurity, low incomes, and poverty. Consequently, income level is the best predictor of food security/insecurity (Che & Chen, 2001; Vozoris & Tarasuk, 2003; McIntyre et al., 2002). Income levels, of course, are also linked to buying "healthy foods" and "healthy eating" (Tarasuk, 2001; Kirkpatrick & Tarasuk, 2003; McIntyre et al., 2003; Vozoris, Davis & Tarasuk, 2002). Individuals in food insecure households are more likely to have poor health, chronic health conditions, and poor self-rated health than those in secure households (Che & Chen, 2001; Vozoris & Tarasuk, 2003; McIntyre et al., 2000).

In light of the above presentation, the problem of food insecurity lies in income inequalities and poverty and not in either poor budgeting or poor lifestyles in vulnerable populations (McLaughlin et al., 2003; Bolaria & Bolaria, 2002). The solution also lies, therefore, in reducing inequalities and eliminating poverty. However, what has been happening is increasing inequalities, economic restructuring in the context of globalization, and reduced social spending. If the problem of food insecurity is to be addressed, the focus has to be on public policy initiatives to reduce inequalities and eliminate poverty, that is, reduce differences among Canadians in social-structural determinants of health.

CONCLUSION

Data presented in this chapter indicate that wide income disparities and poverty persist in Canada. Economic and social imbalances produce inequalities of opportunities, differential life chances, and different social consumption patterns. A duality of social consumption patterns is linked to income levels – while upper-income and rich Canadians have disposable income for luxury goods, at the other extreme, low-income and poor Canadians are often unable to buy even necessary subsistence goods, including food. Since the early 1980s, it has become increasingly evident that a large number of Canadians depend upon food banks. The continuing existence of food banks indicates that food insecurity and food dependency have become permanent features of Canadian society.

Material and social deprivations force upon people many debilitating conditions that produce poor health, shorter lives, high infant mortality, and other physical and mental health problems. Food insecurity and compromised dietary intakes only exacerbate these conditions and further increase the health risks for the vulnerable populations.

STUDY QUESTIONS

1. *Discuss the statement that material and social deprivations produce poor health and shorter lives for the disadvantaged.*
2. *Discuss the physical and psychological health consequences of dependency on food banks.*
3. *Canada is one of the richest countries in the world and certainly produces abundant food. How, then, can we explain food insecurity and hunger in this country?*
4. *Discuss the relationships among inequality, poverty, food insecurity, and health.*
5. *Negative social attributes such as social stigma, disrepute, and shame, which are usually associated with poverty, are likely to be exacerbated by dependency on food banks. Discuss the linkages between negative social attributes and social, psychological, and physical wellness.*

GLOSSARY

feminization of poverty conditions in which women face a higher risk of poverty than men and comprise a growing population of the poor.

food banks voluntary agencies established to distribute food to the hungry; sustained by public and private sector donations of time, food, and money.

food insecurity the inability to acquire nutritionally adequate and safe foods in socially acceptable ways.

income inequality a pattern of income distribution in which relatively stable disparities exist in the relative share of income received by different segments of the population.

life chances opportunities to acquire material goods, necessary services, and desirable living conditions.

social stigma negative social and personal characteristics that are often attributed to individuals as a result of their dependency on public and private agencies and programs.

REFERENCES

Auger, N., Raynault, M-F., Lessard, R., & Choiniere, R. (2004). Income and health in Canada. In D. Raphael (Ed.), *Social determinants of health: Canadian perspectives* (pp. 39–52). Toronto: Canadian Scholars' Press.

Bolaria, B.S. (2002). Income inequality, poverty, food banks and health. In B.S. Bolaria & H.D. Dickinson (Eds.), *Health, illness and health care in Canada* (3rd ed., pp. 131–143). Toronto: Thomson Nelson.

Bolaria, B.S., & Bolaria, R. (2002). Personal and structural determinants of health and illness: Lifestyles and life chances. In B.S. Bolaria & H.D. Dickinson (Eds.), *Health, illness and health care in Canada* (3rd ed., pp. 445–459). Toronto: Thomson Nelson.

Bolaria, B.S., & Wotherspoon, T. (2000). Income inequality, poverty and hunger. In B.S. Bolaria (Ed.), *Social issues and contradictions in Canadian society* (pp. 73–90). Toronto: Harcourt.

Campaign 2000. (2006). *One million too many: Implementing solutions to child poverty in Canada. 2004 Report Card on Child Poverty in Canada.* Ottawa.

Canadian Association of Food Banks. (CAFB). (2006). *Time for action: Hunger count 2006.* Toronto.

Canadian Association of Food Banks. (CAFB). (2003). *Hunger count 2003: Something has to give; Food banks filling the policy gap in Canada.* Toronto.

Canadian Institute of Child Health. (1994). *The health of Canada's children: A CICH profile* (2nd ed.). Ottawa: CICH.

Canadian Institute of Child Health. (2000). *The health of Canada's children* (3rd ed.). Ottawa: CICH.

Canadian Labour Congress. (2003). Economy. *Economic Review and Outlook, 14*(2).

Che, J. & Chen, J. (2001). Food insecurity in Canadian households. *Health Reports, 12*, 11–22.

Chossudovsky, M. (1983). Underdevelopment and the political economy of malnutrition and ill health. *International Journal of Health-Services, 13*(1), 69–87.

Curry-Stevens, A. (2001). When market fails: Exploring the widening gap between the rich and poor in Canada. Toronto: CSJ Foundation for Research and Education.

Curry-Stevens, A. (2004). Income and income distribution. In D. Raphael (Ed.), *Social determinants of Health: Canadian perspectives* (pp. 21–38). Toronto: Canadian Scholars' Press.

Davey-Smith, G. (Ed.). *Inequalities in health: Life course perspectives.* Bristol: Policy Press.

Galabuzi, G.E. (2004). Social exclusion. In D. Raphael, (Ed.), *Social determinants of health: Canadian perspectives* (pp. 235–252). Toronto: Canadian Scholars' Press.

Galabuzi, G.E. (2006). *Canada's economic apartheid.* Toronto: Canadian Scholars' Press.

Hamelin, A.M., Beaudry, M., & Habicht, J.P. (2002). Characterization of household food insecurity in Quebec: Food and feelings. *Social Science and Medicine, 54*, 119–132.

Hamelin, A.M., Habicht, J.P., & Beaudry, M. (1999). Food insecurity: Consequences for the household and broader social implications. *Journal of Nutrition, 129*, 5175–5205.

Health Canada. (2003). *The health of Aboriginal women.* Ottawa: Health Canada.

Kirkpatrick, S. and Tarasuk, V. (2003). Income and household food expenditure in Canada. *Public Health Nutrition, 6*, 589–597.

Ledrou, I., & Gervais, J. (2005). Food insecurity. *Health Reports, 16*, 47–51.

McIntyre, L. (2004). Food insecurity. In D. Raphael (Ed.), *Social determinants of health: Canadian perspectives* (pp. 173–186). Toronto: Canadian Scholars' Press.

McIntyre, L., Connor, S.K., & Warren, J. (2000). Child hunger in Canada: Results of the 1994 National Longitudinal Survey of Children and Youth. *Canadian Medical Association Journal, 163*(8), 961–965.

McIntyre, L., Glanville, N.T., Officer, S., Anderson, B., Raine, K.D., & Dayle, J.B. (2002). Food insecurity of low-income lone mothers and their children in Atlantic Canada. *Canadian Journal of Public Health, 93*, 411–415.

McIntyre, L., Glanville, N.T., Raine, K.D., Dayle, J.B., Anderson, B., & Battaglia, N. (2003). Low-income lone mothers compromise their nutrition to feed their children. *Canadian Medical Association Journal, 168*, 686–691.

McIntyre, L., Walsh, G., & Connor, S.K. (2001). *A follow-up study of child hunger in Canada.* Ottawa: Human Resources Development Canada.

McLaughlin, C., Tarasuk, V., & Kreiger, N. (2003). An examination of at-home food preparation activity among low-income, food-insecure women. *Journal of the American Dietetic Association, 103*, 1506–1512.

National Council of Welfare. (2006a). *Poverty facts 2003.* Ottawa: National Council of Welfare.

National Council of Welfare. (2006b). *Poverty profile 2002 and 2003.* Ottawa: National Council of Welfare.

Olson, C.M. (1999). Nutrition and health outcomes associated with food insecurity and hunger. *Journal of Nutrition, 129*, 5215–5245.

Pederson, A., & Raphael, D. (2006). "Gender, race and health inequalities." In D. Raphael, T. Bryant, & M. Rioux (Eds.), *Staying alive: Critical perspectives on health, illness and health care* (pp. 159–192). Toronto: Canadian Scholars' Press.

Phipps, S. (2003). The impact of poverty on health: A scan of research literature. Canadian Institute for Health Information, Canadian Population Health Initiatives.

Phipps, S., & Lethbridge, L. (2006). *Income and the outcomes of children.* Ottawa: Statistics Canada, Analytical Studies, Research Paper Series (Statistics Canada Cat. no. 11F0019MIE, no. 281).

Rainville, B. & Brink, S. (2001). *Food insecurity in Canada, 1998–1999.* Ottawa: Applied Research Branch, Human Resources Development Canada.

Raphael, D. (2004). Introduction to the social determinants of health. In D. Raphael (Ed.), *Social determinants of health: Canadian perspectives* (pp. 1–18). Toronto: Canadian Scholars' Press.

Ross, N., Wolfson, M., Dunn, J., Berthelot, J.M., Kaplan, G., & Lynch, J. (2000). Relations between income inequality and mortality in Canada and in the United States: Cross sectional assessment using census data and vital statistics. *British Medical Journal*, 320, 898–902.

Shah, C.P. (2004). The health of Aboriginal peoples. In D. Raphael (Ed.), *Social determinants of health: Canadian perspectives* (pp. 267–280). Toronto: Canadian Scholars' Press.

Statistics Canada. (2004, November 16). Study: Disparities in birth outcomes by neighbourhood income in British Columbia, 1958 to 2000. *The Daily*, Nov. 16, 2004.

Statistics Canada. (2006, June 6). Study: Neighbourhood income, maternal education and birth outcomes in Quebec, 1991 to 2000. *The Daily*, June 6, 2006.

Tarasuk, V. (2001). Household food insecurity with hunger is associated with women's food intakes, health and household circumstances. *Journal of Nutrition, 131*, 2670–2676.

Tarasuk, V. (2004). Health implications of food insecurity. In D. Raphael (Ed.), *Social determinants of health: Canadian perspectives* (pp. 187–200). Toronto: Canadian Scholars' Press.

Tarasuk, V.S., & Beaton, G.H. (1999). Household food insecurity and hunger among families using food banks. *Canadian Journal of Public Health, 90*, 109–113.

Tarasuk, V.S., & Davis, B. (1996). Response to food insecurity in the changing Canadian welfare state. *Journal of Nutrition Education, 28*, 71–75.

United Nations Food and Agriculture Organization (FAO). (2002). *The state of food insecurity in the world.* Washington: FAO.

Vozoris, N., Davis, B., & Tarasuk, V. (2002). The affordability of a nutritious diet for households on welfare in Toronto. *Canadian Journal of Public Health, 93*, 36–40.

Vozoris, N., & Tarasuk, V.S. (2003). Household food insufficiency is associated with poorer health. *Journal of Nutrition, 133,* 120–126.

Wilkins, R., Berthelot, J.M., & Ng, E. (2000). Trends in mortality by neighbourhood income in urban Canada from 1970–1996. *Health Reports, 13,* 1–28.

Wilson, B., & Steinman, C. (2000). *Hunger count 2000. A surplus of hunger.* Toronto: Canadian Association of Food Banks.

Wilson, B. & Tsoa, E. (2002). *Hunger count 2002. Eating their words: Government failure on food security.* Canadian Association of Food Banks.

Yalnizyan, A. (1998). *The growing gap: A report on growing inequality between the rich and the poor in Canada.* Toronto: Centre for Social Justice.

Yalnizyan, A. (2000). *Canada's great divide: The politics of the growing gap between rich and poor in the 1990s.* Toronto: Centre for Social Justice.

10

Overcoming Hurdles: Health Care and Aboriginal People

JAMES S. FRIDERES University of Calgary

INTRODUCTION

Over the past century, colonization, globalization, domestic restructuring, and a belief in the ethos of privatization have combined to dramatically impact the way of life of Aboriginal people in Canada. Beginning with a philosophy of genocide guiding its relationship to First Nations, the Canadian state moved to assimilation and more recently a policy of integration in its dealings with Aboriginal people. However, the effects of colonialism have had major long-term impacts on the way of life of Aboriginal people. In addition, the smallpox, measles, and tuberculosis epidemics of the 19th and 20th centuries destroyed a large proportion of the Aboriginal population. Finally, the residential school system, racism, and reserve life have further contributed to the marginalization of Aboriginal peoples with respect to their integration into mainstream society (Stubben, 2006). This chapter will show how, over time, colonialism, medical, social, and economic policies adopted by Canada have penetrated Aboriginal institutional orders, specifically their traditional health care system and the health practices now provided to Aboriginals (Rodriguez-Pinero, 2005). The end result is that Aboriginal people now occupy the lowest ten percent of income category and have the lowest level of quality of life of all ethnic groups in Canada.

Social scientists have speculated for some time that the widening income inequalities among groups of people in Canada exacts a heavy social cost in terms of social exclusion, the eroding of civil society, and lower productivity. Scholars in the field of Aboriginal health have now turned their attention to the consequences of income inequality on the well-being of this minority population (Kawachi, Wilkinson & Kennedy, 1999; Newbold, 1998; Coburn, 2000). This developing body of empirical literature has demonstrated that economic inequality has real costs in the form of worsening health for Aboriginal people (Kennedy et al., 1998; Berkman & Kawachi, 2000; Cooke, Beavon & McHardy, 2004; Canadian Institute for Health Information, 2004). The next question is whether or not inequality still remains, and has it either decreased or increased? The data is clear that the gap has increased over the past three decades. In the 1960s, the top 20 percent of North American households made over $70,000 per year while the lowest 20 percent had an annual income of just over $7,000. Thirty years later, the top 20 percent had increased their annual income by 44 percent, whereas the bottom 20 percent had increased their income by seven percent. Forbes Magazine noted that of the world's top 200 working billionaires, their average worth increased over 100 percent ($2.2 billion to $4.7 billion) from 1995–2000, while a greater percentage of the North American population is now living below the poverty line.

Does it matter that the rich are getting richer and the poor are getting poorer? Put more bluntly, what are the health consequences of such a growing inequity? For some minority groups (e.g., Aboriginal people) their health levels have declined over the past quarter century. Others (Abella, 1984; Frideres & Gadacz, 2005) have noted that economic inequalities have spawned latent social conflict, declining support for public institutions, and increasing ethnic tensions. As such, the health of a people is a sensitive indicator of such inequalities, reflects the social and economic costs incurred by a society, and should be of concern of Canadians (Navarro & Muntaner, 2004). Certainly, Canada has improved its ability to increase its economic output, yet the real key is how the economic profits are divided among the people (e.g., the more unequal the distribution of economic rewards the lower the life expectancy of the people) (Coburn, 2000).

The most recent evidence from Canada indicates that neo-liberalism is associated with rapidly increasing inequality. It is not that inequalities did not exist before neo-liberal regimes (pre-1970 in Canada); it is simply that inequality has been exacerbated under nearly forty years of neo-liberalism. In Canada, with the decline of the welfare state and the concomitant rise of neo-liberal policies that oppose measures to redistribute income resources, inequality is increasing in Canada.

Neo-liberalism refers to the ideology that champions markets and the market economy. Its basic philosophy is that markets are the best, most effective, and most efficient manner by which resources in production and distribution are allocated. It also embodies the view expressed by Margaret Thatcher that there is no such thing as "society," only individuals and families. Thus, neo-liberals view society as a combination of autonomous individuals motivated by economic consideration that is at odds with a sociological perspective that views society as something more than the sum of the individual parts.

Finally, a central tenet of their philosophy is that competition is the only way in which innovation will occur. In the end, the neo-liberal extols the virtues of a market economy and argues there should be no state intervention in any economic activity. As such, they are not concerned about inequality and in fact argue that inequalities are "just" because they reflect the ratio of input to output (i.e., your rewards are proportional to what you invest). In Canada today, we see the ethos of neo-liberalism permeating all aspects of our lives, particularly in the area of health.

In the area of health, the "bio-medical model" (the belief that sickness is generated and located totally within an individual's body) supports this philosophy. The locus of cause tends to be focused on the individual. Thus, Canadians are encouraged to view health care and health risks in terms of the individual, rather than in the context of either society or of the actions taken by vested interest groups such as the Canadian Medical Association or multinational corporations (Bush et al., 1996). As Bolaria (1979) points out, this individual-centred conceptualization has led to a curative orientation, in which technical bio-medical solutions are offered to solve the individual's problems, and the social, economic, and political causes of ill health are ignored. He goes on to point out that this position obscures the extent to which health and illness depend on socially determined ways of life.

Recent research has shown that we must incorporate the social context into explanations about why some people stay healthy and others get sick. This perspective rejects the conceptualization that specific behaviours are within the realm of individual choice, and asserts, rather, that individual choice operates within a social context (Marmot & Wilkinson, 1999). The social behaviour exhibited by people is shaped by such factors as patterns of social control, norms and mores, facilitating or reducing opportunities to engage in specific behaviours, and presenting different coping strategies to deal with stress related activities.

SOCIAL DEMOGRAPHIC PROFILE OF ABORIGINAL PEOPLE

Just under a million people identified themselves as being of Aboriginal (First Nations/Indian, Metis, Inuit) origin. In the present chapter we will focus on one of those subgroups – First Nations. We will see that over the past quarter century, there has been a major increase in the number of Aboriginal people. Bill C-31 (1985) is one of the biggest reasons why there has been a major increase in the First Nations population over the past quarter century (it redefined who was an Aboriginal), although the increasing birth rate and concurrent decrease in the death rate have added to the unusually high population increase (see Table 10.1). These individuals reside in 600 First Nations communities that fall into approximately 50 different culturally and linguistically distinct groups across the country. Table 10.2 reveals the urbanization of Aboriginal people and their distribution in major urban centres throughout Canada.

There are many socio-demographic dimensions in which Aboriginal people differ from other Canadians. For example, Aboriginal children live in a very different family structure: fewer than half (41%) of Aboriginal families include married couples, compared with nearly three quarters of the general Canadian population. Over one third of Aboriginal families are common-law couples (compared with only 20 percent of the general Canadian population), and one quarter of the Aboriginal families are "lone parent" families, while 16 percent of other Canadian families are of this type. Aboriginal people have, on average, more children than do non-Aboriginals (3.2 compared with 1.57), and they show a high dependency ratio-65.8 vs. 47.4 for all Canadians.

The Aboriginal population is considered very young: nearly 40 percent of Aboriginal people (compared with 22 percent of non-Aboriginal) are under 15 years of age, and only three percent are over 65 (compared with nine percent of non-Aboriginal). The First Nations birth rate is 23 births per 1,000 population – twice the Canadian rate. First Nations girls age 15–19 have a birth rate five times higher than the national rate. Table 10.3 reveals some additional socio-demographic attributes of First Nations that distinguishes them from the general Canadian population.

Canadians have, for many years, chosen to employ strategies embedded in the principle of Jeremy Bentham's Panopticon – a building designed so that guards could watch prisoners but prisoners were unable to see the guards. The principle of such a building was that prisoners would know they were being watched and thus would always be on their best behaviour. In the end, they would internalize their "model" behaviour and strive to act and think as the dominant society dictated. The Panopticon model underlies Canada's assumptions and conceptualization of its relationship to Aboriginal people – unidirectional, hierarchical, and controlling. It is the belief that coercive control directed toward Aboriginal peoples will eventually result in them losing their Aboriginal characteristics and assimilating into Canadian society. Under Panopticon principles, the central objective in creating a special Department (e.g., Indian and Northern Affairs Canada) to deal with Aboriginal people, has always been to maintain close control over them in all aspects of their lives.

TABLE 10.1 *Total Canadian Aboriginal Population by Province and by Aboriginal Group, 2001*[a]

Province	Aboriginal	North American Indian	Metis	Inuit
Canada	976,305	608,850	292,305	45,070
Nfld & Lab.	18,775	7,040	5,480	4,560
PEI	1,345	1,035	220	20
N.S.	17,010	12,920	3,135	350
N.B.	16,990	11,495	4,290	155
Quebec	79,400	51,125	15,855	9,530
Ontario	188,315	131,560	48,340	1,375
Manitoba	150,045	90,340	56,800	340
Saskatchewan	130,185	83,745	43,695	235
Alberta	156,225	84,995	66,060	1,090
British Columbia	170,025	118,295	44,265	800
Yukon	6,540	5,600	535	140
NWT	18,730	10,615	3,580	3,910
Nunavut	22,720	95	55	22,560

[a] The Aboriginal identity population comprises those individuals who reported identifying with at least one Aboriginal group – Indian, Metis, or Inuit.

Source: Adapted from 2001 Census; Siggner and Costa, 2005; Frideres and Gadacz, 2005; Indian Affairs and Northern Development, Basic Departmental Data, 2002.

TABLE 10.2 *Aboriginal Population in Selected Metropolitan Areas, 2001*

City	Population	Percentage	Growth Rate % (1981–2001)
Victoria	6,570	2.2	NA
Vancouver	36,140	1.7	140
Calgary	21,915	1.9	213
Edmonton	40,925	3.8	205
Saskatoon	20,260	7.5	382
Regina	15,685	6.9	145
Winnipeg	55,750	6.9	247
Ottawa/Hull	13,487	1.2	238
Thunder Bay	8,205	2.6	172
Sudbury	7,385	4.6	245
Toronto	20,300	1.1	56
Montreal	11,085	1.6	42
All Canada	976,305	3.9	105

Source: Siggner and Costa, 2005; Statistics Canada, 2001 Census; Frideres and Gadacz, 2005.

TABLE 10.3 *Selected Socio-Demographic Attributes of First Nations People, 1981 and 2001*

	1981	2001
Life Expectancy (years)		
First Nations	65.7	72.9
Canadian	75.6	78.7
Deaths by Suicide (per 100,000)		
First Nations	26.5	28
Canadian	14.5	13
Self Rated Health Status (excellent %)		
First Nations	NA	40
Canadian	NA	61
Proportion completed High School		
First Nations	0.33	0.57
Canadian	0.60	0.75
Unemployment Rate		
First Nations	26.4	22.0
Canadian	11.2	7.0
Average Annual Income [(a)]		
First Nations	6,840	10,094
Canadian	16,554	22,489

[(a)] Constant 2000 dollars (This means that inflation is accounted for so one can compare the 1981 and 2001 figures as controlling for the year. Both sets of data have been standardized to the value of a dollar in 2000.)

Source: Statistics Canada, 1984; Nault et al., 1993; Verma, et al., 2003; Cooke, Beavon, and McHardy, 2004; Statistics Canada, 2003; Canadian Population Health Initiative, 2004.

FIGURE 10.1
Total Federal Expenditures and Source for Indian Affairs, 2004–05

Note: "Other" consists of National Defense, Justice Canada, Natural Resources Canada, Correctional Services of Canada, Canadian Heritage, Industry Canada, Fisheries and Oceans Canada, Indian Residential Schools Resolution Canada, and Public Safety and Emergency Preparedness.

Source: Canada, Government of, 2006. 2005–2006 Estimates, Part II., The Government Expense Plans and the Main Estimates, Ottawa, Canadian Government Publisher, Section 17.

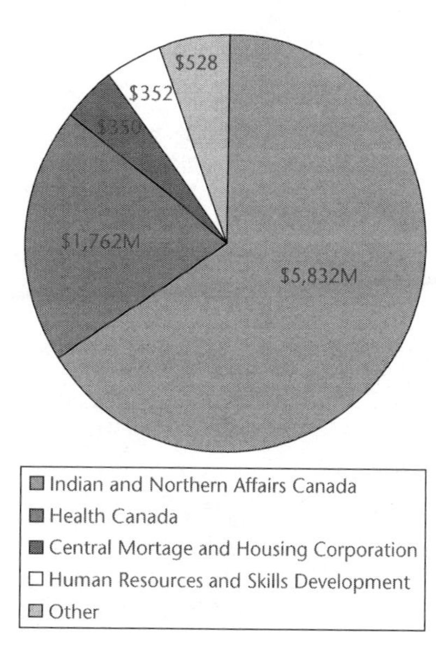

TRADITIONAL ABORIGINAL HEALTH CARE

The practice of medicine among Aboriginal people has always been closely linked to their world view. The traditional aboriginal understanding of the body was that it was a vessel where the human and non-human realms overlap. While early Indian medicine was not based on anatomy and physiology, it was based on practical knowledge that had been acquired on an empirical basis. Medicine men/women accumulated an extensive knowledge of plants and herbs for both internal and external use for such effects as analgesia, circulatory stimulation, diuresis, and laxative effects. They knew about vitamins (e.g., vitamin C and D) and their effects on the health of an individual long before Western society attained this information. While the dispensation of medicine was permeated with rules and rituals to ensure the collective health of the community, medicine men/women could recognize and immobilize a fractured bone and had effective methods of handling hemorrhages and other major illnesses. In short, these individuals had a genuine body of useful practical knowledge with regard to disease and illness (Whitaker, 2006).

Bodies, from an Aboriginal perspective, were affected both individually and collectively by activities in both the human and spiritual realms (Helm, 1998). Aboriginal people traditionally identified three kinds of illness: visible injuries that were a result of physical causes, such as bone fractures and lacerations; diseases caused by some invisible external event, confirmed indirectly by the behaviour of the sick person (e.g., smallpox, influenza, or cancer); and a residual category, which included mental illness (Harter et al., 2004). Moreover, the distinction between these illnesses was blurred.

Traditional health care, as practiced by Aboriginal societies, was not only a way of dealing with private troubles and uncertainties but also an integral part of social relationships and cultural patterns of belief. It involved both a practitioner and a patient within a community and the actions taken by the medical practitioner reinforced the existing social order as well as "cured" the patient (Assembly of First Nations, 1994; Lajeunesse, 1993). Like other systems, it aimed at producing a healthy person who could work and produce goods for domestic consumption and enhance the viability of the community.

At the outset of his or her curative regimen, the traditional Aboriginal health care practitioner generally applied routine medicines and practiced the rituals associated with them. The assumption was that there was some metaphysical basis for the illness and that the rituals and medicines would have a curative power to treat a variety of illnesses. However, if the illness did not pass, more powerful shamanistic methods – prayers and chants – would be employed (Sealy & McDonald, no date). Because Aboriginal people viewed illness as a result of some foreign object or spirit having entered the space surrounding an individual, the task of the medicine man/woman, or **shaman**, was to remove the foreign object or spirit.

Aboriginal healing circles and the medicine wheel reflect the world and the events taking place as a circle – a view different from the Euro-Canadian view of order, which is hierarchical and uni-directional. In the Aboriginal circle perspective, the community is interconnected, consisting of the land, the people, and the non-physical world. A central value of Aboriginal culture is to live life to its fullest, not only for oneself but also for one's family and community. In short, a balance between all aspects of the physical and spiritual world is necessary if healing is to take place (Sanguins, 2005).

Throughout the 19th century and well into the 20th century, traditional Aboriginal health care activities were increasingly discouraged and discontinued as various government agencies declared them inappropriate or even sometimes illegal. The major problem confronting Aboriginal people was the precipitous intrusion of white society into their way of life; high rates of neurosis and alcoholism resulted as they attempted to deal with the rapid changes imposed upon them.

In general, the Aboriginal belief systems define health as "living in balance" with other systems of which the individual is a part. As such, a health care system must be holistic, flexible, and responsive to the individual, the community, and the disease/illness. Thus, for Aboriginals, all aspects of life must be lived in "balance and respect" in order to achieve wellness. Health is holistic because it integrates and gives equal emphasis to the physical, spiritual, mental, and emotional aspects of the person (Royal Commission on Aboriginal Peoples Report, 1996). However, with the rapid social change impacting First Nations' communities, these beliefs and values became increasingly difficult to practice.

HEALTH CARE POLICY: WHO IS RESPONSIBLE?

Meilicke and Storch (1980) point out that prior to Confederation there was little government involvement in health care issues. The government's position was that the health and social needs of Canadians were family concerns and were to be dealt with by families and voluntary or religious organizations. Few actions were taken by the provincial or federal governments to prevent the spread of smallpox, typhus, and other diseases that frequently decimated the Aboriginal population (Heagerty, 1934), unless such an epidemic threatened the local non-Aboriginal population (Hasting & Mosley, 1964).

Beginning in 1905, the federal government created the office of the General Medical Superintendent in the Department of Indian Affairs, and a mobile nurse visitor program in 1922. Until 1945, the Department of Indian Affairs was the sole provider of medical health care services to Aboriginals on reserves. In that year, these services were transferred to the Department of Health and Welfare, where they have remained. In 1962, Indian Health Services (a division of Health and Welfare) was merged with six other federal health programs to form the Medical Services Branch.

The current national health care system was established in 1970, and it is a publicly financed and administered system that is managed by the provinces under the umbrella of the *Canada Health Act*. Under this legislation, primary, secondary, and tertiary health care can be accessed at no cost to the individual Canadian. At the same time, on-reserve primary health services complement this system but are separately funded by the federal government. However, First Nations patients requiring either secondary or tertiary care must go to a provincial service centre for which the province may receive remuneration by the federal government for services rendered.

In 1986, Health and Welfare (Medical Services Branch) announced a new policy initiative: the Indian Health Transfer Policy. This new policy was created to facilitate a developmental approach to health care and services to Aboriginal communities, and was centred on the concept of self-government. It was hoped that it would lead to First Nations autonomy and community control of health care services (Speck, 1989).

The transfer policy in health care is a continuation of the "devolution policy" developed by Indian and Northern Affairs Canada a decade earlier, in that it proposes that a larger share of the responsibility for Aboriginal people now allocated to the federal government be taken on by First Nations.

The Medical Services Branch's transfer policy (enacted in 1989) reflects an agreement between the two levels of government on the best way to deal with the health inequalities existing between Aboriginal peoples and the rest of Canada. It builds on the 1979 Indian Health Policy that recognized three pillars: community development, the traditional relationship of the Indian people to the federal government, and the Canadian health system. In 2000, the division of Medical Services dealing with Aboriginal people was renamed the First Nations and Inuit Health Branch.

Of the twenty-seven programs and services under the Medical Service Health Branch programs, fourteen are targeted and NOT transferable to First Nations Communities (e.g., tobacco control initiative, Head Start, HIV/AIDS, and dental/oral health). Of the programs/services transferable, over 80 percent of First Nations communities are now managing some of these programs/services. Evaluations of these transfers by the federal government took place throughout the 90s, and although the evaluations were positive, a moratorium on further transfers was announced in 2005. Today, the First Nations and Inuit Health Branch support the delivery of public health services on reserves and in Inuit communities. It also provides drug, dental, and ancillary health services to First Nations and Inuit people regardless of residence. The Branch also provides primary care services on reserves in remote and isolated areas where there are no provincial services available. Throughout Canada, six major programs are carried out by the Branch ranging from non-insured health benefits to nursing services to community medicine.

The federal government argues that the current community health services to First Nations and Inuit are provided as a matter of policy and NOT legislative or treaty responsibility. There are some exceptions, such as the references to the provision of a "Medicine chest" in Treaty Six. In this **treaty**, the Cree of Alberta were able to force the government to add a provision that would ensure that their medical needs would be the responsibility of the crown. However, in general, the Government of Canada argues there is no constitutional obligation or treaty that requires the Canadian government to offer health programs or services to Aboriginal peoples. As a result, the federal government limits its responsibility to being the "payer of last resort." A 1974 ministerial policy statement describes federal responsibility for Aboriginal health issues as voluntary and aimed at ensuring the availability of services by providing it directly where normal services are not available.

First Nations disagree and claim that the *Royal Proclamation of 1763* and the subsequent *British North America Act, 1867* established federal responsibility for health care for First Nations. They link federal health programs to statutory or treaty obligations (AFN, 2002; Ahenakew & Sanderson, 2001). These differences were most clearly articulated in the final report of the *Royal Commission on Aboriginal People*. Disputes between First Nations and the federal government over health issues revolve around three components: the definitions of health; the difference in the way health policy is implemented for Aboriginal people; and the funding of First Nations health services, including the statutory, constitutional, and fiduciary obligations of the federal government regarding the provision of health services to Aboriginal people (Speck, 1989).

Today, Health Canada acknowledges that the government, private/non-profit organizations, and non-government organizations are the three main sectors in the delivery of health care services. Recently, however, a fourth sector, the First Nations primary health care services, has emerged. It is funded with public money to provide services to an Indigenous constituency and is involved in the delivery of non-commercial social services. This new "level" of delivery is tied to an Indigenous governance structure designed by First Nations communities, and reflects the federal government's commitment to devolve their responsibility. This new level of health care services reflects a need to be responsive to local First Nations communities, provides increased opportunities for employment, and reflects local cultural expression. In addition, it is argued that this new mechanism will improve Aboriginal participation in health care, increase access, and reduce inequities (Lavoie, 2004).

There is considerable tension between the two parties with regard to this transfer. Speck (1989) points out that First Nations people are denied self-determination, which in turn denies them the opportunity to create conditions whereby Aboriginal health could be improved. For example, she notes that the federal government continues to administer health services as an isolated "thing" that is separate from the political, social, and economic dimensions of life – a fact that Aboriginal people and others have consistently identified as one of the major problems in Aboriginal health care.

The transfer of health and health care responsibilities for Aboriginal communities has spawned a fear that the end result will be the gradual withdrawal of the federal government in supporting the delivery of health to Aboriginal people. Others argue that new emerging needs are not being considered under the transfer agreements (e.g., HIV/AIDS and diabetes) and thus these will be unfunded in the future. The Auditor General of Canada has noted that the transfer of responsibilities to Aboriginal communities makes them not directly accountable to Parliament for how the funds are used. However, the *Accountability Act* recently introduced (2006) in the House of Commons would make Aboriginal communities more accountable in their use of funds.

PROGRAMS AND THE PROVISION OF MEDICAL SERVICES

The federal government has assumed jurisdiction over the health of Aboriginal people throughout Canada. Although the *Indian Act* says little about specifics (see section 73[1]), and its main focus is on preventing the spread of infectious diseases, there remains strong financial commitment to Aboriginal health care through a variety of programs (Woodward, 2005).

A large proportion of First Nations and Inuit Health funding ($1.3 billion) is provided to individuals through the non-insured health benefits program that acts as a kind of insurance plan. Figure 10.2 shows the distribution of funds from this branch toward non-insured health benefits and the changes that have taken place in the last decade.

In addition to federal programs, Aboriginal people have to rely upon hospital and medical care available in their home province as other Canadians do. However, the federal government does not compensate provincial health care services unless special agreements have been signed between the two parties. In addition, as noted previously, Aboriginal organizations may receive funding for health services.

FIGURE 10.2

Non-Insured Health Benefits for Aboriginal Peoples, 1991/92 and 2000/01

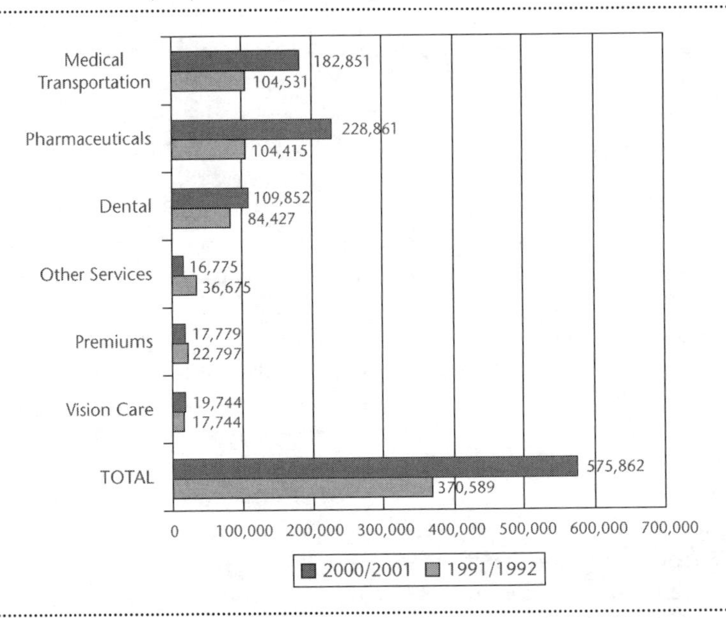

Source: Adapted from First Nations and Inuit Control, Annual Report, 2001–02 (http://www.hc-sc.gc.ca/fnihb-dgspni/fnihb/bpm/hfa/fnic_annual_report_2001_2002.htm).

The overall structure for providing medical and health services to Aboriginal people is complex and involves multiple jurisdictions. At the national level, several government agencies interact to set policies, determine programs, and establish funding levels. They include the deputy minister of health and welfare, director general, policy and evaluation, the treasury board, and the directors of Indian/**Inuit** policy, planning, and evaluation. At the provincial level, the regional director oversees the implementation of the programs for each health zone, which involves doctors, nurses, and environmental health officers. In addition, provincial authorities provide health services for which Aboriginal people may be recipients. At the local level, for those bands involved in health care delivery, band councils make decisions regarding training programs and determine who will be admitted to various health programs (Frideres & Gadacz, 2005). In the end, there is considerable difficulty in coordinating the provision of services. Finally, the fragmentation and short term funding does not allow for efficient cost outlays or the continuation of programs.

DOMINANT CULTURE VIEWS ON ABORIGINAL HEALTH AND ILLNESS

Over the years, the practitioners of modern Western medicine have ridiculed traditional Aboriginal health care practices. Non-Aboriginal people, unfamiliar with the substances and methods used in Aboriginal medicine, saw its practices as primitive, irrational, and ignorant. From their ethnocentric and racist perspective, the use of medicine men/women or shamans was evidence of paganism and heathenism; they persistently argued that shamans were evil and that Christian prayers were more efficacious in curing illness (Sealy & McDonald, no date). These moral entrepreneurs, who carried out their destruction of Aboriginal health care practices with relentless zeal, were aided by the government's willingness to accept the medical profession's definition of what was appropriate and acceptable in health care methods. To secure the primacy of this definition, laws were introduced that would ensure that traditional Aboriginal ways would be phased out and new Western ways legitimized. As a result, the Western bio-medical model became the dominant model and many traditional medicinal practices and products were forced underground or lost. As Rowe (2006) points out, Aboriginal identity is positively related to level of health.

Although Aboriginal people may utilize the dominant society's medical system, their traditional health care provides them with a sense of security not obtainable through Western practices. Thus, they tend to retain and utilize some of the traditional approaches, under specific conditions, along with more modern health care practices. On many reserves today, we find that traditional health care remains viable, if not universally used. To the extent that Aboriginal people are isolated and **institutionally complete** on the reserve, the use of such traditional techniques is reinforced (Sivell-Ferri, 1997).

MODERN MEDICINE: UNDERLYING ASSUMPTIONS

For modern medicine to be effective, a number of assumptions must be made. For example, if an individual is ill, the assumption is that treatment will be sought as soon as the symptoms appear. Moreover, it is assumed that if medicines are prescribed, the individual will purchase them, carry out the medicinal regime, and stop behaviours that counter the prescribed medicine. While this model may be a workable one for middle-class families, it is not always successful for those who are poor or have different cultural values. The resurgence of tuberculosis and the high rate of diabetes in Aboriginal communities are perhaps the best modern examples of how modern medical assumptions are not always workable. To provide an individual with a prescription and a set of instructions as to how to use the medicine does not necessarily mean that the individual is able to purchase the medicine, take the dosage in the manner instructed, or change his or her lifestyle (e.g., eat regular meals, eat meals that reflect proper nutritional standards, or have funds to maintain proper housing). On many reserves, less than 50 percent of the population has easy access to an automobile, and this has major implications for health care and provision.

The basic assumptions upon which Canadian medical thinking, and hence the health care system, rest are the acceptance of germ theory, the dominance of the individual as the locus of cause, and the ability of people to diagnose and take steps to cure an illness. These assumptions presuppose that health is solely the concern of the individual. Most Canadians accept the first condition with little reservation; the second also does not seem to be problematic for many people. However, certain sectors of the population, for example, Aboriginal people, do not accept the second assumption and find the third difficult to implement. Obviously, those who reject or are unable to accept or implement all these assumptions (and have no access to alternative health services) are at a distinct disadvantage in maintaining good health and a high quality of life.

INFLUENCES ON HEALTH STATUS

The health of an individual is influenced by four factors: lifestyle, environment, the organizational structures of health care, and biological (genetic) makeup (LaFramboise, 1980). Lifestyle consists of decisions made by an individual that have an impact on overall health, for example, his or her use of alcohol and tobacco, occupation, and physical fitness. There is a tendency to define this component only in terms of "voluntary" decisions. However, many of these seemingly voluntary decisions are actually involuntary or at least severely circumscribed. For example, smoking is a means to reduce hunger pangs, unskilled labourers are forced to take jobs with a high risk of accidents, and one's financial resources may determine the nutritional value of one's diet.

The environmental element is the individual's physical and social environment, which includes factors such as air quality, potable water, place of residence, and housing. Health care organization refers to the quality, arrangement, nature, and relationships of people and resources within society to its health care services. This component, usually referred to as the "health care delivery system," includes such elements as medical practices, hospitals and extended care facilities, and the use of antibiotics and other drugs. The final component – biological makeup – refers to the individual's physical and genetic makeup. There is a tendency to view this component as a constant and to consider all people as biologically the same, although there are some known biological predispositions for specific human groups (e.g., sickle-cell anemia among Black people of West African descent).

Health problems experienced by the individual are, theoretically, the result of a "crack" in any one of the above four components. However, each of these components can contribute differently to illness among different groups of people. Moreover, as noted earlier, there is a tendency to assume that all Canadians have access to the same health care system, have the same biological makeup, and operate within a similar environment. Thus, there is a tendency for researchers to focus on the individual's lifestyle as determining the quality of health, since it is considered the only variable in the formula (Wirick, 1966).

In other words, politicians, health care practitioners, and the employment system view the Canadian population as homogeneous. There is a continued insistence that one health care model (the individual bio-medical curative model) is correct and that no others should be recognized. Policies and programs established by the government reflect this fundamental bias. However, it is clear that many social classes and cultural groups outside the mainstream have fundamental problems in adapting to the health care model propounded by the medical profession. Aboriginal people do not have equal access to health services (e.g., hospitals) nor do they live in a physical environment comparable to other Canadians. Recent assessments show that two thirds of First Nations communities do not have safe drinking water. Others cannot eat fish from their nearby lakes because of mercury or PCB contamination. Clearly, external factors very much influence the health of an Aboriginal individual. Thus, even though there are 800 Aboriginal nurses and 67 Aboriginal doctors (less than one percent of the health care providers in Canada), they are required to carry out Western bio-medical medicine when working on First Nations communities.

ABORIGINAL PEOPLE: A HEALTH STATUS REPORT

Many of the statistics about disease and illness among Aboriginal people have been published and are well known. Diseases of poverty, overcrowding, and poor housing have led to chronic and acute respiratory diseases that take a heavy toll among Aboriginal people. The standardized death rate for the Aboriginal population is similar to that of the general Canadian population – 6.6 deaths per 1,000 population (Nuttall, 1982; Tjepkema, 2002; Canada, 1997; Health Canada, 2003). However, these figures mask the fact that the majority of deaths for First Nations occur at younger ages, but at older ages for other Canadians.

The overall trend in Aboriginal mortality shows that it has improved substantially over the past two decades. However, there is still a considerable gap between Aboriginals and the general Canadian population. Although the overall death rate among Aboriginal people has decreased by nearly one third since 1978, it is still about 1.5 times the national rate. Life expectancy at birth for Aboriginal people continues to improve each year, yet the gap between Aboriginal people and the general Canadian population is still more than six years. One of the major factors contributing to the increase in the life expectancy of Aboriginal people is the declining infant mortality rate. Over the past two decades, the rate has decreased by more than 50 percent, from a high of 24 per 1,000 in 1980 to less than 10 per 1,000 in 2001; but Aboriginal infant mortality rate is still twice as high as the overall Canadian rate.

Research has shown that young Aboriginals are more often exposed to problems such as alcohol and drug abuse, pervasive poverty, persistent racism, and a legacy of colonialism; they are caught in a cycle that has been perpetuated across generations (Romanow, 2002). What are the specific causes of death among Aboriginal people? For the past decade, over one third of all Aboriginal deaths (compared to eight percent in the general population) are due to accidents and violence. For all age groups up to 63, Aboriginal people are four times as likely as non-Aboriginals to die from these causes.

Table 10.4 reveals the leading causes of death for Aboriginal people by age group. While the two major causes (injury and poisoning, and the circulatory system) have shown dramatic decreases over the past two decades, the data also show that the third leading cause, neoplasm (cancers) is on the increase. Another health problem facing Aboriginal people is the resurgence of tuberculosis. From a high of 84 cases per 100,000 population in 1980, the incidence steadily decreased into the 1990s. By 1994, the incidence of tuberculosis was at an all-time low at 46 cases per 100,000 population for Aboriginal people. However, in recent times, the rate has dramatically increased, and today the rate stands at 62.1 cases per 100,000 population, seven times the national rate (Health Canada, 2003). To fully appreciate this level, consider that today, Africa has a rate of 80.0. Nevertheless, the data in Table 10.4 reveal the stability of these statistics for Aboriginal people over time. As such, it is clear that government efforts to deal with the causes have not been successful.

Other health issues facing Aboriginal people include diseases previously unknown to them. For example, prior to 1950, diabetes was practically unknown in the Aboriginal

TABLE 10.4 *Leading Causes of Death in First Nations, by Age Group, 1999*

Age Group	Cause of Death	Percentage
1–9	Fire and Flames	26%
	Motor Vehicle Accidents	24%
	Other Injuries	24%
	Other	26%
	Total Number of Deaths = 34	
10–19	Suicides and Self-Inflicted Injury	38%
	Motor Vehicle Accidents	30%
	Drowning and Submersion	10%
	Other	23%
	Total Number of Deaths = 80	
20–44	Suicides and Self-Inflicted Injury	23%
	Motor Vehicle and Traffic Accidents	15%
	Homicide	7%
	Accidental Poisoning by Drugs	6%
	Drowning and Submersion	5%
	Other	43%
	Total Number of Deaths = 367	
45–64	Ischemic Heart Disease	17%
	Lung Cancer	6%
	Motor Vehicle and Traffic Accidents	5%
	Diabetes	4%
	Liver Disease and Cirrhosis	4%
	Other	64%
	Total Number of Deaths = 390	
65+	Ischemic Heart Disease	20%
	Other Forms of Heart Disease	9%
	Cerebrovascular Disease	7%
	Lung Cancer	7%
	Pneumonia and Influenza	6%
	Other	50%
	Total Number of Deaths = 575	

Source: Adapted from First Nations and Inuit Control, Annual Report, 2001–2002 (http://www.hc-sc.gc.ca/fnihb-dgspni/fnihb/bpm/hfa/fnic_annual_report_2001_2002.htm).

population; today, its incidence is two to five times higher than for the non-Aboriginal population. Today, we find that for those individuals over 60, nearly one quarter of the Aboriginal population has diabetes (compared to about 11 percent of the general Canadian population). Younger Aboriginal people are also being diagnosed with high rates of diabetes. Health officials in British Columbia report increases of 50–100 percent between 1992 and 1999. AIDS has also become a major health issue for Aboriginal people, and its incidence is reported to be five times the national level. Today, the proportion of AIDS cases among Aboriginal persons has climbed from one percent of all cases before 1990 to over ten percent by 2003.

In present-day Aboriginal communities, compared with the rest of the Canadian population, suicide and self-inflicted injuries are three times higher (six times higher for the 15–24 age groups), homicide rates are twice as high, congenital anomalies are one and a half times higher, and pneumonia is over three times higher. Aboriginal people have five times the rate of child welfare, four times the death rate, three times the number of violent deaths, four times the suicide rate, and twice the rate of hospital admissions of Canada's non-Aboriginal population. Aboriginal people are also exposed to severe environmental hazards: industrial and resource development have polluted water, and disrupted fish and game stock for many reserve communities, seriously affecting their quality of life.

Considerable effort and funds have been allocated to deal with Aboriginal medical services. However, the social environmental issues that are linked to health have not been attended to. For example, when mercury contaminates a river or lake that Aboriginal people use as a daily food source, community members who eat the fish will become ill and suffer the consequences, both in the short and the long term. On the other hand, if they do not eat the fish, they must look for an alternative source of food. Either course of action will cause health, social, and economic disruption in the community, which in turn has indirect impacts upon the community and its residents.

In summary, the quality of life experienced by Aboriginal people is far inferior to that of non-Aboriginals. During the past century, the federal and provincial governments have been funding Aboriginal health care programs. However, given their lack of success to date, it is unlikely that simply increasing the Aboriginal health budget will resolve these problems. Even if the health care budget for Aboriginal people were substantially increased, it would not be sufficient to remove health differences. Improving the health of Canadian Aboriginals will depend on improving their social and economic situation.

ETIOLOGY IN SOCIETY

Definitions of disease and illness or health have a social as well as pathological component. The physical condition of an individual must be defined as one of illness before the individual can perceive that she or he is ill (Berliner, 1977). If the group, neighbourhood, or community defines the condition as an illness, then certain steps are taken to correct the condition. On the other hand, if the condition is not so defined by the individual's reference group, it would be inappropriate for the individual to assume a sick role and the individual would not seek treatment (Kane, Kasteler & Gray, 1976). Thus, the definition of illness in a community will determine the norm of health or state of health considered normal for its members. An Aboriginal individual living in an Aboriginal community thus interprets his or her own health status, as do others in the community. What constitutes illness or sickness will be determined by the definition of the group and the group's reaction to people who exhibit certain symptoms or behaviour. As Kane, Kasteler, and Gray (1976), among others, argue, the Aboriginal definition of reality means living with other Aboriginal people who share the same perspective, values, and beliefs, which are passed from one generation to the next (Frideres, 1998).

At the same time, professional health care practitioners reflect middle-class, white values with regard to health and health care. Any patient not sharing their values is at a distinct disadvantage. Health care practitioners do not understand the attitudes and lifestyles of patients from the lower class or from a different culture. Health care professionals, socialized in a middle-class milieu to accept Western bio-medical care, are ill-prepared to deal with patients whose behaviour does not conform to middle-class values (National Aboriginal Health Organization, 2001). They assume that Aboriginal patients share their perspective on illness and health care, and that they have the same resources (or access to the same resources) as the middle-class patient or the medical professional. In reality, however, Aboriginal people are generally poor and can manage only the barest of material necessities: heat, food, and clothing. Thus, their desires are for subsistence goods (e.g., food and housing) in order for them and their children to stay alive. The day-to-day experience of medical practitioners clearly reinforces the notion that Aboriginal patients do not follow their orders and heal themselves. As a result, Aboriginal people are stereotyped as irresponsible, dirty, and incapable of carrying out orders or taking responsibility for themselves. Negative attitudes are expressed more or less openly, making encounters with health care providers unpleasant for Aboriginal people. Every time they return to the health care facility, they must undergo this experience. The alternative and common Aboriginal strategy is to avoid the unpleasant situation by not returning to the practitioner or facility.

Aboriginal people prefer to deal with others from a more holistic, inter-connective perspective – being cognizant of all the dimensions of an individual with whom they are interacting. In the health care system of the dominant society, there is an elaborate division of labour: nurses are interested only in one aspect of the patient, the X-ray technician in another, the orthopedic surgeon in still another. Aboriginal people find this a foreign experience that is both confusing and frustrating (Suchman, 1963). They also perceive the rational, objective, and unemotional manner of health care professionals, inculcated in medical school, not as the mark of a good professional but rather as the mark of a cold, heartless person, unsympathetic to the patient (Knowlton, 1971; Dutton, 1986).

Finally, another barrier to change in Aboriginal health is jurisdiction. The long-standing arguments between the federal and provincial governments have created two jurisdictional issues: 1) The argument by the provinces that the federal government has sole responsibility for the health care services to First Nations people as defined under the *Indian Act*, and 2) what are the health rights held by different groups of Aboriginal people created by the *Indian Act*. Provincial governments disallow First Nations access to certain health programs not covered under the Canada Health Act. At the same time, the federal government also disallows certain Aboriginal groups (e.g., Metis, off-reserve First Nations, and urban Inuit) from certain federal health services.

CONCLUSION

The successful adaptation of Aboriginal people to the dominant society requires the denial, or at least the repression, of traditional models of health care in favour of those of the dominant society. In this process, there is a fundamental inequity and dehumanization (Weidman, 1980). The dominant group has taken the position that its patterns of behaviour and institutions are not only the best but also morally superior to others. Behaviours that do not match the dominant group norms are viewed as undesirable. As a result, while Aboriginal people publicly utilize the dominant society's medical service, it is not uncommon for individuals to seek help simultaneously from the traditional health care system. Although Aboriginal people use the dominant health care systems, they continue to regard their own understanding of the natural world as antecedent and superior knowledge (Press, 1978). Unfortunately, modern orthodox practitioners ignore the existence of a traditional health care culture in Aboriginal communities. They are not trained to be aware of it, nor do they have any ability to evaluate it; they deny its existence, or if they acknowledge it, discount its significance to the medical world or to those people using it.

The dominant society, particularly its health care practitioners, dismiss medicine men or women and shamanism among Aboriginal people as meaningless, even though many prescribed modern medicines are pharmacologically inert (Sealy & McDonald, no date). Despite this, the dominant medical profession still relies upon these medicines and – perhaps more startling – the patients using them get well. This suggests that medicine is not just a function of its pharmacological ingredients, but also of suggestion and social support.

Although health services tend to be concentrated in urban areas, many Aboriginal people live in rural areas. When health professionals enter the rural areas, the "drop-in" mentality resulting from occasional visits is seldom conducive to delivery of adequate service. Medical specialists have little understanding of Aboriginal culture, and language also poses a barrier to communication. When Aboriginal people must travel to distant urban centres to obtain health services, disruptions are even more acute.

Most service and delivery systems are centralized and insensitive to input from local communities, operating on the assumption that Aboriginal patients are passive recipients who should have little or no say in what services are offered, by whom, or where. Even though the First Nations Inuit Health Branch was created, the bureaucracy of Health Canada shows that policies emanate from Ottawa and are then implemented by regional administrators and on-site health care workers. There are few ways in which the bureaucracy can be responsive to local concerns or medical issues. In addition, professional autonomy in medical issues at the local level inhibits the involvement of Aboriginal clients (National Aboriginal Health organization, 2003). Those services that are offered undermine Aboriginal culture by explicitly or implicitly providing incentives for Aboriginal people to abandon their heritage and be assimilated into the larger, non-Aboriginal society. The dominant society perpetuates this situation despite the obvious fact that one of the most effective ways of improving a people's health lies in individual and community maintenance. This is more important than having more doctors per capita or increasing the number of hospitals. An individual's quality of life is highest when she or he functions at a high level, is free from morbidity or impairment, and when his or her vitality and emotional health are high (Lerner, 1973). Rather than denigrating traditional medicine, the dominant society should spend more time learning about Aboriginal health care and how to utilize and integrate it with modern health care practices.

The effectiveness of the entire health care system is related as much to the environmental conditions of Aboriginal communities as to the treatment and facilities provided. Too often, the need for care is engendered by problems associated with overcrowded living conditions leading to contagion and infection, by generally poor nutrition associated with chronic unemployment, by family and community violence, and by the re-emergence of medical problems after effective treatment, when the patient returns to the conditions from which the problems arose. Nevertheless, the Medical Services

Branch treats the symptoms, and little is done to address the basic causes of poor health conditions in areas of housing, economic development, employment opportunities, and sanitation – all of which lie within the mandate of Indian and Northern Affairs Canada (Canada, 1985).

As we move into the 21st century, we are increasingly directing our attention to preventative health care activities. For example, stop-smoking programs are based on the belief that preventing tobacco use will result in a better quality of life, and advocates of physical exercise promote exercise for the same reasons. Thus, governments are investing in "health promotion" activities that are based on the belief that not only will the health of individuals be better in later life but also that this will, in turn, be economically beneficial to society. Unfortunately, this conceptualization is not being applied to Aboriginal communities. Although the federal government spends more than $10 billion annually to deal with the "Indian problem," little has been done to promote the health of Aboriginals. Almost all programs are reactive and attempt to solve a health or health-related problem.

Over the past quarter century, Aboriginal people have experienced a more positive quality of life, particularly in the area of health. However, in comparison with the general Canadian population, they do not exhibit the same profile. A major gap persists that reflects the poverty in which most Aboriginal people live. Until a more integrated approach is taken to dealing with the problems faced by Aboriginal people, there is no reason to anticipate a great change in their quality of life.

STUDY QUESTIONS

1. *How have historical actions precipitated today's crisis in Aboriginal health care?*
2. *What are the health conditions of Aboriginal people compared with those of non-Aboriginals?*
3. *What are some of the reasons for Aboriginal people not using modern health practices?*
4. *Why has the current health care system failed Aboriginal people?*
5. *How is modern health care similar to the traditional health care practices of Aboriginal people?*
6. *Why should Canadian health care professionals have an understanding of traditional Aboriginal approaches to health care?*

GLOSSARY

Aboriginal people the descendants of the original inhabitants of North America. The Canadian Constitution recognizes three groups of Aboriginal peoples: Indians, Metis, and Inuit.

dependency ratio the number of people who are either too young or too old to work relative to the number of people of working age – usually defined as ages 15–65.

fiduciary obligations obligations based on a relationship between Aboriginal people and the government of Canada that involves a trust or trusteeship.

First Nation a term that came into common usage in the 1970s to replace the term "Indian"; there is no legal definition of this term.

Indian an Aboriginal person who is not Inuit or Metis; a legal term embedded in the Constitution Act, 1982.

institutionally complete of an ethnic community, controlling a variety of institutions, such as religion, education, and commerce, that influence the society in which it operates.

Inuit an Aboriginal people of northern Canada.

life expectancy on average, the number of years an individual may expect to live at birth.

Metis people of mixed First Nations and European ancestry who identify themselves as Metis; a legal term in Alberta and British Columbia.

mortality rate the number of deaths per year in a cohort of people.

reserve a parcel of land set aside by the federal government for use and occupancy by status Indians but not owned by Indians.

shaman individuals in the Aboriginal community who are called upon to diagnose a health-related problem or to restore balance on behalf of a community.

treaty a negotiated agreement regarding land and governance between the federal government and a group of Indians. Hundreds of treaties have been signed over the past 200 years.

treaty Indian a status Indian who belongs to a band that signed a treaty with the government of Canada.

REFERENCES

Abella, R. (1984, October). *Report of the commission on equality in employment.* Ottawa: Government of Canada.

Assembly of First Nations. (1994). *Breaking the silence.* Ottawa: Assembly of First Nations Health Commission.

Assembly of First Nations. (2002, April 4). Presentation to the Commission of the Future of Health Care in Canada, Public hearings in Ottawa, ON.

Ahneakew, D., &. Sanderson, S. (2001). Sovereignty and treaty relations between First Nations and Canada. Paper presented at First Nations Health: Our Voice, Our Decision, Our Responsibility, February 25–27, Ottawa, ON.

Berkman, L., & Kawachi, I. (2000). *Social epidemiology.* New York: Oxford University Press.

Berliner, H. (1977). Emerging ideologies in medicine. *Review of Radical Political Economics, 9*(1), 189–218.

Bolaria, B.S. (1979). Self-care and lifestyles: Ideological and policy implications. In J.A. Fry (Ed.), *Economy, class and social reality* (pp. 350–363). Toronto: Butterworths.

Bush, P., et al. (1996). *Children, medicines, and culture.* New York: Pharmaceutical Products Press.

Canada, Government of, 2006. 2005–2006 Estimates, Part II., The Government Expense Plans and the Main Estimates, Ottawa, Canadian Government Publisher, Section 17.

Canada. (1997). *Basic departmental data 1996.* Ottawa: Departmental Statistics Section, Public Works and Government Services Canada.

Canadian Institute for Health Information. (2004). *Improving the health of Canadians.* Ottawa, Canadian Institute for Health Information.

Coburn, D. (2000) Income inequality, social cohesion and the health status of populations: The role of neo-liberalism. *Social Science and Medicine, 51*, 135–146.

Cooke, M., Beavon, D., & McHardy, M. (2004). *Measuring the well-being of Aboriginal people.* Ottawa: Strategic Research and Analysis Directorate, Indian and Northern Affairs Canada.

Dutton, P. (1986). Financial, organizational and professional factors affecting health care utilization. *Social Science and Medicine, 23*(7), 721–735.

Dyck, N. (1997). Tutelage, resistance and co-optation in Canadian Indian administration. *Canadian Review of Sociology and Anthropology, 34*(3), 333–348.

Frideres, J. (1998). Indigenous peoples of Canada and the United States of America: Entering the 21st century. In L. d'Haenens (Ed.), *Images of Canadianness* (pp. 167–196). Ottawa: University of Ottawa Press.

Frideres, J., & Gadacz, R. (2005). *Aboriginal people in Canada.* Scarborough: Prentice-Hall.

Harter, L., Japp, P., & Beck, C. (Eds.). (2004). *Narratives, health, and healing.* London, Lawrence Erlbaum Associates Pub.

Hasting, J., & Mosley, W. (1964). *Introduction: The evolution of organized community health service in Canada.* Royal Commission on Health Services. Ottawa: Supply and Services.

Heagerty, J. (1934). The development of public health in Canada. *Canadian Journal of Public Health, 25*, 53–59.

Health Canada. (2003). *A statistical profile on the health of First Nations in Canada.* Ottawa: Health Canada.

Kane, R., Kasteler, J., & Gray, R. (1976). *The health gap: Medical services and the poor.* New York: Springer.

Kawachi, I., Kennedy, B., & Wilkinson, R. (1999). *The society and population health reader.* New York: The New Press.

Kelm, M.E. (1998). *Colonizing bodies: Aboriginal health and healing in British Columbia.* Vancouver: University of British Columbia Press.

Kennedy, B., Kawachi, I., Glass, R., & Prothrow-Stith, D. (1998). Income distribution, socioeconomic status and self-rated health: A US multi-level analysis. *British Medical Journal, 317*, 917–921.

Knowlton, C. (1971). Cultural factors in the non-delivery of medical services to southwestern Mexican Americans. In M. Riedesel (Ed.), *Health-related problems in arid lands* (pp. 118–131). Tempe: Arizona State University Press.

LaFramboise, H. (1980). Health policy: Breaking the problem down into more manageable segments. In C. Meilicke & J. Starch, *Perspectives on Canadian health and social services policy: History and emerging trends* (pp. 159–212). Ann Arbor, MI: Health Administration Press.

Lajeunesse, T. (1993). *Community holistic circle healing.* Ottawa: Ministry of the Solicitor General.

Lavoie, J. (2004, January). Governed by contracts: The development of Indigenous primary health services in Canada, Australia and New Zealand. *Journal of Aboriginal Health, 1*(1), 6–24.

Marmot, M., & Wilkinson, R. (1999). *Social Determinants of Health.* Toronto: Oxford University Press.

Meilicke, C., & Storch, J. (1980). *Perspectives on Canadian health and social services policy: History and emerging trends.* Ann Arbor, MI: Health Administration Press.

National Aboriginal Health Organization. (2001). *Making a difference.* Ottawa: Submission to the Commission on the Future of Health Care in Canada.

National Aboriginal Health Organization. (2003). *Public opinion poll on health care. First Nations views on their health and health care.* Ottawa: National Aboriginal Health Organization.

Navarro, V., & Muntaner, C. (Eds.). (2004). *Political and economic determinants of population health and well-being.* New York: Baywood Publishing Company, Inc.
Newbold, K.B. (1998). Problems in search of solutions: Health and Canadian Aboriginals. *Journal of Community Health, 23*(1), 59–72.
Nuttall, R. (1982). The development of Indian boards of health in Alberta. *Canadian Journal of Public Health, 73,* 300–303.
Rodriguez-Pinero, L. (2005). *Indigenous peoples, post colonialism and international law.* New York: Oxford University Press.
Romanow, R. (2002). *Building on values: The future of health care in Canada – Final report.* Ottawa: Commission on the Future of Health Care in Canada.
Rowe, C. (2006). *Aboriginal identity and knowledge within Canada's social gradient in health.* Unpublished master's thesis, University of Calgary.
Royal Commission on Aboriginal Peoples. (1996). *People to people, nation to nation: Highlights from the report of the Royal Commission on Aboriginal Peoples.* Ottawa: Minister of Supply and Services.
Sanguins, J. (2005). *Living well: Understanding the experience of diabetes and cardiovascular disease in First Nations peoples.* Unpublished doctoral dissertation, University of Calgary.
Sealy, B., & MacDonald, N. (no date). *The health care professional in an Aboriginal community.* Ottawa: Department of National Health and Welfare.
Sivell-Ferri, C. (1997). *The Ojibwa circle: Tradition and change.* Ottawa: Ministry of Solicitor General, Supply and Services Canada.
Speck, D.C. (1989). The Indian health transfer policy: A step in the right direction, a revenge of the hidden policy? *Aboriginal Studies Review, 5*(1), 187–214.
Stubben, J. (2006). *Native Americans and political participation.* Denver, CO: ABC-CCIO Inc.
Suchman, E. (1963). *Social patterns of health and medical care.* New York: New York City Department of Health.
Tjepkema, M. (2002). *The health of the off reserve Aboriginal population, supplement to health reports, 13,* 1–16.
Waldram, J., Herring, D., & Young, T.K. (1995). *Aboriginal health in Canada: Historical, cultural and epidemiological perspectives.* Toronto: University of Toronto Press.
Weidman, H. (1980). Dominance and domination in health care: A transcultural perspective. In M. Staum & D. Larsen (Eds.), *Doctors, patients, and society* (pp. 133–145). Waterloo, ON: Wilfrid Laurier University Press.
Whitaker, E. (2006). *Health and healing in comparative perspective.* Upper Saddle River, NJ: Prentice Hall.
Wirick, G. (1966, Winter). A multiple equation model of demand for health care. *Health Services Research,* 301–346.
Woodward, J. (2005). *Aboriginal law.* Toronto: Carswell.

11

IMMIGRATION, ETHNICITY, AGING, AND HEALTH

KAREN M. KOBAYASHI University of Victoria

INTRODUCTION

Canada's changing ethno-cultural profile – the result of significant increases in the proportions of both visible minorities and immigrants in the population over the past few decades – has important implications for policy and research in the population health and health care domains. This is due, in large part, to the historical and contemporary experiences of social exclusion that visible minorities and immigrants have faced in this country. Some of the key implications of such experiences, the results oftentimes of the intersection between socio-demographic, socio-economic, and cultural factors, that have been noted in the literature on health and well-being are lower health status (both subjective and objective) and increased health risks (particularly for chronic illnesses) among visible minority and immigrant adults (Bolaria & Bolaria, 1994; Galabuzi, 2004; Hyman, 2001; Meadows, Thurston & Melton, 2001). Such disparities in health status and health care utilization between groups (visible minorities and non-visible minorities; the foreign-born and the Canadian-born) have been the focus of research on ethnic inequality in health both at the individual and population levels (Dunn & Dyck, 2000; Globerman, 1998; Wilkinson, 1996; Halpern & Nazroo, 2000; Kawachi & Kennedy, 2002). More recently, however, research interest in the health – both physical and mental – of immigrants post-immigration has given rise to a growing body of literature on the healthy immigrant effect, an hypothesis that maintains that recent immigrants are actually healthier than those born in Canada, and consequently, that they use the health care system less; over time, however, this health status advantage decreases (for example, Ali, 2002; Chen, Ng & Wilkins, 1996a, b; Perez, 2002). Both areas of research then, ethnic inequality in health and immigrant health over time, can be regarded as salient to policy discussions on ethno-cultural and immigrant health in Canada.

This chapter provides an overview of four key issues pertaining to immigration, ethnicity, aging, and health in Canada. Beginning with a profiling of the increasing ethno-cultural diversity in Canada, we then move to a discussion of the health of immigrants, with a particular emphasis in this section on the healthy immigrant effect literature. The topic of ethnicity, immigration, and health, focusing on health disparities as they are influenced by social structural, lifestyle, and cultural factors between visible and non-visible minorities and immigrants and non-immigrants, is then covered. The chapter concludes with a section on ethnicity, aging, and social policy in an attempt to provide some guidance to health care policy-makers on the development of relevant services and programs to the growing populations of visible minorities and immigrants.

INCREASING DIVERSITY

According to the 2001 Census, visible minority Canadians represent 13.4 percent (4,000,000) of the population – a significant increase from 1991 when fewer than 10 percent of Canadians were members of visible minority groups (see Table 11.1). To add to the demographic complexity of the visible minority population, over two-thirds (70%) of visible minority Canadians are foreign-born. Table 11.1 also indicates that in 2001 the majority of the nearly four million visible minority Canadians were residents of either Ontario or British Columbia, a reflection of the overall settlement pattern of immigrants. Although projections indicate that the visible minority population will remain younger than their non-visible minority counterparts over the next decade, this population is aging with proportionally more older adults and fewer young people (Statistics Canada, 2005).

TABLE 11.1 *Proportion of Visible Minorities[1], Canada, Provinces and Territories, 1991, 1996, and 2001*

	1991	1996	2001
	%		
Canada	9.4	11.2	13.4
Newfoundland and Labrador	0.8	0.7	0.8
Prince Edward Island	1.0	1.1	0.9
Nova Scotia	3.4	3.5	3.8
New Brunswick	1.2	1.1	1.3
Quebec	5.6	6.2	7.0
Ontario	13.0	15.8	19.1
Manitoba	6.9	7.0	7.9
Saskatchewan	2.6	2.8	2.9
Alberta	9.4	10.1	11.2
British Columbia	14.2	17.9	21.6
Yukon Territory	2.7	3.3	3.6
Northwest Territories	3.5	3.8	4.2
Nunavut	0.9	0.6	0.8

[1]The Canadian Employment Equity Act defines visible minorities as "persons, other than Aboriginal peoples, who are non-Caucasian in race or non-white in colour." Specifically, Statistics Canada considers that the visible minority population includes the following groups: Chinese, South Asian (East Indian, Pakistani, Sri Lankan, etc.); Black, Filipino, Latin American, Southeast Asian (Cambodian, Indonesian, Laotian, Vietnamese, etc.); Arab, West Asian (Afghan, Iranian, etc.); Japanese, Korean, and Pacific Islander.

Source: Statistics Canada, http://www12.statcan.ca/english/census01/Products/Analytic/companion/etoimm/provs.cfm.

Results from the 2001 Census indicate that 18.4 percent (5,400,000) of the Canadian population is foreign-born, the highest proportion in 70 years (see Table 11.2). This figure, up from 16.1 percent in 1991, reflects the increasing number of immigrants entering Canada, particularly in the past two decades. Further, of those who are born outside of the country, one-third (1,800,000) are recent immigrants who arrived between 1991 and 2001.

In addition to the growth of the foreign-born population over time, the make-up of this population according to country of birth has also changed. Until the early 1970s, the primary sources of immigrants were European countries. In the last decade, however, immigrants were most likely to be from Asia, with China and India being the major source countries. Concomitantly, an increasing proportion of new immigrants

TABLE 11.2 *Proportion of Foreign-Born Population, by Census Metropolitan Area (1991–2001 Censuses)*

	1991	1996	2001
	% of the total population		
Canada	16.1	17.4	18.4
St. John's	2.8	2.9	2.9
Halifax	6.4	7	6.9
Saint John	4.3	4	3.8
Saguenay	0.7	0.7	0.9
Quebec	2.2	2.6	2.9
Sherbrooke	3.8	4.3	4.6
Trois-Rivières	1.3	1.6	1.5
Montreal	16.4	17.8	18.4
Ottawa-Gatineau	14.7	16.3	17.6
Ontario Part	17.7	19.8	21.1
Quebec Part	5.4	5.6	6.6
Kingston	13.5	12.8	12.4
Oshawa	17.2	16.5	15.7
Toronto	38	41.9	43.7
Hamilton	23.5	23.6	23.6
St. Catharines-Niagara	18.9	18.3	17.8
Kitchener	21.5	21.8	22.1
London	18.8	19.2	18.8
Windsor	20.6	20.4	22.3
Greater Sudbury/Grand Sudbury	8.1	7.5	7
Thunder Bay	13.1	12.2	11.14
Winnipeg	17.4	16.9	16.5
Regina	8.4	8	7.4
Saskatoon	8.2	7.6	7.6
Calgary	20.3	20.9	20.9
Edmonton	18.3	18.5	17.8
Abbotsford	19.8	20.3	21.8
Vancouver	30.1	34.9	37.5
Victoria	19.5	19.3	18.8

Source: Statistics Canada, Census of Population. (Last modified: 2005–09–20).

are allophones – having neither English nor French as their mother tongue – while the proportion with English as their mother tongue has been on the decline. This shift from predominantly European to Asian immigration is also reflected in the changing religious profile of the Canadian population over the last decade, with Muslim, Buddhism, Hinduism, and Sikhism showing percentage increases from 83.8 percent to 128.9 percent over this time period (see Table 11.3). In addition, one of the largest percentage increases (121.1%) among all major religious groups was for individuals reporting "Christian," a religious denomination to which a growing number of Chinese and Korean immigrants report affiliation in large urban settlement centres.

A breakdown of the adult (20+) immigrant population in Canada by age in 2001 indicates that 35.6 percent (the rate is 36 percent for males and 35.3 percent for females) are mid-life (45–64 years) individuals, while approximately 19.4 percent (18.1 percent for males and 20.7 percent for females) are older adults (65 years and over). Further, recent immigrants (<10 years since immigration) comprise 13.6 percent (the rate is 14.2 percent for males and 13.1 percent for females) of the mid-life immigrant population, but only 6.2 percent (6 percent for males and 6.4 percent for females) of the later life group.

An examination of immigrants (excluding refugees) and their length of residence in Canada in these two lifecourse stages is important in that it provides insights into the reasons for immigration by age; it also reflects their expectations for employment and/or support post-immigration, trajectories that both intersect with health. For example, it is assumed that recent immigrants who are currently 65 years of age or older have moved to Canada to join adult children, as they have most likely completed their work-force

TABLE 11.3 *Major religious denominations, Canada, 1991 and 2001*[1]

	2001	1991			Percentage change 1991–2001
	Number	%	Number	%	
Roman Catholic	12,793,125	43.2	12,203,625	45.2	4.8
Protestant	8,654,845	29.2	9,427,675	34.9	–8.2
Christian Orthodox	479,620	1.6	387,395	1.4	23.8
Christian, not included elsewhere[2]	780,450	2.6	353,040	1.3	121.1
Muslim	579,640	2.0	253,265	0.9	128.9
Jewish	329,995	1.1	318,185	1.2	3.7
Buddhist	300,345	1.0	163,415	0.6	83.8
Hindu	297,200	1.0	157,015	0.6	89.3
Sikh	278,415	0.9	147,440	0.5	88.8
No religion	4,796,325	16.2	3,333,245	12.3	43.9

[1]For comparability purposes, 1991 data are presented according to 2001 boundaries.

[2]Includes persons who report "Christian," as well as those who report "Apostolic," "Born-Again Christian," and "Evangelical."

Source: Statistics Canada, http://www12.statcan.ca/english/census01/Products/Analytic/companion/rel/tables/canada/cdamajor.cfm.

participation, are in the retirement stage of their lives, and are likely to be entering a phase of greater dependency. Longer-term immigrants (10 years or more of residence) who are currently in the mid-life phase (45–64 years), however, are likely to be seeking employment or further education/training in Canada at the time of their immigration (in their mid-30s to early 50s). These variations in reasons for immigration, dependent on age at immigration and other socio-demographic variables like gender, ethnicity, marital status, and socio-economic status, have an impact on physical and mental health over time.

IMMIGRANT HEALTH

It has long been established that due to both the self-selection of healthier individuals into the immigration process and the disqualification of individuals with serious medical conditions in accordance with the health requirements in the Immigration Act, that recent immigrants to Canada are "healthy" (Oxman-Martinez, Abdool & Loiselle-Léonard, 2000). More recently, however, research interest in the changes in health status and utilization patterns over time of ethno-cultural groups has given rise to a number of studies on the health of immigrants across the post-immigration period. Findings from this research have supported the operation of a healthy immigrant effect in Canada, a term that has been used to describe the effect that time since immigration has on the health of immigrants (for example, Ali, 2002; Chen et al., 1996a, b; McDonald & Kennedy, 2004; Perez, 2002). In an attempt to provide insights into this *effect,* social researchers have examined it by a number of factors including age, marital status, socio-economic status, charter language ability, immigration category, and place of birth, in relationship to both physical and mental health.

The Healthy Immigrant Effect

The healthy immigrant effect hypothesis maintains that recent immigrants are healthier (and consequently, that they are less of a "burden" on the health care system because they utilize the system less) than their Canadian-born counterparts, but that over time this health status advantage decreases. It is believed that the effect is strongest among new immigrants for two reasons: (a) healthier (and younger, better-educated) individuals self-select into the immigration process, and (b) the health requirements in the Immigration Act for entrance into Canada tend to disqualify people with serious medical issues (Oxman-Martinez, Abdool & Loiselle-Léonard, 2000). It is thought that the decline in health status over time can be attributed to the adoption of mainstream (Canadian) beliefs, attitudes, and lifestyle behaviours (e.g., smoking, dietary changes, increased alcohol consumption) by immigrants, resulting in a convergence in health status (and health care utilization) between the foreign- and non-foreign-born populations (Ali, 2002; Chen, Ng & Wilkins, 1996a; Hull, 1979; Perez, 2002; Zambrana, Scrimshaw, Collins & Dunkel-Schetter, 1997). This argument is supported by Canadian studies comparing immigrants by time since immigration, which tend to show that longer-term immigrants (> =10 years residence) are not as healthy as newly arrived individuals due to a deterioration in their health over time.

Using data from the 1994–95 NPHS in one of the first studies to test the hypothesis, Chen and his colleagues (1996a) find the following support for the healthy immigrant effect: immigrants, particularly recent immigrants, are less likely than the Canadian-born population to have chronic conditions or disabilities. Further, their results indicate that the effect is strongest for those from non-European source countries (e.g., China, Hong Kong, Taiwan, India), who constitute the majority of recent immigrants to Canada.

Recent research by Perez (2002) and Ali (2002), based on analyses of 2000–01 CCHS data, provides further support for the healthy immigrant effect in Canada. In examining health status and health behaviour in the Canadian population, Perez (2002) compares the physical health (incidence of heart disease, diabetes, high blood pressure, and cancer) of immigrants with that of the Canadian-born, while Ali (2002) focuses on variations in mental health (incidence of depression and dependence on alcohol). Both studies observe the healthy immigrant effect with respect to selected physical and mental health indicators. In addition, the findings show that time since immigration is also related to variations in the health of immigrants; that is, the longer the period of residence in Canada, the more likely the health status of immigrants is to converge with the Canadian norm. Additionally, these findings remain significant when a number of demographic, socio-economic, and lifestyle variables are held constant.

Further research, using a number of different measures of health (e.g., disability, dependency, life expectancy, incidence of chronic conditions), also finds evidence for the healthy immigrant effect in Canada (Chen, Ng & Wilkins, 1996b, 1995; Dunn & Dyck, 2000; Hyman, 2001; McDonald & Kennedy, 2004; Parakulam, Krishnan & Odynak, 1992). These studies indicate that length of residence in Canada (along with country of birth and demographic–SES factors) contributes to variations in the health of immigrants.

Despite overwhelming support confirming the existence of a healthy immigrant effect with regard to health status, however, Globerman (1998), in his study on the health care utilization patterns of immigrants, concludes that "age is the strongest single determinant of health problems" (p. 31), regardless of immigrant status. In fact, his research suggests that immigrants and the Canadian-born utilize health care resources in similar ways at all stages of the lifecourse, including in old age. According to Globerman then, a healthy immigrant effect does not exist with regard to the use of health care services, even in later life.

The issue of age as a key health determinant for immigrants is taken up in a recent study by Gee, Kobayashi, and Prus (2004) examining the healthy immigrant effect in mid- to later life. Using data from the 2000–01 CCHS, the study examines how age at immigration affects the health of mid- to later life immigrants, compared to Canadian-born persons. After controlling for age, marital status, cultural-ethnic origin, language proficiency, education, income adequacy, alcohol consumption, number of years smoked, and fruit-vegetable consumption, the results indicate strong support for the healthy immigrant effect among the 45–64 age group: new immigrants have better self-reported and **functional health**. However, this advantage decreases with time spent in Canada. Second, and again in support of the healthy immigrant effect hypothesis, the results also suggest that there may be a gradient of deterioration in health with time since immigration (i.e., a convergence in health differences between immigrants and Canadian-born persons). In contrast to new arrivals, longer-term immigrants aged 45–64, compared to Canadian-born persons, are just as likely to experience a disability or to have a comparable level of overall functional health (HUI) and are even less likely to rate their health as good or better. The findings from this study then are consistent with the assumptions of the healthy immigrant effect hypothesis; that is, when socio-demographic, SES, and lifestyle factors are controlled, recent immigrants still have the lowest risk of disability, the highest odds of reporting positive health, and the highest average functional health score. Hence, these factors do not appear to explain the healthy immigrant effect.

The results for persons aged 65 years of age and older, however, differ from those reported for the 45–64 year age group in a few important ways. First, the healthy immigrant effect does not apply to the older adult population. In fact, recent older adult arrivals have significantly poorer functional health compared to their Canadian-born counterparts. Further, recent older arrivals are less likely to rate their health in a positive manner relative to Canadian-born older adults.

In conclusion, the findings from the Gee et al. study indicate that the healthy immigrant effect applies to mid-life immigrants in Canada. Specifically, recent mid-life (45–64 years) immigrants – those who immigrated less than 10 years ago – have better functional and **self-rated health** compared to their longer-term counterparts – those who immigrated 10 or more years ago. The latter group's health status is similar to that of Canadian-born persons. Interestingly, a different picture emerges in later life (65 years and over), where recent immigrants have poorer overall health compared to longer-term residents and the Canadian-born. This disadvantage, however, disappears when socio-demographic and socio-economic status and health-related behaviour factors are held constant.

ETHNICITY, IMMIGRATION, AND HEALTH

Ethnic inequality in Canada as it pertains to the different dimensions of health – health status, health care utilization, and access to health care – is an area that has only recently begun to receive adequate research attention. Its emergence as a topic of interest for social researchers has been a response, in part, to key statements in federal government-funded reports like the 1999 publication, *Toward a Healthy Future: Second Report on the Health of Canadians*; this report noted that, although the provision of health care services in our existing universal health care system "does not [yet] seem to be related to the income of the patient...there continue to be language and cultural barriers to the provision and/or utilization of services in certain circumstances" (p. 145). This report, a collaborative effort by government and researchers in population health, was the most comprehensive summary of then current information on the health of Canadians, and, in particular, provided evidence that in the face of growing ethno-cultural diversity in the population, the ability of all groups to access (and utilize) health care was an important issue for social policy.

In order to address the disparities in health status and health care utilization of visible minorities and immigrants over the lifecourse, it is important to acknowledge and understand the factors (and their intersection) that affect differential access to health care services and programs among these groups; factors include employment, income, work conditions, gender, housing, geographic place of residence, and experiences of discrimination – both by gender and race. Visible minorities and immigrants, like Aboriginal Canadians and other disadvantaged groups, are more likely to experience social exclusion or marginalization on the basis of their socio-economic status/position than non-visible minorities and the Canadian-born, and consequently, to have lower health status and higher health risk at a number of different stages in their lives (Bolaria & Bolaria, 1994; Galabuzi, 2004; Hyman, 2001). This intersection between ethnicity and socio-economic status, although salient in its implications for the health of visible minority and immigrant Canadians, has not, unfortunately, been adequately addressed in the literature on the social determinants of health (Galabuzi, 2004).

It is surprising that despite the increased representation in the population of visible minority and foreign-born Canadians, there remains a paucity of empirical research on the social determinants of health for these groups. That is, even though there has been incredible growth in research on the health of Canadians overall, this literature has emerged with very little attention paid to the roles of ethnicity and immigration in discussions on health and health care. Recent exceptions include studies by Dunn and Dyck (2000); Kopec, Williams, and Austin (2001); Sheth, Nair, Nargundkar, Anand, and Yusul (1999); Wu and Schimmele (2005); and an important edited volume for health professionals by Waxler-Morrison, Anderson, Richardson, and Chambers (2005) addressing the need for culturally sensitive health care and support services.

Of the Canadian research that has been undertaken, much of it has focused on the health of immigrants and the majority has been quantitative in nature; these studies have, for the most part, focused on comparing the health status and health care utilization patterns of immigrants and the Canadian-born using both secondary data from national health surveys and primary data collected for research projects targeting particular ethno-cultural groups. For example, a number of studies have used National Population Health Survey (NPHS) data to examine the relationships between immigration and health status (Dunn & Dyck, 2000) and health care utilization (Globerman, 1998); another has involved the collection of health status and health care utilization data from mid-life Chinese and South Asian immigrants in the Lower Mainland (Kobayashi, 2003). While secondary data analysis is important for population health research, primary data collection is increasingly necessary given the limitations imposed on researchers interested in ethno-cultural and immigrant dimensions of health by national health datasets like the NPHS and the Canadian Community Health Survey (CCHS). Limitations are due to (1) the under-representation of visible minority and immigrant Canadians in the overall samples; (2) the exclusion of questions on important cultural characteristics (e.g., ethnic identity, adherence to non-Western value/belief systems) that may be important determinants of health status and/or health care use; and (3) the close-ended structure and cross-sectional nature of questions on ethnicity, immigrant status, and health; such questions tend to fail to recognize ethnic identification, immigration, and health care as dynamic social processes.

One such study that addresses this last point, authored by Meadows, Thurston, and Melton (2001), focuses on the under-researched topic of immigrant women's health. In one of the few qualitative studies to explore the relationship between health determinants and the immigration-related experiences of mid-life women, the authors find that the immigration process itself is salient in determining health, and that an understanding of a number of different factors (i.e., income, education, health beliefs and behaviours, family relationships, spirituality and religious practices) as they are related to immigration is important in developing relevant and appropriate health services for immigrant women in middle age. The inclusion of women (and their *voices*) as active participants in the research process, a more phenomenological approach to health research, recognizes the need for experiential data to make sense of the population health profiles generated by secondary data analyses.

This critique of secondary data sources, however, is in no way meant to negate the important, albeit mixed, findings on ethnic inequality and health from studies using these datasets. Indeed, a key comparative study between immigrants and the Canadian-born using the 1994–95 NPHS by Dunn and Dyck (2000) was one of the first to address ethnic inequality in the health domain; the findings indicate that despite the absence of a relationship between socio-economic and immigration characteristics and self-reported health status, socio-economic variables are salient factors in terms of health outcomes for immigrants (versus non-immigrants). Further, in a cross-cultural, comparative study of health status in Canada using the same dataset, Kopec and his colleagues (2001) find that even after controlling for socio-economic status, significant differences in health status, as measured by scores on the Health Utilities Index (HUI), still exist amongst the immigrant and Canadian-born populations. From this, the authors conclude that although immigration factors might possibly explain some of the variance in the HUI across different ethno-cultural groups, there is a strong likelihood that other cultural factors (i.e., country of birth and charter language ability) influence the reporting of chronic illness, particularly pain and mental health issues, in these groups.

In another study examining the association between ethnicity and chronic disease, Wang and colleagues (2000) use data on arthritis prevalence obtained from the 1994–95 NPHS. After adjusting for age, gender, socio-economic variables, and body mass index, the findings show that the risk for arthritis is significantly lower among Asian immigrants than among North American-born Canadians. Thus, both immigrant status and ethnicity are factors influencing the self-reported prevalence of arthritis in the Canadian population. Similarly, Acharya (1998) finds variations in mental health status and its predictors by the country of birth of Canadian immigrants, while Wu, Noh, and Kaspar (2003) observe that East and Southeast Asian, Chinese, South Asian, and Black populations experience the lowest rates of depression in Canada.

Further, with regard to mental health, from the mid-1980s onward a number of studies have focused on stress, coping, and adaptation in ethno-cultural groups concluding that certain groups like the Chinese and Koreans, who are largely foreign-born populations, experience high levels of stress and may not possess adequate coping resources to adapt to/deal with difficult life events/circumstances (Kim & Berry, 1987; Wong & Reker, 1985). This finding may partially be explained by the difficulties older adult immigrants face in trying to rebuild social capital (beyond their family networks) in unfamiliar environments, which may, in turn, contribute to the increased distress and anxiety they experience on a day-to-day basis.

In a later study, exploring the relationship between cultural factors and health satisfaction in a sample of Asian Canadian (Japanese, Chinese, and Korean) older adults, Ujimoto, Nishio, Wong, and Lam (1993) find that there are variations across groups on health satisfaction with the Chinese reporting the highest degree of satisfaction followed by the Japanese and then the Koreans. Interestingly, the Japanese, a largely post-immigrant group, are the most likely to be ambivalent – have mixed feelings – about their health. These findings, however, must be interpreted with caution given that Western mental health scales and instruments are not easily translated (i.e., some of the items may not be relevant or understood in traditional Asian cultures) particularly when they are administered to recent Asian Canadian immigrants (Lai, 2000, 2004). It is therefore important to undertake comparative research across different ethno-cultural groups in order to get at the underlying cultural mechanisms that may be responsible, either in whole or in part, in producing a particular health pattern or finding.

In a comparative study on cardiovascular and cancer mortality among European, South Asian, and Chinese Canadians from 1979–93, Sheth and his colleagues (1999) conclude that there are significant differences in the rates of death from ischemic heart disease and cancer by ethnic group. Their findings also indicate, however, that there is a notable decline and convergence in mortality rates for heart disease and stroke for the three groups. In a related commentary on ethnicity and chronic disease, O'Loughlin (1999) points out that this result provides evidence that existing inequalities between ethnic groups are narrowing, and that due to the rapidity with which these health patterns are changing, two of the key contributing factors may in fact be lifestyle and environment. This convergence may lead us to believe then that cultural factors are not playing as salient a role in determining health status as are socio-structural and lifestyle variables. But what about the inter-relationship between cultural and other factors?

Dunn and Hayes (2000) examine the ways in which housing-related factors (e.g., type of dwelling, neighbourhood location, tenure), in conjunction with cultural factors like ethnicity, affect the health status of individuals and populations. With regard to culture, their findings indicate that ethnic origin, coupled with housing factors, is an important indicator of self-rated health. In particular, respondents are more likely to report good health if they are of non-Western ethnic origin (e.g., Chinese, Filipino, Vietnamese, East Indian) and feel that they can purchase goods and services that will meet their ethno-specific needs in their residential community or close by. Thus, living in or in close proximity to a culturally and/or linguistically-sensitive environment (i.e., a community with a high degree of **institutional completeness**) may positively influence self-perceived health status for Asian and South Asian Canadians.

How does this translate into life expectancy? According to the 2000–01 CCHS, the city of Richmond, with 59 percent of its population reporting Chinese ethnic origin, also boasts the highest life expectancy in the country at 81.2 years, almost three years longer than the national average. Richmond residents also self-report healthy lifestyle practices including the country's lowest smoking and obesity rates. Lifestyle factors, however, may not help to explain the increased life expectancy finding in this predominantly immigrant municipality. In a study on the health status and health behaviour among immigrants using data from the 2000–01 CCHS, Perez (2002) finds that although health behaviours (i.e., smoking and alcohol consumption) differ between Canadian-born and immigrant respondents and vary with the length of time since immigration, these differences do not explain, in general, health outcome patterns.

What do all of these studies, despite the variability in their findings, have in common? From this body of mainly quantitative research, we find support for the use of a **population health perspective** to examine the relationship between ethnicity, immigration, and health. Such a perspective recognizes that the socio-economic, demographic (i.e., gender, language, age, marital status, residential arrangements), cultural, and lifestyle characteristics of individuals and their interactions, rather than "medical care inputs and health behaviours" (Dunn & Dyck, 2000, p. 2) are the most important predictors of health status and health care utilization over the adult lifecourse. Recognizing the complex and multidimensional nature of ethnic inequality in relationship to health outcomes, a number of researchers have, in recent studies, used this perspective to examine health disparities at different stages of the lifecourse.

The finding of Gee and her colleagues (2004) that there is a health gap between Canadian- and foreign-born older adults (65+ years), provides a good opportunity for researchers examining ethnic and/or immigrant-based health disparities to explore why this may be the case in later life and not at earlier lifecourse stages. In an attempt to explain this gap using data once again from the 2000–01 CCHS, Kobayashi and Prus (2005) set out to test two hypotheses, one on **differential vulnerability** and the other on **differential exposure**.

The first hypothesis, the **differential exposure hypothesis**, suggests that immigrant status differences in health in later life are attributable to the different social locations (and resulting life experiences) of foreign-born (FB) and Canadian-born (CB) older adults, and to their differential exposure to various lifestyle behaviours such as smoking, alcohol consumption, and quality of diet. The second hypothesis, the **differential vulnerability hypothesis**, suggests that differences in the health status of FB and CB older adults are attributable to differences in their "vulnerability" (their reaction) to particular social structural and lifestyle determinants of health.

The results indicate that foreign-born older adults have significantly poorer health compared to their Canadian-born counterparts. The findings, however, do not generally support the differential exposure hypothesis: when the data are adjusted for socio-demographic, SES, and lifestyle differences, the health of immigrants does not become more similar to that of non-immigrants. Interestingly, the overall findings do reveal significant immigrant status differences in "vulnerability" to specific indicators of structural and behavioural determinants of health, providing support for the differential vulnerability hypothesis. Of the socio-demographic factors, the relationships between health and ethnicity (visible minority status) and language tend to vary the most by immigrant status. English/French language proficiency (as opposed to neither English nor French) is more strongly associated with better health for immigrants, and ethnicity (visible minority status) is generally only important for FB (i.e., FB visible minorities have better health than FB whites). Further, analyses reveal that immigrant-based health inequalities are significantly explained by differential vulnerabilities to SES factors between CB and FB persons – having higher education and income tend to be more beneficial to the health of FB persons than it does for CB persons. Finally, there are also significant immigrant status differences in lifestyle behaviours, with alcohol consumption having a stronger (positive) influence on health for FB, but smoking a more important (negative) determinant of health for CB.

In conclusion, these findings indicate support for the differential vulnerability hypothesis but not for the differential exposure hypothesis in explaining the health gap between Canadian- and foreign-born older adults. What this suggests is that differences in health status between these two groups, rather than being the result of different social locations and/or lifestyle behaviours, can instead be attributed to the different "reactions" of Canadian- and foreign-born older adults to various social and lifestyle determinants of health. Indeed, the effects of ethnicity (i.e., visible minority status), charter language proficiency, education, and income, all important structural determinants of health for both Canadian- and foreign-born older adults, vary by immigrant status, as do the effects of lifestyle behaviours like smoking and alcohol consumption.

It is no surprise that charter language proficiency for immigrants is an important determinant of health as it facilitates "access" to health care in mainstream society. In trying to make sense of the *ethnicity effect* (visible minority immigrants have better health than their white counterparts), however, it is important to consider the breakdown of the visible minority category. The majority of visible minority immigrant older adults in Canada are of Chinese or South Asian ethnic origin. Given this, we might speculate that the use of ethno-culturally-grounded complementary and alternative health practices (i.e., traditional Chinese medicine, Ayurvedic treatment) by older adults in this group may contribute to their better self-reported health status. With regard to the differential effects of socio-economic status – education and income – on the health of older adults in the sample, perhaps the effect is greater for foreign-born older adults because higher education and income work to offset the negative impact of delayed acculturation (i.e., decreased charter language proficiency, decreased social/political participation).

The effects of lifestyle behaviours on the health of Canadian- and foreign-born older adults indicate that alcohol consumption has a stronger positive influence on the health of immigrant older adults than it does for their Canadian-born counterparts. In many European (e.g., France, Spain, and Italy) and Asian (e.g., Japan, South Korea) countries, the consumption of alcohol in moderation is recognized as an important part of overall health maintenance. Such practices, carried over into their new home countries, may continue to provide a protective function for foreign-born older adults against chronic illness and disease. Finally, the more pronounced negative effect of smoking on the health of Canadian-born older adults (versus foreign-born older adults) may be partially explained by their generation's higher propensity to take up (at an earlier lifecourse stage) and continue smoking into later life.

Ethnicity, Aging, and Social Policy

Canada is undergoing profound changes in the overall make-up of its population. Not only is the population aging rapidly, it is fast becoming more ethno-culturally diverse. What are the implications for social policy of these concurrent demographic shifts? With regard to immigrant health, Globerman (1998) and McDonald and Kennedy (2004) refer to the health of immigrants as an important determinant of the costs and benefits of immigration policy, particularly in the context of the health care system. This is especially true for older mid- to later life immigrants who are at stages in the lifecourse when they are likely to undergo more dramatic changes in health status, thereby affecting their need for health care. This holds in spite of the fact that with the compression of morbidity to the last years of life there may be a delay in the acute need for care, as the *healthy immigrant effect* literature gives us some indication that there will inevitably be more intense pressure placed on the health care system at some point by these individuals later in their lives.

Based on findings from Canadian studies on ethnic inequality and health, there are a number of implications for the development of Canadian health care policy and program planning for visible minorities and immigrants, individuals who make up over one-half of the foreign-born adult population. First, health care policies must begin to address the differential needs of ethno-cultural and immigrant adults by age group. A mid-life group of recent immigrants, for example, will have fewer needs for services and programs in the early years of their residency in Canada, while certain sub-groups of older new immigrants may have an increased need for services, due to poor health status. Policies must be developed at both the federal and provincial levels (particularly in Ontario (Toronto), Quebec (Montreal), and British Columbia (Vancouver), provinces (and cities) in which the majority of immigrants choose to reside) that (a) target immigrants, especially visible minority immigrants, as they age over time, and (b) respond to the needs of an older immigrant population from the outset.

Second, with respect to physical health status, older immigrants from large South Asian or Asian source countries like India or Taiwan may experience nutritional deficiencies, as diet and dietary behaviours change at an accelerated rate after immigration. The rate at which lifestyle behaviours converge with the Canadian norm will, of course, vary according to a number of different factors related to assimilation and acculturation processes, including age at immigration, country of birth, level of adherence to traditional (country of birth) value and belief systems, place of residence (urban vs. rural), and degree of institutional completeness of the immigrant's ethno-cultural group in the place of residence. In the end, these and other related factors must be considered in any comprehensive Canadian health care policy and program planning initiatives for mid- to later life adults.

CONCLUSION

This chapter has provided an overview of recent research on the health of visible minority and immigrant Canadians – focusing on the changes in immigrant health status and health care utilization over time, and ethnic and immigrant-based health inequality – and has highlighted a number of key studies in these areas. In Canada, despite evidence that a healthy immigrant effect operates in the population, this effect varies according to a number of different demographic and cultural factors including age, country of origin/birth, and length of residency – time since immigration. Further, in trying to explain health disparities in later life, it is important to use a perspective that acknowledges the multiple and complex nature of the factors – social structural, cultural, and lifestyle – that contribute to these variations. For example, Kobayashi and Prus (2005) tested two hypotheses – differential exposure and differential vulnerability – and found that differences in health status between immigrant and non-immigrant older adults, rather than being the result of different social locations and/or lifestyle behaviours, can instead be attributed to the different "reactions" of older adults in these two groups to various social and lifestyle determinants of health.

With regard to policy, in planning for the future it is clear that health care policy-makers need to recognize and take into account the diversity inherent in visible minority and immigrant populations. While social exclusion may be the experience for many individuals, it is not the lived reality for all. And, for those who are marginalized, the reasons for this exclusion may vary according to a number of different reasons from socio-economic status to charter language ability to racial discrimination in the workplace, factors that may work either alone or in intersection with one another to produce negative health outcomes. Thus, the process of developing appropriate health policies, programs, and services for visible minority and immigrant Canadians as they age, will require an ongoing dialogue between governments at different levels (municipal, provincial, and federal) and across departments or ministries (e.g., immigration, health, and seniors). It is only through such coordinated efforts that we can continue to ensure access to health care for all Canadians and thereby promote the health and well-being of all citizens.

STUDY QUESTIONS

1. *How have the visible minority and immigrant populations in Canada changed over the past two decades?*
2. *Why is an examination of the adult immigrant population at different lifecourse stages (i.e., middle and later life) important?*
3. *Why is a population health perspective an appropriate framework for examining the intersection between immigrant status, time since immigration, health, and age?*
4. *According to the research findings presented, can we differentiate the healthy immigrant effect by age? If so, how?*
5. *Among the older adult population, how does the author explain the health gap between immigrant and non-immigrant Canadians?*

GLOSSARY

differential exposure hypothesis one of two hypotheses used to explain immigrant status differences in health status; it suggests that health status differences are attributable to the different social locations (and resulting life experiences) of immigrant and non-immigrant older adults, and to their differential exposure to various lifestyle behaviours like physical activity level, smoking, alcohol consumption, and quality of diet.

differential vulnerability hypothesis one of two hypotheses used to explain immigrant status differences in health status; it suggests that health status differences are attributable to differences in immigrant and non-immigrant older adults' vulnerability (their reaction) to certain social structural and lifestyle determinants.

functional health refers to an individual's physical health and capacities in the domains of vision, hearing, speech, mobility, dexterity, cognition, emotions, and pain and discomfort.

healthy immigrant effect a hypothesis that maintains that recent immigrants are healthier (and consequently, they use the health care system less) than their Canadian-born counterparts but that over time this health status advantage decreases.

institutional completeness a term developed by Breton (1964) to describe the extent to which various social organizations are developed in an ethno-cultural community.

population health perspective an approach that addresses a broad range of factors (e.g., social, physical/biological, environmental, lifestyle, health care system) and their interactions that determine health.

self-rated health refers to subjective health status and is an indicator of how an individual perceives his/her physical health on a Likert scale ranging from poor to excellent.

REFERENCES

Ali, J. (2002). Mental health of Canada's immigrants. *Health Reports,* Vol. 13 (Statistics Canada, Catalogue No. 82–003). Ottawa: Health Canada.

Bolaria, B.S., & Bolaria, R. (1994). Immigrant status and health status: Women and racial minority immigrant workers. In B.S. Bolaria & R. Bolaria (Eds.), *Racial Minorities, Medicine, and Health* (pp. 149–168). Halifax: Fernwood.

Bolaria, B.S., & Bolaria, R. (2002). Women's lives, women's health. In B.S. Bolaria & H.D. Dickinson (Eds.), *Health, illness, and health care in Canada* (3rd ed., pp. 169–184). Toronto: Nelson.

Chen, J., Ng, E., & Wilkins, R. (1995). Life expectancy and health expectancy of Canadian immigrants from 1986 to 1991. In *Immigration and life expectancy in Canada* (Statistics Canada, Catalogue No. 89F0084XPE, pp. 9–22). Ottawa: Statistics Canada.

Chen, J., Ng, E., & Wilkins, R. (1996a). The health of Canada's immigrants in 1994–95. *Health Reports* (Statistics Canada, Catalogue No. 82–003), *7*(4), 33–45.

Chen, J., Ng, E., & Wilkins, R. (1996b). Health expectancy by immigrant status. *Health Reports* (Statistics Canada, Catalogue No. 82–003), *8*(3), 29–37.

Denton, M., Prus, S., & Walters, V. (2004). Gender differences in health: A Canadian study of the psychosocial, structural and behavioural determinants of health. *Social Science and Medicine, 58,* 2585–2600.

Dunn, J.R., & Dyck, I. (2000). Social determinants of health in Canada's immigrant population: Results from the National Population Health Survey. *Social Science and Medicine, 51,* 1573–1593.

Dunn, J.R., & Hayes, M. (2000). Social inequality, population health, and housing: A study of two Vancouver neighborhoods. *Social Science and Medicine, 51,* 563–587.

Galabuzi, G-E. (2004). Social exclusion. In D. Raphael (Ed.), *Social Determinants of Health: Canadian Perspectives* (pp. 235–251). Toronto: Canadian Scholars' Press.

Gee, E., & Kimball, M. (1987). *Women and aging.* Toronto: Butterworths.

Gee, E.M., Kobayashi, K.M., & Prus, S.G. (2004). Examining the healthy immigrant effect in mid- to later life Canadians: Findings from the Canadian Community Health Survey. *Canadian Journal on Aging, 23*(Supplement 1), S61-S69.

Globerman, S. (1998). *Immigration and health care utilization patterns in Canada.* RIIM Working Paper Series, No. 98–08.

Halpern, D.S., & Nazroo, J. (2000). Mental health and ethnic group concentration: A confirmation of the ethnic density effect. *International Journal of Social Psychiatry, 46*(1): 34–46.

Hull, D. (1979). Migration, adaptation and illness: A review. *Social Science and Medicine, 13A,* 25–36.

Hyman, I. (2001). *Immigration and health.* Ottawa: Health Canada. Retrieved 3 July 2004 from http://www.hc-sc.gc.ca/iacb-dgiac/arad-draa/english/rmdd/wpapers/wpapers1.html.

Kawachi, I.R., & Kennedy, B. (2002). *The health of nations: Why inequality is harmful to your health.* New York: New Press.

Kim, U., & Berry, J. (1986). Predictors of acculturative stress: Korean immigrants in Toronto, Canada. In L.H. Ekstrand (Ed.), *Ethnic minorities and immigrants in cross-cultural perspectives* (pp. 159–179). Lisse: Swets and Zeitlinger.

Kobayashi, K.M. (2003, March). Exploring the determinants of health status and health care utilization among mid-life Chinese and South Asian immigrants in the Lower Mainland. Paper presented at the 6th National Metropolis Conference, Edmonton, AB.

Kobayashi, K.M., & Prus, S.G. (2005). Explaining the health gap between Canadian- and foreign-born older adults: Findings from the 2000/2001 Canadian Community Health Survey. *Recent Advances and Research Updates: Journal of the International Research Promotion Council, 6*(3), 269–273.

Kopec, J.A., Williams, J.I., To, T., & Austin, P.C. (2001). Cross-cultural comparisons of health status in Canada using the Health Utilities Index. *Ethnicity and Health, 6*(1), 41–50.

Lai, D.W.L. (2000). Measuring depression in Canada's elderly Chinese population. Use of a community screening instrument. *Canadian Journal of Psychiatry, 45*, 279–284.

Lai, D.W.L. (2004). Impact of culture on depressive symptoms of elderly Chinese immigrants. *Canadian Journal of Psychiatry, 49*, 820–827.

Laroche, M. (2000). Health status and health services utilization of Canada's immigrant and non-immigrant populations. *Canadian Public Policy, 26*(1), 51–73.

McDonald, J.T., & Kennedy, S. (2004). Insights into the "healthy immigrant effect": Health status and health service use of immigrants to Canada. *Social Science and Medicine, 59*(8), 1613–1627.

McDonough, P., & Walters, V. (2001). Gender and health: reassessing patterns and explanations. *Social Science and Medicine, 52*, 547–559.

Meadows, L.M., Thurston, W.E., & Melton, C. (2001). Immigrant women's health. *Social Science and Medicine, 52*, 1451–1458.

Oxman-Martinez, J., Abdool S., & Loiselle-Léonard, M. (2000). Immigration, women and health in Canada. *Canadian Journal of Public Health, 91*, 394–395.

Parakulam, G., Krishnan, V., & Odynak, D. (1992). Health status of Canadian-born and foreign-born residents. *Canadian Journal of Public Health, 83*, 311–314.

Perez, C.E. (2002). Health status and health behaviour among immigrants. *Health Reports*, Vol. 13 (Statistics Canada, Catalogue No. 82–003). Ottawa: Statistics Canada.

Saldov, M. (1991). The ethnic elderly: Communication barriers to health care. *Canadian Social Work Review, 8*, 269–277.

Statistics Canada. (2005). Population Projections of Visible Minority Groups, Canada, *Provinces and Regions, 2001–2017* (Demography Division).

Ujimoto, K.V., Nishio, H., Wong, P.T.P, & Lam, L. (1993). Cultural factors affecting self-assessment of health satisfaction of Asian Canadian elderly. In R. Masi, K.A. Mcleod, & L. Mensah (Eds.), *Multicultural health and culture: Exploring the relationship* (p. 229). Toronto: Multicultural Health Coalition.

Waxler-Morrison, N., Anderson, J.M., Richardson, E., & Chambers, N.A. (2005). *Cross-cultural caring: A handbook for health professionals* (2nd ed.). Vancouver: University of British Columbia Press.

Wilkinson, R.G. (1996). *Unhealthy societies: The afflictions of inequality*. London: Routledge.

Wong, P.T.P., & Reker, G.T. (1985). Stress, coping, and well-being in Anglo and Chinese elderly. *Canadian Journal on Aging, 4*, 29–37.

Zambrana, R.E., Scrimshaw, S.C.M., Collins, N., & Dunkel-Schetter, C. (1997). Prenatal health behaviors and psychosocial risk factors in pregnancy in women of Mexican origin: The role of acculturation. *American Journal of Public Health, 87*, 1022–1026.

PART 4
WOMEN, FAMILY, AND HEALTH

The overarching theme of this section is that human experiences of health and illness are embedded in economic, social, and cultural contexts, and these factors play an important role in the social distribution of health and illness. Gender is an important part of life; women's and men's different life experiences are shaped by socially structured gender inequality and socially constructed gender roles. Race and class intersect with gender to produce subgroup differences in health and illness patterns. Women are health caregivers and receivers. In both roles, women's experiences are profoundly influenced by the gendered inequality pervasive in Canadian society.

Bolaria and Bolaria begin this section with a chapter that links women's health status and health care needs to the structured social and economic inequality of their lived experiences. Chapter 12 presents a brief review of gender differences in health and illness patterns and discusses "artefact," genetic, and social-structural explanations of these differences in morbidity and mortality. Differential exposure theory and differential vulnerability theory are discussed to explain general differences in psychological health. Bolaria and Bolaria conclude by addressing various forms of violence against women living in low-income countries and the consequences for women's health and morbidity and mortality. These issues are important in the context of globalization, migration, and increasing social, cultural, and religious diversity in Canada.

In Chapter 13, Berenson, Miller, and Findlay focus on the medicalization of women's bodies. Medicalization is the process whereby certain processes and phenomena come to be understood as properly belonging in the domain of medical knowledge and professional control. Two core aspects of women's existence historically have been medicalized: pregnancy, childbearing, and childrearing; and physical appearance, especially as it relates to body weight. The authors outline reasons for, and the means by which, the medicalization of pregnancy, childbearing, and childrearing occurred. They also examine the way in which a concern for women's health, rooted in their role as bearers of future generations, was manifested as a concern with diet, exercise, and weight. In particular, fat was seen as a major health problem that also was symptomatic of an underlying failure of will and self-control. It is in this context that the authors link women's eating disorders such as anorexia and bulimia, to women's subordinate social status, socialization, and the struggle for autonomy and control. They argue that although the medicalization of women's bodies is indicative of their general social subordination, women also have an interest in at least some aspect of the medicalization of their bodies and have learned how to use it to their advantage. They conclude that the relationship between women and the medical profession will continue as an ongoing negotiation for control over the definition of health problems and the best means to deal with them.

Varcoe picks up the theme of women's social subordination and links it to their experiences of violence and health in Chapter 14. In this regard she makes three points. First, she argues that various dimensions of inequality compound the impact of violence on women's health. Second, the various dimensions of inequality experienced by women sustain violence by creating barriers to securing adequate means for dealing with it. Finally, she argues that those dynamics sustain privilege and distance from the problem for some women, so they tend not to fully understand the problem or the social foundation of its cause.

12

WOMEN'S LIVES, WOMEN'S HEALTH

B. SINGH BOLARIA University of Saskatchewan, University of Victoria

ROSEMARY BOLARIA Researcher and Medical Writer

INTRODUCTION

Socially structured gender inequalities have important consequences for women's lives and their life chances. Women's positions and experiences in society are shaped by their social roles, conventions, economic opportunities, and access to resources. Social and economic inequalities in turn produce variations in health and illness patterns between men and women. Women, however, are not a homogeneous group. The life experiences of some groups of women differ markedly from those of other women and the female population as a whole. For instance, race, ethnic, and class position intersect with gender to produce variations in gender inequality and social variability in health status among women. Racial minority women are doubly disadvantaged because they may encounter inequality due to their race or colour in addition to sex discrimination. Social and economic differentiation and heterogeneity among women produce subgroup differences in health effects and health outcomes. The first part of this chapter presents a brief review of gender differences in health and illness patterns and the sociological explanations often advanced to account for these differences. The last section of the chapter addresses the health consequences of life experienced by women in different social, cultural, and economic contexts, and variations in the health consequences of different life experiences.

GENDER, HEALTH, AND ILLNESS

"Women get sicker, but men die quicker" sums up the morbidity and mortality patterns of men and women in developed countries (Lorber, 2000). Improved living conditions, better public health and sanitation, better nutrition, and improved medical care and services have benefited both men and women. Mortality rates have fallen and life expectancy has consistently increased for both men and women (Federal, Provincial and Territorial Advisory Committee on Population Health, 1999a, pp. 323–324; Miles, 1991; Lorber, 2000; Trypuc, 1994). However, health gains have been greater for women. Current lower mortality for women is a relatively recent occurrence, and the present patterns of longer life expectancy for women emerged at the end of the 19th century and only in developed industrialized countries (Miles, 1991; Lorber, 2000). Before the mid-19th century, women suffered from excess mortality, attributable to a comparatively harsher life for women and factors such as frequent pregnancies and poor maternal care (Trypuc, 1994). Social and health advantages have not accrued to all women because women are not a homogeneous group, however. Social diversity and social stratification among women produce different life chances and variations in health status across individuals and subgroups (McMullen, 2004; Health Canada, 2003a, b; Jackson et al., 2004; OPHA, 2000; Rieker & Bird, 2000; MacIntyre, Hunt & Sweeting, 1996; Muszynski, 1994).

The health of Canadians in regard to one of the basic indicators of population health has been consistently improving over the years. In 1996, the total (male and female) life expectancy at birth reached new heights, 78.6 years, as a result of the decline in mortality rates. A female born in 1996 could expect to live to the age of 81.4 and a male to the age of 75.7, a difference of 5.7 years. The life expectancy at birth continues to narrow slowly between sexes. For example, the difference was 7.5 years in 1978 and 5.9 years in 1995 (Federal, Provincial and Territorial Advisory Committee, 1999a, p. 324). In 1999, the average life expectancy at birth was 79 years. The sex differences in life expectancy remained: women 81.7 years and men 76.3 years (Health Canada, 2002). In 2001, Canada had the ninth-highest life expectancy, 2.1 years behind Japan with the longest life expectancy at 81.4 years (Statistics Canada, 2005). Canada had the eleventh-highest life expectancy for women and the seventh-highest life expectancy for men (Statistics Canada, 2005). While Canada compares favourably in life expectancy with other industrialized countries, wide variations exist within Canada by regions and socio-economic status. Northern and isolated communities and those with low incomes have the lowest life expectancies. For instance, Region de Nunavik in Quebec has the lowest life expectancy, at 66.7 years for both sexes, which is close to life expectancies in countries like Dominican Republic (67.0 years) and Egypt (66.5 years). On the other hand, the health regions with the highest life expectancies are typically urban communities characterized by high incomes and high educational attainment. For instance, Richmond, in British Columbia, has the highest life expectancy, at 83.4 years (Statistics Canada, 2005).

In advanced countries, females enjoy a decided advantage over males in life expectancy. Women living in poor, less industrialized countries, however, do not fare as well as men in those countries and women in industrialized countries (United Nations Population Fund [UNFPA], 2000; Miles, 1991; United Nations [UN], 1995; Lorber, 2000). Men live longer than women in some Asian and African countries (Miles, 1991). The lives of women in these countries continue to be harsher, due to factors such as feudal cultural practices, excessive violence, lack of control by women over their bodies, and reproduction, frequent pregnancies, poor nutrition, and poor obstetric care (UN, 1995; UNFPA, 2000). Women in poor countries also have shorter lives than do their sisters in more advanced countries. The differences in women's life expectancies between rich and poor countries in some cases are 20 years or more (UN, 1995). Racial, ethnic, and class differences among women in advanced countries produce subgroup variations in life expectancy. For example, the estimated life expectancy for a registered Indian woman born in 1991 is considerably shorter than that of other Canadian females born that year – 74 and 81 years, respectively (Statistics Canada, 1995, p. 149). The life expectancy of First Nations people continues to improve, but differences still persist between First

Nations and other Canadians. The average life expectancy at birth in 1999 for First Nations was 76.6 years for women and 68.9 for men (Health Canada, 2002). As noted before, the northern communities in Canada, which have a high proportion of Aboriginal population, have the lowest life expectancy in Canada. Data from the United States indicate that longevity rates vary considerably by race and income (Rieker & Bird, 2000; Syme & Yen, 2000).

It is evident that gender differences in life expectancy are closely linked to a nation's level of economic development. The higher the level of development, the longer the overall life expectancy of the population, the greater the increase in women's longevity, and the wider the differences between men and women (Miles, 1991; UN, 1995). Subgroup differences by race and income levels continue to persist in advanced countries.

While women on average live longer than men, they also report more illness than men, and there is some variation in mortality and causes of death (Statistics Canada, 1999; Federal, Provincial and Territorial Advisory Committee on Population Health, 1999a). Overall, Canada has one of the lowest mortality rates in industrialized countries. The major causes of deaths for both men and women are cardiovascular diseases and cancers. Among the specific causes of deaths, coronary heart disease (CHD) was the most important. Male mortality rates are significantly higher than female rates for general and specific causes such as cardiovascular diseases, cancers, CHD, and respiratory illnesses. It should also be noted that since 1970, the death rates for most of the primary causes have declined. This decline is particularly significant in the case of heart disease in general and coronary heart disease in particular (Federal, Provincial and Territorial Advisory Committee on Population Health, 1999a, p. 317).

There are gender differences in both objective and subjective health status. Women report a greater number of health problems such as disability, more symptoms of illness, and more stress and anxiety than males.

The data on hospital separations by diagnostic group and sex are important because they provide information on morbidity and health problems requiring hospitalization. The highest rate of separations was for pregnancy. This is followed by circulatory diseases, digestive diseases, and respiratory diseases (CIHI, 2001a).

Women were more likely than men to be hospitalized in 1998–99. While pregnancy accounts for much of this difference, women were also more likely to have been hospitalized for cancer, mental disorders, digestive diseases, genitourinary diseases, and musculoskeletal diseases. Men, on the other hand, were more likely to have been hospitalized for circulatory and respiratory diseases and for injuries and poisoning (CIHI, 2001a; Federal, Provincial and Territorial Advisory Committee on Population Health, 1999a, b).

The data on mental disorders treated in psychiatric and acute-care hospitals show that overall, female rates are markedly higher than male rates. For particular causes, female rates are higher than male rates for affective psychoses, neurotic disorders, adjustment reaction, depressive reaction disorder, and senile and pre-senile organic psychotic conditions. On the other hand, male rates are higher than female rates for schizophrenic psychoses and alcohol and drug dependency (CIHI, 2001b; Federal, Provincial and Territorial Advisory Committee on Population Health, 1999a, b).

These data indicate that women are more likely than men to be hospitalized for physical illness and mental disorders. The causes of hospitalization are also different for male and female populations.

Differences in morbidity and mortality patterns between men and women are evident in other areas (DesMeules, Turner & Cho, 2003; DesMeules, Manuel & Cho, 2003; Federal, Provincial and Territorial Advisory Committee on Population Health, 1999a; Statistics Canada, 1995; Trypuc, 1994). For instance, while men are more likely than women to commit suicide, women are twice as likely as men to be depressed and their depression lasts longer. Women are also more likely than men to report conditions such as allergies, migraine headaches, and arthritis and rheumatism. These conditions impair women's functional health and cause activity limitations. While conditions such as arthritis as a cause of activity limitation are reported more frequently by women, men report conditions such as heart, back, and limb problems as causing activity limitation. Women also report more long-term disability and chronic conditions than men.

Women are more likely than men to visit health professionals, visit a general practitioner, make more frequent visits to doctors, and use emergency health services. Women are more likely than men to have had a recent eye examination and physical examination. Women also use more antidepressant drugs than men, which is consistent with higher levels of depression experienced by women.

Similar patterns of morbidity and mortality in male and female populations exist in other advanced countries (see, for example, Miles, 1991; Lorber, 2000; Rieker & Bird, 2000). How can these differences and contradictions in morbidity and mortality be explained? The following section discusses the explanations most often advanced.

EXPLANATIONS OF GENDER DIFFERENCES IN MORBIDITY AND MORTALITY

The subject of male and female differences in morbidity and mortality patterns has received considerable attention. While acknowledging that these explanations are not mutually exclusive, Miles (1991, pp. 10–12) lists three possible ways to account for these differences: "artefact," genetic causation, and social causation. Some researchers argue that these differences are an "artefact" rather than real. Their main argument is that while women's health status is not any worse than men's, women are more likely to take notice of their symptoms, are inclined to see a physician and seek treatment, and are more willing to respond to health surveys (see Miles, 1991, pp. 10–12).

Biological and genetic differences (sex chromosomes and hormones) have also been used to explain morbidity and mortality differences between men and women. Statistics that are often used to show female "superiority" refer to differences in male and female conception, fetal mortality, stillbirths, and infant mortality rates (for review, see Trypuc, 1994; Miles, 1991). It is also argued that females, due to their biological and genetic constitution, reproductive anatomy, and physiology, may be endowed with resistance to certain diseases.

The third general explanation focuses on the social–structural context of women's and men's lives. Social and economic inequalities and socially constructed gender roles have important consequences for men's and women's lives, and produce variations in health and illness patterns. Women are more likely than men to be poor, a phenomenon commonly referred to as the "feminization of poverty." In 2003, the poverty rate was 17.1 percent for women and 14.1 percent for men; for unattached women the rate was 42.1 percent and for unattached men it was 34 percent (National Council of Welfare, 2006a).

Social and economic inequalities produce differential opportunities and life chances; social roles and related activities expose men and women to different health risks (Pederson & Raphael, 2004; Muszynski, 1994; Trypuc, 1994; Rieker & Bird, 2000; Miles, 1991; Lorber, 2000). The focus here is on the social production of health and illness. Social and economic inequality produces negative health outcomes and poor health status for women. Also, it is argued that male socialization and lifestyles expose men to riskier, aggressive, and dangerous behaviour. For instance, men have higher mortality due to motor vehicle accidents. Men are also more likely to indulge in excessive smoking, drinking, and substance abuse, with negative health consequences (Federal, Provincial and Territorial Advisory Committee on Population Health, 1999a, b; Trypuc, 1994). On the other hand, it is pointed out that the often demanding and contradictory social roles of women produce negative health outcomes. For instance, domestic work responsibility and a caring role in the family, combined with the increasing participation of women in the paid work force, may contribute to elevated stress levels among women.

Two theoretical perspectives are advanced to explain gender differences in psychological health: differential exposure theory and differential vulnerability theory. Rieker and Bird (2000, p. 102) state: "Both theories attribute gender differences in psychological well-being to the social organization of men's and women's lives. The former emphasizes the extent to which men and women are exposed to particular stressors, whereas the latter focuses on men's and women's responses to those stressors." According to the differential exposure theory, women experience hardships and stressors to a greater extent than do men because of their disadvantaged position relative to men in the work force and the inequitable division of work in the household. Married women in particular experience work overload due to paid work outside the home as well as a majority of the household work; this overload may produce higher levels of psychological distress. Women "caught" in these circumstances may also perceive a lack of control over their lives, which in turn can increase psychological distress and depression.

According to the differential vulnerability theory, the effects of particular stressors differ for men and women for a variety of reasons. For instance, men and women may attach different meanings and significance to paid work and family roles because of different normative expectations about work and family responsibilities (Simon, 1995). Socio-cultural beliefs and normative expectations may affect men's and women's self-evaluations as parents and spouses. Women are more likely than men to experience role conflict and to see their work and family roles as competing rather than integral, and thus they experience more guilt and stress than men (Simon, 1995). That the consequences of housework and employment differ for men and women and produce different health outcomes is supported by other research evidence (for review, see Miles, 1991; Rieker & Bird, 2000; Trypuc, 1994; Lorber, 2000; Muszynski, 1994). Normative socio-cultural expectations and society's treatment of women affect their mental health. As Paltiel (1987, p. 234) states: "Every woman's mental health is affected by the way her society regards and treats unmarried or married women, childless women, mothers, poor women, assaulted women, divorced women, minority women, disabled women, widows, aged women, or women with aspirations."

Patterns of health and illness have everything to do with women's lives, work, employment opportunities, life experience, and social and economic circumstances. However, it should be noted that social, economic, and other disadvantages do not accrue to all women equally (MacIntyre, Hunt & Sweeting, 1996). Women are not a homogeneous group, but, rather, are diversified and stratified by class, race, and ethnicity. The social patterning of health and disease are also differentially experienced by various subgroups (Walters, Lenton & McKeary, 1995). For instance, women with low income and low education levels report poorer health, and "unhealthy" lifestyles are also associated with lower income and lower education (Walters, Lenton & McKeary, 1995). Racial minority women often experience ill health because of unhealthy work environments and harsher working conditions in areas such as farm labour, textiles and sewing, and domestic work (for review, see Bolaria & Bolaria, 1994a, b, c). Aboriginal people overall show lower life expectancy and greater incidence of morbidity and premature deaths than non-Aboriginal people (Shah, 2004; Tjepkema, 2002). Aboriginal women in Canada have poor health status, greater incidence of sickness and disease, and shorter life expectancies than the overall female population (Health Canada, 2003b). The differential health of Aboriginal, immigrant, and visible minority women is linked to the racial and gender differences in a number of social-structural determinants of health, such as income, living conditions, employment, working conditions, and social exclusion (Chard, Badets & Howatson-Lev, 2000; Chard, 2000; Tait, 2000; Pederson & Raphael, 2004; Galabuzi, 2004, 2006; Picot, 2004). It should be noted that immigrants initially have better health status than persons born in Canada. This is generally referred to as the healthy immigrant effect. This effect is attributed to health screening tests for immigrants before entry and to the fact that young and healthy people are more likely to emigrate. However, this healthy immigrant effect disappears over time (Ali, 2002; Perez, 2002). This is because of labour market discrimination, low incomes, poor living and working conditions, and high incidence of poverty among recent immigrants and some racial minority groups (McPherson, 2004).

Differential opportunity structure and the work histories and work experience of most women place them at a disadvantage not only throughout their working lives but also in old age. Senior women have relatively low incomes and have the highest incidence of low income of any age group (Lindsay, 2000). Economic disadvantage produces health disadvantage for many senior women (McPherson, 2004). Health status inequalities and the social patterning of disease between diverse groups of women are supported by research findings from other countries (see Walters, Lenton & McKeary, 1995; Rieker & Bird, 2000).

In summary, sociological research on gender and health has focused on how socially structured gender inequalities and socially constructed gender roles contribute to differences in women's and men's physical and mental health. Social patterning of health and disease are also differentially experienced by various subgroups of women, according to their social class, race, and ethnicity. Race, class, and gender are important determinants of life experiences and contribute to differences in physical and mental health.

GLOBAL CONTEXT: PERILS OF BEING FEMALE

While conditions for women and their lives continue to improve, women and girls still face considerable economic exploitation, sexual exploitation, violence, and discrimination (United Nations Population Fund, 2000; UNICEF, 2005; United Nations 2003, 2004; ILO, 2003; Ehrenreich & Hochschild, 2003). The situation for women and girls remains particularly precarious in many low income countries where patriarchal relations and social, cultural, and religious practices continue to victimize women and girls, and expose them to extensive and various forms of violence. In this section we are particularly concerned with violence and health outcomes.

Violence against women, its consequences for women's health, and its impact on morbidity and mortality are being increasingly recognized. Violence and abuse are associated with numerous health and social problems, including depression, child abuse, suicide, and substance abuse. Battered women face higher risk of miscarriage and low birth weight babies, and are four to five times more likely to require psychiatric treatment and five times more likely to commit suicide. Dealing with violence, abuse, and rape accounted for five percent of the global health budget (World Bank, 1993; Stark & Flitcraft, 1991).

Given the importance of violence against women and its health consequences, it is important to discuss the extent of violence and the link between specific forms of violence and their health impact. Violence against women is widespread; cuts across social, economic, and national boundaries; and tends to be much more common in some lower-income countries. Women face the risk of violence throughout their lives, from infancy to old age, and even before birth (prenatal) in the form of sex-selective abortions (United Nations Population Fund, 2000).

Table 12.1 summarizes the type of violence women may face during their lifecourse. Some forms of violence are more prevalent in some countries than in others, and the extent and risk of violence is mediated by the economic and legal position and rights of women. In early life, the risks girls face include genital mutilation, incest, infanticide, and child prostitution. During adolescence, girls and women face the risk of date and courtship violence, coercive sex and rape, workplace sexual abuse, and forced prostitution. During their reproductive phase, the types of violence women face include **dowry deaths**, partner homicide, and rape. Women are also at a high risk of abuse and violence in old age.

The universality of this phenomenon threatens women's lives, health, and well-being everywhere, but more so in some low-income countries. In addition to experiencing

TABLE 12.1 *Gender Violence at Various Stages in a Woman's Life*

Phase	Type of Violence
Prenatal	Sex-selective abortions, battering during pregnancy, coerced pregnancy (rape during war)
Infancy	Female infanticide, emotional and physical abuse, differential access to food and medical care
Childhood	Genital mutilation, incest and sexual abuse, child prostitution; differential access to food, medical care, and education
Adolescence	Dating and courtship violence, economically coerced sex, sexual abuse in the workplace, rape, sexual harassment, forced prostitution
Reproductive	Abuse of women by intimate partners, marital rape, dowry abuse and murders, partner homicide, psychological abuse, sexual abuse in the workplace, sexual harassment, rape, abuse of women with disabilities
Old Age	Abuse of widows, elder abuse (which mostly affects women)

Source: United Nations Population Fund (2000, p. 28).

greater economic disparities, men and women in these countries face social and cultural customs and practices that legitimize subordination, sexual abuse, and violence. In some instances, women even face death if they violate or are suspected of violating certain customs and cultural practices (UNFPA, 2000; UN, 1995; Fischbach & Donnelly, 1996).

The following section discusses certain forms of violence and their associated health and other consequences for women. These forms of violence are prevalent only in certain low-income countries.

TRAFFICKING, VIOLENCE, AND HEALTH

Millions of young girls and women are victims of international sex trafficking and forced prostitution (UN, 1995; UNFPA, 2000). It is estimated that every year about four million girls and women are bought and sold worldwide for prostitution, slavery, or forced marriage (UNFPA, 2000; Stewart & Gajic-Veljanoski, 2005). The greatest problem with trafficking is occurring in Asia (UNICEF, 2000; UNFPA, 2000).

Victims of sex trafficking face considerable physical, psychological, and sexual abuse. They are usually isolated, and if they attempt to leave they are faced with physical violence. They are forced to comply with the sexual demands of their clients. Forced and unprotected sex and frequent intercourse with multiple partners put women at risk of sexually transmitted diseases, including HIV and AIDS. Frequent sex and sexual abuse also increase their risk of gynecological problems, including adhesions, infections, chronic pelvic pain, and vaginal bleeding. Sexual abuse, violence, and isolation also have negative psychological consequences for these girls and women. These victims of trafficking have almost no access to health care, and their health problems go untreated, which often leads to early deaths (UNFPA, 2000). Stewart and Gajic-Veljanoski (2005) summarize the physical and psychological health risks faced by women who are trafficked (Table 12.2).

TABLE 12.2 *Physical and Psychological Health Risks Faced by Women Who Are Trafficked*

Food and sleep deprivation
Repeated rape
Physical injury such as bruising, broken bones or teeth, mouth injuries, cuts, burns
Emotional manipulation, including threats, blackmail
Persistent sexual exploitation, social marginalization
Sexually transmitted diseases and unwanted pregnancies from unsafe sexual practices such as condom refusal
Forced or unsafe abortion
Absence of gynecologic care and HIV testing
Anxiety, post-traumatic stress disorder, depression, suicidal tendencies
Somaticized symptoms and other sequelae of abuse (e.g., headaches, back and body aches, dizziness, nausea, vision disturbances)
Inability to recuperate and integrate into society

Source: Donna E. Stewart and Olga Gajic-Veljanoski, Trafficking in Women: The Canadian Perspective. *Canadian Medical Association Journal (CMAJ)*, July 5, 2005, *173*(1), 1–25.

FEMALE GENITAL MUTILATION

Female genital mutilation (FGM), often referred to as female circumcision, is practiced in many countries, mostly in Africa and western Asian regions. Recent estimates indicate that at least 130 million women have been forced to undergo female genital mutilation or cutting or **social surgery**; another two million are at risk each year from this dangerous practice (UNFPA, 2000, p. 26). The procedure may be performed on infants, females a few years old, or adolescent girls, and is often performed without anesthesia, in unsanitary conditions, and rarely with proper surgical instruments (UNFPA, 2000; Fischbach & Donnelly, 1996). The practice is intended to preserve the virginity of young girls and the control of female sexuality until marriage. If not circumcised, women may be viewed as sexually permissive. There are many health risks associated with female circumcision, including hemorrhage, infections due to crude and unsanitary instruments, pelvic infections, **chronic conditions** such as urinary tract infections, and, in some cases, infertility. This procedure may also increase the risk of neonatal deaths and stillbirths (UNFPA, 2000; Fischbach & Donnelly, 1996).

SEX-SELECTIVE ABORTIONS AND INFANTICIDE

Another form of violence against women and girls involves sex-selective abortions and infanticide. UNFPA (2000, p. 25) states that "at least 60 million girls who would otherwise be expected to be alive are 'missing' from various populations, mostly in Asia, as a result of sex-selective abortions, infanticide or neglect." Prenatal gender tests are used to abort female babies in many Asian countries. In countries where these tests are banned, illegal tests are readily available. This practice is most common in countries where male children are preferred and females are considered a liability to the family because of various social customs and cultural practices. One of these costly customs, discussed in the following section, is the institution of dowry, practiced in many Asian countries. Female infanticide also takes many girls' lives. The result is that in some Asian countries, there are 105 men for every 100 women (UNFPA, 2000). Neglect, inadequate nutrition, and poor health services also take their toll on girls.

For women these practices pose considerable health risks, including unsafe abortions, frequent and unwanted pregnancies in pursuit of a male child, lack of emergency obstetric care, and infections and hemorrhaging due to complications associated with abortions. Life-saving emergency care is unavailable to women in many low-income countries, particularly in rural areas. Unsafe abortions account for a significant number of maternal deaths. It is estimated that about 20 million unsafe abortions are performed each year, causing injuries, suffering, and illnesses to millions of women; approximately 78,000 die from these procedures each year as well (UNFPA, 2000; Sernau, 2006).

DOWRY DEATHS AND HONOUR KILLINGS

Women and girls are also victims of "dowry deaths," "accidental kitchen deaths," and "bride burning" in many low-income countries. **Honour killings** are often linked to the family's demands for chastity and virginity, a woman's refusal to marry the person chosen by the family, a woman's refusal to stay in an abusive relationship, pregnancy outside of marriage, and even the "dishonour" of having been a victim of rape (World Bank, 1993; UNFPA, 2000; UN, 1995). Rape in some societies is considered a crime against the woman's family and family honour rather than a violation of women. The perpetrators of these killings, who are often members of the victims' own families, often go unpunished by courts because the defense of family honour under these circumstances is often approved and sanctioned by the community and is treated by the courts as a mitigating circumstance (UN, 2000; UNFPA, 2000). These notions of "family honour" have cost thousands of women their lives; as many as 5,000 girls and women are murdered every year for "dishonouring" their families (UNFPA, 2000).

While the true mortality figures related to dowry disputes and unmet dowry demands by the husband and his family remain unknown, these deaths have been reported with increasing frequency on the Indian subcontinent (Bolaria & Bolaria, 2002). Typically, the husband and his family make ongoing demands for additional dowry from the bride and her family, which they may not be able to meet. This often leads to an increasing frequency of domestic abuse culminating in the bride's "accidental death," often claimed by the husband to be the result of a "kitchen fire" caused by overheated cooking oil or the bursting of a stove. These deaths are rarely investigated and sometimes may be treated as suicides. With the wife's death, the husband and his family are then free to pursue another, more lucrative, marriage.

Such is the plight of women in societies where they are considered expendable. If they survive sex-selective abortion, infanticide, "honour killings," and "accidental kitchen deaths," many women face social subordination, exploitation, physical and sexual abuse, and violence during their lifecourse. Domestic violence is also linked to various forms of mental disorder, including depression, **post-traumatic stress disorder** (PTSD), phobia, substance use and abuse, and suicide (Fischbach & Donnelly, 1996).

CONCLUSION

The overarching theme of this chapter is that health and illness cannot be understood with reference only to biological phenomena and medical knowledge. Human experiences of health and illness are embedded in economic, social, and cultural contexts, and these factors play an important role in the social distribution of health and illness. Gender is an important part of life; women's and men's different life experiences are shaped by socially structured gender inequality and socially constructed gender roles. Different life circumstances and experiences in turn produce variations in health and illness patterns between men and women. Women, however, are not a homogeneous group. Race and class intersect with gender to produce subgroup differences in health and illness patterns. Women living in poor countries do not fare well relative to women in rich industrialized countries.

In developed industrialized countries, women live longer than men but also experience more illnesses. Women are also more likely than men to be hospitalized for physical illness and mental disorders. The causes of hospitalization are different for male and female populations. Men are more likely to have been hospitalized for circulatory and respiratory diseases, injuries, and poisoning. In addition to being hospitalized for pregnancy, women are more likely to have been hospitalized for cancer and digestive, genitourinary, and musculoskeletal diseases. Men are more likely than women to have been hospitalized for schizophrenic psychoses and alcohol and drug dependency. Female rates are higher in areas such as neurotic disorders, affective psychoses, and depressive reaction disorder.

Women are also more likely than men to report conditions such as migraine headaches and allergies, which impair women's functional health and cause activity limitations. Men, on the other hand, report conditions such as heart and back problems causing activity limitations. Women visit health professionals more often than men do.

To account for differences in morbidity and mortality, three possible explanations are discussed: "artefact," genetic causation, and social causation, with particular emphasis on the social-structural context of men's and women's lives. Differential exposure theory and differential vulnerability theory are discussed to explain general differences in psychological health. Sociological explanations focus on how socially structured inequality and gender roles contribute to differences in men's and women's physical and mental health. Social and economic subgroup differences among women produce subgroup differences in health status.

The last section of the chapter addressed women's situation in the global context with particular focus on various forms of violence against women in low-income countries. It examined violence involving female genital mutilation, dowry deaths and honour killings, trafficking in girls and women, sex-selective abortions, female infanticide, and their health consequences for women, and the impact of various forms of violence on morbidity and mortality patterns.

STUDY QUESTIONS

1. *Why do sex differences in mortality and morbidity continue to exist? Give evidence to support the argument that women's health care will not improve until women's position in society improves.*
2. *Discuss the statement that the differential treatment that women receive both as providers and consumers of health care is a manifestation of patriarchal culture and gender inequality in the larger society.*
3. *Discuss the extent of violence against women and the relationship between health and various forms of violence.*
4. *Discuss the differential exposure theory and differential vulnerability theory to explain gender differences in psychological well-being.*
5. *Discuss how socio-economic position, race, and other dimensions of social status interact with gender to produce variations in gender inequality and its health consequences.*
6. *Discuss how socially constructed gender roles and differential opportunities shape men's and women's lives and in turn affect their health.*

GLOSSARY

battered women women subjected to repeated attacks or multiple blows by a partner.

cardiovascular diseases all diseases of the circulatory system, including ischemic heart disease and stroke.

chronic conditions conditions having duration of at least six months.

dowry deaths deaths related to unmet demands of wealth from a bride's family by a husband's family. The most common form of dowry death is the "kitchen accident," in which a woman is "accidentally" burned to death by overheated oil or the bursting of a cooking stove.

honour killings the killing of rape victims, women suspected of adultery, women who refuse to marry the person chosen by their families, or women who refuse to stay in an abusive marriage.

hospital separations patients who are discharged from or die in hospitals.

post-traumatic stress disorder (PTSD) a complex set of symptoms in the aftermath of a psychologically traumatic event and experience; characteristic symptoms include depression, trouble concentrating, sleep disturbance, and memory impairment.

social surgery female circumcision; the cultural practice of surgically altering female genitalia, including genital mutilation (circumcision and infibulation).

violence an act involving force or coercion, with the intention of causing physical, psychological, and emotional harm.

REFERENCES

Ali, J. (2002). Mental health of Canada's immigrants. *Health Reports,* Vol. 13 (Statistics Canada, cat. no. 82–003). Ottawa: Statistics Canada.

Bolaria, B.S., & Bolaria, R. (Eds.). (1994a). *Racial minorities, medicine and health.* Halifax and Saskatoon: Fernwood.

Bolaria, B.S., & Bolaria, R. (Eds.). (1994b). *Women, medicine and health.* Halifax and Saskatoon: Fernwood.

Bolaria, B.S., & Bolaria, R. (1994c). Immigrant status and health status: Women and racial minority immigrant workers. In B.S. Bolaria & R. Bolaria (Eds.), *Racial minorities, medicine and health* (pp. 149–168). Halifax and Saskatoon: Fernwood.

Bolaria, B.S., & Bolaria, R. (2002). Women's lives, women's health. In B.S. Bolaria & H.D. Dickinson (Eds.), *Health, illness and health care in Canada* (pp. 169–184). Toronto: Thomson Nelson.

Canadian Institute for Health Information. (CIHI). (2001a). *Hospital morbidity database, 1995–1996.* Compiled from Federal, Provincial and Territorial Advisory Committee on Population Health (1999). *Statistical report on the health of Canadians.* Ottawa: Minister of Public Works and Government Services.

Canadian Institute for Health Information. (CIHI). (2001b). *Mental health database, 1995–1996.* Compiled from Federal, Provincial and Territorial Advisory Committee on Population Health (1999). *Statistical report on the health of Canadians.* Ottawa: Minister of Public Works and Government Services.

Canadian Research Institute for the Advancement of Women (CRIAW). (2002). *Women's experience of racism: How race and gender interact.* Ottawa: CRIAW.

Chard, J. (2000). Women in a visible minority. In Statistics Canada, *Women in Canada 2000: A gender based statistical report* (pp. 219–246). Ottawa: Statistics Canada.

Chard, J., Badets, J., & Howatson-Lev, L. (2000). Immigrant women. In Statistics Canada, *Women in Canada 2000: A gender based statistical report* (pp. 189–218). Ottawa: Statistics Canada.

Delahanty, J. (1999). *From social movements to social clauses: Grading strategies for improving conditions for women garment workers*. Ottawa: North-South Institute.

DesMeules, M., Manuel, D., & Cho, R. (2003). *Women's health surveillance report: A multidimensional look at the health of Canadian women* (pp. 19–20). Ottawa: Health Canada, Canadian Population Health Initiative.

DesMeules, M., Turner, L., & Cho, R. (2003). Morbidity experiences and disability among Canadian women. In M. DesMeules et al. (Eds.), *Women's health surveillance report: A multidimensional look at the health of Canadian women*. Ottawa: Health Canada, Canadian Population Health Initiative.

Dixon-Mueller, R. (1994). Abortion policy and women's health in developing countries. In E. Fee & N. Krieger (Eds.), *Women's health, politics and power: Essays on sex/gender, medicine, and public health* (pp. 191–210). Amityville, NY: Baywood.

Doyal, L. (1995). *What makes women sick: Gender and the political economy of health*. London: Macmillan.

Doyal, L. (2004). Gender and the 10/90 gap in health research. *Bulletin of the World Health Organization, 82*, 162.

Ehrenreich, B., & Hochschild, A.R. (2003). *Global women: Nannies, maids, and sex workers in the new economy*. New York: Metropolitan Books.

Federal, Provincial and Territorial Advisory Committee on Population Health. (1999a). *Statistical report on the health of Canadians*. Ottawa: Minister of Public Works and Government Services.

Federal, Provincial and Territorial Advisory Committee on Population Health. (1999b). *Toward a healthy future: Second report on the health of Canadians*. Ottawa: Minister of Public Works and Government Services.

Fee, E., & Krieger, N. (Eds.). (1994). *Women's health, politics and power: Essays on sex/gender, medicine and public health*. Amityville, NY: Baywood.

Findlay, D.A., & Miller, L.J. (1994). Medical power and women's bodies. In B.S. Bolaria & R. Bolaria (Eds.), *Women, medicine and health* (pp. 115–139). Halifax and Saskatoon: Fernwood.

Fischbach, R.L., & Donnelly, E. (1996). Domestic violence against women: A contemporary issue in international health. In J. Subedi & E.B. Gallagher (Eds.), *Society, health, and disease: Transcultural perspectives* (pp. 316–345). Upper Saddle River, NJ: Prentice-Hall.

Galabuzi, G.E. (2004). Social exclusion. In D. Raphael (Ed.), *Social determinants of health: Canadian perspective* (pp. 235–252). Toronto: Canadian Scholars' Press.

Galabuzi, G.E. (2006). *Canada's economic apartheid: The social exclusion of racialized groups in the new century*. Toronto: Canadian Scholars' Press.

Hale, A. (1996). The deregulated global economy: Women workers and strategies of resistance. *Gender and Development, 4*(3), 8–15.

Health Canada. (2002). *Healthy Canadians: A federal report on comparable health indicators 2002*. Ottawa: Health Canada.

Health Canada. (2003a). *Exploring concepts of gender and health*. Ottawa: Women's Health Bureau.

Health Canada. (2003b). *The health of Aboriginal women*. Ottawa: Health Canada.

Hubbard, R. (1990). *The politics of women's biology*. New Brunswick, NJ: Rutgers University Press.

Hyman, I. (2001). *Immigration and health. Working Paper Series*. Ottawa: Applied Research and Analysis Directorate, Health Canada.

International Labour Organization (ILO). (2003). *Global employment trends*. Geneva: ILO.

Jackson, B., Pederson, A., Armstrong, P., Boscoe, M., Chow, B., Grant, K.R., Gubermahn, N., & Wilson, K. (Fall 2004). Quality care is like a carton of eggs: Using a gender based diversity analysis to assess quality of health care. *Canadian Women Studies, 24*(1), 15–22.

Lindsay, C. (2000). Senior women. In Statistics Canada, *Women in Canada 2000: A gender based statistical report* (pp. 269–294). Ottawa: Statistics Canada.

Lorber, J. (1997). *Gender and the social construction of illness.* Thousand Oaks, CA: Sage.

Lorber, J. (2000). Women get sicker but men die quicker: Gender and health. In P. Brown (Ed.), *Perspectives in medical sociology* (3rd ed., pp. 40–70). Prospect Heights, IL: Waveland Press.

MacIntyre, S., Hunt, K., & Sweeting, H. (1996). Gender differences in health: Are things really as simple as they seem? *Social Science and Medicine, 42*, 617–624.

McLeod, K., & Baris, E. (2000). Globalization and international trade in the twenty-first century: Opportunities for and threats to the health sector in the south. *International Journal of Health Services, 30*(1), 187–210.

McMullen, J. (2004). *Understanding social inequality: Intersections of class, age, gender, ethnicity and race in Canada.* Toronto: Oxford University Press.

McPherson, B.D. (2004). *Aging as a social process: Canadian perspective.* Don Mills, Ont.: Oxford University Press.

Messing, K. (1991). *Occupational safety and health concerns of Canadian women.* Ottawa: Minister of Supply and Services Canada.

Miles, A. (1991). *Women's health and medicine.* Milton Keynes, PA: Open University Press.

Muszynski, A. (1994). Gender inequality and life chances: Women's lives and health. In B.S. Bolaria & R. Bolaria (Eds.), *Women, medicine and health* (pp. 57–72). Halifax and Saskatoon: Fernwood.

National Council of Welfare (2006a). *Poverty facts 2003.* Ottawa: National Council of Welfare.

National Council of Welfare (2006b). *Poverty facts 2002 and 2003.* Ottawa: National Council of Welfare.

Newbold, K.B., & Danforth, J. (2003). Health status and Canada's immigrant population. *Social Science and Medicine, 57*, 181–199.

Ontario Public Health Association (OPHA). (2000). *Improving the access to and quality of public health services for lesbian and gays.* Toronto: OPHA.

Organisation for Economic Co-operation and Development (OECD). (1998). *OECD health data 98.* Paris: OECD.

Paltiel, F.L. (1987). Women and mental health: A post-Nairobi perspective. *World Health Statistics Quarterly, 40*, 233–266.

Perez, C.E. (2002). Health status and health behaviour among immigrants. *Health Reports*, Vol. 13 (Statistics Canada, cat. no. 82–003). Ottawa: Statistics Canada.

Peterson, A. & Raphael, D. (2006). Gender, race and health inequalities. In D. Raphael, T. Bryant & M. Rieux (Eds.), *Staying alive: Critical perspectives on health, illness and health care* (pp. 159–192). Toronto: Canadian Scholars' Press.

Phipps, S. (2003). *The impact of poverty on health.* Ottawa: Canadian Institute of Health Information.

Picot, G. (2004). *The deteriorating economic welfare of immigrants and possible causes.* Ottawa: Statistics Canada.

Rieker, P.P., & Bird, C.E. (2000). Sociological explanations of gender differences in mental and physical health. In C.E. Bird, P. Conrad, & A.M. Fremont (Eds.), *Handbook of medical sociology* (5th ed., pp. 98–113). Upper Saddle River, NJ: Prentice-Hall.

Robbins, R.H. (2005). *Global problems and the culture of capitalism.* Toronto: Pearson Education.

Santow, G. (1995). Social roles and physical health: The case of female disadvantage in poor countries. *Social Science and Medicine, 40,* 147–161.

Sernau, S. (2006). *Global problems: The search for equity, peace and sustainability.* Toronto: Pearson Education.

Shah, C.P. (2004). The health of Aboriginal peoples (pp. 267–280). In D. Raphael (Ed.), *Social determinants of health: Canadian perspective.* Toronto: Canadian Scholars' Press.

Simon, R.W. (1995). Gender, multiple roles, role meaning, and mental health. *Journal of Health and Social Behavior, 36*(2), 182–194.

Stark, E., & Flitcraft, A. (1991). Spouse abuse. In M. Rosenberg & M. Fenley (Eds.), *Violence in America: A public health approach* (pp. 123–157). New York: Oxford University Press.

Statistics Canada. (1998, April 16). Deaths 1996. *The Daily.* Ottawa (cat. no. 11–001-XIE).

Statistics Canada, Health Statistics Division. (1999). *Health indicators, 1999.* Ottawa (cat. no. 82–221-XCB).

Statistics Canada (2005, February 1). Health Indicators, *The Daily.* Ottawa.

Stewart, D.E. & Gajic-Veljanoski, O. (July, 2005). Trafficking in women: The Canadian perspective. *Canadian Medical Association Journal (CMAJ), 173*(1), pp. 25–26.

Subedi, J., & Gallagher, E.B. (Eds.). (1996). *Society, health and disease: Transcultural perspectives.* Upper Saddle River, NJ: Prentice-Hall.

Sundari, T.K. (1994). The untold story: How the health care systems in developing countries contribute to maternal mortality. In E. Fee & N. Krieger (Eds.), *Women's health, politics and power: Essays on sex/gender, medicine, and public health* (pp. 173–190). Amityville, NY: Baywood.

Syme, S.L., & Yen, I.H. (2000). Social epidemiology and medical sociology: Different approaches to the same problem. In C.E. Bird, P. Conrad, & A.M. Fremont (Eds.), *Handbook of medical sociology* (5th ed., pp. 365–376). Saddle River, NJ: Prentice-Hall.

Tait, H. (2000). Aboriginal women. In Statistics Canada, *Women in Canada 2000: A gender based statistical report* (pp. 247–268). Ottawa: Statistics Canada.

Theobald, S. (1996). Employment and environmental hazard: Women workers and strategies of resistance in northern Thailand. *Gender and Development, 4*(3), 16–21.

Tjepkema, M. (2002). The health of the off-reserve Aboriginal population. *Health Reports Supplement, 13,* 1–17.

Trypuc, J.M. (1994). Gender based mortality and morbidity patterns and health risks. In B.S. Bolaria & R. Bolaria (Eds.), *Women, medicine and health* (pp. 73–88). Halifax and Saskatoon: Fernwood.

United Nations (UN). (1995). *The world's women: 1995 trends and statistics.* New York: UN.

United Nations (UN). (2000). *Civil and political rights, including questions of disappearances and summary executions: Report of the special rapporteur, Asma Janhangir.* New York: UN Commission on Human Rights.

United Nations (UN) (2003). *Human development report. United Nations development program.* New York: Oxford University Press.

United Nations (UN) (2004). *Human development report. United Nations development program.* New York: Oxford University Press.

United Nations AIDS (UNAIDS). (2004). *Report on the global AIDS epidemic.* New York: United Nations.

United Nations Children's Fund (UNICEF). (2000, January 20). UNICEF: Child sex trafficking must end. Press Release. New York: UNICEF.

United Nations Children's Fund (UNICEF). (2005). *Monitoring the status of women and children: Education*. New York: UNICEF.

United Nations Population Fund (UNFPA). (1999). *Violence against girls and women: A public health priority*. New York: UNFPA.

United Nations Population Fund (UNFPA). (2000). *The state of world population: Lives together, worlds apart, men and women in a time of change*. New York: UNFPA.

Walters, V., Lenton, R., & McKeary, M. (1995). *Women's health in the context of women's lives*. Ottawa: Minister of Supply and Services.

World Bank. (1993). *World development report 1993: Investing in health* (Report No. 11778). Washington, DC: World Bank.

World Health Organization (WHO). (1994). *Ninth general programme of work, 1996–2001*. Geneva: WHO.

World Health Organization (WHO). (1997). *Abortion: A tabulation of available data on the frequency and mortality of unsafe abortion* (3rd ed.). Geneva: WHO.

Yanz, L., Jeffcott, B., Ladd, D., & Atlui, J. (1999). *Policy options to improve standards for women garment workers in Canada and internationally*. Ottawa: Status of Women Canada.

Zimmerman, S. (2000). The medical management of femininity: Women's experiences with silicone breast implants. In P. Brown (Ed.), *Perspectives in medical sociology* (3rd ed., pp. 256–281). Prospect Heights, IL: Waveland Press.

13

Through Medical Eyes: The Medicalization of Women's Bodies and Women's Lives

CAROL BERENSON University of Calgary

LESLIE J. MILLER University of Calgary

DEBORAH A. FINDLAY Dalhousie University

INTRODUCTION

It has been said that the influence of professional medicine has transformed the body from an arena of sacred forces to the mundane reality of diet, cosmetics, exercise, and preventative medicine (Turner, 1984, p. 216). The writer's point is that the human body, once the concern of the priest, is now the business of the doctor. This chapter examines the **medicalization** of women's bodies and women's lives. It begins by considering the historical emergence of modern medical knowledge as a powerful and prestigious perspective on the world and goes on to ask why it is that the lives of women, in particular, have become favoured territory for medical intervention. The second part of the chapter looks at three examples of medicalization in women's lives, in order to examine the process, and to assess the outcome when these activities and conditions are defined as medical problems. In the final section, we ask what women stand to gain, as well as lose, when they and others come to see their lives through medical eyes.

THE RISE OF MEDICAL DISCOURSE AND THE PROFESSIONALIZATION OF MEDICINE

Medicalization refers to the process whereby an activity or a condition becomes defined by society at large as an illness (either physical or psychological) and is thereby moved into the sphere of control of the medical profession (Zola, 1972, 1975). Habitual gambling, for example, has been regarded by a minority as a sin and by most people as a leisure pursuit, perhaps wasteful, but a pastime nevertheless. Lately, however, gambling has been described as a psychological illness – compulsive gambling. It is in the process of being medicalized. The consequences of this shift in **discourse** (i.e., in the way of thinking and talking) about gambling are considerable: for doctors and counselors, who now have in gamblers a new market for their services or treatment; perhaps for casinos, which may find themselves subject to new regulations, insofar as they are deemed to contribute to the "disease"; and, finally, for gamblers themselves, who are no longer treated as sinners or wastrels but as patients, with claims on our sympathy and on our medical insurance plans (Conrad & Schneider, 1980).

The concern in this chapter is the medicalization of women's bodies and lives. The modern view is to see the body through medical eyes (as a site of health and sickness); thus, it is hard to grasp that the traditional way of seeing and knowing the body was a religious one. The traditional world view regarded the body as the outward aspect of the soul, and on it appeared the marks of the unending struggle between Good and Evil. Thus, a whole range of problems now taken for granted as medical issues – bodily deformities (e.g., missing limbs, birthmarks), infertility, contagious diseases like the plague, and madness – were customarily regarded as signs of God's displeasure. Similarly, many of the things people did on and with their bodies (e.g., "mortification of the flesh") were done to obtain God's favour; and people dieted (fasted) not for the health of their bodies but for the health of their souls. As Durkheim pointed out, these conditions, and the social reactions they provoked, were visible to all and thus stood as stark reminders of the moral order to which all members of the community were bound (Durkheim, 1964). While we can still see lingering remnants of an older world view (the idea that AIDS is God's punishment for sexual sin, for example), the secular discourse of modern medicine has emerged, at least in the West, as the dominant way of thinking and speaking about the body.

HEALING BECOMES MEN'S WORK

As medicine began to emerge as a profession in its own right, the lives of ordinary women were of little concern to doctors and other powerful groups, a situation that reflected women's inferior status. For centuries, their health needs and the major social events in their lives, notably pregnancy and childbirth, had been left to other women in the community. But as the modern state emerged and began to take a proprietary interest in the health and well-being of its citizens, women, as the creators of those citizens, were gradually encompassed within the sphere of state and medical observation and control. At this point, healing came to be defined as a medical matter (Rothman, 1989, p. 77).

But instead of working to improve the skills and training of traditional female healers and midwives, the young, overwhelmingly male medical profession moved to take over their role in the management of women's health. After a long struggle, doctors succeeded in discrediting women's traditional expertise (as "ignorance," "superstition," and "incompetence") and, by the early 20th century, in driving them from the field. The result of this successful poaching operation is that male doctors became society's accepted experts on the subject of women and had the power to define what counted as health and illness (Lorber, 2000). Twentieth-century science went on to take the male body as the norm for research on women (Tavris, 1992), with the immediate result that many of women's basic functions were seen as "problems" and became subject to medical intervention. This has not, however, occurred without women's compliance. Sometimes this compliance arose out of women's own choices, such as a preference for medically supervised hospital births over home births. At other times, however, women have complied out of fear, ignorance, or misinformation (recall, for example, the adoption of, then flight from, Hormone Replacement Therapy (HRT) as a treatment for the problems of menopause).

The great prestige that doctors currently enjoy is a relatively recent phenomenon. Until the mid-19th century, surgeons occupied the same low rung on the ladder as barbers – the low status of both owing to the undesirable association with blood. What accounted then, for the rapid rise in power and prestige of the medical perspective? The dominance of medical discourse is related to the professionalization of medical practice. Professionalization occurs when an occupational group attains a monopoly over a certain area of expertise. First, the emerging profession must lay claim to an area of knowledge, and then create a clientele or market for its services. The new profession must also maintain its power, especially by controlling standards of training and certification for those who would enter the field, and by keeping the status of, income, and demand for its practitioners high (Torrance, 1987, p. 15; Freidson, 1970). Finally, the power of the medical profession was aided by medicine's crucially important alliance with science (Ludmerer, 1985, pp. 107, 231). By defining itself as a scientific endeavour, then, medicine was able to share the prestige that contemporary society accorded to fields that presented themselves as rational, scientific enterprises.

Many factors, then, contributed to the dominance of the medical perspective, and some scholars argue persuasively that social and political factors rather than strictly medical achievements (e.g., the ability to "conquer" disease) led to that prominence (Fisher, 1988, p. 134; Rothman, 1989). Whatever the case, the medical profession continues to struggle today to maintain its dominant position by warding off competitors (e.g., midwives, practitioners of "alternative" medicine), and by expanding its services into ever-new markets – most recently, sexuality. Once again, women's bodies offer a lucrative new territory for profit-making.

Feminists have argued that the medicalization of women's problems amounts to a real reduction in women's control over their own lives. Such a loss has important practical implications. The medical profession may discover a problem with women's bodies when women themselves feel that none exists, thus needlessly enmeshing them in the medical system. Or it may perceive interactional or structural problems as medical ones, prescribing pills and surgery when social and political change is called for (as when sexual problems, for example, are extracted from the larger issue of women's social relationships). In short, the issue of who gets to define women's needs and problems is an important aspect of power, for that group also gets to determine the solutions.

In the following sections we provide some concrete examples of how women's lives have been medicalized and of how that development has influenced their own understanding of these phenomena. First, the ongoing medicalization of menstruation is examined; then the creation of a medical discourse on appearance is discussed. Finally, we look at the very recent attempt to see women's sexuality and sexual problems through medical eyes.

THE MEDICALIZED MENSTRUATING BODY: THE NET WIDENS

When we recognize that the universal male body has been taken by researchers as the standard for what is normal and healthy (Tavris, 1992), then it is not surprising that women's bodies have been medicalized around those aspects that most strikingly differentiate them from the so-called normal male. Thus, it is the female reproductive body, and its various related bodily processes, that have been the site of disproportionate medical labeling and attention from a masculine medical profession.

The menstrual cycle is one aspect of the reproductive body that has been increasingly medicalized over the course of the 20th century. According to 19th-century medical doctrine, menstruation was regarded as a physically debilitating and pathological condition best dealt with by rest, in order to protect and revitalize the woman's reproductive capacities (Ratcliff, 2002, p. 151). Women, supposedly weakened by their menstruating bodies, were to limit activities to the less stressful private sphere and leave the rigors of public life to their non-menstruating male counterparts. Nineteenth-century thinking about women as fragile, delicate, and in need of male protection (Nelson, 2006, p. 74) fit well with a medicalized discourse around menstruation, and the exclusion of women from higher education and the world of business and politics could be justified as biological, and therefore inevitable.

The past century has seen dramatic changes in the lives of women and their involvement in the public sphere of activities and institutions. The weak and fragile 19th-century woman has been replaced by a 21st-century superwoman who can presumably have it all (an equally problematic construction of womanhood, it is noted) (Nelson, 2006, p. 255). Realistic or not, this contemporary image of successful womanhood involves juggling multiple roles and responsibilities such as mother, professional, wife, entertainer, and homemaker. This woman's experience flies in the face of earlier medical thinking that had her energy and reproductive capacities diminished by activity and stress. What then of the medicalized menstruating body? One might speculate that 19th-century ideas about women's bodies as inherently weak and incapable would no longer be prevalent in medical discourses. But when we survey the terrain of medical labels and interventions connected to menstruation over the 20th century, we see that today's menstruating woman is actually more medicalized than her 19th-century counterpart; the process is simply less overt and explicit than it once was.

Throughout the 20th century, the actual time of bleeding was no longer the focus of medical attention, unless it was perceived as abnormally late, early, long, or short by medical standards (Lorber, 2000, p. 59). While these standards were (and continue to be) unrealistically narrow and restricted, at least their existence removed the labeling of all menses as abnormal. Presumably now the blanket labeling of all women as frail because of their menstruation was over.

However, the medical "discovery" of a new disorder connected with menstruation, called the Pre-Menstrual Syndrome, has today created a new period of "disease" for women. While the menstrual period itself may have become a non-issue medically, now it seems that women are suffering and in need of medical attention for a period of time prior to the menses. The initial research and subsequent creation of the PMS label evolved from the accounts of individual women reporting menstrual-related difficulties in their doctors' offices. Though this group of sufferers would scarcely constitute a representative sample of all menstruating women, somehow the thinking about PMS has expanded to include *all* menstruating women as sufferers.

The ongoing research on PMS has helped to support this thinking by attributing a vast and poorly defined list of symptoms to the disorder. This "diagnostic slipperiness" (Lorber, 2000, p. 59) on the part of the medical establishment makes the label apply to practically all menstruating women, at least some of the time. This construction of pre-menstruating women as unwell is not unlike the 19th-century view, in that all women are grouped into the illness category by virtue of their menstruating bodies.

Another diagnostic issue connected to the PMS label deals with the length of time during which it is thought to occur. Exactly how long does the so-called "pre-menstrual" time last? The research here is also confusing, with evidence ranging from a few days to a few weeks in duration (Fausto-Sterling, 1986, p. 334). Whether PMS lasts either a few days or a few weeks, the ultimate outcome of this labeling is to lengthen the time during which women are seen to be unwell. If, for example, one's premenstrual symptoms start to occur about two weeks prior to menstruation and continue for one week after (Dalton cited in Fausto-Sterling 1986), we see that a woman can be rendered less than well for approximately three weeks out of four. This leaves her with one fully functional, productive week a month! If we then combine PMS with the actual time of menstrual bleeding, there is *no* disease-free time in her life. Thus the net of medicalization widens.

A further aspect of the PMS designation is its emphasis on women as emotionally unstable.[1] While this psychiatric labeling may serve some women, concerns about the labeling of all menstruating women as potentially mentally ill abound amongst feminist critics (Figert, 1996; Tavris, 1992). Some critics argue that the medicalization of so-called inappropriate female emotions (such as anger) is a way to subsume women's discontent under a medical label, and cure it with a medical solution focused on the individual woman. When women themselves use the PMS label to dismiss their own behaviour ("Don't mind me, I'm PMSing") the question arises as to why an excuse is necessary in the first place. Perhaps gender scripts that label angry or assertive women as unwomanly are operating here. Ultimately, medicalization locates the problem and the solution in the individual woman, and does not require an examination of the broader context of her life in which her anger might be understood to be about something other than her fluctuating hormones. Moreover, the PMS label has moved so completely into mainstream popular culture that husbands, boyfriends, and women themselves are quick to either assign or take up this syndrome today. Once the medical establishment has provided the initial label and credibility for it, the mainstream will ensure its continuance.

It is surprising to realize that, despite the advances in their lives since the 19th century, 20th-century women continued to be seen as fragile, weak, and mentally unstable in connection with their menstruating bodies. In fact, the net of medicalization around menstruation actually widened over this period, as PMS defined the 20th-century woman as ill for an even longer period than her 19th-century counterpart.

As we enter the 21st century, we see a new twist in the medicalizing process, as the net widens still further. Now girls can suppress menstruation altogether. In today's world, many young women see their opportunities as limitless and their power gains in the public sphere have become increasingly evident. In the face of these social gains for women, it seems that today's liberated woman can opt to reduce or eliminate her menstrual bleeding with the help of 21st-century technological advancements in the medical field. A new and improved birth control pill boasts the benefits of its capacity to reduce a woman's menstrual cycle frequency to four times a year (marketed as "Seasonale"); another will suppress it altogether (marketed as "Anya").[2] Where previously it might have been seen as unnatural or unhealthy to manipulate one's period through unorthodox taking of the pill, today it has become a medically legitimate practice in some circles, and the health benefits of not bleeding at all are now front and centre in the medical discourses. From concerns about a loss of iron, to the discomforts of cramps and

PMS, the health justifications for hormonally eliminating one's period altogether are moving into the cultural climate as never before.

Underlying the discussion about the effects of not menstruating, we see another set of messages geared toward the 21st-century liberated woman. As with other medicalizing labels, the net here is cast beyond so-called sufferers to include all menstruating women, whether suffering or not. It seems that, not only can women with particularly problematic periods seek help to eliminate them, but now all women can opt to get rid of the pesky, inconvenient, and distasteful experience of menstruating.

For example, endometrial ablation is a procedure that removes the uterine lining through cauterizing or lasering and is sometimes the recommended treatment for uterine fibroids (Dionne, 2001, p. 52). One Calgary physician advertises the procedure electively to any woman who cares to eliminate monthly bleeding cycles without the use of birth control pills.[3] This advertisement, found in a health and fitness magazine, shows a woman in workout gear resting on a park bench, water bottle in hand, a towel flung around her neck. The copy reads "Simplify your life ... no more periods cramping your lifestyle."[4] The message here is clear: any smart, active, 21st-century liberated woman would jump at the chance to "simplify her life" by eliminating her periods. The mainstreaming of this message is internalized by women themselves; otherwise there would be no market for this elective procedure.

Here we see the powerful interplay between the medical discourse and the idea of the **"plastic"** or **postmodern body** – a recent view of the body which suggests that there is nothing about it that cannot be changed (see the next section). Was not menstruation once the unalterable, natural mark of what it meant to be a woman? Or, as a writer in *Macleans* put it, "Isn't the whole point of 'the curse' that it's *not* optional?" (George, 2005, p. 41). But the medicalizing of menstruation has made it just that, a choice, part of "giving women control." And this message is being taken up by women themselves, such as Dr. Shari Brasner, a 40-year old Manhattan gynecologist, who "just doesn't have time to menstruate." "I have an incredibly busy day," she says, "and the reality is I just don't have time to get to the bathroom every two or three hours to change a tampon or a sanitary napkin" (quoted in George, 2005, p. 41). So while the medical profession promotes the suppression of menstruation through surgical procedures or medication, in a market where profits are considerable and the risk to women and girls remains unclear, some women appear happy to adopt this "solution."[5] The *Macleans* writer concludes: "Health experts are predicting that by this time next year, menstruation will no longer be an inevitable function but rather an optional feature, at bit like power steering or pay-per-view" (George, 2005, p. 41).

Ultimately, this history of medical discourses around menstruation has highlighted the idea that, despite the range of medical interventions into women's menstruating bodies, there has been a consistent commitment to the need for such intervention. Although the diagnosis and treatment is clearly different (thanks in part to technological advances), the underlying story is the same: the menstruating body remains a problem and abnormal in comparison to the normal male body which does not bleed. Ideas about what constitutes normal menstruation seem to vary across time, and are inextricably linked to the gains in status for women over the past century. Ironically, it seems that with a rise in women's status over the years, the net of medicalization has widened, encompassing more women, more of the time, over a longer period of their lives.

THE MEDICALIZATION OF WOMEN'S APPEARANCE

In this section, we consider how the physical appearance and shape of women's bodies has come under medical control. This development has been part of a broader socio-historical trend toward **social control** of all bodies, and we discuss this trend first. Then, we turn to some of the forms that this control takes for women in particular, and the part that the medical perspective plays in that outcome. We end with a discussion of a shift in the way we have come to see bodies in the postmodern world. Throughout, it is important to keep in mind the question of how women themselves perceive and deal with this medicalization process.

POLICING THE BODY

The earliest attempts to regulate the individual body occur in the early modern era, according to Foucault: for the first time, an interest was taken in the ordinary person who until then, had been an undifferentiated part of a faceless "horde" or "rabble." Foucault argues persuasively that the source of this new interest was the modern state, which began, with emerging professional groups as its instruments, to observe and document the lives and bodies of the masses in the interest of producing useful and productive citizens (Foucault, 1979; Donzelot, 1979). The most important of these professional groups was the medical doctors, and an emerging powerful alliance between general practitioners and mothers allowed the state an important point of entry into, and control over, the private sphere of the family, especially the bodily habits of its members, including the mother herself (Donzelot, 1979; Turner, 1984; Miller 1991). An emphasis on useful and productive bodies, the raw material for the creation of a productive labour force, was aided by the 17th-century Cartesian model of the body as a machine (Bordo, 1990, p. 86).

This mechanical image contributed to the development of the medical rationalization and classification of the body, including diet regimens, in which input and output could be mathematically calculated and managed (Turner, 1982, pp. 258–259). In contrast to the earlier religious treatises on diet – which promoted fasting and the "denial of the flesh" as a route to spirituality – 19th- and 20th-century medical writings had a more worldly aim: the promotion of healthy diet as a way of increasing the labour productivity of the working class (Turner, 1984, p. 170).

Fat Becomes Unhealthy

One important mark of the modern, secular discourse on diet is its relentless focus on body weight. As the modern "scientific" approach to diet and food intake slowly diffused down the social ladder, a large stomach – the old symbol of wealth – faded into history. In the early 20th century, the modern concept of the calorie allowed the quantification of nutrition based on an economist's notion of physiological equilibrium (as energy flow in and out of the body). Following the emergence of calorie-counting, insurance companies and the medical profession constructed an association of overweight or "obesity" with death, an association based on studies of men but automatically applied to women as well (Schwartz, 1986, pp. 154–156). These and later developments (the linking of fat to heart disease and the classification of bodies into types, like "mesomorph") united to focus on overweight as the major threat to the worker's productivity under capitalism; as a result, the medical profession, backed by the state and business interests, began to recommend a lifelong vigilance over body weight in the form of dieting and exercise (Schwartz, 1986, pp. 189, 223). This approach to diet, while still heavy with moral overtones, was a far cry from earlier religious conceptions. In the transition to modernity, concludes Turner, "The vocabulary of passions, desires and humours was replaced by the discourse of calories and proteins" (1984, p. 170).

Doctors' Group Taking Aim in Fight Against Fat

A new group launched Monday by doctors wants obesity treated and funded as a disease as part of a united front against fat.

Doctors can't bill the provinces for treating obesity on a regular basis because it's not considered an illness, Dr. David Lau, president of Obesity Canada, told a news conference.

But the World Health Organization says a global epidemic of obesity is behind a range of illnesses, said Lau, a University of Ottawa professor and endocrinologist...

About half of Canadians are overweight, including one-third who are obese, and that puts them at increased risk of diabetes, heart disease, high blood pressure and other common health woes...

"You're dealing with a complex disease that has a whole bunch of consequences, and there are a lot of costs involved," said Lau...

But while ample girths are driving up health care costs, the issue of how much weight is too much has become a heavy topic.

Lau recognizes the mixed messages. While one Australian company is raking in proceeds for an anti-cellulite pill now sold in Canada, eating disorders especially among teen girls and the lobby for fat acceptance have never been more high-profile.

Lau said that's one reason Obesity Canada is focusing on feeling good, and not looking good. "We're concerned about the health risk of obesity, and not the body image."

As Obesity Canada becomes a "credible source of information" and does more research on weight problems, it may ask the provinces to work weight counselling and treatment into fee schedules because doctors are the gatekeepers of health, said Lau...

Source: Marlene Habib, *The Mail-Star,* Halifax, Tuesday, April 13, 1999, pp. A1–A2. Reprinted with permission of The Halifax Herald Limited.

In general, the monitoring of health and body weight, which originated outside the individual in the state and the medical profession, has been largely taken over by individuals, bearing out arguments for a shift in the form of social regulation from policing by others to self-policing in modern Western society (Foucault, 1979; Elias, 1978). However, there are important gender and class exceptions to this rule. First, men have traditionally been less interested in their own health, and less likely to engage in **body-work** than women (Miller and Penz, 1991), though their interest in appearance is increasing, as we see in the following section. This difference is rooted in a broad cultural tendency to value men for their economic power rather than their appearance, and in a cultural script that makes women the custodians of health care for the whole family, not just themselves (Charles & Kerr, 1988, pp. 82–83, 237; Trypuc, 1994, pp. 268, 270-271). Second, the working class is less likely to self-police body weight and health than is the middle class (Shilling, 1993, pp. 127–149). Pressure on the working class to do so is largely exerted externally by the state, the medical profession, and the middle class (Edgely & Brissett, 1990).

Critics of the contemporary obsession with fitness argue that the middle class equates health (or at least a fit appearance) with success and worldly achievement and is in favour, moreover, of regulating those in society who will not conform to the middle-class standard (Edgely & Brissett, 1990). Early in the 1990s, for example, the Alberta government considered a proposal allowing doctors to give patients an annual "report card" covering health indicators like blood pressure, weight, smoking, and cholesterol levels. More recently, the Premier ruminated publicly about ways to return tax dollars to fit citizens.

It is interesting to note that the cultural fear of fat (currently described in the media as the "epidemic of obesity") is now focused on children, and has even led to the control of women's bodies out of medical concern for the fat of the fetus (Schwartz, 1986, p. 269). The idea that too many fat cells in fetal life and childhood will lead to adult obesity has led doctors and mothers to restrict the weight gain that occurs in pregnancy (Schwartz, 1986, pp. 296–297). To that end, it became necessary to monitor pregnant women's bodies more closely through prenatal care. Here again, the degree to which women have taken up or resisted this medical discourse is unclear. However, faced with the prospect of having fitness and body weight monitored and graded from the womb to the workplace, and perhaps into old age, one begins to grasp the far-reaching authority society has granted to the medical profession.

RENOVATE YOUR BODY!

The obsession with fat remains at centre stage and the medical discourse of health, especially as it is strategically employed in the lucrative fitness industry, continues to pressure women to conform to the slim ideal. But fat is not the only bodily "flaw" we are asked to correct. One look at the spectacular rise – not to mention the normalization – of cosmetic surgery over the last decade shows that virtually all parts of the body have become sites for body "modification." And while the medical profession is, as usual, ready with the tools and techniques to assist these changes, we suggest that doctors alone are not responsible for the rush to "nip and tuck."

Underlying the popularity of cosmetic surgery is a deeper shift in the way we in the West, especially in North America, have come to see the body. Cultural theorists have pointed to the rise of the "postmodern" body[6] whose hallmark is its **plasticity**. Whereas we once regarded our bodies as natural, with features we were stuck with for the most part (breast size, for instance), we now see these features as entirely malleable, and our bodies as unfinished projects or "works in progress" (Williams & Bendelow, 1998, Ch. 4; Davis, 1992).

Instead of the traditional or "communal" body whose appearance functioned to mark our membership in society (the traditional Hutterite women's hairstyle, for example, or ritual circumcision), our bodies are now seen as canvases on which we can exercise our choice and creativity, and display our individuality to others (the "communicative" body) (Featherstone, 1982; Howson, 2004, Ch. 4). The postmodern body, these theorists argue, knows no limits and is endlessly modifiable; with effort and the application of technology we can redesign our thighs, our hairline, and as Michael Jackson and others have shown, two of the oldest "unchangeables" of all – our skin colour and our gender.

Cultural theorists attribute this change to several factors. One is the increasing importance of visual culture and technology since the mid-1800s (notably the development of photography and the cinema, the mass production of magazines, and the associated rise of the advertising industry). The resulting exponential increase in the circulation of images, they suggest, has led to a new attention to "how we look" to others, and an escalating social premium placed on "looking good."[7] A second factor is the emergence of consumer culture since World War II, which forged a new connection between self and the consumption of goods. Advertisements began to tell us that our social worth would be transformed by the goods we bought, and we were encouraged to recreate ourselves through our purchases – including the new commodity, designer bodies.

There are several noteworthy consequences of this new view of bodies. First, the gender gap is narrowing: where appearance historically carried more social significance in women's lives than in men's, as we noted earlier, the new cultural message – about the link between appearance and social worth – targets men and women both; hence men's increasing consumption of cosmetics and cosmetic surgery.[8] Second, the medical promotion of cosmetic surgery combines with the new cultural view of the plastic postmodern body to exert relentless pressures on women (and increasingly on men) to "work on" their bodies endlessly. It is no coincidence that popular TV "makeover" programs like *The Swan* appear in the TV guide right next to home and wardrobe renovation shows. The message is the same: Redesign! Renovate!

In consequence, we suggest that the new deviant is not the person with a bodily "flaw" or problem, but the one who refuses to "do something about it," especially when the technology is ready to hand. While we refer here mainly to appearance, the very same impetus to "fix what's fixable" in our lives, through surgery or a pill, also pushes us to "fix" our menstrual periods, as we have seen; and as we discuss in the next section, this same trend pushes us to "fix" our sexual problems.

For feminist scholars, the willingness, even enthusiasm of women to redesign their bodies surgically, or through fitness or diet regimes, does not disguise their deep insecurity regarding their bodies, an insecurity underwritten by medicine and popular culture as normal and right (MacNevin 1992, pp. 26–27). Many women's groups attempt to persuade women that the problem is not in their bodies but in the cultural forces that create the demand for the ideal appearance.[9] They argue that the woman's body is the site but not the source of her problems, and they attempt to support women who would challenge cultural demands for the one "right" body. Undercutting this message, however, is the picture of the designer body as increasingly easy to "get," and the contempt that, in an era that glorifies activity, attaches to the woman who will "do nothing" to improve herself.

THE FINAL FRONTIER? MEDICALIZING WOMEN'S SEXUALITY

The final example we consider is the medicalization of women's sexuality. We refer here to the effort to define women's orgasmic response – specifically, the inability of a woman to experience orgasm in intercourse – as a medical disease or dysfunction. The move to medicalize this issue is of special interest. First, the process has a definite starting point, unlike the much more gradual process of medicalizing women's appearance. Second, the push for medicalization has come from the pharmaceutical industry, not the medical profession. Third, the process itself has been open to scrutiny from the outset, and has been loudly denounced by feminist groups and others, especially for the way it distorts women's dissatisfaction with their sexual lives. Finally, this instance of the medicalization process is a relatively recent one, and its story is still unfolding.

The story begins with Viagra, and the background is this: in 1997, after considering the phenomenal financial success of Pfizer's Viagra (sildenafil citrate), a group of nine drug companies sponsored a meeting of clinicians, researchers, and drug company representatives to discuss "female sexual dysfunction" and the lucrative possibility of a similar drug for women. Other meetings followed, and in 1999 researchers with links to Pfizer published a study to "assess" women's sexual "dysfunction." This study, whose research methodology has been severely criticized especially for its vagueness, claimed that for women aged 18-59, the "total prevalence of sexual dysfunction" was 43 percent, a figure taken up by the popular press; ergo, 43 percent of women were therefore in need of a Viagra-like drug to cure their "disease" (Moynihan, 2003[10]; see also Bordo, 2001). In this way, the pharmaceutical industry gained the research legitimacy it needed to argue that a real medical disorder – one that needed treating – existed in a substantial segment of the female population, and by 2002, new drug trials for "female sexual arousal disorder" were underway.

Almost from the start, women's groups and other observers protested the unseemly haste to discover a disease; in 2001, Leonore Tiefer commented on the parallel between Viagra as a medicalized version of men's sexual problems, and the "discovery" of women's sexual dysfunction, in her article which asked "A New View of Women's Problems: Why New? Why Now?" In 2003, a journalist brought discussion to a head in his article called "The Making of a Disease: Female Sexual Dysfunction." The article began with the question "Is a new disorder being identified to meet unmet needs or to build markets for a new medication?" (Moynihan, 2003).

It is important to note that these and other writers do not deny that women – or men – experience sexual problems. Rather, they criticize the way the medicalization process (as we have seen in other instances) routinely reduces a large and complex social matter (here, the sexual experience) to its purely physical aspects (erection in men and orgasm in women); and how it tends to focus on physical causes – the kind that can be solved with a quick fix (a pill) – rather than by looking at the broader social, political, and psychological aspects of relationships that might cause women (and men) to lose their enthusiasm for a sexual encounter. Tiefer, the psychologist whose writing has taken the lead here, has noted other factors which have contributed to the failure to resist this narrow view of sexual problems, such as, the lack of comprehensive sexuality education in schools and communities which continue to leave people (especially the young) anxious and misinformed about sexuality generally, sensational popular magazine articles offering questionable information ("50 Ways to Drive your Man Wild in Bed"), incessant Internet drug promotion, and the failure of physicians, parents, and teachers to promote forms of arousal and pleasure other than intercourse ("outercourse") (Tiefer 2000). Tiefer also points out that feminists have for many years attempted to broaden our understanding of female sexuality (away from the **phallocentric** focus on intercourse, and toward a social as well as physical concept of sex) but now find their voices drowned out by the force of the recent medicalization campaign.[11]

But while Viagra might be an important part of the story as to why women's sexuality is being medicalized at this particular historical moment, it is clearly not the whole story. Another factor is at work here, we suggest: a new cultural ideal of young womanhood, one highly visible in the media. Popular magazines and TV shows tell us that today's liberated woman is not only about corporate success and technology-controlled menstruation, she is also a sexually aware and adventurous "Sex and the City" girl. This woman explores her sexuality and fearlessly places it front and centre as a part of who she is and what she deserves. She knows how to have an orgasm and she is self-assured enough to make sure he knows how to provide her with one as well. No fears of being called a "slut" here, this 21st-century diva deserves to have it all. Although this sexy liberated woman is different from her 1990s predecessor, the theme of superwoman lives on in this media construct, and the expectations for women – more orgasms, more often – seem to be getting higher all the time.

The rise of this performance-oriented ideal of the young hip woman raises a number of issues. First, it suggests a shift on women's part in the direction of a masculine model of sexuality – in effect, a move away from the cultural story that used to prevail in the social science literature (i.e., that "men want sex" but "women want relationships"; see Tolman, 2003). Second, it may set up an unreal expectation for women – the Vixen who can keep up with the Viagra-enhanced performance of her male partner – whose actual existence in real life is unknown.[12] (And if the Vixen too needs a pill, one will soon be on the market; but we wonder whether these two pill-enhanced performers will ever need to actually talk about how things are going sexually, when they have medical solutions such as these at hand.) Most importantly, we see how smoothly this performance-centred image of the "Sex and the City" girl combines with the entrepreneurial drive of the drug industry in a powerful cultural-economic-medical nexus that forcefully asserts one narrow medicalized picture of women's sexual lives and problems.

In sum, then, the campaign to medicalize women's sexuality has borrowed the mechanical view of sexuality taken from research into male erectile dysfunction or "impotence,"[13] and more generally, has followed the path blazed by the successful promotion of Viagra. More than any other example of medicalization we have discussed, this campaign seems to suggest a conspiracy – or at least, a blatant commercially-inspired manipulation of women – by an identifiable group of professionals. But on closer examination we see that even in a case such as this, these "agents" of medicalization do not act in isolation from the larger social context, and seem to be supported in complex ways by larger developments at the cultural level (here, a new view of the sophisticated young woman whose sexuality invites a medical "fix"). How the campaign to bring women aboard the Viagra bandwagon will fare will be interesting to watch.

CONCLUSION

This final section weighs the consequences of medicalization on women's lives. First, it reviews the main negative effects, then it considers whether there are positive outcomes as well. Finally, it asks whether recent "woman-centred" health movements are able to provide significant alternatives to mainstream professional medicine.

The Pros and Cons of Medicalization

Perhaps the most important negative result of the medical perspective on women's lives is its tendency to individualize and depoliticize their problems. In all of the examples discussed, women's problems are blamed on themselves (that is, they are viewed as personal, psychological, or physical matters), and this diagnosis leads to an avoidance of essential social and institutional remedies. The medical model tells women, "The problem is with you, so you must do the changing." The authors of this chapter find this approach misguided: it treats the female, but leaves dominant patriarchal conceptions of femininity untouched.

The second negative result of medicalization concerns the manner in which the medical rhetoric of illness is deployed to produce conformity to social norms. The idea that sickness will befall women who deviate from their "natural" – that is, social – gender roles runs through the history of Western thought. In the 19th century, we noted, medical opinion held that women who were active during menstruation would suffer an array of ailments, from depression to an atrophied uterus; thus, inactivity was often the medical prescription for restoring them to health. The point of this example is not to ridicule the medical knowledge of the past, but to show how medical discourse has been, and continues to be, deployed in ways that limit women's options – in behaviour, in appearance, and in relationships (Fausto-Sterling, 1986; Lorber, 2000).

But while the negative effects of medicalization on women's lives are considerable, it would be a mistake to portray women as the inevitable victims of medical discourse (Davis 1995; Walters 1994).[14] The medical rhetoric of health and illness originated with the medical profession, but it is not wholly owned by doctors, and this means that it is available to be used by other groups, including women, to achieve their own ends. Women have discovered, for example, that the visibility of formerly "invisible" problems like woman abuse, or PMS, is increased substantially once they are labeled as "medical problems." As such, these conditions are more likely to draw public attention and sympathy, to attract research funding, and to appear on the political agenda. Thus, even if women's groups are wary of the medical view and its implications, they have also recognized that certain advantages may flow from adopting it as a strategy. In these instances, women, like other relatively low power groups in society, see that if they cannot change the system that favours the medical perspective, they can at least borrow its discourse and reap some of its benefits for themselves.

Second, women may welcome a medical approach to some issues just because it releases them from stigma and moral responsibility for the problem; you cannot be blamed (at least not explicitly) for a "disease" you did not choose to get. The stigma of alcoholism is reduced when it is medicalized as a chemical disorder, for example, and obesity is more acceptable when it is no longer called "the sin of gluttony" but rather a "glandular disorder" or a psychological problem called "compulsive eating." As noted in the first section of this chapter, the consequences of such discursive shifts are quite concrete: instead of shunning the guilty parties, or locking them up, we extend them our sympathy and send them for treatment. Furthermore, medicalization not only lightens the burden of stigma, it also transfers the responsibility for the treatment of the problem from the sufferer to the doctor: the behaviour is now the doctor's problem (Conrad & Schneider, 1980, p. 248). The relief and security such a transfer provides may serve a real therapeutic purpose.

Alternatives to the Medical Model: A Realistic Assessment

What alternatives are there to the powerful medical model? As noted previously, women can sometimes turn medical rhetoric to their own advantage. They have also resisted medicalization in a more radical fashion by trying to change mainstream medical practices or by sidestepping them altogether. For example, they have tried to escape the control of the medical profession by supporting midwifery and natural childbirth movements, by challenging the power hierarchies within doctor-patient relationships, and by forming self-help groups that emphasize self-help care (Fox, 1990, p. 410). In addition, strong advocacy has emerged for patients' "right to know" and to decide on matters of their own health. The Internet has become a source of information, self-diagnosis, and support for an increasing segment of the population. These developments all represent a move toward "client control" (de Swaan, 1990, p. 71; Fox, 1990, p. 410).

But, while these movements are sometimes touted as a **demedicalization** of women's lives, they do not represent a wholesale rejection of modern medicine (Fox, 1990, p. 412). Most people can scarcely imagine, nor would they choose, a world without modern medical expertise. It is far more likely, then, that women will achieve not a demedicalization of their bodies, but a greater voice in the ways they are treated by the medical profession – in short, informed choice and a greater degree of power. Moreover, there are signs that mainstream medicine is permeable to a range of consumer demands, notably alternative and traditional techniques and philosophies (e.g., acupuncture), and will be broadened by these inclusions.

What is occurring, then, is not a demedicalization but an ongoing negotiation between two power groups, a two-way relationship in which the underdogs (women and other clients of the medical profession) are gaining increased leverage and muscle. It would appear, however, that these gains must be constantly defended, for with each new development (the new reproductive technologies, for example), the medical profession seems to be ready to disempower women anew.

We conclude that women are not the passive victims of medical institutions. They have been controlled by mainstream professional medicine, but they have also influenced it on occasion (Findlay, 1990). Like other groups, they have turned the profession's prestigious rhetoric to their own advantage. In the end, the encounter between women and the medical profession is much like women's encounter with other institutions of social control – neither victory nor defeat, but an ongoing struggle.

STUDY QUESTIONS

1. *Recently we have read of two new "diseases": SAD (seasonal affective disorder) and micromastia (small breasts). Discuss the consequences for women and for doctors when these conditions are medicalized.*
2. *Would you choose to get rid of your menstrual period if it seemed safe to do so? Would the "loss" of menstruation have any special significance to you as a woman? If so, what would it symbolize? (Compare this idea, for example, with the woman who has a mastectomy and says that loss of her breast makes her feel like she is "no longer a woman.") Are there equivalent "losses" of essential masculinity in your life as a man, and if so what are they? To what gender scripts are these "essential aspects" related?*
3. *Consider the current popularity of "working out" and fitness classes. What messages are conveyed to women and girls – in the media but also in the youth subculture – about the relationships between health and fitness? How are women and girls persuaded to participate in these goods and practices?*
4. *Do men and women these days want the same things from sex? How well does the "Sex and the City" scenario describe you and your friends?*

GLOSSARY

bodywork all effort expended in the maintenance or improvement of physical appearance and health; shopping for cosmetics and clothing, dyeing one's hair, exercising, cosmetic surgery, and dieting all fall into this category.

demedicalization the removal of a condition or activity from the category of disease, at which point the medical profession no longer has the sole responsibility for defining and treating that condition.

discourse the broad linguistic frameworks within which people perceive, think, and speak about the world and/or actors' everyday language.

medicalization the process that defines a condition or activity as a disease or an illness; treatment of the condition is then considered the responsibility of the medical profession.

phallocentric sexuality the dominant view of sexuality that restricts sexual pleasure to penetration and heterosexual intercourse.

plastic/postmodern body a term used by cultural theorists to describe a new view of the body in the postmodern era. In this view, the body is seen as infinitely changeable or plastic, rather than fixed and natural, and is used as a canvas to display identity to others.

policing the process by which powerful social groups, such as physicians, control others through scrutiny and documentation (rather than force), in order to bring them into line with dominant or "normal" social standards of acceptability. While the term is borrowed from the legal sphere, it is used by sociologists to refer to forms of social and moral, rather than legal, constraint.

social control the result of formal and informal rules or pressures being imposed on individuals or groups to influence their activities and behaviours. Teasing is an example of informal social control.

REFERENCES

Bordo, S.R. (1989). The body and reproduction of femininity: A feminist appropriation of Foucault. In A.M. Jagger & S.R. Bordo (Eds.), *Gender/body/knowledge* (pp. 13–33). New Brunswick, NJ: Rutgers University Press.

Bordo, S.R. (1990). Reading the slender body. In M. Jacobus, E. Fox Keller, & S. Shuttleworth (Eds.), *Body politics: Women and the discourses of science* (pp. 83–112). New York: Routledge.

Bordo, S.R. (1993). *Unbearable weight: Feminism, western culture and the body*. Berkeley: University of California Press.

Bordo, S.R. (2001). Pills and power tools. In M.S. Kimmel & M.A. Messner (Eds.), *Men's lives* (5th ed., pp. 344–349). Boston: Allyn and Bacon.

Charles, N., & Kerr, M. (1988). *Women, food and families*. Manchester & New York: Manchester University Press.

Conrad, P., & Schneider, J.W. (1980). *Deviance and medicalization: From badness to sickness*. St. Louis, MO: C.V. Mosby.

Currer, C., & Stacey, M. (Eds.). (1986). *Concepts of health, illness and disease: A comparative perspective*. Leamington Spa, UK: Berg.

Davis, D. (1996). The cultural constructions of the premenstrual and menopause syndromes. In C.F. Sargent & C.B. Brettell (Eds.), *Gender and health: An international perspective* (pp. 57–86). Upper Saddle River, NJ: Prentice Hall.

Davis, K. (1995). *Reshaping the female body: The dilemma of cosmetic surgery*. New York: Routledge.

Davis, K. (1997). My body is my art: cosmetic surgery as feminist utopia? In K. Davis (Ed.), *Embodied practices: Feminist perspectives on the body* (pp. 168–181). London: Sage.

de Swaan, A. (1990). *The management of normality: Critical essays in health and welfare*. London & New York: Routledge.

Dionne, C. (2001). *Sex, lies and the truth about uterine fibroids: A journey from diagnosis to treatment to renewed good health*. New York: Avery.

Donzelot, J. (1979). *The policing of families*. New York: Pantheon Books.

Durkheim, E. (1964 [1933]). *The division of labour in society*. New York: Free Press.

Edgley, C., & Brissett, D. (1990). Health Nazis and the cult of the perfect body: Some polemical observations. *Symbolic Interaction, 13*(2), 257–279.

Ehrenreich, B., & English, D. (1979). *For her own good: 150 years of the experts' advice to women*. Garden City, NY: Anchor Books.

Elias, N. (1978 [1939]). *The history of manners*. New York: Urizen Books.

Fausto-Sterling, A. (1986). Hormonal hurricanes: Menstruation, menopause, and female behavior. In L. Richardson & V. Taylor (Eds.), *Feminist frontiers III* (pp. 329–430). New York: McGraw-Hill.

Featherstone, M. (1982) The body in consumer culture. *Theory, Culture and Society, 1*, 18–33.

Figert, A.E. (1996). *Women and the ownership of PMS: The structuring of a psychiatric disorder*. Hawthorne, NY: Aldine De Gruyter.

Findlay, D.A. (1990). Women and medical knowledge in the 1950s: A study of the process of social construction. Unpublished doctoral dissertation, McMaster University, Hamilton.

Fisher, S. (1988). *In the patients' best interest: Women and the politics of medical decisions*. New Brunswick, NJ: Rutgers University Press.

Foucault, M. (1979). *Discipline and punish: The birth of the prison*. New York: Vintage.

Fox, R.C. (1990). The medicalization and demedicalization of American society. In P. Conrad & R. Kern (Eds.), *The sociology of health and illness: Critical perspectives* (3rd ed., pp. 390–394). New York: St. Martin's Press.

Freidson, E. (1970). *Professional dominance: The social structure of medical care.* New York: Aldine.
George, L. (2001, March 17). In search of the perfect man. *Calgary Herald,* p. OS1.
George, L. (2005, December 12). The end of menstruation. *Macleans, 188*(50), 41–46.
Habib, M. (April 13, 1999). Doctors group taking aim in fight against fat. *The Halifax Mail-Star,* pp. A1–A2.
Howson, A. (2004). *The body in society*. Cambridge, UK: Polity.
Kamerman, S., & Hayes, C.D. (Eds.). (1982). *Families that work: Children in a changing world.* Washington, DC: National Academy Press.
Lavie-Ajayi, M. (2005). "Because all real women do": The construction and deconstruction of "female orgasmic disorder." *Sexualities, Evolution and Gender, 7*(1), 57–72.
Lorber, J. (2000). *Gender and the social construction of illness.* Walnut Creek, CA: AltaMira Press.
Ludmerer, K.M. (1985). *Learning to heal: The development of American medical education.* New York: Basic Books.
MacNevin, A.L. (1992). Step 'n pump: A social inquiry into aerobically exercised femininity. Unpublished master's thesis, Dalhousie University, Halifax.
Martin, E. (1987). *The woman in the body. A cultural analysis of reproduction.* Boston: Beacon Press.
Martin, E. (1991). The egg and the sperm: How science has constructed a romance based on stereotypical male-female roles. *Signs: A journal of women in culture and society, 16*(3), 485–499.
Miller, L. (1991). Family problems and problem families. In B.S. Bolaria (Ed.), *Social issues and contradictions in Canadian society* (pp. 57–85). Toronto: Harcourt Brace Jovanovich.
Miller, L., & Penz, 0. (1991, August). Talking bodies: Female body builders colonize a male preserve. *Quest, 43*(2), 148–163.
Moynihan, R. (2003). The making of a disease: female sexual dysfunction. *British Medical Journal, 326,* 45–47.
Nelson, A. (2006). *Gender in Canada* (3rd ed.). Toronto: Pearson Prentice Hall.
Nicholson, P. (2003). Feminism and the debate about female sexual dysfunction. *Sexualities, Evolution and Gender, 5*(1), 37–39.
Ratcliff, K.S. (2002). *Women and health: Power, technology, inequality, and conflict in a gendered world.* Boston: Allyn and Bacon.
Rothman, B.K. (1989). Women, health and medicine. ln J. Freeman (Ed.), *Women: A feminist perspective* (4th ed., pp. 77–86). Mountain View, CA: Mayfield.
Schwartz, H. (1986). *Never satisfied. A cultural history of diets, fantasies and fat.* New York: Anchor Books.
Shilling, C. (1993). *The body in social theory*. London: Sage.
Spitzack, C. (1990). *Confessing excess: Women and the politics of body reduction.* Albany: State University of New York Press.
Szekely, E. (1988). *Never too thin.* Toronto: Women's Press.
Tavris, C. (1992). *The mismeasure of woman.* New York: Simon & Schuster.
Tiefer, L. (2002). Beyond the medical model of women's sexual problems: a campaign to resist the promotion of "female sexual dysfunction." *Sexual and Relationship Therapy, 17*(2), 127–35.
Tiefer, L. (2001). A new view of women's sexual problems: Why new? Why now? *Journal of Sex Research, 38*(2), 89–96.
Tiefer, L. (2000). The medicalization of women's sexuality. *American Journal of Nursing, 100*(12), 11–12.

Tolman, D. (2003). Daring to desire: Culture and the bodies of adolescent girls. In R. Weitz (Ed.), *The politics of women's bodies* (pp. 100–121). Oxford and Cambridge: Oxford University Press.

Torrance, G.M. (1987). Socio-historical overview. In D. Coburn, C. D'Arcy, G.M. Torrance, & P. New (Eds.), *Health and Canadian society* (2nd ed., pp. 13–22). Markham, ON: Fitzhenry & Whiteside.

Trypuc, J.M. (1994). Women's health. In B.S. Bolaria & H.D. Dickinson (Eds.), *Health, illness, and health care in Canada* (2nd ed., pp. 260–275). Toronto: Harcourt Brace.

Turner, B.S. (1982, June). The government of the body: Medical regimens and the rationalization of diet. *British Journal of Sociology, 33*(2), 254–269.

Turner, B.S. (1984). *The body and society*. Oxford: Basil Blackwell.

Turner, B.S. (1987). *Medical power and social knowledge*. London: Sage.

Williams, S.J., & Bendelow, G. (1998). *The lived body: Sociological themes, embodied issues*. London and New York: Routledge.

Wolf, N. (1991). *The beauty myth*. Toronto: Vintage Books.

Zola, I.K. (1972). Medicine as an institution of social control. *Sociological Review, 20*, 487–504.

Zola, I.K. (1975). In the name of health and illness: On some sociological consequences of medical influence. *Social Science and Medicine, 9*, 83–87.

ENDNOTES

1. Debates about whether or not PMS should be understood as a psychiatric disorder and therefore appear in the Diagnostic and Statistical Manual (DSM) of the American Psychiatric Association manual have been ongoing since the 1980s. While PMS itself has never actually been included, labels such as LLPDD (Late Luteal Phase Dysphoric Disorder) and, most recently, PMDD (Pre Menstrual Dysphoric Disorder) have appeared in the manual.
2. The birth control pill has always worked by shutting down a woman's normal menstrual cycles, however, a pseudo-period was built into the pill-taking cycle so that women would maintain a sense of having a "normal" period. Today's new and improved birth control pill simply makes this medical manipulation of the menstrual cycle explicit by highlighting a woman's capacity to skip her so-called period by simply continuing to take hormonal pills everyday, rather than taking the standard week off once a month.
3. It is important to note that many health professionals would not support the use of endometrial ablation as an elective procedure for non-medical purposes.
4. Permission to reproduce this advertisement was denied by the physician in question.
5. *Macleans* cites a recent American survey by the Association of Reproductive Health Professionals, saying that 69 percent of respondents "would try using a birth control method that stopped [their period] altogether if they could be sure it wouldn't hurt them" (cited in George, 2005, 46).
6. Some scholars dispute this terminology, arguing that we are not in a postmodern age, but in "high modernity." Others talk about the body in "consumer society"; whatever the terminology, however, they are in agreement about the effect: the emergence of the plastic or malleable body.
7. This point is captured in Bourdieu's argument that the body counts as "cultural capital"; that is, ownership of the ideal body represents both symbolic and economic value in that society.

8. Men's increasing interest in their appearance is now widely covered in the popular press. A recent article in the *Calgary Herald* entitled "In Search of the Perfect Man" states that Canadian men spent $16 million on hair-colouring products in 2000, and that 11 percent of all cosmetic surgery (mainly liposuction) is performed on men (a figure based on combined American and Canadian statistics) (*Calgary Herald*, March 17, 2001, p. OS1). It is notable that these procedures, however, still tend to be framed within the stereotypical gendered cultural discourses: men who undergo cosmetic surgery typically say that they are doing it "to give themselves a competitive edge in the workplace," while women claim that they are doing it "for themselves."
9. At the same time, however, feminists have become less intolerant of women who choose cosmetic surgery for their own purposes. This shift has occurred as they have listened more closely to (and engaged in more research into) women's own accounts of these kind of body modification practices. At a more general level, women's agency and empowerment – rather than victimization – has figured more importantly in their analyses. See for example Davis (1995; 1997), whose work has led the way here.
10. This study, undertaken by two researchers including a sociologist, gave about 1,500 women a checklist of seven problems, including anxiety about sexual performance, and a lack of desire for sex. Those who said they had experienced even one of these problems for more than two months in the previous year were characterized as having "sexual dysfunction" (in Moynihan, 2003). Moynihan notes that the researchers' caveat (that the data were "not equivalent to clinical diagnosis") is "regularly overlooked" (Moynihan, 2003, p. 46).
11. It is discouraging that while men too have been encouraged over the last decade and more to broaden their understanding of what counts as masculinity, the success of Viagra threatens to reduce masculinity again to sexual performance.
12. On this important matter, scholars are beginning to realize how little research has been done into what women themselves want, say, and experience regarding their sexualities and desires (Nicholson, 2003). A very recent study based on interviews with 50 women suggests that women's "problems with orgasm" are less a problem for themselves than one they attribute to their male partners. These woman are heavily influenced by dominant discourses of heterosexual relationships that glorify orgasm – the "orgasmic imperative" that defines it as "the peak" – and the author finds evidence that the media play a real role in the "pervasive and profound expectation that a man can satisfy a woman by giving her an orgasm...[such] that its absence introduces a pressure on the relationship that 'something needs to be done'" (Lavie-Ajayi, 2005, p. 63). The author underlines the hegemony of this story and deplores the lack of alternative discourses concerning satisfying sexual relationships. In terms of this issue, Lavie-Ajayi's research reasserts the conventional story about what women want; to some extent, Tolman (2003) argues the opposite, however, asserting that culture has stifled women's sexual desires with the story that "they want relationships not sex."
13. Beyond the similarities, however, lie some important differences in the taken-for-granted ways we think about the sexuality of men and women – especially the relationship between sex and power. The popular term for erectile dysfunction – impotence (literally, without power) – made a clear connection between men's sexual performance and power, the root of their masculinity. This is a connection never made in discussions of women's sexuality (that is, "orgasmic dysfunction" is never called "impotence"). Though the language has changed in medical circles (erectile dysfunction is intended to describe merely the malfunctioning body part), the sentiment among men has likely

not, hence the popularity of the "quick fix" that Viagra provides. As Bordo points out, taking a simple pill to deal with a hydraulics problem is certainly preferable, in the view of many men, to a lengthy and in-depth consideration of one's relationships and the conditions within which one's "power tool" might fail (Bordo, 2001).

14. See Walters (1994) for a more general discussion of the limits of medicalization and the resilience of lay perspectives on health issues. Walters concludes that "women borrow from medicine as appropriate, transform and integrate this information with their own understandings" (p. 312). She argues that women's own perceptions are too rarely examined, and that when they are, they reveal that they have not been medicalized to the degree that critics suppose.

14

INEQUALITY, VIOLENCE, AND WOMEN'S HEALTH

COLLEEN VARCOE University of British Columbia

INTRODUCTION

Although violence is understood to be gendered and women are understood to be the primary victims of violence, violence also interacts with other intersecting forms of inequality. Inequalities along the lines of class, age, ability, sexual orientation, and racialization[1] compound and are compounded by the effects of violence on women's health. Thus, violence against women must be understood in the context of these forms of inequity.

The purpose of this chapter is to explore the ways in which certain pervasive forms of inequality (particularly gender, **racialization**, and poverty) interact with violence to affect women's health. This chapter will draw on literature as well as the author's research to explicate the links between violence, various forms of inequality, and women's health in Canada. In doing so, this chapter is intended to contribute to the developing understanding of violence against women that goes beyond a gender analysis and to contribute to the promotion of strategies to counter violence that are rooted in an understanding of women's diversity. In particular, it draws attention to the ways in which people in positions of professional privilege and power can either reproduce and reinforce, or resist and oppose, the dynamics of inequality and violence.

This chapter will draw on studies the author has conducted in partnership with others. An ethnographic study conducted over two years in two hospital emergency units and their communities examined health care practice in relation to violence against women (Varcoe, 1997, 2001). This study also included an analysis of women's experiences of formal support services in relation to abuse and explored how those experiences were shaped both by professionals and by the women themselves. Second, an action research study with women who have been battered by partners (Project Violence Free) aimed to improve the ways in which services in the health care, legal, and social welfare systems respond to violence against women (Varcoe, 2006; Varcoe & Irwin, 2004; Varcoe, Jaffer & Kelln, 2002). Third, a qualitative study (Risks of HIV and Violence) examined the intersecting risks for intimate partner violence (IPV) and human immunodeficiency virus (HIV) for rural and Aboriginal women (Dick & Varcoe, 2004; Varcoe & Dick, in press). Finally, a longitudinal study of the health and economic effects of violence for women after they have left abusive partners (the Women's Health Effects Study, WHES) is underway.

EVOLVING UNDERSTANDINGS OF VIOLENCE

Violence against women has been recognized as a significant social problem only since the late 1960s and early 1970s (Barnett, Miller-Perrin & Miller, 2005). The intervening decades have seen efforts, primarily by women themselves, to have the scope of the problem *believed* by the public. There is now wide acceptance that violence against women is a global problem of epidemic proportions. Further, the gendered nature of violence has been increasingly understood. Data from many countries shows that "Although women can be violent in relationships with men, and violence is also sometimes found in same-sex partnerships, the overwhelming burden of partner violence is borne by women at the hands of men" (WHO, 2002, p. 114). Violence in the home (often referred to by the somewhat diminishing and gender-neutral term "domestic violence"), sexual assault and **sexual harassment** (by known and unknown assailants), and **corporate violence** are deeply gendered. This chapter focuses on these forms of violence, although it should be noted that other forms of violence, such as the violence of war, also have gendered effects (Lutz, 2002) that are relevant to Canada.

The Scope and Gendered Nature of Violence

In Canada, the enormity of the problem of violence and its gendered nature have been clearly established. In 1993, Statistics Canada conducted a national population survey, the Violence Against Women Survey (VAWS). In this survey, researchers interviewed a randomly selected national sample of 12,300 women by telephone. Various researchers, including Rodgers (1994), Ratner (1995), Johnson (1996), and Kerr and McLean (1996), analyzed the data from this study, providing the most comprehensive picture of the problem in Canada to date. Although Statistics Canada produces annual reports on the broader concept of "family violence," these reports rely on different data sources, such as the General Social Survey on Victimization (Statistics Canada, 2005), and use methodological approaches that do not take into account issues such as safety when responding, as was done with the VAWS.

The VAWS estimated that one in every two women in Canada over the age of 18 had experienced at least one incident of sexual or physical assault, and that 10 percent were the victims of assault in the year preceding the survey (Johnson, 1996; Rodgers, 1994). In congruence with global statistics on wife abuse (Heise, Pitanguy & Germain, 1994) and numerous U.S. studies (see Barnett, 2000; Koss, 1990; Tjaden & Thoennes, 1998), 29 percent of women in Canada who had ever been married or lived in a common-law relationship reported being physically or sexually assaulted by a marital partner at least once during the relationship (Johnson, 1996; Rodgers, 1994). Johnson extrapolated these figures to the population, estimating that over 2.6 million Canadian women have experienced physical or sexual assault, and that of the 6.69 million women currently in a marital relationship, 1.02 million (15%) have been assaulted. More recently, Cohen and MacLean (2003) analysed data from the 1999 General Social Survey (GSS) and found that lifetime sexual assault by someone other than a partner (which could include family members, non-family members, or strangers) was reported by 11.6 percent of the women.

Corporate violence, which encompasses hazardous working conditions and environments, including sexual harassment, has been less well studied but is also gendered (Hinch & DeKeseredy, 1994). Some studies show that women report more workplace violence than men, whereas other studies show no significant gender difference; however, women report more incidents of sexual harassment in the workplace than men (MacIntosh, 2005; Findorff, 2005). Although no national studies have been conducted to estimate the full extent of violence in the workplace, the scope and gendered nature of the problem can be appreciated from the many small-scale studies, especially those conducted in occupations where women predominate. For example, a survey of 8,780 nurses found that 21 percent and 16.9 percent, in British Columbia and Alberta respectively, experienced some form of physical assault in a period of five shifts (Duncan, Estabrooks & Reimer, 2000; Duncan et al., 2001). Poster (1996) found that 75 percent of 999 psychiatric nursing staff in Canada, the United States, the United Kingdom, and South Africa reported being assaulted at least once during their careers. Coombes (1998) reported a survey that indicated that one of every two nurses was at risk of physical assault, and Carroll and Morin (1998) reported that one third of nurses working in general areas were affected by workplace violence. Arnetz, Arnetz, and Soderman (1998) found that the incidence of violence toward practical nurses was 31 incidents per 100 person years.

While sexual harassment is usually discussed in relation to employment contexts and in the context of power relations, such as between teachers and students or between doctors and patients, this narrow definition is problematic (Kelly & Radford, 1998). Kelly and Radford explain that women in positions of authority are harassed (e.g., female teachers by male students), many women's places of employment are also their homes (e.g., "domestic" workers), and many women are harassed outside of employment contexts. The VAWS illustrates this clearly as it found that 23 percent of Canadian women had been assaulted by a non-spousal known man and 23 percent by a stranger, with sexual violence (including unwanted sexual touching and violent sexual assault) being much more common than physical assault outside of spousal relationships (Johnson, 1998).

Evolving Theoretical Perspectives

In addition to the scope and gendered nature of violence being delineated, during the past three decades, the ways violence is understood have also evolved. Theorists from across disciplines have attempted to understand violence by focusing attention on and seeking causal explanations for violence in three spheres: individuals, couples or dyads, and society (Bograd, 1988; Gelles, 1993). Stark and Flitcraft (1991) labelled these three perspectives the interpersonal model, the family violence model, and the gender-politics model. *Interpersonal Models* dominated early work on violence and focused on individual and interpersonal relationships. These views emphasized the psychology of the victim and perpetrator and their interrelationships. Initially, focus on the characteristics of victims diverted attention from the situation to the victim. Later, attention to the psychology of the perpetrator shifted attention regarding the causes of violence to the psychopathology of the perpetrator. Dobash and Dobash (1992) argue that the media popularize the focus on the individual in ways that perpetuate understandings of violence as a problem of abnormal individuals who need psychiatric help. Causal explanations of violence related to the psychology of the individual leave power and gender relations unexamined and consider violence in isolation from the social and historical contexts in which it occurs.

Family Violence Models focus attention on either couples or families, and seek to explain the causes of violence in social relations within couples and families. These perspectives, predominant in most research on violence in the 1970s–1990s (Silva, 1994), tend to be gender-neutral, treat power inequities as only one factor among many, and explain violence as resulting from external stresses and breakdown of the family (Bograd, 1988; Stanko, 1988). As with the focus on individuals, a focus on dyads or families, limits an analysis of the influence of the social context and leaves the role of women and families in society unexamined.

Gender-Political Models which include feminist perspectives tend to explain violence as arising from the social context and contribute an analysis of the influence of gender and power relations to theorizing violence (Yllö, 1993). Feminist perspectives take into account the gendered nature of violence but have been criticized as inadequate for understanding violence from at least two positions. First, some authors (e.g., Dutton, 1994; Gelles, 1993; Letellier, 1994) argue that **feminism** is insufficient because it is limited to using a single variable (**patriarchy**) to explain the existence of wife abuse, and overlooks how evidence of men who are not violent and violence in same-sex relationships illustrate that patriarchal ideology does not account fully for male violence. These authors tend to reject feminism in favour of continued support for the interpersonal or family violence model or in favour of an integration of the various perspectives (e.g., Dutton, 1994; Miller, 1994; Tolman & Bennett, 1990; Renzetti, 1994). Others critique feminist perspectives by pointing out that while violence is deeply gendered, other forms of oppression are as important in understanding violence against women (Crenshaw, 1994; Mahoney, 1994; Mosher, 1998; Phillips, 1998; Bannerji, 2000). These authors argue that although important, gender can be seen as "overly determinate" in understanding violence: "While gender is a significant factor, other kinds of oppression, such as that based on race and class, are seen to be equally important" (Mosher, 1998, p. 140). Mosher categorizes the various perspectives somewhat differently than earlier authors do. She combines individual and family-oriented approaches under what she terms the "therapeutic" perspectives, and distinguishes feminist perspectives, which foreground gender, from the "intersecting oppression perspective," which considers how other forms of oppression are magnified by each other and magnify the violence in women's lives. From this perspective, the experience of violence is seen as being influenced profoundly by the intersections of multiple social locations of privilege and oppression.

Understanding violence at the intersection of multiple forms of oppression does not mean reinforcing or subscribing to stereotypes that associate violence primarily with certain groups. Dobash and Dobash (1992) claim that "by the late 1980s, public accounts had chipped away at persistent images of the violence as a problem confined to the working class, ethnic groups or the poor" (p. 5). Yet, such images persist today, informing individual and state responses to violence against women. At every stage of this author's research on violence, she was referred repeatedly by members of the public and service providers to places associated with poor and racialized people. Most recently, when conducting a study of the intersecting risks of violence and HIV for rural women (Dick & Varcoe, 2004; Varcoe & Dick, in press), the community had to position the research cautiously to prevent the problem from being interpreted as a problem only for Aboriginal women.

Acceptance is growing that violence is an enormous social problem that is deeply gendered. However, understandings of violence against women have been largely viewed in abstraction from women's lives, and the interpersonal-therapeutic models continue to dominate common understandings of violence. Thus, attention to violence has largely focused on individuals and on discrete acts of violence rather than on the social context within which violence occurs. Such understandings lead to interventions that deal with individuals and their specific acts rather than with the patterns from which those acts arise. When attention is turned to the socio-political context of violence, feminist analyses tend to focus on gender oppression, and the influences of other intersecting forms of oppression are rarely taken into account. Although feminist perspectives have increased public awareness of the gendered nature of violence, violence and its impact on women's lives must be understood within the context of a culture of violence that encompasses the violence of racism, poverty, heterosexism, and other forms of inequity. It is thus from this perspective that the remainder of this chapter will proceed.

VIOLENCE AND WOMEN'S HEALTH AT THE INTERSECTIONS

The limitations of a gender-only analysis of violence against women have been forcefully articulated and attention has been turned toward the importance of other forms of oppression by authors such as Hooks (1984), Richie and Kanuha (1993), Walker (1995), Agnew (1998), Bannerji (2000), and Anderson (2000). Moving beyond a gender analysis of violence, recent theorists use the concept of **intersectionality** to understand violence (Crenshaw, 1994; Mahoney, 1994; Mosher, 1998; Phillips, 1998). "Intersectionality" refers to the interaction between forms of oppression (e.g., racism, classism, sexism) in ways that magnify one another (Brewer, 1993; Collins, 1993). For example, the experience of being poor (or racialized, or disabled, or aged) is not simply an "added" form of oppression for a woman; rather, being poor co-constitutes the oppression inherent in being a woman. Similarly, being racialized amplifies poverty, as does disability, and so on. Intersectionality addresses the ways in which various forms of oppression reinforce each other and interact. Thus, for example, an Aboriginal woman who finds it difficult to find employment because of racism is kept poor, and so on.

Women's health also is analyzed increasingly from an intersectional perspective (Anderson, 2000; Morrow, Hankivsky & Varcoe, 2007). Gender-based analysis, or gender mainstreaming as it is known internationally, has been used to show not only how women's health varies by gender but also by a wide range of intersecting determinants of health (Hankivsky, 2006). Intersectional approaches to violence against women, women's health, and the impacts of violence on women's health produce more complex and finely nuanced understandings, and thus provide a better platform for policy, practice, and further research.

The central purpose of the remainder of this chapter is to illustrate that understanding how violence impacts women's health requires understanding how intersecting forms of inequality interact with violence to affect women's health. There are three major points to this argument. The first is that inequities compound the impact of violence. The second is that the dynamics of inequity and violence create barriers to obtaining meaningful support in dealing with violence, and thus sustain violence in the lives of more oppressed women. The third point is that these dynamics also sustain privilege and notions of superiority, and thus they distance persons of privilege from violence.

VIOLENCE AFFECTS WOMEN'S HEALTH

Women experience a wide range of health impacts as a consequence of violence including direct physical consequences of injuries and sexual abuse (such as gynaecological problems, including pelvic inflammatory disease), long term consequences of physical injuries (such as arthritis and chronic pain), and the consequences of stress and mental and emotional abuse (such as depression, post traumatic stress disorder, and gastrointestinal problems such as irritable bowel syndrome) (Ali, Toner, Stuckless, Gallop, Diamant, Gould et al., 2000; Campbell, 2002; Champion, Piper, Holden, Korte & Shain, 2004; Coker, Smith, Bethea, King & McKeown, 2000; Coker, Smith, King & McKeown, 2000; Green, Flowe-Valencia, Rosenblum & Tait, 1999; Reilly & Warshaw, 1998). These health effects are also seen in higher costs for the health care and social services systems (Hathaway, Mucci, Silverman, Brooks, Mathews & Pavlos, 2000; Yodanis, Godenzi & Stanko, 2000), with women who experience abuse requiring more surgical interventions, physician and pharmacy visits, hospital stays, and mental health consultations than other women even when controlling for other factors affecting health care utilization (Heise et al., 1999). However, violence against women and its impacts are not borne equally by all groups of women.

INEQUITIES COMPOUND THE IMPACT OF VIOLENCE

Intersecting inequities magnify the experience of violence in women's lives, and thus their health, in at least three ways. First, less privileged women are exposed to more forms of violence, and thus to more violence. Second, the less privileged a woman, the greater are the costs of disclosure of IPV. Third, the more forms of oppression a woman experiences, the more constrained are her "choices."

Less Privilege Means More Violence

Less privileged women are exposed to more violence. This is not to say that less privileged people are more violent, but rather that less privilege renders people more vulnerable. For example, women with disabilities are made vulnerable to violence by their disabilities and by the fact that they often must rely on others to provide many forms of support; they are thus vulnerable to a large range of people. Using the Health Utility Index with a random sample of Canadians, 22.6 percent of women report having a disability compared to 19.6 percent of men (Desmeules, Turner & Cho, 2003), and earlier work suggests that women with disabilities are at least 1.5–2 times as likely to be abused as non-disabled women (Statistics Canada, Centre for Justice Statistics, 1994; Stimpson & Best, 1991; Sobsey, 1988). To take another example, women who are racialized are exposed to the violence of racism as a matter of course. Thus, for racialized women, violence in intimate relationships occurs within a context of daily exposure to racism. Aboriginal women in Canada are much more likely than non-Aboriginal women to experience violence by a male partner (Brownridge, 2003) and are eight times more likely than non-Aboriginal women to be killed by their partner (Trainor & Mihorean, 2001). Brownridge's analysis of Statistics Canada's General Social Survey, however, supports the theory that the unique experience of colonization of Aboriginal people in Canada, which includes ongoing racism and discrimination, plays a large role in their disproportionate likelihood of violence against women. Importantly, poverty constitutes a significant risk factor for abuse by male partners (Browne & Bassuk, 1997; Grana, 2001). As economic independence is central to determining whether women will enter, remain in, or leave abusive partnerships, with a persistent gender wage gap in Canada, income is salient. For example, women have more precarious employment than men, with those in full-time temporary, part-time permanent, and part-time temporary wage work earning roughly seventy percent of the average wage received by full-time permanent men of the same age (Cranford, Vosko & Zukewhich, 2003). These various forms of disadvantage compound one another – so, for example, disabled women are further disadvantaged by lower levels of income and social support: 20–27 percent of disabled women have low income compared to 13–18 percent of disabled men; 35–41 percent of disabled women report receiving social support all of the time compared to 40–58 percent of disabled men (Desmeules, Turner & Cho, 2003).

Less Privilege Means More Costly Disclosure

Disclosure of abuse incurs costs for all women. For most women, disclosure of abuse is constrained by cultural norms, religious beliefs, and family pressures.[2] According to the women interviewed by the author, the disclosure of IPV means at least embarrassment and shame. As Koss notes: "When people acknowledge their status as victims, inevitably some degree of devaluation is incurred" (1990, p. 374). In addition, decision making is often taken out of women's hands following a disclosure of intimate violence. Therefore, disclosure often has personal, social, and economic costs that extend beyond the initial act of disclosure. For example, after her husband had beaten her particularly badly, one woman described weighing the costs of disclosure (which she saw as ruining her son's chances for a scholarship and university, and potentially causing her to lose her home):

> If I go to the cops tonight (and I knew damn well if I made a complaint it was out of my hands)—what I really wanted to do was get this documented, okay? I knew if I went there it was out of my control so I had to sit back and "What am I going to do?" (Interview, Project Violence Free, 2001)

There are costs associated with disclosure for the woman, her family, and her community regardless of her level of privilege. In the author's various studies, many women spoke of those constraints in terms of the loss of privilege:

> [My husband] was earning somewhere around two hundred to three hundred thousand a year, he covered the mortgage but it was very difficult, I mean I didn't have enough money

> to buy myself a pair of jeans, it was awful, very, very difficult....I didn't realize the legal system, once he moved out, how awful it was for women, I didn't realize the cost of child care, I didn't realize the difficulty of getting care for my kids if I was working nights or evenings...all of that was not known to me, and the year that I was separated, that all became known to me....I had so little support from anyone...because of him being a [professional], it really felt that people were really biased against me...even in my family you know, and they didn't really understand that I should be leaving a marriage. (Interview, Project Violence Free)

For most women, disclosure and the subsequent pressure to leave abusive partners means a drastically reduced income. For example, early findings of the WHES show that while the women's personal income increased slightly, their household income declined dramatically after leaving an abusive male partner. Disclosure may be particularly costly for women who experience more inequities, because they have fewer options and resources.

Inequities mean that women have fewer resources and fewer choices about how much violence they have to endure. Women who must rely on others for various forms of support and care (such as women who are disabled or frail, and elderly women) often must choose between enduring the abuse or losing the care. This may mean not only the loss of a home and income but also the irreplaceable loss of direct care. Women who have fewer employment opportunities (due to age, racism, and so on) must tolerate more sexual harassment, not only because they need their jobs but also because they have less power to expose the harassment. Given the invisibility of lesbian battering (Bernhard, 2000; Ristock, 1991; Turrell, 2000), lesbians are unlikely to find meaningful social support among formal services, and disclosure may incur homophobic and heterosexist responses. Lesbians may fear such responses, fear disbelief, and fear the impact of disclosure on the lesbian community – fears that may be exploited by abusive partners. For example, in a recent study (Varcoe, Jaffer & Irwin, 2000), a lesbian who had been battered by her partner did not call the police when beaten because her partner threatened to tell the police that the woman who had been beaten had "started it" and because she thought "of course the cops would believe her or treat us both like freaks."

The costs of disclosure are particularly evident in the especially toxic consequences for racialized women (Bannerji, 2000). Dobash and Dobash (1992) note that for racialized women to seek assistance in dealing with intimate violence is considered unacceptable both by racialized communities and by the women themselves because responses (such as arrest) are seen as "further act(s) of racial oppression against men of colour" (p. 52). Women from racialized communities must choose between exposing their communities to further racism (itself a form of violence) or tolerating violence. In her study of resources for Canadian women from Asia, Africa, and the Caribbean, Agnew (1998) illustrates how seeking help risks "the loss of sympathy and support from their families and other members of the ethnic or racial community" (p. 8). Bannerji notes that particularly for immigrant women of colour, "silence means anything from complicity to resistance" and that such women are in "double jeopardy since speaking and not speaking both entail problems" (p. 153). Despite the documentation of these problems, the impact on women's use of the formal systems is unknown. In the United States, studies such as the National Violence Against Women Survey (Tjaden & Thoennes, 1998) and others (see Barnett, 2000) indicate that African American women are more likely to seek help than Anglo-American women, suggesting that women from racialized communities are to some extent paying the costs of disclosure. Thus, in Canada, Guruge and Khanlou (2005) argue that understanding the impact of male violence on the health and well-being of immigrant and refugee women must be understood within the context of post-migration loss of financial and social stability, racism and discrimination, and the stress of negotiating and navigating through various institutional and structural systems that are designed to serve the dominant groups.

Less Privilege Means Fewer Choices

The more forms of oppression a woman experiences, such as poverty, racialization, and disability, the more constrained are her "choices." Poverty is particularly constraining. Women's vulnerability to violence is increased by economic and social disparities between men and women. Gurr, Mailloux, and Kinnon (1996) point out that financial and psychological independence are key factors that deter women from either entering or staying in abusive relationships. Women's lack of economic independence often limits their ability to leave abusive situations, and poverty limits access to services in multiple ways. Levinson's (1989) comparative study of 90 small-scale and peasant societies indicated that the strongest predictor of wife abuse was sexual economic inequality. Wife abuse occurred more frequently in societies in which husbands controlled family wealth and thus had more economic and decision-making power. In Canada, the VAWS indicated that the one-year incidence of wife assault was twice as high for women who were unemployed or earned less than $15,000 per year than for all other socio-economic groups. Lambert and Firestone (2000) note that "women who are able to at least equalize their occupational prestige with their partner suffer fewer types of abuse than women whose prestige is lower than their partner's and women from lower socio-economic households" (p. 50). Further, while research suggests that intimate partner violence does not prevent victims from working, it prevents victims from maintaining long-term stable jobs (Swanberg, Logan & Macke, 2005). Abusive partners interfere with work through both work disruption and work-related stalking. As a result of these behaviours, some victims of partner violence struggle to be employed, others manage to obtain employment but fail to maintain it, whereas still others cannot obtain employment at all. These economic barriers to living violence-free are magnified by the effects of racism, cultural norms, language, disabilities, and age.

Thus, in Canadian society, where men tend to have more economic and decision-making power, violence against women occurs at disgraceful rates, and the same inequities that foster abuse also limit women's options for either entering or leaving abusive relationships, and exposes them to other forms of violence. Inequities compound one another and compound violence by increasing women's vulnerability to abuse, thus increasing the costs of disclosure and limiting options for dealing with violence. These dynamics affect and are affected by women's health.

INEQUITIES CREATE BARRIERS TO SUPPORT

Intersecting forms of oppression limit women's possibilities of obtaining meaningful support in several interacting ways. First, inequities limit access to support. Second, because services have become professionalized and are now largely provided by "mainstream" well-educated members of the dominant culture, services tend to be designed with similar women in mind. Thus, services are fewer and less appropriate for women who are further from the dominant culture. Third, women who are more disadvantaged or marginalized have less power in relation to those providing service.

Inequities Mean Less Access

Access to support is limited both directly and indirectly by inequities. Poverty, which is of course compounded by racism, disability, age, and so on, particularly limits access. At the most concrete level, the costs of services (such as legal fees and counselling), of transportation to services in both urban and rural settings, and of child care during support can directly limit access. The understanding of complex legal and social welfare systems may be limited by education and literacy levels. Further, women's paid and unpaid work may leave little time to sort through these complex systems. A woman who has casual, part-time, minimum-wage employment will not have the luxury of paid time off to attend services such as support groups or counselling, or to consult lawyers, police, and so on. Language barriers will further compound all of the access issues (Agnew, 1998).

Geography is a source of inequity of particular importance to Canadian women. Women in rural and isolated communities have considerably less access than urban women to all forms of social support. For example, MacIntosh (2005) points out that the problems associated with addressing workplace bullying may be compounded in rural communities where employers and fellow workers may also be neighbours. In our study of the intersecting risks of violence and HIV for rural women (Dick & Varcoe, 2004; Varcoe & Dick, in press), poverty worked with the rural context and violence to keep women isolated. The women in the study who lived in rural or remote settings described geographic isolation as part of the dynamics of abuse and as a barrier to assistance. Indeed, one of the transition houses predicted staffing based on when "spring break up" (of snow and ice) might permit women to get to help. In the VAWS, the number of rural women who contacted or stayed in a transition house or shelter, got their own place, or stayed in a hotel was too small to report, compared with 15 percent of urban women who did so (Levett & Johnson, 1997). Although they were somewhat more isolated from family, friends, and neighbours, rural women relied on family and friends to the same extent as did urban women, but were somewhat more likely than urban women to return home (79 percent compared with 67 percent). However, rural women were slightly more likely to contact a social service agency, and, despite being geographically more distant from medical services, rural women who were injured were as likely as urban women to receive medical attention for their injuries (Levett & Johnson, 1997). This suggests that rural women often do the added work to overcome the additional barriers to access.

Inequities Mean Less Appropriate Support

Even when women can access services, those services are often inappropriate or inadequate, reflecting and further magnifying existing inequities based on age, language, disability, sexual orientation, and racialization. For example, services for older women are often lacking and/or inappropriate. In the United States, researchers have pointed out that older women have quite different services needs depending on whether they were abused by spouses or by others such as adult children, and may get little help from adult protection services which are designed for the latter (Grossman & Lundy, 2003; Zink, Jacobson, Regan & Pabst, 2004). In a study of services offered by transition houses in British Columbia, Hightower et al. (1999) found that only 1–2 percent of the women served were over 60 years of age, although women over 60 years of age comprise 22 percent of the adult female population. Some of the reasons suggested for this discrepancy included a lack of staff training and awareness of the dynamics of abuse of older persons, lack of facilities for those with disabilities, and challenges in providing assistance with medications and physical care to those who require such care. The services were thought to be particularly inadequate for older women with disabilities or language barriers, and older women living in poverty. Overall, Hightower et al. and others (e.g., Vinton, 1997) conclude that service has been oriented to the needs of younger women with children. Services for older abused women are often guided by a medical model that views all older adults as vulnerable and dependent, creating services that are more in line with a child abuse model.

The appropriateness and accessibility of services for women who are racialized, women who speak little of the official languages, and lesbians have also been questioned. Racism pervades human-service provision in Canada (Henry et al., 2005). With particular regard to services for women who have experienced abuse, Agnew (1998) conducted an extensive study of services in Canada (primarily Eastern Canada). She described widespread racism in mainstream social and legal services for women who had experienced abuse. She also described institutionalized racism, such as employment practices that lead to service providers who are not representative of the diversity of the communities they serve, and inadequate funding for community-based services. In Canada and other Western countries, women seeking assistance in relation to abuse within health care services commonly encounter racism and classism (Campbell et al., 1994; Dobash & Dobash, 1992; Hampton & Newberger, 1988; Varcoe, 2001), factors that likely deter access and disclosure and certainly diminish the benefit of service.

Women who speak limited English (this includes some immigrant women, francophone women in English-dominated regions, and women who speak Aboriginal languages) find services less accessible and appropriate in most areas. For example, a survey of resources in Greater Vancouver illustrated that services for francophone women experiencing abuse are difficult to find and may not be affordable (e.g., psychologists), thus limiting French-speaking women's support for dealing with abusive partners (Dubois, Dussault & Lévesque, 1994). For women who are immigrants, citizenship issues and unfamiliarity with institutional systems further compound the problems of access throughout the legal, health care, and social welfare systems, and for many language, isolation, and economic fears are also barriers to support (Guruge & Khanlou, 2005; Varcoe, Jaffer & Irwin, 2000).

While over the past two decades researchers and service providers have increasingly acknowledged and attended to violence in lesbian relationships, such "non-prototypical" victims continue to be overlooked as individuals and in service planning (Renzetti, 1996; Ristock, 2002; VanNatta, 2005; Burke & Owen, 2006; Seelau & Seelau, 2005). Lesbians commonly encounter barriers to health care (Stevens & Hall, 1988; Davis, 2000), and evidence exists that in other systems, responses by service providers in relation to violence may be particularly compromised for lesbian women (e.g., Agnew, 1998; Wise & Bowman, 1997). Indeed, VanNatta (2005) argues that shelter workers are likely to perceive women abused by women rather than by men as outside of their model of the "real battered woman."

Inequities Mean Less Power

When service is obtained, women of less privilege have less power in relation to those providing service. With less power in relation to service providers, women are more at the mercy of service providers and thus even less likely to find those services useful. Women with less power are more readily scrutinized, have less power to resist the contingencies that professionals place on the provision of service, and may be viewed as less deserving of service.

Poverty, racialization, and other forms of inequity make individuals more open to the health care provider's scrutiny. In this author's study of emergency units (Varcoe, 1997, 2001), she observed and was told by health care providers that they were less likely to ask questions about abuse of wealthy, non-racialized people. One nurse working in a setting that served a large First Nations reserve as well as a wealthy population said:

> I'll just say "Maybe this could be," rather than really "Look let's deal with this, I think there is some violence here," which I would do with the [Native] Indian women, which I probably wouldn't do with the [wealthier] ladies. (Varcoe, 1997)

Health care providers commonly associated and anticipated violence with poor and racialized people, despite the fact that they were aware that violence crosses all socioeconomic levels and cultures. Paradoxically, although they were likely to assume abuse as an issue among poor and racialized women, they also tended to view poor and racialized women as less deserving of care and support. In a disturbing example, nurses reported that a physician refused to call the sexual assault team to examine a First Nations woman who had been drinking, calling her "a societal derelict." Such judgments were not based directly on class and race alone, but rather on a complex of judgments in which individual women were seen as deserving to different extents. Women who were seen as undeserving of support in relation to violence included women who abused alcohol and drugs, women who had been offered help before and "refused" help, or women who returned frequently – behaviours that were seen as individual choices rather than as reflecting larger social issues. For example, a social worker told of supporting a particular woman:

> She had been in a transition house, left the house to go and try to reconnect with this partner, been badly beaten again and was now in Emerg awaiting some repair surgery...her situation was quite appalling to some of the nurses, [and my role was] also dealing with the judgment that she was the undeserving patient because of the drug addiction. (Varcoe, 1997)

Health care providers also made support contingent on women accepting professional definitions of the problem and solutions. Describing how friends and family members of women who experience violence make help conditional on the woman accepting their evaluation of her situation, Lempert (1997) called such a dynamic "definitional contingency." Support was often not offered or was withdrawn from women who were perceived as not making decisions that health care providers thought best. Because women with less privilege have less power in relation to service providers, these dynamics are more likely to play out along the lines of existing inequities. So, for example, the dynamics between health care providers and Aboriginal women more generally (Browne & Fiske, 2001; Browne, 2005) are likely to shape interactions in relation to violence.

Intersecting inequities mean that certain women have less service and support for dealing with violence. The more inequity a woman experiences, the less likely she is to find appropriate, meaningful support in dealing with violence in her life. And, the more inequity she experiences, the less power she has in relation to those providing support.

THE DYNAMICS OF INEQUITY AND VIOLENCE SUSTAIN PRIVILEGE

The dynamics between violence and inequity are self-perpetuating, sustain positions of privilege and notions of superiority, and distance persons of privilege from violence. This maintenance of the status quo of inequity and violence is actualized primarily through stereotyping. These stereotypes include associating violence with people of less privilege (particularly poor and racialized people) and associating certain characteristics such as passivity and acceptance of abuse with those same people (Agnew, 1998; Browne, 2005; Varcoe, 2001).

Inequity fosters violence, which in turn fosters inequity. The greater the inequities a given woman experiences, the more forms of violence she is exposed to and the less likely she is to receive meaningful support. The more violence she must endure, the more inequity is entrenched. So, for example, a woman who is poor and unable to afford independent housing, legal fees, and other services that might help decrease the violence in her life, is kept in violence and kept poor, both of which affect health.

These dynamics also sustain positions of privilege and notions of superiority. When women who are marginalized in some way are recognized as abused, rather than associating violence with vulnerability and visibility, service providers may judge them as being more "prone" to being battered. In a study of emergency units and their communities (Varcoe, 1997, 2001), health care providers commonly associated violence with the racialized groups in their community but attributed the association to race, rather than to the vulnerabilities associated with racism or to the visibility occasioned by appearance. When asked about their experiences in dealing with violence against women, health care providers tended to recall only racialized women. They more easily recalled women they identified by race, tended to anticipate and observe violence among racialized women, and thus more often recognized abuse among racialized women, reinforcing their ideas about among which people and communities violence occurred.

When increased scrutiny of racialized and poor women identifies violence, the identification of violence is interpreted as further evidence that the particular group is *more violent* rather than *more visible* to those in positions of power. Such interpretations of personal experience are exacerbated by racialized media depictions of violence (e.g., Wilcox, 2005). Rather than the disproportionate barriers to disclosure being seen and being attributed to inequities, women are seen as not wanting help. When women do not use or access services, this is not seen as reflecting inadequate service but rather, in a victim-blaming manoeuvre, they again are judged as not wanting help. Limited choices are not seen for what they are, but rather are considered choices women make (see also Mahoney, 1994; Mosher, 1998). Thus, if a woman must choose between poverty and abuse, she is blamed either for tolerating abuse or for being poor. If a woman must choose between abuse and exposing her community to racial stereotypes about violence, either the stereotypes are reinforced or she is blamed for tolerating abuse (and other racial stereotypes about women in certain groups – such as passivity and tolerance for violence – are reinforced).

The dynamics of inequality and violence are often dismissed by using the concept of culture. In Canadian society, "culture" is often conflated with "race" and used to explain all sorts of social problems and behaviours. With respect to violence, such ideas can be used to dismiss abuse as a "cultural problem" among certain people. Thus, culture is a concept often used to mask the dynamics between inequity and violence. For example, in an ethnographic study (Varcoe, 1997) referring to racialized groups, both racialized and non-racialized people told the author that it was "against their culture" to disclose abuse. Individualist understandings of health issues feed into these dynamics. For example, understanding poverty and drug and alcohol use as individual responsibilities (rather than considering the complex relations among violence, drug and alcohol use, and poverty) supports blaming individuals and "cultures" rather than examining the contribution of social inequities to violence.

The dynamics of inequality and violence reinforce stereotypes that associate violence with the less privileged. Women who are seen to endure violence (despite the fact that they may be doing so partially in resistance to other forms of oppression) may be judged as being accepting of violence. Increased exposure to violence may be seen as a failing on the part of the woman. Similarly, if less service decreases the effectiveness of women's attempts to limit the violence they endure, then that ineffectiveness may be attributed to the woman. Finally, given the greater scrutiny of less privileged women by powerful service providers, less privileged groups may be perceived as being more violent.

These stereotypes in turn serve to maintain the superiority of more privileged people (particularly racial and class superiority) and to distance those more privileged from violence. The logic here is that violence is a problem of the "other" and thus is not a problem of those with more privilege; it is a problem of "those people" and by contrast, is *not* a problem of "my" people. Thus, a person of privilege is superior because of membership in a seemingly less violent group, and violence is a problem that is at a distance from those persons and groups. Stereotypical ideas about violence work to maintain notions of racial superiority among those with racial privilege, and ideas about race and class work to keep violence at a distance from those with privilege.

Dynamics of inequality and violence "work" for people in privileged positions. And professional service providers are at the interface between the worlds of privilege and women who require service. The increased visibility of marginalized people and increased scrutiny by professionals are fuelled by stereotypical thinking and biased expectations, all of which magnify the appearance of an increased incidence of violence among poor and racialized people, an appearance that in turn fosters demeaning stereotypes. Health is worsened by the interplay among various forms of inequity and violence, both through the social determinants of health and the limitations to health care access.

IMPLICATIONS

Attempts to address inequities and violence in relation to women's health generally focus on the accessibility and appropriateness of services rather than on the correction of fundamental inequities within our society. Improvements to service provision generally take the form of providing services for particular marginalized groups and of promoting "cultural sensitivity" in mainstream services. These strategies are inadequate and must be replaced with strategies that address fundamental social inequities and strategies to provide services that are based on critical awareness of inequity and actively seek to redress those inequities, particularly poverty and racism.

Address Fundamental Social Inequities

Anti-violence work must be accompanied by active strategies to address social inequities. Lack of economic resources seriously compromises women's ability to change their circumstances and live in safety (Browne & Bassuk, 2000). Strategies that increase the financial and psychological independence of women – particularly women who are marginalized by other inequities such as racialization, disability, and age – are far more likely to have an impact on reducing violence against women than violence-specific programs. Social policies that promote equity in hiring practices and wages, social housing, subsidized child care, legal aid, divorce, and child-support laws that foster equity should be supported by all who wish to reduce violence against women. Health issues as diverse as mental illness, HIV, and bowel disease can be better understood if the complex interplay among health disparities, social inequities, and violence are taken into account.

Base Services on a Critical Awareness of Inequities

Anti-violence services need to be based on a critical understanding of all forms of inequity and integrated with services that attempt to address such inequities. The World Health Report on Violence and Health (2002) recommends that violence prevention be integrated into social and educational policies, thereby promoting gender and social equality. The intersecting impacts of disability, mental illness, poverty, racism, ageism, and heterosexism must be considered in the planning, improvement, and delivery of services. Individual women's experiences of violence must be understood within the context of their lives and the inequities they experience, and support must be provided based on that understanding. This means that support must be woman-centred and promote economic independence. Mills (1996) argues that rather than insisting that a woman leave her partner, a woman-centred approach to economic independence is required to explore all the woman's options and recognize "that her uncertainty and emotional and cultural loyalties demand a safe and non-judgemental space in which to explore these issues" (p. 266).

Mills (1996) has argued for replacing the criminal model of response with an integrated social response in the form of "domestic violence commissions" that would place control in the hands of women themselves and address economic independence as well as the violence the woman has experienced. Wuest and Merritt-Gray (1999) concur and argue that helpers must go beyond simply facilitating access to resources. Rather, they argue, women need more than just access to financial aid; they need to know how to create long-term financial security. Women need more than police protection; they need the judicial system to support their economic independence through the division of assets, child support, and the maintenance of their personal boundaries.

Addressing the inequities that women face that are based on gender and are magnified by all other forms of inequity must begin with dealing with economic issues. Simultaneously, active strategies to address particular forms of oppression are essential to interrupt the dynamics of inequality and violence. Considering anti-racist strategies may provide ideas for approaches that are also consciously anti-heterosexist, anti-ageist, anti-ableist, and so on.

Replace "Multiculturalism" with Anti-Racism

The improvement of mainstream anti-violence services must move beyond the ideology of **multiculturalism**, which pervades Canadian society (Bannerji, 2000; Henry et al., 2005; Ng, 1993a, b), and beyond the passive notion of "cultural sensitivity." Multiculturalism is inadequate to the goal of eradicating racism because its focus is on improving the behaviour of "**prejudiced** individuals," which overlooks the ways in which racism is deeply embedded in language, structures, and institutions. In a multicultural analysis of service, the problem is defined as mismatches between "minority" and dominant cultures, which overlooks political and economic forces and makes the "different" culture the problem. From a multiculturalist perspective, services are improved by bringing "culture" into care, which often confuses culture with "ethnicity," and perpetuates the use of racial categories. Multiculturalism assumes a "level playing field" between individuals, which overlooks the historical impact of colonization, immigration, and racism. The related notion of cultural sensitivity is similarly insufficient. Such an idea relies on the passive "sensitivity" of members of dominant groups to the "difference" of "others" and leaves inequity unexamined.

Actively anti-racist approaches would include changing language, structures, and institutions. Racism is manifest in structures and service delivery through lack of access to appropriate programs and services for racialized women, inadequate funding for ethno-racial community-based agencies, lack of minority representation in social agencies, ethnocentric values and counselling services, and monocultural or ad hoc "multicultural" models of service delivery (Henry et al., 2005). Meaningful change would thus include improved funding for community-based agencies (without further entrenching racial stereotypes), hiring practices that ensure that the diversity in any given community is reflected in the social locations of those providing service, and the development of anti-racist models of service delivery that take into account the inequities that women experience and the impact of those inequities on women's lives and communities.

In contrast to the common social responses that require women to "leave," Mosher (1998) asks if it would not be preferable to discern what would make it possible for a woman "to take care of her race, her community, her husband [or partner] and herself without having to choose among them" (p. 148). To move toward that preferable option, those who are in positions of professional privilege must examine their stance in relation to inequities and violence. People in such positions have the option of using their privilege in ways that oppose the dynamics of inequality and violence toward improving women's health rather than maintaining the status quo.

ACKNOWLEDGEMENTS

This research was supported by a National Health Research and Development Program fellowship, by a research grant from the Canadian Nurses Foundation, and by two grants from the British Columbia Health Research Foundation. The author gratefully acknowledges all the research participants, the members of "Women in Action," and Dr. Joan Anderson for her guidance.

STUDY QUESTIONS

1. *What privileges do you personally experience? How do these privileges shape your assumptions, values, and beliefs? What sensitivities and "blind spots" do your privileges create?*
2. *In what ways are your beliefs about the demographics of violence against women shaped by stereotypical ideas and images, and your own privilege?*
3. *What do you believe is the extent of violence within the community with which you identify? What influences the ideas you hold?*
4. *In what ways has the ideology of multiculturalism influenced your thinking about how human services ought to be provided?*

GLOSSARY

classism an assumption of superiority in relation to a group of people of a given rank or status (usually socio-economic) in the community.

corporate violence behaviour and actions of persons in authority within the corporation, including acts of omission that endanger the health and safety of employees and other persons.

feminism a point of view that considers women as oppressed and exploited; includes both a commitment to changing the condition of women and the adoption of a critical perspective toward dominant intellectual traditions and methodologies.

gendered of a given phenomenon, influenced and varied by the gender of the persons involved; for example, work, caregiving, and income are different for men and women and thus are "gendered."

intersectionality the interaction between forms of oppressions (such as racism and sexism) in ways that magnify one another; for example, being racialized is not an "added" form of oppression for a woman; rather it magnifies that oppression (Brewer, 1993; Collins, 1993).

multiculturalism an approach to culture and "difference" in diverse, multiracial, multilingual societies that has arisen from the general social theory of cultural pluralism. Cultural pluralism holds that all cultures are "equal" but different. Multiculturalism emphasizes culture as a determinant of behaviour and "difference" (rather than, for example, structural inequities), and is often associated with cultural relativism, the idea that each culture has its own values and should be judged by its own standards. Multiculturalism is enshrined in Canadian society, in various laws, and in commonsense understandings of Canada. In health care, multiculturalism has been increasingly associated with calls for "cultural sensitivity," meaning that health care providers should be "tolerant" of and sensitive to the "differences" of "other" cultures (non-dominant groups).

patriarchy the system of male domination over women – the rule of husbands, male bosses, and other men in social, economic, and political institutions.

prejudiced holding an unreasonable, unjustified bias; having a preconceived opinion that is usually unfavourable.

racialization the process by which people are labelled according to particular physical characteristics or arbitrary ethnic or racial categories, and then dealt with in accordance with beliefs related to those labels (Agnew, 1998). This process is based on the concept of race, "a socially constructed phenomenon based on the erroneous assumption that physical differences such as skin colour, hair colour, and texture, and facial features are related to intellectual, moral, or cultural superiority. The concept of race has no basis in biological reality and as such has no meaning independent of its social definitions" (Henry et al., 2005, p. 4).

sexual harassment conduct that occurs in a gender-stratified context and in a context of differential power relationships, and that often involves sexual remarks, sexual touching, demands for sex, sexual impositions, and other unwanted and offensive conduct.

violence an act involving force or coercion and that causes physical, psychological, or emotional harm to others.

REFERENCES

Agnew, V. (1998). *In search of a safe place: Abused women and culturally sensitive services.* Toronto: University of Toronto Press.

Ali, A., Toner, B., Stuckless, N., Gallop, R., Diamant, N., Gould, M., et al. (2000). Emotional abuse, self-blame, and self-silencing in women with irritable bowel syndrome. *Psychosomatic Medicine, 62*(1), 76–82.

Allman, K.K.M. (1992). Race, racism, and health: Examining the "natural" facts. In J.L. Thompson, D.G. Allen, & L. Rodrigues-Fisher (Eds.), *Critique, resistance and action: Working papers in the politics of nursing* (pp. 35–52). New York: NLN.

Anderson, J.M. (2000). Gender, "race," poverty, health and discourses of health reform in the context of globalization: A postcolonial feminist perspective in policy research. *Nursing Inquiry, 7*, 220–229.

Arnetz, J.E., Arnetz, B.B., & Soderman, E. (1998). Violence toward health care workers: Prevalence and incidence at a large regional hospital in Sweden. *American Association of Occupational Health Nurses Journal, 46*(3), 107–114.

Bannerji, H. (2000). A question of silence: Reflections on violence against women in communities of colour. In H. Bannerji (Ed.), *The dark side of the nation: Essays on multiculturalism, nationalism and gender* (pp. 151–174). Toronto: Canadian Scholars' Press.

Barbee, E.L. (1992). Ethnicity and woman abuse in the United States. In C.M. Sampselle (Ed.), *Violence against women: Nursing research, education and practice issues* (pp. 153–166). New York: Hemisphere.

Barnett, O.W. (2000). Why battered women do not leave: Part 1: External inhibiting factors within society. *Trauma, Violence & Abuse, 1*(4), 343–372.

Barnett, O.W., Miller-Perrin, C.L., & Miller, R.D. (2005). *Family violence across the life span: An introduction* (2nd ed.). Thousand Oaks, CA: Sage.

BC Task Force on Family Violence. (1992). *Is anyone listening? Report of the British Columbia Task Force on Family Violence.* Victoria, BC: Ministry of Women's Equality.

Bernhard, L.A. (2000). Physical and sexual violence experienced by lesbian and heterosexual women. *Violence against women, 6*(1), 68–79.

Bograd, M. (1988). Feminist perspectives on wife abuse: An introduction. In K. Yllö & M. Bograd (Eds.), *Feminist perspectives on wife abuse* (pp. 11–26). Newbury Park, CA: Sage.

Brewer, R.M. (1993). Theorizing race, class and gender: The new scholarship of Black feminist intellectuals and Black women's labour. In S.M. James & A.P.A. Busia (Eds.), *Theorizing black feminisms: The visionary pragmatism for Black women* (pp. 13–30). London: Routledge.

Browne, A. (2005). Discourses influencing nurses' perceptions of First Nations patients. *CJNR: Canadian Journal of Nursing Research, 37*(4), 62–87.

Browne, A., & Bassuk, S.S. (1997). Intimate violence in the lives of homeless and poor housed women: Prevalence and patterns in an ethnically diverse sample. *American Journal of Orthopsychiatry, 67*(2), 261–278.

Browne, A.J., & Fiske, J. (2001). First Nations women's encounters with mainstream health care services. *Western Journal of Nursing Research, 23*(2), 126–147.

Brownridge, D. (2003). Male partner violence against Aboriginal women in Canada: An empirical analysis. *Journal of Interpersonal Violence, 18*(1), 65–83.

Burke, T.W., & Owen, S.S. (January 2006). Same-sex domestic violence: Is anyone listening? *The Gay & Lesbian Review Worldwide,* 6–7.

Campbell, J. (2002). Health consequences of intimate partner violence. *The Lancet,* 359, 1331–1336.

Campbell, J.C., Pliska, M.J., Taylor, W., & Sheridan, D. (1994). Battered women's experiences in the emergency department. *Journal of Emergency Nursing, 20*(4), 280–288.

Carroll, V., & Morin, K.H. (1998). Workplace violence affects one-third of nurses: Survey of nurses in seven SNAs reveals staff nurses most at risk. *American Nurses, 30*(5), 15.

Champion, J.D., Piper, J., Holden, A., Korte, J., & Shain, R.N. (2004). Abused women and pelvic inflammatory disease. *Western Journal of Nursing Research, 26*(2), 176–191.

Coker, A.L., Smith, P.H., Bethea, L., King, M.R., & McKeown, R.E. (2000). Physical health consequences of physical and psychological intimate partner violence. *Archives of Family Medicine, 9*(5), 451–457.

Coker, A.L., Smith, P.H., McKeown, R.E., & King, M.R. (2000). Frequency and correlates of intimate partner violence by type: physical, sexual, and psychological battering. *American Journal of Public Health, 90*(4), 553–559.

Cohen, M.M., & MacLean, H. (2003). Violence against Canadian women. In M. Desmeules, D. Stewart, A. Kazanjian, H. Maclean, J. Payne, & B. Vissandjée (Eds.), *Women's health surveillance report: A multidimensional look at the health of Canadian women* (pp. 45–47) Ottawa: Canadian Institute for Health Information.

Collins, P.H. (1993). Toward a new vision: Race, class, and gender as categories of analysis and connection. *Race, Sex & Class, 1*(1), 25–45.

Coombes, R. (1998). Violence: The facts. *Nursing Times, 94*(43), 12–13.

Cranford, C.J., Vosko, L.F., & Zukewhich, N. (2003). The gender of precarious employment in Canada. *Relations Industrielles/Industrial Relations, 58*(3), 454–482.

Culley, L. (1996). A critique of multiculturalism in health care: The challenge for nurse education. *Journal of Advanced Nursing, 23*, 564–570.

Crenshaw, K.W. (1994). Mapping the margins: Intersectionality, identity politics, and violence against women of color. In M.A. Fineman & R. Mykitiuk (Eds.), *The public nature of private violence* (pp. 93–118). New York: Routledge.

Davis, V. (2000). Lesbian health guidelines. *Journal of the Society of Obstetricians and Gynaecologists of Canada, 22*, 202–205.

Desmeules, M., Turner, L., & Cho, R. (2003). Morbidity experiences and disability among Canadian women. In M. Desmeules, D. Stewart, A. Kazanjian, H. Maclean, J. Payne, & B. Vissandjée (Eds.), *Women's health surveillance report: A multidimensional look at the health of Canadian women* (pp. 19–20). Ottawa: Canadian Institute for Health Information.

Dick, S., & Varcoe, C. (2004). Violence against women and substance use in a rural context. *Visions: BC's Mental Health and Addictions Journal, 2*(4), 15–16.

Dobash, R.E., & Dobash, R.P. (1988). Research as social action: The struggle for battered women. In K. Yllö & M. Bograd (Eds.), *Feminist perspectives on wife abuse* (pp. 51–74). Newbury Park, CA: Sage.

Dobash, R.E., & Dobash, R. (1992). *Women, violence and social change*. London: Routledge.

Dubois, M.-F., Dussault, M., & Lévesque, M. (1994). *Que ça change!! Rapport du comité consultatif sur la violence*. Vancouver: Réseau-Femmes Columbie-Britannique.

Duncan, S., Estabrooks, C., & Reimer, M. (2000). Violence against nurses. High rates of workplace violence against nurses: Findings of the Alberta Nurse Survey. *Alberta RN, 56*(2), 13–14.

Duncan, S., Hyndman, K., Estabrooks, C., Hesketh, K., Humphrey, C., Wong, J., et al. (2001). Nurses' experience of violence in Alberta and British Columbia hospitals. *Canadian Journal of Nursing Research, 32*(4), 57–78.

Dutton, D. (1994). Patriarchy and wife assault: The ecological fallacy. *Violence and Victims, 9*(2), 167–182.

Findorff, M., McGovern, P., Wall, M., & Gerberich, S. (2005). Reporting violence to a health care employer: a cross-sectional study. *American Association of Occupational Health Nurses Journal, 53*(9), 399–406.

Gelles, R.J. (1993). Introduction. In R.J. Gelles & D.R. Loseke (Eds.), *Current controversies on family violence* (pp. 1–9). Newbury Park, CA: Sage.

Grana, S.J. (2001). Sociostructural considerations of domestic femicide. *Journal of Family Violence, 16*(4), 421–435.

Green, C.R., Flowe-Valencia, H., Rosenblum, L., & Tait, A.R. (1999). Do physical and sexual abuse differentially affect chronic pain states in women? *Journal of Pain and Symptom Management, 18*(6), 420–426.

Grillo, T., & Wildman, S. (1995a). Obscuring the importance of race: The implications of making comparisons between racism and sexism (or other isms). In R. Delgado (Ed.), *Critical race theory: The cutting edge* (pp. 564–572). Philadelphia: Temple University Press.

Grillo, T., & Wildman, S. (1995b). Sexism, racism and the analogy problem in feminist thought. In J. Adleman & G.M. Enguídanos (Eds.), *Racism in the lives of women: Testimony, theory and guides to antiracist practice* (pp. 171–180). New York: Harrington Park Press.

Grossman, S.F., & Lundy, M. (2003). Use of domestic violence services across race and ethnicity by women aged 55 and older. *Violence Against Women, 9*(12), 1442–1452.

Gurr, J., Mailloux, L., & Kinnon, D. (1996). *Breaking the links between poverty and violence against women.* Ottawa: Health Canada.

Guruge, S., & Khanlou, N. (2004). Intersectionalities of influence: Researching the health of immigrant and refugee women. *CJNR: Canadian Journal of Nursing Research, 36*(3), 33–47.

Hamberger, L.K. (1994). Domestic partner abuse: Expanding paradigms for understanding and intervention. *Violence and Victims, 9*(2), 91–94.

Hampton, R.L., & Newberger, E.H. (1988). Child abuse incidence and reporting by hospitals: Significance of severity, class and race. In G.T. Hotaling, D. Finkelhor, J.T. Kirkpatrick, & M.A. Straus, *Coping with family violence: Research and policy perspective* (pp. 212–221). Newbury Park, CA: Sage.

Hankivsky, O. (2006). Beijing and beyond: Women's health and gender-based analysis in Canada. *International Journal of Health Services, 36*(2), 377–400.

Hathaway, J.E., Mucci, L.A., Silverman, J.G., Brooks, D.R., Mathews, R., & Pavlos, C.A. (2000). Health status and health care use of Massachusetts women reporting partner abuse. *American Journal of Preventive Medicine, 19*(4), 302–307.

Health Canada. (1993). *Family violence against women with disabilities.* Ottawa: National Clearinghouse on Family Violence.

Heise, L.L. (1994). Gender-based abuse: The global epidemic. In A.J. Dan (Ed.), *Reframing women's health: Multidisciplinary research and practice* (pp. 233–250). Thousand Oaks, CA: Sage.

Heise, L.L., Pitanguy, J., & Germain, A. (1994). *Violence against women: The hidden health burden.* World Bank Discussion Paper #255. Washington, DC: World Bank.

Henderson, A. (2003). Research leadership. Nurses and workplace violence: nurses' experiences of verbal and physical abuse at work. *Canadian Journal of Nursing Leadership, 16*(4), 82–98.

Henry, F., Tator, C., Mattis, W., & Rees, T. (2005). *The colour of democracy: Racism in Canadian society* (3rd Edition). Toronto: Harcourt.

Higginbotham, E.B. (1992). African-American women's history and the metalanguage of race. *Signs: Journal of Women in Culture and Society, 17*(21), 251–274.

Hightower, J., Smith, M.J.G., Ward-Hall, C., & Hightower, H. (1999). Meeting the Needs of Abused Older Women? A British Columbia and Yukon Transition House Survey. *Journal of Elder Abuse & Neglect, 11*(4), 39–57.

Hinch, R., & DeKeseredy, W. (1994). Corporate violence and women's health at home and in the workplace. In B.S. Bolaria & H.D. Dickinson (Eds.), *Health, illness, and health care in Canada* (pp. 326–344). Toronto: Harcourt Brace.

Hooks, B. (1984). *Feminist theory: From margin to center.* Boston, MA: South End Press.

Johnson, H. (1996). *Dangerous domains: Violence against women in Canada.* Toronto: Nelson.

Johnson, H. (1998). Rethinking survey research on violence against women. In R.E. Dobash & R.P. Dobash (Eds.), *Rethinking violence against women* (pp. 23–51). Thousand Oaks, CA: Sage.

Kelly, L., & Radford, J. (1998). Sexual violence against women and girls. In R.E. Dobash & R.P. Dobash (Eds.), *Rethinking violence against women* (pp. 53–76). Thousand Oaks, CA: Sage.

Kerr, R., & McLean, J. (1996). *Paying for violence: Some of the costs of violence against women in BC.* Victoria, BC: Ministry of Women's Equality.

Koss, M.P. (1990). The women's mental health research agenda: Violence against women. *American Psychologist, 45*(3), 374–380.

Lambert, L.C., & Firestone, J.M. (2000). Economic context and multiple abuse techniques. *Violence Against Women, 6*(1), 49–67.

Lempert, L. (1997). The other side of help: Negative effects in the help-seeking processes of abused women. *Qualitative Sociology, 20*(2), 289–309.

Letellier, P. (1994). Gay and bisexual male domestic violence victimization: Challenges to feminist theory and responses to violence. *Violence and Victims, 9*(2), 95–106.

Levett, A., & Johnson, H. (1997). *A statistical comparison of women's experiences of violence in urban and rural settings.* Ottawa: Canadian Centre for Justice Statistics, Statistics Canada.

Levinson, D. (1989). *Family violence in cross-cultural perspective.* Newbury Park, CA: Sage.

Lutz, C. (2002). Making war at home in the United States: Militarization and the current crisis. *American Anthropologist, 104*, 723–735.

MacIntosh, J. (2005). Experiences of workplace bullying in a rural area. *Issues in Mental Health Nursing, 26*(9), 893–910.

Mahoney, M.R. (1994). Victimization or oppression? Women's lives, violence, and agency. In M.A. Fineman & R. Mykitiuk (Eds.), *The public nature of private violence* (pp. 59–92). New York: Routledge.

Miller, S.L. (1994). Expanding the boundaries: Toward a more inclusive and integrated study of intimate violence. *Violence and Victims, 9*(2), 183–194.

Mills, L. (1996). Empowering battered women transnationally: The case for postmodern interventions. *Social Work, 41*(3), 261–268.

Morrow, M., Hankivsky, O., & Varcoe, C. (2007). *Women's health in Canada: Critical theory and policy.* Toronto: University of Toronto.

Mosher, J. (1998). Caught in tangled webs of care: Women abused in intimate relationships. In C.T. Baines, P.M. Evans, & S.M. Neysmith (Eds.), *Women's caring: Feminist perspectives on social welfare* (2nd ed., pp. 139–159). Oxford: Oxford University Press.

Ng, R. (1993a). Sexism, racism, Canadian nationalism. In H. Bannerji (Ed.), *Returning the gaze: Essays on racism, feminism and politics* (pp. 182–196). Toronto: Sister Vision Press.

Ng, R. (1993b). Multiculturalism as ideology: A textual analysis. In M. Campbell & A. Manicom (Eds.), *Knowledge, experience and ruling relations: Studies in the social organization of knowledge* (pp. 35–48). Toronto: University of Toronto Press.

Phillips, D.S.H. (1998). Culture and systems of oppression in abused women's lives. *Journal of Obstetric, Gynecologic, and Neonatal Nursing, 27*, 678–683.

Poster, E.C. (1996). A multinational study of psychiatric nursing staffs' beliefs and concerns about work safety and patient assault. *Archives of Psychiatric Nursing, 10*(6), 365–373.

Ratner, P. (1995). Societal responses as moderators of the health consequences of wife abuse. Unpublished doctoral dissertation. University of Alberta, Edmonton.

Rattansi, A. (1995). Just framing: Ethnicities and racisms in a "postmodern" framework. In L. Nicholson & S. Seidman (Eds.), *Social postmodernism: Beyond identity politics* (pp. 250–286). Cambridge: Cambridge University Press.

Reilly, M.A., Warshaw, C., & Center for Research on Women and Gender/The University of Illinois at Chicago. (1998). *Health aspects of violence against women.* US Public Health Services Office on Women's Health US Department of Health and Human Services.

Renzetti, C.M. (1994). On dancing with a bear: Reflections on some of the current debates among domestic violence theorists. *Violence and Victims, 9*(2), 195–200.

Renzetti, C.M. (1996). *Violence in gay and lesbian domestic partnerships.* New York: Haworth Press.

Richie, B.E., & Kanuha, V. (1993). Battered women of color in public heath care systems: Racism, sexism and violence. In B. Bair & S.E. Cayleff (Eds.), *Wings of gauze: Women of color and the experience of health and illness* (pp. 288–299). Detroit: Wayne State University Press.

Ristock, J. (1991). Beyond ideologies: Understanding abuse in lesbian relationships. *Canadian Women's Studies, 12*(1), 74–79.

Ristock, J.L. (2002). *No more secrets: Violence in lesbian relationships.* New York: Routledge.

Rodgers, K. (1994). Wife assault: The findings of a national survey. *Juristat: Service Bulletin, Canadian Centre for Justice Statistics, 14*(9), 1–22.

Seelau, S., & Seelau, E. (2005). Gender-role stereotypes and perceptions of heterosexual, gay and lesbian domestic violence. *Journal of Family Violence, 20*(6), 363–371.

Silva, N. (1994). Towards a feminist methodology in research on battered women. In A.J. Dan (Ed.), *Reframing women's health: Multidisciplinary research and practice* (pp. 290–298). Thousand Oaks, CA: Sage.

Stanko, E.A. (1988). Fear of crime and the myth of the safe home: A feminist critique of criminology. In K. Yllö & M. Bograd (Eds.), *Feminist perspectives on wife abuse* (pp. 75–88). Newbury Park, CA: Sage.

Stark, E., & Flitcraft, A. (1991). Spouse abuse. In M. Rosenburg & M. Fenely (Eds.), *Violence in America: A public health approach* (pp. 123–155). New York: Oxford University Press.

Statistics Canada. (2000). *Women in Canada: A gender-based statistical report.* Ottawa: Author (cat. no. 89–503-XPE).

Statistics Canada. (2005). *Family violence in Canada: A statistical profile 2005.* Ottawa: Canadian Centre for Justice Statistics.

Stevens, P.E., & Hall, J.M. (1988). Stigma, health beliefs and experiences with health care in lesbian women. *Image: Journal of Nursing Scholarship, 20*(2), 69–73.

Swanberg, J.E., Logan, T., & Macke, C. (2005). Intimate partner violence, employment, and the workplace: Consequences and future directions. *Trauma, Violence & Abuse, 6*(4), 286–312.

Tjaden, P., & Thoennes, N. (1998). *Prevalence, incidence, and consequences of violence against women: Findings from the national violence against women survey.* Washington, DC: U.S. Department of Justice, National Institute of Justice and Centers for Disease Control and Prevention.

Tolman, R.M., & Bennett, L.W. (1990). A review of quantitative research on men who batter. *Journal of Interpersonal Violence, 5*, 87–118.

Turrell, S.C. (2000). A descriptive analysis of same-sex relationship violence for a diverse sample. *Journal of Family Violence, 15*, 281–293.

VanNatta, M. (2005). Constructing the battered woman. *Feminist Studies, 31*(2), 416–443.

Varcoe, C. (1996). Theorizing oppression: Implications for nursing research on violence against women. *Canadian Journal of Nursing Research, 28*(1), 61–78.

Varcoe, C. (1997). Untying our hands: The social context of nursing in relation to violence against women. Unpublished doctoral dissertation. University of British Columbia, Vancouver.

Varcoe, C. (2001). Abuse obscured: An ethnographic account of emergency unit nursing practice in relation to violence against women. *Canadian Journal of Nursing Research, 32*(4), 95–115.

Varcoe, C. (2006). Doing participatory action research in a racist world. *Western Journal of Nursing Research, 28*(5), 525–540.

Varcoe, C. & Dick, S. (in press). Intersecting risks of violence and HIV for rural and Aboriginal women in a neocolonial Canadian context. *Journal of Aboriginal Health,* 4.

Varcoe, C., & Irwin, L. (2004). "If I killed you, I'd get the kids": Women's survival and protection work with child custody and access in the context of woman abuse. *Qualitative Sociology, 27*(1), 77–99.

Varcoe, C., Jaffer, F., & Kelln, P. (2002). *Protecting women? Women's experiences of seeking protection from abuse by intimate partners.* Victoria: University of Victoria.

Vinton, L. (1997). Questions and answers about older battered women. Retrieved on April 15, 2000. http://www.state.fl.us/doea/Home/Publications/Older_Battered_Women/older_battered_women.html.

Walker, L.E.A. (1995). Racism and violence against women. In J. Adleman & G.M. Enguídanos (Eds.), *Racism in the lives of women: Testimony, theory, and guides to antiracist practice* (pp. 239–249). New York: Harrington Park.

Wilcox, P. (2005). Beauty and the beast: Gendered and raced discourse in the news. *Social & Legal Studies, 14*(4), 515–532.

Wildman, S., & Davis, A.D. (1995). Language and silence: Making systems of privilege visible. In R. Delgado (Ed.), *Critical race theory: The cutting edge* (pp. 573–579). Philadelphia: Temple University Press.

Wise, A.J., & Bowman, S.L. (1997). Comparison of beginning counselors' responses to lesbian vs. heterosexual partner abuse. *Violence and Victims, 12*(2), 127–135.

World Health Organization. (2002). *World report on violence and health.* Geneva: World Health Organization.

Wuest, J., & Merritt-Gray, M. (1999). Not going back: Sustaining the separation in the process of leaving abusive relationships. *Violence Against Women, 5*(2), 110–133.

Yassi, A., Tate, R., Cooper, J., Jenkins, J., & Trottier, J. (1998). Causes of staff abuse in health care facilities: Implications for prevention. *American Association of Occupational Health Nursing Journal, 46*(10), 484–491.

Yllö, K. (1993). Through a feminist lens: Gender, power and violence. In R.J. Gelles & D.R. Loseke (Eds.), *Current controversies on family violence* (pp. 47–62). Newbury Park, CA: Sage.

Zink, T., Jacobson Jr., C.J., Regan, S., & Pabst, S. (2004). Hidden victims: The healthcare needs and experiences of older women in abusive relationships. *Journal of Women's Health, 13*(8), 898–908.

ENDNOTES

1. "Racialization" refers to the social process by which people are labelled according to particular physical characteristics or arbitrary ethnic or racial categories, and then dealt with in accordance with beliefs related to those labels (Agnew, 1998).
2. "Culture" is often conflated with ethnicity and thought of only in relation to racialized people. Such thinking is a common feature of Canadian democratic racism (Henry et al., 2005) that is especially problematic in relation to violence.

PART 5

THE HEALTH OF CHILDREN, YOUTH, MID-LIFE, AND THE ELDERLY

Current thinking and research are increasingly of the view that the advantages and disadvantages that characterize one phase of life carry over into the subsequent stages of life. The implications of this perspective for policy-makers are clear; those things that determine the health and well-being of children and youth will continue to determine the health and status of adults and the elderly. Although concern about the health and well-being of children and youth is a policy objective in its own right, the prevailing view gains increased policy relevance in the context of an aging society. The four chapters in this section examine the determinants of health for children, youth, mid-life, and the elderly.

It is widely believed that one's experiences from conception to the age of six years are the most important in connecting and sculpting the brain's neurons. Healthy development during this phase of the life cycle improves learning, behaviour, and health into adulthood. Bolaria and Bolaria, in Chapter 15, explore the relationship between inequality (particularly income inequality), poverty, family environment, and child health. Specifically, they look at changing patterns of infant mortality and at a number of key determinants of child health status including an examination of low birth weight and lifelong morbidity, the nature of family life and health status, and child mental health and the psychosocial environment. The pattern that emerges is very clear: the various dimensions of inequality, particularly income inequality, are directly related to poor child health status.

Schissel, in Chapter 16, picks up the theme of inequality and health status as it relates to adolescents. His main argument is that the health problems of youth are the result of their social, economic, and political marginalization in contemporary Canadian society. To develop this argument, he provides an overview of the physical and emotional jeopardy faced by youth in the contexts of their lived experiences in school, athletics, the labour market, the underworld of crime, and the criminal justice system. An overarching reality for an increasing proportion of youth is poverty, which exposes them to increased health risks.

In Chapter 17, Meadows, using a combination of social determinants of health and population health promotion approaches, examines well-being at mid-life. Her discussion of social determinants of health, population health, the lifecourse, life choices, and life chances provide the context in which mid-life and well-being are discussed. Meadows then discusses prevention and preventative health at mid-life – biomedical prevention and prevention in everyday life – and links them to various social determinants of health including turning points, that is, significant events in one's lifecourse. The mechanisms which affect well-being of people at mid-life range from personal practices and coping skills, to the larger social structural and cultural contexts in which health and well-being are pursued. Meadows argues that the health of populations cannot be understood solely with reductionist approaches without attention to the broader determinants of health.

In Chapter 18, Penning and Votova look at the social construction of aging and health and its consequences in the Canadian health care context. They argue that the application of biomedical concepts and criteria for understanding the aging process results in the medicalization of aging and the aged – the view that aging is a clinical condition. Because the concerns of the aged and the consequences of aging often are not amenable to effective management in the context of the hospital-based acute health care system, the elderly are often stigmatized as both inappropriate and problematic users of health care services. As a result, they are increasingly channeled into community-based facilities and home care. The paradox is that, unlike medicare, community-based care and home care are not always covered by public health care insurance. Thus, the rise of community-based care corresponds to a trend toward the re-privatization of the Canadian health care system. This re-privatization takes at least two forms: an increase in private, for-profit health care services, and an increased reliance on unpaid, voluntary health care provisions, usually by family members, mainly women. The implications of these processes, both for the nature and organization of the Canadian health care system and for the health status of volunteer caregivers in the community, warrant close attention.

15

INEQUALITY, FAMILY, AND CHILD HEALTH

B. SINGH BOLARIA University of Saskatchewan, University of Victoria

ROSEMARY BOLARIA Researcher and Medical Writer

INTRODUCTION

In the past few years, children's lives and well-being have received considerable attention from researchers, health experts, politicians, and policy-makers. Much of the study and discussion has focused on the links between inequality and opportunities. Inequalities of wealth and income produce unequal life chances – the opportunities for material and social rewards. Poverty translates into homelessness, ill health, short **life expectancy**, malnutrition, and hunger, to mention only a few of its effects (Bolaria & Wotherspoon, 2000).

Political and social concerns about child poverty led in 1989 to an all-party resolution in the House of Commons to end child poverty by the year 2000. One of the first publications to present a comprehensive picture of the health profile of Canada's children was prepared by the Canadian Institute of Child Health (CICH, 1994). Although public awareness of many of the issues of child health has increased, poverty and its consequences remain prominent in many areas of children's lives. This chapter focuses on the health risks and health outcomes associated with socio-economic inequalities and the physical and social environments in which children live.

INEQUALITY AND POVERTY

Income inequality is an important dimension of social stratification. An examination of income distribution data reveals wide income disparities among Canadians. The data also show the small change in the share of income held by Canadians in different income categories over time (Bolaria & Wotherspoon, 2000; National Council of Welfare, 2006a; Curry-Stevens, 2004). Income inequalities persist in Canada. More recent figures indicate that while the average family income in Canada is on the rise, the richest fifth of the population gained the most (Little & Stinson, 2000). In 2003, the share of total after-tax income of the richest 20 percent of the family units was 43.7 percent while for the poorest 20 percent it was 5 percent (National Council of Welfare, 2006a).

A significant number of Canadians live in poverty. The number of poor people was nearly 5 million in 2003 and the poverty rate was nearly 16 percent (National Council of Welfare, 2006b). Poverty figures fluctuate with economic conditions, particularly fluctuations in the labour market. Poverty rates have increased amid high unemployment rates, economic restructuring that has forced job losses and wage cuts, and cutbacks in social spending.

Child poverty figures follow the same general patterns as the statistics for the general population. In 2003, 1.2 million children lived in poverty, a rate of 16.7 percent (National Council of Welfare, 2006b). Obviously, children are poor because they live in poor families. Poverty rates vary by family structure. Poverty rates are relatively low for two-parent families and quite high for families with single-parent mothers. Certain groups face a high risk of poverty. These include unemployed persons, people whose participation in the labour force is irregular, those with low educational levels, and those in certain occupations.

These income disparities produce an inequality of opportunities and life chances, and have negative outcomes for individuals in low-income and poor families. "Poverty of opportunity" and family income levels are factors detrimental to healthy child development and child well-being (Ross & Roberts, 1999).

Most relevant to the discussion in this chapter is the link between income inequality, poverty, family environment, and child health, which is the focus of the following sections. First, the chapter discusses the health status of low-income and poor children in areas such as **infant mortality**, birth weight, injuries, and emotional development. Then it focuses on the health risks and health outcomes associated with specific family environments.

INEQUALITY, POVERTY, AND HEALTH STATUS

Social medicine is primarily concerned with the social, economic, and environmental conditions in society that produce patterns of **morbidity** and mortality. **Epidemiological** data in Canada and elsewhere show a persistent and pervasive association between socio-economic status and health status (Link & Phelan, 2000; Mirowsky, Ross & Reynolds, 2000; Syme & Yen, 2000; Davey-Smith, 2003; Auger et al., 2004). Those who are advantaged with respect to socio-economic status are also advantaged in health status. Those with high incomes, for instance, live longer, healthier, and more disability-free lives on average than those who are poor. Similar patterns of disease, illness, and mortality prevail for children (Reading, 1997; CICH, 1994; 2000; Browne, 2004; Ross & Roberts, 1999; Ross, Scott & Kelly, 1996; Health Canada, 1999; Saskatchewan Institute on Prevention of Handicaps, 1997). Poor housing, poor nutrition, poor neighbourhoods, and poor environments all contribute to high morbidity and mortality in low-income and poor populations.

The research findings on specific dimensions of child health provide persuasive evidence of the association between social-structural determinants and the variation in health risks and health outcomes for children.

INFANT MORTALITY

Infant mortality is one of the most important indicators of population health of a country because of its association with both adult mortality and life expectancy. The infant **mortality rate** in Canada has declined steadily. In 1960, the **infant mortality rate** for Canada was slightly over 27. By 1993, it had dropped to 6.3 (Statistics Canada, 1995; Ross, Scott & Kelly, 1996). In 1996, for the first time, the infant mortality rate dropped below 6 to 5.6 per 1,000 live births, and a little more than half these deaths (3.3 per 1,000) occurred in the first seven days of life (Federal, Provincial and Territorial Advisory Committee on Population Health [FPTAC], 1999b; Statistics Canada, 1999b; Statistics Canada, Health Statistics Division, 1999). The most recent available data show a further decline in infant mortality rates. In 2003, the infant mortality rate was 5.3 (Statistics Canada, 2006).

Although overall infant deaths have declined substantially, class, race, and regional differences persist in affecting child health (FPTAC, 1999a; Ross & Roberts, 1999). The infant mortality in the Aboriginal population is almost twice that of the general population (Frideres, 2000, p. 205; CICH, 1994, 2000). Children of parents in the poorest neighbourhoods have twice the infant mortality rates of children in the richest neighbourhoods (Ross, Scott & Kelly, 1996; CICH, 1994, 2000). Disparities in birth outcomes are linked to neighbourhood income (Statistics Canada, 2004, 2006).

Infant mortality rates vary by income groups. Those in the lower-income groups experience above-average infant mortality rates (FPTAC, 1999a, p. 75). The infant mortality rate in 1996 was highest in the Northwest Territories (12.2 per 1,000); among the provinces, Saskatchewan ranked highest (8.4) and Quebec lowest (4.6) (FPTAC, 1999b, p. 307, Table 78). These differences were also apparent in 2003. The infant mortality rate was the highest in Nunavut (19.8); among the provinces, Manitoba ranked the highest (8.0), and New Brunswick and British Columbia the lowest (4.1 and 4.2) (Statistics Canada, 2006).

With respect to infant mortality, Canada does not rank very favourably with other advanced countries; its standing has declined in recent years. For instance, in 1990, Canada ranked fifth among the seventeen OECD countries; its ranking dropped to twelfth by 1996 (FPTAC, 1999b, p. 306). In 1996, Japan had the lowest infant mortality rate (3.8) and the United States the highest (7.8). Finland, Sweden, and Norway all had infant mortality rates of 4. Other countries with infant mortality rates above 7 were Greece and New Zealand. It is apparent that the association between socio-economic status and health status arises very early in life – "the first injustice" (Gortmaker & Wise, 1997) – and "this first injustice" is followed by an enduring association between socio-economic status and the risk of death that persists throughout adult life (Link & Phelan, 2000, p. 34). This association is persistent across time and in many countries. There are various reasons for variations in infant mortality rates, including low birth weights, preventable communicable diseases, malnutrition, injuries, household income, neighbourhood, and the mother's education (Price, 1994; Kloos, 1994; Singh & Yu, 1995; Reading, 1997; Statistics Canada, 2004, 2006; Safe Kids Canada, 2006; Phipps & Lethbridge, 2006).

HEALTH AT BIRTH: BIRTH OUTCOMES AND BIRTH WEIGHT

Weight at birth is one of the most important measures of overall health and well-being later in life (McCormick, 1985; McCormick et al., 1992; Wilkins, Sherman & Best, 1991). The standard definition of low birth weight is less than 2,500 grams (5.5 pounds) at birth (Statistics Canada, 1999). The average weight at birth of a full-term infant is 3,400 grams (7.5 pounds). Low birth weight is the major cause of infant mortality.

Children who survive face a high risk of other developmental and health-related problems, such as impaired learning and neurodevelopment, and loss of sight and hearing (McCormick, 1985; McCormick et al., 1992). The negative effect of low birth weight extends into adult life and contributes to differences in mortality (Reading, 1997). Several factors are associated with low birth weight, including the mother's age, health, tobacco and alcohol use during pregnancy, nutrition, and premature delivery.

Almost 6 percent of all live births in Canada in 1996 resulted in low birth weight (Statistics Canada, 1998b). Low-birth-weight children are likely to be born to very young mothers (10–14 years) and to older mothers (45 and older). For instance, 9.3 percent of the low-birth-weight children were born to mothers 10–14 years of age, and 10 percent to mothers 45 years of age and older (Statistics Canada, 1998b). The risk of low-birth-weight children increases for mothers 40 years of age and older. Mothers younger than 15 years of age and those 45 years of age and older are almost twice as likely as the average Canadian mother to have an underweight newborn infant. Premature births account for over half of low-birth-weight infants. Teen mothers are more likely to have babies with low birth weight and prematurity (Ng & Wilkins, 1994), and both the teen mother and the unborn child are at risk of poor nutrition and poor health outcomes (Schor, 1995, p. 97).

Children born into poverty encounter a wide range of negative health outcomes. Children born to low-income parents are at a high risk for low birth weight. The low birth weight rate was seven percent in households with incomes less than $30,000 and 4 percent in households with incomes greater than $60,000 (CICH, 2000).

Maternal health and nutrition during pregnancy are important factors in healthy pregnancy, and in the weight and health of the newborn. These are linked to income levels. Food availability, food security, food deprivation, and hunger are problems faced by low-income Canadians (CICH, 1994, 2000; Bolaria & Wotherspoon, 2000). The contradictions associated with "hunger in the midst of plenty" are starkly illustrated by the rise of food banks across Canada in the past two decades. There was "serious deterioration in household food security in Canada" in the 1990s, and the growing demand for their services has forced food banks to expand their distribution services beyond their own centres to various other programs, centres, and service organizations (Canadian Association of Food Banks (CAFB), 2003, 2006; Wilson & Tsoa, 2002; McIntyre, 2004; Che & Chen, 2001). The provision of food in itself cannot be equated with nutritional and dietary adequacy. Women and children, in particular, face high health risks and negative health outcomes (CICH, 2000; Wilson & Steinman, 2000; McIntyre, Connor & Warren, 2000; Tarasuk & Beaton, 1999; Tarasuk, 2001, 2004; McIntyre et al., 2002, 2003). Factors that need to be considered here include women's reproductive health and nutritional health needs during pregnancy, and children's nutritional needs. The effects of malnutrition and vitamin deficiencies have begun to appear in some cases (see Bolaria & Wotherspoon, 2000).

Mothers' lifestyle and social consumption patterns can also contribute to poor birth outcomes. Tobacco and alcohol consumption during pregnancy may be implicated in negative health outcomes for children. Smoking during pregnancy may contribute to low birth weight and high rates of respiratory illness (see Bolaria & Bolaria, 2002). Lower education and lower incomes are implicated in high tobacco consumption. Fetal Alcohol Spectrum Disorder (FASD) is the term used to describe a range of effects that can occur in children whose mothers drank during pregnancy (Stade et al., 2006; Chudley et al., 2005).

FASD is a result of maternal alcohol consumption during pregnancy and its effects may include developmental and cognitive disabilities – physical, mental, behavioural, learning problems – which have lifelong implications. FASD covers a spectrum of cases which range from more severe abnormalities and more visible manifestations (Fetal Alcohol Syndrome [FAS]) to cases of less severity in terms of cognitive function and other abnormalities (Fetal Alcohol Effect [FAE]; Partial FAS [FFS]). The point is that affected individuals exhibit a wide range of cognitive, developmental, and behavioural expressions. The incidence of FASD in Canada is estimated at 1-6 in 1,000 live births (Stade et al., 2006). There are serious health, social, and economic consequences to FASD. The risk factors for prenatal alcohol exposure include lower maternal socio-economic status, lower education, paternal drinking, and poor developmental environment (Chudley et al., 2005).

Low incomes, poverty, dependency on food banks, poor nutrition, and inadequate health care all contribute to low birth weight and high infant mortality. The low-birth-weight rate is significantly higher in poor than in rich neighbourhoods (CICH, 1994, 2000). Disparities in birth outcomes are linked to neighbourhood income and maternal education (Statistics Canada, 2004, 2006; Phipps & Lethbridge, 2006). Social and economic inequities are also manifested in growth and height of children (see Reading, 1997). In short, socio-economic differences are implicated in a wide range of variations in health outcomes for children.

INJURIES

Injuries are one of the least-recognized public health problems in Canada today. The costs associated with injuries are enormous, not only in direct dollar costs but also, more importantly, in the loss of life and human potential (CICH, 1994, 2000; Safe Kids Canada, 2000a; Saskatchewan Institute on Prevention of Handicaps, 1996; FPTAC, 1999b; Cushman, 1995). According to one estimate, childhood injuries cost $4 billion a year in Canada (Health Canada, 1998).

Injuries are the leading cause of death for Canadian children and youth between the ages of 1 and 19. In addition, nonfatal injuries result in impairment and disabilities for many young people (CICH, 1994, 2000). Fatalities account for only a small proportion of the health and economic costs of injuries. Recent figures on young people indicate that "for every injury related death, there are 40 hospitalizations and an estimated 670 emergency room visits for treatment of injuries" (Herbert et al., 1999, p. 39). Injury mortality rates are also higher for males than for females (Herbert et al., 1999, p. 40).

The recognition of injuries as a leading cause of death in children has resulted in more research and comprehensive information on this subject. The data from hospitals participating in the Canadian Hospitals Injury Reporting and Prevention Program (CHIRPP) is one of the primary sources on types, sites, location, and activity at the time of injury (Health Canada, 1998; see also CICH, 1994, 2000). Home and school are the primary location of injuries. Younger children are more frequently injured at home than adolescents, who are more likely to be injured while involved in sports and leisure activities.

A recent report (Safe Kids Canada, 2006a) on unintentional child injury between 1994 and 2003 indicates that during this period an estimated average of 390 Canadian children age 14 and under died each year, and an estimated average of 25,500 children were hospitalized each year. The overall injury death rate among these children declined by 37 percent and the overall injury hospitalization rate declined by 34 percent between 1994 and 2003. The deaths declined from 500 in 1994 to 300 in 2003, and hospitalizations from 32,500 to 20,500. The three leading causes of injury-related deaths were motor vehicle collision, drowning, and threat to breathing (suffocation, choking, and strangulation). The primary cause of injury-related hospitalization was falls, which accounted for 44 percent of all injury-related hospital admissions. The causes of death and hospitalization varied by age group and by sex.

Despite this decline in death rates among children age 14 and under, unintentional injury remains the leading cause of death for children ages 1–14. Canadian parents, however, believe the leading health risks to their children are obesity, inactivity, and nutrition (Safe Kids Canada, 2006b).

Childhood injuries are a worldwide problem. According to a World Health Organization (WHO) report, in 2002, over 700,000 children ages 14 and under were killed by an injury, and 90 percent of these injuries were unintentional (WHO, 2006 [cited from Safe Kids Canada, 2006]).

Injuries, in addition to causing suffering and death, also are a major financial cost to society. The economic cost of injuries to Canadians of all ages is in the billions of dollars, and other related costs, such as property damage and insurance claims, add billions to the total cost (Moore, Mao & Zheng, 1997).

A comprehensive study by the Saskatchewan Institute on Prevention of Handicaps (1996) on child injury, hospitalization, and deaths in Saskatchewan for the period 1989–1994 indicates that during this period, nearly 69 percent of all deaths to children and youth aged 1–19 years were due to injuries. A large number of injuries result in hospitalization.

The leading cause of injury deaths for all Saskatchewan children and youth under 20 years of age was motor vehicle traffic (31%), and the leading cause of injury-related hospitalization was falls (25%). The causes of death and hospitalization among children vary considerably by age. For instance, older children were more likely to die due to motor vehicle traffic injuries and younger children more likely to die due to drowning, choking, and fires. For younger children, the leading causes of injury-related hospitalization were falls and poisoning, and for the older group the leading causes were motor vehicle traffic and self-injuries (Saskatchewan Institute on Prevention of Handicaps, 1996).

The Saskatchewan study also found differences among various groups in injury-related hospitalizations and deaths. The highest rates of injury-related hospitalizations occurred among treaty Indian children, followed by northern children. There were also variations in injury-related deaths among various groups. For instance, for urban, rural, and northern children, and youth under 20 years of age, the leading cause of injury death was motor vehicle traffic. For treaty Indian children and youth, however, the leading cause of injury death was self-injury, followed by drowning or choking, fire and flame, and motor vehicle-pedestrian accidents. In Canada, the death rate for Aboriginal children as a result of injuries is much higher than that of the total population of Canadian children: almost four times higher for infants; five times higher for preschoolers; and three times higher for teenagers (MacMillan, Walsh & Jamieson, 1999).

Differential risk of injury and death is associated with the socio-economic background of children, and the physical and social environments in which children live. Poor children face a high risk of injury, illness, and death because they often live in

substandard housing, houses with damp walls and ceilings, rotting porches and steps, and crumbling foundations (Ross, Scott & Kelly, 1996; CICH, 1994, 2000). Social variations in accidents, accidental injury, and accident rates are evident from research in other countries (Reading, 1997). Writing on this topic, Reading (1997, p. 464) states: "Because accidents are 'place-specific' – that is, they happen in part because of the risks associated with the place they occur – these geographical variations indicate more clearly the links between social disadvantage, environmental risk, and accidental injury."

PSYCHOSOCIAL, MENTAL HEALTH, AND CHILD WELL-BEING

Other dimensions of child development and child health also deserve consideration. For instance, low birth weight, as well as being linked to infant mortality and adult morbidity and mortality, can also result in physical and mental disabilities. Since low birth weight is more prevalent in poor families and poor neighbourhoods, child disabilities are also linked to low-income and poor families. Poor children are also more likely to suffer from psychological and mental health problems, and have higher rates of behavioural and emotional disorders (Ross, Scott & Kelly, 1996; Ross & Roberts, 1999; CICH, 1994, 2000; Canadian Education Statistics Council, 2000). Poor children are more likely than non-poor children to have chronic health problems, problems at school, and psychiatric problems, and they are less likely to feel good about themselves (CICH, 1994, p. 128; see also CICH, 2000). They are also more likely to have vision, hearing, speech, or mobility problems (Ross & Roberts, 1999). Other evidence also indicates poor social and emotional health of children from low-income and poor families in areas such as school performance, social relations, emotional disorders, high levels of indirect aggression, hyperactivity, and conduct disorders (CICH, 1994, 2000; Canada, 1991; Ross & Roberts, 1999; Ross, Roberts & Scott, 2000; Boyle & Lipman, 2002).

Other indicators raise concerns about the well-being of Canadian children and youth: low self-esteem, depression, high life stress levels, substance abuse, smoking, and intentional injuries. The continuing high rate of suicide among youth, particularly in Aboriginal populations, points to young people's distress (FPTAC, 1999a).

Canadian children and youth are, however, doing well in many areas, and there is a continuous decline in morbidity and mortality in this group. For instance, child and youth injury death rates and injury-related hospitalizations have been decreasing (CICH, 1994, 2000; Safe Kids Canada, 2006). In Canada, there is also a steady decline in infant mortality rates and increasing life expectancy. While these are positive signs, social variations in health status, opportunities, quality of life, and well-being persist because of socioeconomic disparities.

FAMILY, SOCIAL ENVIRONMENT, AND CHILD HEALTH

Increasingly, social scientists, policy-makers, and social epidemiologists are recognizing the family as an important factor in the health of infants, children, and youth. Social relations and interaction among family members, family environment, early childhood education and care, and public policies regarding family and children have important impacts on children's development and health (Cleveland & Krashinsky, 2001; Browne, 2004; Friendly, 2004).

One area which has received considerable attention is the incidence of abuse and violence in the family, and the resulting health outcomes for mothers and children. Family violence, and sexual and physical assaults against spouses and children, are extensive in Canada and other countries (Statistics Canada, 2005; AuCoin, 2005; Brzozowski, 2004; Bolaria & Bolaria, 2002b; Varcoe, 2002). While violence is implicated in adverse health outcomes for women (Bolaria & Bolaria, 2002b; Varcoe, 2002), this section is concerned with health outcomes for children. Violence affects the physical, emotional, and psychological health and well-being of victims. Children are victimized when mothers have to escape to shelters or transition homes from abusive and violent homes.

Children living in violent situations experience emotional distress as a consequence of witnessing or being subjected to violent behaviour by either their fathers or their mothers' partners. Children who witness spousal abuse are also at a high risk of substance abuse in later life and risk depression and emotional problems. Neglect, verbal abuse, and maltreatment contribute to negative health and development outcomes.

Family violence against children and youth is extensive; in 2003, while children and youth under the age of 18 represented 21 percent of the population, they accounted for 21 percent of victims of physical assault and 61 percent of the victims of sexual assault. Parents were implicated in most of the cases of sexual and physical assault. Girls were the victims in 80 percent of family related sexual assaults, and rates were higher for girls 12–14 years of age (AuCoin, 2005, p. 11).

Violence during pregnancy in particular carries very serious health consequences for mothers and fetuses (Cokkinides et al., 1999; Peterson et al., 1997; Health Canada, 2004). The estimate of abuse during pregnancy ranges from 5.7–6.6 percent (cited in Health Canada, 2004). According to the 2004 General Social Survey (GSS), 7 percent of the women 15 years of age and over in previous or current or common-law unions experienced spousal violence representing about 653,000 women (AuCoin, 2005, p. 8). The adverse maternal outcomes include rupture of uterus, spleen, liver, and diaphragm. The adverse fetal health outcomes include miscarriage, fetal death, spontaneous abortion, fetal injuries, and preterm labour and delivery. Certain women are at a high risk of violence and abuse. Rates of violence are high among younger women, who are in relationships of three years or less, and those who are in common-law relationships. Aboriginal women are at a much higher risk of violence than non-Aboriginal women. Low-income women are also more vulnerable than their high-income counterparts (Varcoe, 2002; Bolaria & Bolaria, 2002b; Health Canada, 2004; AuCoin, 2005).

Family relationships and level of family functioning are also implicated in child health. Income appears to be a primary factor in the overall well-being of families. Ross and Roberts (1999, p. 5) show that "children in low-income families are twice as likely to be living in poorly functioning families as children in high-income families. The incidence of poor family functioning decreases steadily as family incomes rise from under $20,000 to $50,000." Children in low-income families are also more likely to be living with a parent who often exhibits signs of depression, and to grow up with parents who themselves suffered childhood trauma and who are chronically stressed (Ross & Roberts, 1999, pp. 6–8). Children and adolescents in these circumstances are more likely than others to exhibit behavioural and emotional problems.

Other social environmental factors in the family that are linked to child health and development include family structure (e.g., single- or two-parent family), parenting skills, and an emotionally stable family environment (Saskatchewan Institute on Prevention of Handicaps, 1997, 2000; FPTAC, 1999a, pp. 71–93). Children living in two-parent families as compared to those living in single-parent or step-families have more favourable behavioural and psychological outcomes (Kerr & Beaufort, 2001). The physical environment, including adequate housing and safe neighbourhoods, is also linked to child health (Ross, Scott & Kelly, 1996, p. 14; CICH, 1994, 2000; Reichert, 1995, p. 17; Ross & Roberts, 1999, pp. 14–16). Low-income families are more likely to live in inadequate and unsafe housing, in problem neighbourhoods, and in poorly functioning families (Ross, Roberts & Scott, 2000). Children living in low income households (less than $20,000) are at high risk of hyperactivity and delinquent behaviours (CICH, 2000).

The socio-economic status of the family is crucial in the family's ability to cope with the child health issues previously discussed. Children in low-income families are less likely to have access to health services, particularly services that are not socially funded, such as dental care and eye care.

CONCLUSION

Child health and well-being have received considerable attention in the past few years. Although there has been a steady improvement in the health status of Canadian children, variations by socio-economic status persist. Whereas overall infant mortality rates and infant deaths have steadily declined, class, race, and neighbourhood differences persist in influencing child health. Inequality and poverty are linked to high infant mortality, low birth weight, high risk of injury deaths, child disabilities, and poor psychosocial development and mental health. The social and economic health of the family, as well as the social and economic forces external to the family, have important effects on child health.

Improvement in the social and material conditions of children's lives and the elimination of child poverty and child hunger have been in the forefront of public policy debate in Canada and internationally. Although the House of Commons voted unanimously to "seek to achieve the goal of eliminating poverty among Canadian children by the year 2000," income inequality and child poverty persists. Food insecurity and hunger remain daily experiences of thousands of children in Canada (Wilson & Steinman, 2000; CICH, 2000; Tarasuk & Beaton, 1999; McIntyre, Connor & Warren, 2000). Millions of children in poor countries face poverty, exploitation, abuse, hunger, and poor health (UNICEF, 2000). In view of this, a broad strategy is required to address issues of child health: accessibility to and the availability of a wide range of health services, the elimination of child poverty and hunger, and programs and policies to provide safe and secure physical and social environments for healthy child development.

STUDY QUESTIONS

1. *Discuss the relationship between family income and factors critical to the well-being of children.*
2. *Discuss the factors associated with differential infant mortality rates by class and race.*
3. *Discuss the relationship between the family's social environment and children's health.*
4. *Discuss the association between infant mortality and adult mortality. Why is infant mortality one of the most important indicators of population health?*

5. *What is meant by poverty of opportunity? How does poverty of opportunity relate to children's health?*
6. *Discuss the relationship between maternal lifestyle, the availability of and accessibility to maternal care, and children's health.*
7. *Discuss the statement that "Infant mortality is the best available overall indicator of health and development status of a country."*

GLOSSARY

epidemiological relating to epidemiology; the study of factors related to the distribution of disease in a population.

infant mortality the death of a live-born infant in the first year of life.

infant mortality rate the number of deaths in the first year of life per 1,000 live births.

life expectancy the length of time a person born in a given year is expected to live.

morbidity the distribution of sickness and disease in a given population.

mortality rate the total number of deaths in a population in a specific time period divided by the total population.

perinatal mortality combination of stillbirths and deaths within the first seven days of life.

substandard housing houses with major problems, such as poor plumbing, poor sanitation, and broken windows.

REFERENCES

AuCoin, K. (Ed.). (2005). *Family violence in Canada: A statistical profile, 2005*. Ottawa: Statistics Canada, Canadian Centre for Justice Statistics.

Auger, N., Raynault, M.-F., Lenard, R., & Choiniere, R. (2004). Income and health in Canada. In D. Raphael (Ed.), *Social determinants of health: Canadian perspectives* (pp. 39–52). Toronto: Canadian Scholars' Press.

Bolaria, B.S., & Bolaria R. (2002a). Inequality, family and child health. In B.S. Bolaria & H.D. Dickinson (Eds.), *Health, illness and health care in Canada* (3rd ed., pp. 247–264). Toronto: Thomson Nelson.

Bolaria, B.S., & Bolaria, R. (2002b). Women's lives, women's health. In B.S. Bolaria & H.D. Dickinson (Eds.), *Health, illness and health care in Canada* (3rd ed., pp. 169–184). Toronto: Thomson Nelson.

Bolaria, B.S., & Wotherspoon, T. (2000). Income inequality, poverty, and hunger. In B.S. Bolaria (Ed.), *Social issues and contradictions in Canadian society* (3rd ed., pp. 73–90). Toronto: Harcourt Brace.

Boyle, M.H., & Lipman, E.L. (2002). Do places matter? Socioeconomic disadvantage and behavioural problems of children in Canada. *Journal of Consulting and Clinical Psychology, 70*, 378–389.

Browne, G. (2004). Early childhood education and health. In Dennis Raphael (Ed.), *Social determinants of health* (pp. 125–137). Toronto: Canadian Scholars' Press.

Brzozowski, J. (Ed.). (2004). *Family violence in Canada: A statistical profile, 2004*. Cat. no, 5–224-XPE. Canadian Centre for Justice Statistics. Ottawa: Statistics Canada.

Canadian Association of Food Banks. (2003). *Hunger count 2003: Something has to give: Food banks filling the policy gap in Canada.* Toronto: Canadian Association of Food Banks.

Canadian Association of Food Banks. (2006). *Time for action: Hunger count 2005.* Toronto: Canadian Association of Food Banks.

Canadian Education Statistics Council. (2000). Education indicators in Canada. Report of the Pan-Canadian Education Indicators Program 1999. Ottawa: Statistics Canada.

Canadian Institute of Child Health (CICH). (1993). Prevention of low birth weight in Canada: Literature review and strategies. Prepared for Health Promotion Branch, Ontario Ministry of Health.

Canadian Institute of Child Health (CICH). (1994). *The health of Canada's children: A CICH profile* (2nd ed.). Ottawa: CICH.

Canadian Institute of Child Health (CICH). (2000). *The health of Canada's children: A CICH profile* (3rd ed.). Ottawa: CICH.

Che, J., & Chen, J. (2001). Food insecurity in Canadian households. *Health Reports, 12,* 11–22.

Chudley, A.E., Conry, J., Cook, J.L., Loock, C., Rosales, T., & LeBlanc, N. (2005). Fetal alcohol spectrum disorder: Canadian guidelines for diagnosis. *Canadian Medical Association Journal, 172,* S1–S15.

Cleveland, G. & Krashinsky, M. (Eds.). (2001). *Our children's future: Child care policy in Canada.* Toronto: University of Toronto Press.

Cokkinides, V.E., Coker, A.L., Sanderson, M., Addy, C., & Bethea, L. (1999). Physical violence during pregnancy: Maternal complications and birth outcomes. *Obstetrics & Gynecology, 93,* 661–666.

Curry-Stevens, A. (2004). Income and income distribution. In D. Raphael (Ed.), *Social determinants of health: Canadian perspectives.* Toronto: Canadian Scholars' Press.

Cushman, R. (1995). Injury prevention: The time has come. *Canadian Medical Association Journal, 152,* 21–23.

Davey-Smith, G. (Ed.). (2003). *Inequalities in health: Life course perspectives.* Bristol: Policy Press.

Federal, Provincial and Territorial Advisory Committee on Population Health (FPTAC). (1999a). *Toward a healthy future: Second report on the health of Canadians.* Ottawa: Minister of Public Works and Government Services.

Federal, Provincial and Territorial Advisory Committee on Population Health (FPTAC). (1999b). *Statistical report on the health of Canadians.* Ottawa: Minister of Public Works and Government Services.

Fischbach, R.L., & Donnelly, E. (1996). Domestic violence against women: A contemporary issue in international health. In J. Subedi & E.B. Gallagher (Eds.), *Society, health and disease* (pp. 316–345). Upper Saddle River, NJ: Prentice-Hall.

Frideres, J.S. (2000). First Nations: Walking the path of social change. In B.S. Bolaria (Ed.), *Social issues and contradictions in Canadian society* (3rd ed., pp. 195–227). Toronto: Harcourt Brace.

Friendly, M. (2004). Early childhood education and care. In D. Raphael (Ed.), *Social determinants of health* (pp. 109–123). Toronto: Canadian Scholars' Press.

Gortmaker, S.L., & Wise, P.H. (1997). The first injustice: Socioeconomic disparities, health services technology, and infant mortality. *Annual Review of Sociology, 23,* 147–170.

Health Canada. (1996). *Wife abuse: The impact on children.* Ottawa: National Clearinghouse on Family Violence.

Health Canada. (1998). Laboratory Centre for Disease Control, Canadian Hospitals Injury Reporting and Prevention Program (CHIRPP) Data Base, 1998.

Health Canada. (1999). *Passive smoking: Nowhere to hide.* Ottawa: Health Canada.

Health Canada, Public Health Agency of Canada, Canadian Perinatal Surveillance System. (2004). Physical abuse during pregnancy. Ottawa. Retrieved on August 19, 2006 (http//www.phac-aspc.gc.ca)_(epssdhe-sc.gc.ca), pp. 1–8.

Herbert, M., Lipskie, T., MacKenzie, S., & Rusen, I.D. (1999). Child injury. In I.D. Rusen & C. McCourt (Eds.), *Measuring up: A health surveillance update on Canadian children and youth* (pp. 39–48). Ottawa: Minister of Public Works and Government Services.

Human Resources Development Canada (HRDC) and Statistics Canada. (1996). *Growing up in Canada: National longitudinal survey of children and youth* (cat. no. 89–550-MPE N01). Ottawa: Statistics Canada and Human Resources Development Canada.

Kerr, D., & Beaujot, R. (May 2001). *Family relations. Low income and child outcomes: A comparison of children in intake, lone and step families.* London, ON: University of Western Ontario, Population Studies Centre.

Link, B.G., & Phelan, J.C. (2000). Evaluating the fundamental cause explanation for social disparities in health. In C.E. Bird, P. Conrad, & A.M. Fremont (Eds.), *Handbook of medical sociology* (5th ed., pp. 33–46). Upper Saddle River, NJ: Prentice-Hall.

Little, B., & Stinson, M. (2000, June 13). Average family enjoying best income in a decade. *The Globe and Mail,* pp. A1, A7.

MacMillan, H., Walsh, C., & Jamieson, E. (1999). Children's health. Ottawa: First Nations and Inuit Regional Health Survey National Steering Committee.

McIntyre, L. (2004). Food insecurity. In D. Raphael (Ed.), *Social determinants of health: Canadian perspectives* (pp. 173–186). Toronto: Canadian Scholars' Press.

McIntyre, L., Connor, S.K., & Warren, J. (2000). Child hunger in Canada: Results of the 1994 national longitudinal survey of children and youth. *Canadian Medical Association Journal, 163*(8), 961–965.

McIntyre, L., Glanville, T., Officer, S., Anderson, B., Raine, K.D., & Dayle, J.B. (2002). Food insecurity of low-income lone mothers and their children in Atlantic Canada. *Canadian Journal of Public Health, 93,* 411–415.

McIntyre, L., Glanville, T., Raine, K.D., Anderson, B., & Battaglia, N. (2003). Do low-income lone mothers compromise their nutrition to feed their children? *Canadian Medical Association Journal, 168,* 686–691.

Mirowsky, J., Ross, C.E., & Reynolds, J. (2000). Links between social status and health status. In C.E. Bird, P. Conrad, & A.M. Fremont (Eds.), *Handbook of medical sociology* (5th ed., pp. 47–67). Upper Saddle River, NJ: Prentice-Hall.

National Council of Welfare. (1990). *Health, health care and Medicare.* Ottawa: Supply and Services Canada.

National Council of Welfare. (2006a). *Poverty facts 2003.* Ottawa: National Council of Welfare.

National Council of Welfare. (2006b). *Poverty profile, 2002 and 2003.* Ottawa: National Council of Welfare.

Petersen, R., Gazamararian, J., Spitz, A., Rowley, D. et al. (1997). Violence and adverse pregnancy outcomes: A review of literature and directions for further research. *American Journal of Preventative Medicine, 13,* 366–373.

Phipps, S. (2003). The impact of poverty on health: A scan of research literature. Canadian Institute for Health Information, Canadian Population Health Initiative.

Phipps, S., & Lethbridge, L. (2006). Income and the outcomes of children. Statistics Canada. Analytical Studies. Research Paper Series (Statistics Canada Catalogue no. 11 F0019MIE, no. 281).

Reading, R. (1997). Poverty and health of children and adults. *Archives of Disease in Childhood, 76*, 463–467.

Reichert, P. (1995). Background information for the development of the Aboriginal head start program in Saskatchewan. Regina: Common Knowledge Social Research.

Ross, D.P., & Roberts, P. (1999). *Income and child well-being: A new perspective on the poverty debate.* Ottawa: Canadian Council on Social Development.

Ross, D.P., Roberts, P., & Scott, K. (2000). Family income and child well-being. *ISUMA – Canadian Journal of Policy Research, 1*(2), 51–54.

Ross, D.P., Scott, K., & Kelly, M. (1996). *Child poverty: What are the consequences?* Ottawa: Centre for International Statistics, Canadian Council on Social Development.

Safe Kids Canada. (2006a). *Child and youth unintentional injury: 10 years in review 1994–2003.* Toronto: Hospital for Sick Children.

Safe Kids Canada. (2006b). National survey of health risks to children 2006. Toronto: Hospital for Sick Children.

Saskatchewan Institute on Prevention of Handicaps. (1996). *Child injury in Saskatchewan: Injury hospitalizations and deaths 1989–1994.* Saskatoon: Saskatchewan Institute on Prevention of Handicaps.

Saskatchewan Institute on Prevention of Handicaps. (1997). *Critical issues in health for Saskatchewan from birth to age nine 1989–994.* Saskatoon: Saskatchewan Institute on Prevention of Handicaps.

Saskatchewan Institute on Prevention of Handicaps. (2000, June). Background paper for the development of a national statement on shaken baby syndrome. Unpublished Paper, Saskatchewan Institute on Prevention of Handicaps, Saskatoon.

Stade, B., Ungar, W.J., Stevens, B., Beyene, J., & Koren, G. (2006, February 5). The burden of prenatal exposure to alcohol: Measurement of cost. *Journal of FAS International, 4*, pp. 1–14.

Statistics Canada. (1994). *Violence against women survey 1993.* Ottawa: Statistics Canada.

Statistics Canada. (1995). *Vital statistics, births and deaths 1993.* Ottawa: Supply and Services.

Statistics Canada. (1996). *Growing up in Canada: National longitudinal survey of children and youth.* Ottawa: Human Resources Canada.

Statistics Canada. (1997). *National population health survey*, 1996–1997. Ottawa: Statistics Canada.

Statistics Canada. (1998b, July 8). Births 1996. *The Daily.* Ottawa: Statistics Canada (cat. no. 11–001-XIE).

Statistics Canada. (1998c, April 16). Deaths 1996. *The Daily.* Ottawa: Statistics Canada (cat. no. 11–001-XIE).

Statistics Canada. (1999). *Compendium of vital statistics 1996.* Ottawa: Statistics Canada (cat. no. 84–214-XPE).

Statistics Canada. (2000). *Women in Canada: A gender based statistical report.* Ottawa: Statistics Canada. (Cat. no. 89–503-XPE).

Statistics Canada. (2004, November 16). Study disparities in birth outcomes by neighbourhood income in British Columbia 1985–2000. *The Daily.*

Statistics Canada. (2005, July 14). Family violence in Canada: A statistical profile, 2005. *The Daily*, (85–224-XIE), Tuesday. July 14, 2005.

Statistics Canada. (2006). Infant mortality rates, by province and territory. Statistics Canada, CANSIM, Table 102–0504.

Statistics Canada. (2006, June 6). Study: Neighbourhood income, maternal education and birth outcomes in Quebec 1991–2000. *The Daily.*

Statistics Canada, Canadian Centre for Justice Statistics. (1997, November). *Assaults against children and youth in the family 1996.* Ottawa: Statistics Canada (cat. no. 85–002-XPE, vol. 17, no. 11).

Statistics Canada, Canadian Centre for Justice Statistics. (1998, May). *Family violence in Canada: A statistical profile 1998.* Ottawa: Statistics Canada (cat. no. 85–224-XPE).

Statistics Canada, Health Statistics Division. (1999). *Health indicators 1999.* Ottawa: Statistics Canada (cat. no. 82–221-XCB).

Syme, S.L., & Yen, I.H. (2000). Social epidemiology and medical sociology: Different approaches to the same problem. In C.E. Bird, P. Conrad, & A.M. Fremont (Eds.), *Handbook of medical sociology* (5th ed., pp. 365–376). Upper Saddle River, NJ: Prentice-Hall.

Tarasuk, V. (2001). Household food insecurity with hunger is associated with women's food intakes, health, and household circumstances. *Journal of Nutrition, 131,* 2670–2676.

Tarasuk, V. (2004). Health implications of food insecurity. In D. Raphael (Ed.), *Social determinants of health: Canadian perspectives* (pp. 187–200). Toronto: Canadian Scholars' Press.

Tarasuk, V.S., & Beaton, G.H. (1999). Household food insecurity and hunger among families using food banks. *Canadian Journal of Public Health, 90,* 109–113.

United Nations Children's Fund (UNICEF). (2000). *The state of the world's children 2000.* New York: Author.

Varcoe, C. (2002). Inequality, violence and women's health. In B.S. Bolaria & H.D. Dickinson (Eds.), *Health, illness and health care in Canada* (3rd ed., pp. 211–230). Toronto: Thomson Nelson.

Wilkinson, R. (1996). *Unhealthy societies: The afflictions of inequality.* New York: Routledge.

Wilson, B., & Steinman, C. (2000). *Hunger count 2000: A surplus of hunger.* Ottawa: Canadian Association of Food Banks.

Wilson, B., & Tsoa, E. (2002). *Hunger count 2002: Eating their words. Government failure on food security.* Toronto: Canadian Association of Food Banks.

World Health Organization. (2006). Child injuries. Geneva: WHO.

16

THE PATHOLOGY OF POWERLESSNESS: ADOLESCENT HEALTH IN CANADA

BERNARD SCHISSEL University of Saskatchewan

INTRODUCTION

Adolescent health is fundamentally an important political-economic and personal issue for several reasons. Firstly, patterns of physical and emotional health for adolescence – including ways of dealing with health problems in either a preventive or therapeutic orientation – quite often follow individuals throughout life. Secondly, the health problems that youth face are often the result of their position as second-class citizens living in a world created by and for adults in a society in which profit is sacrosanct. This second point is important for understanding adolescent health and frames the arguments set out in this chapter. For when you strip away the empty rhetoric of children and youth being our most valued and valuable resource, you will find that problems of adolescent health are largely preventable, are often the result of youth emulating adult behaviour or attempting to live up to the expectations of adults, and are often the result of the stresses and strains of a world in which youth have little political and economic impact on the society they share with adults. This relative powerlessness often places youth in jeopardy, especially youth who live on the margins of the society. The jeopardy of having little political or economic impact coupled with living in conditions of poverty often result in adolescents using and abusing drugs and alcohol to kill the pain (Canada, 2001; Schissel & Fedec, 1999; Webber, 1992). The risk for all youth, but especially marginalized youth, occurs in a political-economic context in which the substances that place youth at risk are largely manufactured by legitimate adult-owned corporations (Males, 2000; Diller, 1998; Chisholm, 1996). I explore the phenomenon of youth substance abuse later in this chapter, but for now, suffice it to say that youth, in many respects, are victims of an adult world where a "business as usual" ethos frames the danger which jeopardizes the health of Canadian adolescents.

This chapter, then, is an exploration of the physical and emotional jeopardy in which Canadian youth find themselves. I explore the primary contexts in which youth live including school, athletics, the labour market, the social world, and the so-called underworld of crime and youth justice. Essentially, this chapter illustrates that the health of youth is a generic issue that involves education, justice, and social welfare as much as it does medicine. In the end, I illustrate that much of the physical and emotional damage to youth is social and political in origin, and that, as a consequence, the public policy reactions to issues of youth health rarely focus on the health of the community in which youth live, and often focus instead on the criminality of youth who are characterized by drug addictions, life in the sex trade, and living on the streets.

HEALTH AND POVERTY

This first section illustrates the overall levels of health for Canadian adolescents and ties these levels to socio-economic factors. The underlying argument is that health status for youth depends on their placement in the socio-economic hierarchy. In short, living on the margins, living below the poverty line, living on the streets, and living in abusive contexts predispose youth to poor health. And it is important to keep in mind that rarely do we conceive of collective health as a focus of intervention; instead, we relegate health to the individual, even as we implement policy focusing on primary health care.

Figures 16.1 through 16.5 illustrate how living in poverty is probably the greatest health risk for adolescents with respect to physical illness, mental health, high risk behaviours, and injury. The data are derived from the National Population Health Survey of Canada (Statistics Canada, 1998). The analysis in the figures is based on the relationship between family income and indicators of health for male and female youth in Canada. Figure 16.1 is based on a self-report indication of general health. Family income is divided into twentieth percentiles in which the population is divided into five numerically equal categories. All the graphs and figures presented in this chapter are based on analyses which are statistically significant (based on two-way analyses of variance and chi-square where appropriate).

FIGURE 16.1
Percentage of Canadian Youth with Poor Health, by Income Level

Source: Based on Statistics Canada (1998).

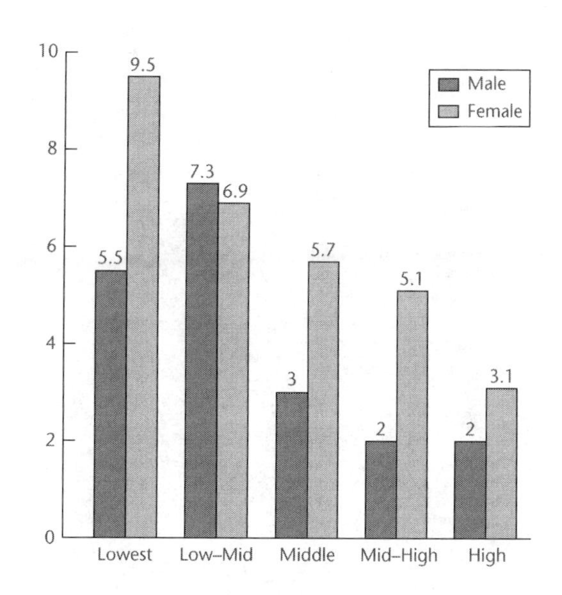

The self-assessment of health variable shows quite clearly that youth in the highest income categories have the lowest levels of poor health and this is especially apparent for female youth. In fact, three times as many female youth express poor health (9.5%) compared to high income female youth (3.1%). Importantly, a greater percentage of females overall reveal poor health than do males, although the poorest youth of both genders are the least healthy.

With regard to adolescent mental health, the estimates in Canada are that between 15–20 percent of youth between 10 and 19 years of age have a major mental disorder (Greenberg et al., 2001; Kutcher, 1996). Consistent with the argument in this chapter, the conventional work on youth and mental health shows quite clearly that psychological and emotional health problems for children and youth are closely tied to adverse life situations including: living in privation, low educational attainment, poor housing conditions, and family dysfunction associated with living as an underclass (Rainwater & Smeeding, 2003; Offord, 1989). Figure 16.2 is based on a self-report of numbers of weeks youth say they are depressed in one year.

Firstly, we notice that, overall, youth experience a significant amount of depression, to the extreme of 15 weeks per year for low income females and 8.29 weeks per year for high income males. Furthermore, in light of our previous discussions, it is significant that depression is more common amongst the poorest youth and that the degree of depression decreases as income increases. It is interesting here that males and females experience generally the same amount of depression, although female percentages are slightly higher. This finding is contrary to almost all research on gender and depression that shows that females of all ages experience more depression than males, at least in clinical contexts (Keyes & Goodman, 2006; Muszynski, 1994; Trypuc, 1994; Northcott, 1991).

Figure 16.3 further illustrates the connections between mental health and socioeconomic circumstance by focusing on levels of stress that Canadian youth experience (based on a series of indicators of stress incorporated into the National Population Health Survey).

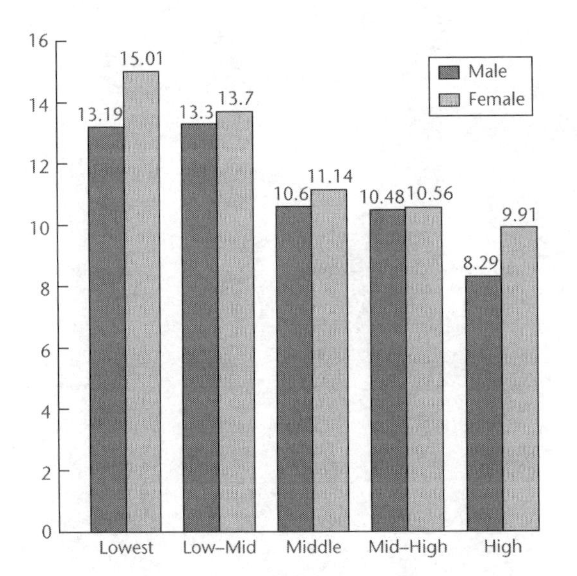

FIGURE 16.2

Number of Weeks of Feeling Depressed for Canadian Youth, by Income Level

Source: Based on Statistics Canada (1998).

FIGURE 16.3

General Chronic Stress Index for Canadian Youth, by Income Level

Source: Based on Statistics Canada (1998).

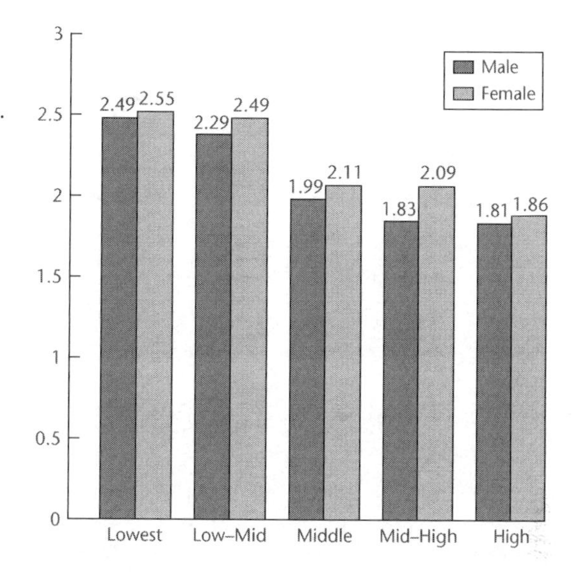

Health research is quite clear that stress leads to both physical and emotional health risk, and that poverty predisposes youth to stress and ultimately to health risk (Newacheck et al., 2003; Abernathy et al., 2002; Canadian Institute of Child Health, 2000; Baxter, 1993). As with previous indicators of health, stress decreases as income increases and levels of stress are highest for the lowest income category for female and male youth. Furthermore, it appears that at all income levels, girls experience higher levels of stress than do boys.

Figures 16.4 and 16.5 are intended to complete this introductory section by illustrating two specific physical manifestations of ill health: asthma and arthritis. I use

FIGURE 16.4

Percentage of Canadian Youth with Asthma, by Income Level

Source: Based on Statistics Canada (1998).

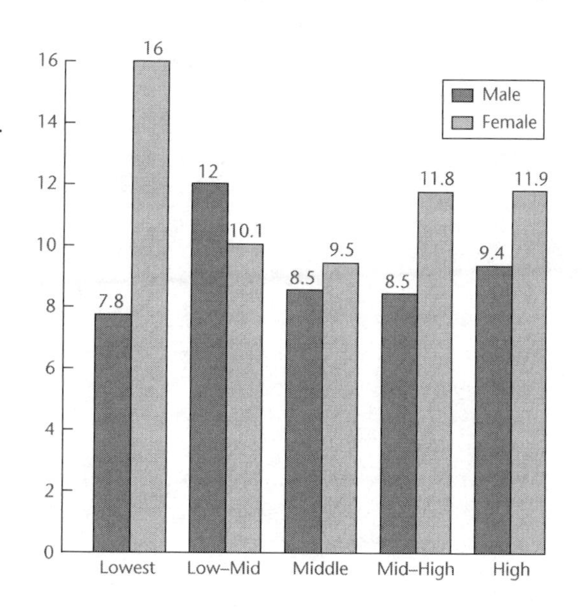

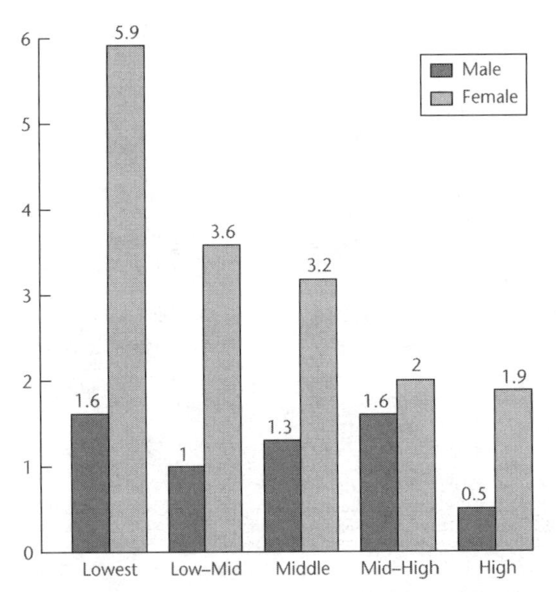

FIGURE 16.5
Percentage of Canadian Youth with Arthritis, by Income Level

Source: Based on Statistics Canada (1998).

asthma as a health indicator because it is purported to have both physical/genetic and psychological origins (McCreary Centre Society, 1999). Several things are important about asthma and youth. Firstly, asthma is the most common chronic illness in children and youth. Secondly, it has been on the rise in the last twenty years in Canada, increasing from 2 percent in 1978 to 12.2 percent in 1997 for children and youth under twenty years of age (Canadian Institute of Child Health, 2000; Canadian Institute of Child Health, 1998; Senthilsevan, 1998). Lastly, American research has indicated that deaths from asthma are four times more prevalent amongst black youth than white youth indicating a rather marked connection to social class (Crater et al., 2001; *Morbidity and Mortality Weekly Report*, 1996). The overall conclusions in most of the research on asthma and children/youth suggest a strong correlation with environmental contaminants and exposure to airborne and ingested substances that trigger asthmatic reactions (Gracey, 2002; Canadian Institute of Child Health, 1998).

Most noticeable in Figure 16.4 is the overwhelming impact that poverty has on rates of asthma for low income girls. Interestingly, the same effect is not apparent for boys. Furthermore, for boys, the rates of asthma vary little across income categories, except for the low-mid income category with a relatively high percentage of 12. Lastly, it is significant that girls have higher rates of asthma overall than do boys. This gender difference may be attributable, in part, to higher rates of smoking amongst girls compared to boys. Income differences are somewhat easier to explain given the higher incidences of smoking amongst lower income youth and the often recorded high levels of exposure to environmental contaminants that lower class people experience relative to their wealthier counterparts.

Arthritis, although thought to be less psychosomatically determined in its origins than conditions like asthma, has a probable socio-environmental antecedent. Adolescent arthritis may originate with impaired nutrition and exposure to environmental threats resulting in triggering factors such as childhood influenza, rubella, and pneumonia.

Research in Manitoba has suggested that these triggering factors and the corresponding incidents of rheumatoid arthritis in adolescents are higher amongst rural Aboriginal youth who tend to live in communities marked by relative privation (Oen, Fast & Postl, 1995). An analysis of levels of arthritis presents a different set of assumptions compared to the study of asthma. Firstly, arthritis is ostensibly more congenitally determined than asthma. Secondly, arthritis is primarily a condition of aging, and in general, is most prevalent amongst the elderly (conditioned by overuse and abuse of the musculoskeletal system). Interestingly, the results here show that arthritis appears often amongst young people, and, for girls, is closely associated with income.

For example, almost six percent of young girls in the low income category have arthritis compared to 1.9 percent in the high income bracket. For some reason, low incomes expose girls to this risk. We might speculate that it has something to do with diet, exercise, and pre-natal and neo-natal care. Even in a system of universal health care, access to adequate diets, healthy lifestyles, and gynecological and pediatric care are determined by social standing (CIHI, 2005; Starfield et al., 2002; McIntyre et al., 2001; Mustard & Roos, 1994). Interestingly, this class phenomenon is not as apparent for boys, although boys in the high income bracket have almost negligible rates of arthritis (5%). Lastly, it is significant that arthritis is much more common amongst girls than boys, and although most clinical evidence suggests similar rates for boys and girls (Woo & Wedderburn, 1998), these results suggest that in a self-report survey, girls are perhaps more aware of their condition and have pursued medical intervention (which reflects the conventional wisdom that suggests women of all ages pursue medical care more often than men).

Overall, the results from the first set of figures illustrate quite clearly that poverty places youth in medical jeopardy. Furthermore, the findings suggest that gender has an influence on levels of health and on how poverty affects health. The following discussions illustrate how many of the medical dangers that threaten the health of adolescents are the result of adult "business as usual." In effect, the health risks faced by youth are the result of the adult pursuit of profit or, at least, the result of youth emulating adult behaviours. And, startlingly, they are, then, largely preventable.

DRUGS, ALCOHOL, AND TOBACCO: ADULT GRATIFICATION, ADOLESCENT DANGER

This section on high-risk substance abuse is significant for several reasons. Firstly, it illustrates that many of the substances that place youth at extreme risk are manufactured legally by adults in the pursuit of profit. Further, youth are in fact the calculated markets for many of these dangerous substances. Secondly, when youth ingest substances that endanger their health, they often do so in emulation of adults or as a response to abuse or neglect in an adult world; their use of chemicals is largely, then, an attempt to normalize a largely unendurable existence. The following discussions illustrate these points.

Tobacco Use

Tobacco is likely the most addictive of available addictive substances and ironically, the one most accessible to young people. While rates of tobacco use have declined in the overall population in recent years, the rates of tobacco use amongst adolescents have increased, especially for female youth, despite the prohibitions surrounding selling cigarettes to underaged youth. In Canada, in 2000, 25 percent of young women aged 15–17 smoked regularly compared to 19 percent of young men; for ages 18 and 19, the rates rise to 31 percent for both girls and boys (Health Canada, 2000). In 1996, Greaves (1996) reported that the rate of smoking amongst adolescent females was on the rise; however, the most recent research indicates that levels of smoking for both girls and boys have leveled off. Interestingly, however, smoking for young people still increases sharply from the ages of 15–17 to 18–19 (Health Canada, 2000).

While smoking is a voluntary activity, tobacco companies target certain demographic markets whether or not those markets are prohibited from smoking. As smoking decreases within the adult population – in response to health campaigns and a general overall awareness of the dangers of smoking especially as people age – children and adolescents provide a new and lucrative market for tobacco advertisers. Tobacco advertisements that promise popularity, thinness, and independence are clearly targeted at young women (Snell, 2005). As an indication of the penetrating impact of advertising on the young, Greaves (1996) reports that the Camel campaign launched in the United States in 1988 (which features the cartoon camel Old Joe) increased Camel's share of the illegal children and youth market from 0.5 percent to 32.8 percent; moreover, ninety-four percent of American high school students reportedly recognize the Old Joe trademark.

Given the widespread knowledge that cigarettes and other forms of tobacco are a proven health risk, what is it that compels children and youth, especially female youth, to smoke in substantial numbers, especially relative to their adult counterparts? Greaves (1996) contends that the explanations lie somewhere in the contemporary ethos of gender equity and potential equal opportunity for girls and boys, and the structural barriers that in reality continue to exist for girls and women. Smoking is emblematic of independence and choice. Tobacco companies foster this in ads that focus on being your own person. The image of independence coupled with the struggle for girls to be equal to boys, fosters an adolescent world in which acceptance and maturity are equated with smoking (Snell, 2005). However, the opportunities for young men and the role models they emulate are much greater for boys than for girls. In this context, young women are faced with a real struggle for equality in a structurally unequal world, and smoking becomes a part of their reality in response to the alienation they feel from the work world and from the constraints of the domestic sphere. Smoking provides:

> symbolic adult status at a time when access to the real thing is undermined...by the paradoxes of femininity, work and adulthood...Once established, the smoking habit may be an important means of managing the inherent tensions between and within paid work, domesticity and constraining notions of appropriate sexual identity in young women's lives (Kostash, 1989, quoted in Greaves, 1996, p. 113).

The notion that smoking is a way of establishing psycho-social identity in a world that promises success often without fulfillment has implications certainly for male smoking as well. Consistent with the overall theme in this chapter, it is relatively easy to argue that children and youth are part of the marginalized classes. They do not vote, they have little policy impact on the world into which they are thrust, and most of the institutions that provide self- and social-fulfillment (clubs, community organization, etc.)

are created by and for adults and are therefore financially and constitutionally unavailable to youth. It is conceivable that both male and female youth – especially the most socio-economically deprived youth (LaGrange & Silverman, 1999; Conrad, Flay & Hill, 1992) – smoke in an attempt to establish control and adult-identify, and ultimately to access, at least symbolically, some sense of influence. This is especially so in relation to the connection between self-empowerment in which smoking is an activity, especially for young girls, that provides a mechanism of immediate self-control, specifically in regard to weight control (Crisp et al., 1999). As Greaves (1996) and others have argued, however, for girls the double jeopardy of living on the margins and living in a patriarchal world dictates unusual vulnerability to the "culture of smoking" and to related pathologies like eating disorders.

Alcohol and Drug Use

As I discuss in a subsequent section, street youth use and abuse alcohol and drugs because, in part, it helps them normalize marginal and traumatic lives. The extent of the trauma faced by street youth is evidenced by the McCreary Centre Society (1994) study of youth in British Columbia in 1994. These findings suggested the rather shocking phenomenon that 98 percent of female youth on the street reported some form of prior abuse, as either a child or an adolescent. More recent works have accentuated the reality that elevated levels of physical, psychological, and emotional harm – either through previous childhood experience or through immediate life circumstances – are linked to the abuse of alcohol and drugs (Hotton & Haans, 2004; Centre for Addiction and Mental Health, 1999; Hagan & McCarthy, 1998), and ultimately linked to high propensities for suicide, self-abuse/**slashing**, and poor levels of health (Votta & Manion, 2004; Schissel & Fedec, 1999; McCreary Centre Society, 1994). For example, Schissel and Fedec (1999), in their study of Saskatchewan children and youth involved in the sex trade, found relatively high levels of both alcohol and drug abuse in a young offender population. However, for the young offenders who were involved in the sex trade, their levels of substance abuse were extremely high to the extent that 100 percent of non-Aboriginal young offenders involved in the sex trade had severe alcohol problems compared to 50 percent of those young offenders not in the sex trade (the corresponding rates for Aboriginal youth were 86 percent and 65 percent respectively).

The reality that substance abuse is associated with trauma is not only characteristic of street youth, however. Despite socio-economic context, youth who have been victims of adult exploitation and abuse show elevated rates of alcohol and drug abuse. For example, the 1992 study entitled *Rape in America* found that serious drinking problems were twelve times higher and serious drug problems were twenty-five times higher in rape victims than in non-victims (Males, 1996). It is significant that in the public discourse surrounding youth alcohol and drug abuse, issues of childhood and youth victimization by adults are rarely addressed in lieu of the more politically expedient focus on dangerous kids. An additional contradiction is that most of the substances abused by children and youth are manufactured legitimately by adults, are often manufactured under the guise of medical care, and are "pushed" to youth by multinational corporations who work very hard at fostering the connections between the use of their substances, academic success (Breggin, 2002; Diller, 1998), and happiness and contentment (Triggle, 2005; Virani, 2004; Cassels, 2003).

While, as we have seen in the previous section, this is especially true for tobacco manufacturers, companies like Labatts, Budweiser, and Coors have so convincingly insinuated themselves into the culture of youth that underage drinking has become almost normative. Of course, when youth are condemned for their potential criminality, drinking and drug use are cited as triggering factors. The therapeutic response, as a result, is to teach abstinence to youngsters, either through law, education, or medicine. In a climate of tolerance for widespread drinking in North America, especially in the context of sports, as Males (1996) argues "any effort to teach youngsters abstinence from these substances is a little like trying to promote chastity in a brothel" (1996, p. 215).

It is pertinent to these discussions to acknowledge that many of the drugs that are produced for therapeutic reasons are harmful to children and youth. For example, in the United States, the drugs that send most teenagers to emergency rooms are Tylenol, Aspirin, and Ibuprofen. Out of all emergency room visit for substance abuse for youth, 71 percent were for pharmaceutical overdoses; 15 percent for alcohol, caffeine, and drugs combined; and only 14 percent for street drugs (Males, 1996). In Canada, the increasing use of Ritalin to control children and youth who are unable to fit into a regular classroom situation – diagnosed as Attention Deficit Hyperactivity Disorder – results in much of the drug ending up on the street and used in combination with other pharmaceuticals. In fact, in the United States, more high school youth use Ritalin illegally than as a prescription, and between 30 and 50 percent of youth in drug treatment centres report Ritalin use (U.S. Department of Justice, 2005). An equally pressing problem is that Ritalin use on hyperactive or children and youth with **ADHD** has increased 4.6 times in Canada since 1990 (Brownell & Yogendran, 2001; Chisholm, 1996). In the United States, the use of Ritalin and associated drugs to control attention disorders in children and youth increases two-fold every four to seven years (Brownell & Yogendran, 2001). The implications of this are staggering given evidence which suggests that Attention Deficit Hyperactivity Disorder is difficult to define let alone diagnose. Some doctors regard Ritalin as a panacea for youth attention problems and prescribe accordingly, while others regard it as a dangerous narcotic. In some communities like Vernon, B.C., 10 percent of 11 year old boys were found to be on the drug (Rees, 1998). Significantly, Sweden banned Ritalin in 1968 because of heavy abuse (U.S. Department of Justice, 2005; Diller, 1998).

Dr. Peter Breggin is probably the most outspoken of health experts who voice extreme caution and concern regarding child and adolescent ADHD. Breggin is the author of nineteen books including *The Ritalin Fact Book* (2002), *Talking Back to Ritalin* (1998, Revised 2001), the founder of The International Centre for the Study of Psychiatry and Psychology (ICSPP), and founder of peer-reviewed journal *Ethical Human Sciences and Services*; he maintains that ADHD and Ritalin are American and Canadian fads (*Talking Back to* Ritalin, 2001). After all, the United States and Canada account for 90 percent and 5 percent of the market for Ritalin, respectively, with the rest of the world sharing the other 5 percent. Breggin's concern is typical of the incredible dissent amongst researchers, clinicians, and physicians. Brownell and Yogendran argue that ADHD is "one of the most controversial conditions of childhood" (2001). Yet, for clinicians, "attention-deficit/hyperactivity disorder (ADHD) has become the psychiatric model or prototype disorder for the medication treatment of children" (Popper, 2002, p. 1).

In the short term, however, Ritalin does make a difference to some of the "symptoms" of ADHD. As a stimulant pharmacologically similar to amphetamines and cocaine

(U.S. Department of Justice, 2005), the stimulant effect is medically understandable. What is neither understandable or ethical, however, is the use of a powerful drug for a condition whose causes and nature are largely unknown, especially for children as their brains are developmentally immature (Popper, 2002).

Another grim reality is that Ritalin has dangerous side effects—including drug dependence, headaches, eye and mouth tics, insomnia, and long-term risks for cancer and chronic depression (Diller, 1998)—but is an extremely lucrative amphetamine for Ciba-Geigy, the primary manufacturer. Social commentators, in response, have argued that in a climate of fiscal restraint resulting in larger classroom sizes, teachers are using Ritalin to manage inordinately large and diverse student contexts. More directly, it appears that we have chosen, very unapologetically, to ignore the environment in which we place our children and youth, and to focus on the more lucrative and more compelling world of individual sickness and deviance:

> In spite of the rhetoric in schools of education about the importance of taking into account the individual needs of the children in a classroom, the current system of public education is designed to make that nearly impossible....Instead, it becomes necessary to find ways of making children able to perform in the environment as they find it. And, in late twentieth-century America, when it is difficult or inconvenient to change the environment, we don't think twice about changing the brain of the person who has to live in it. (Livingston, 1997, pp. 17–18)

The complicity of adults in pushing legitimate pharmaceuticals to youth is illustrated in the following section on sports, popular culture, and body image.

THE PATHOLOGY OF BODY IMAGES

Body weight has for decades been considered a diagnostic indicator of health but only recently has it become a dominant concern for health care professionals and the focus of personal crusades for an increasing number of North Americans (International Obesity Task Force, 2006; Statistics Canada, 2003; Nichols, 1999). The medical argument is simple: insufficient and excess weight statuses are health risks, especially in light of the research on eating disorders and youth (see subsequent section), and obesity and longevity. Importantly, Health Canada's standard weight scale showing acceptable weight per height has become an acceptable standard for judging whether a person is at risk. However, despite the medical validity of this diagnostic tool, the issue of body weight is politically charged. Firstly, body weight and body image are social constructions that have evaluative power. One has to look no further than advertisements for brand name clothing or for cosmetics to see that we place most value on lithe and youthful body types. This socially constructed image of the acceptable body serves industries like clothing and cosmetics. The image is an ideal that we strive to achieve and the struggle is costly and never-ending. As Findlay argues,

> The media and advertising industries, for example, promote their products by suggesting that success and beauty will belong to every woman is she diets properly or purchases the latest stay thin formulas. The medical profession, for its part, advocates a thin build over a

> heavy one, thus reinforcing the dominant norms. Women equate the attainment of the normative appearance with social mobility....Consistent exposure to impossible images of ideal beauty conveys a sense of perpetual deficiency to ordinary women....The effort is often exhausting and painful. (Findlay, 1996, p. 176)

As we will come to see, the effort is not only exhausting and painful, but for young women and men it also has the potential to create permanent physical damage. A fundamental aspect in understanding body weight and health jeopardy for youth is that the struggle to achieve the ideal body type, especially for youth, is often fostered by adults in contexts like athletics, art, and in the business world of fashion, and is based on an ethos that achievement and success are closely tied to, or in fact maybe are equivalent to, maintenance of a certain body image. Cosmetics and clothing industries target youthful audiences, and sports and artistic organizations exploit youth in the search for physical domination and victory. The final irony is that when governments proclaim eating disorders, especially obesity, as a national health problem, they target and blame individuals who are most exploited and disadvantaged, and ultimately they lay blame on the victims for taxing an already heavily burdened health care system.

Before I expand on these issues, however, I would like to illustrate how body weight is closely tied to gender and class. Figures 16.6 and 16.7 are based on the National Population Health Survey, and levels of both underweight and overweight are based on Health Canada standards of acceptable weight per height.

These figures are important for they illustrate how female and male youth differ in the effects of wealth on health. Firstly, for male youth, insufficient weight is most common amongst those in the lowest income category. For girls, the opposite is true, with those in the highest income categories experiencing the highest levels of inadequate weight. This finding for young females is consistent with the socio-medical literature which documents the highest prevalence of eating disorders amongst populations in which the pressures toward thinness are the greatest – including young affluent women

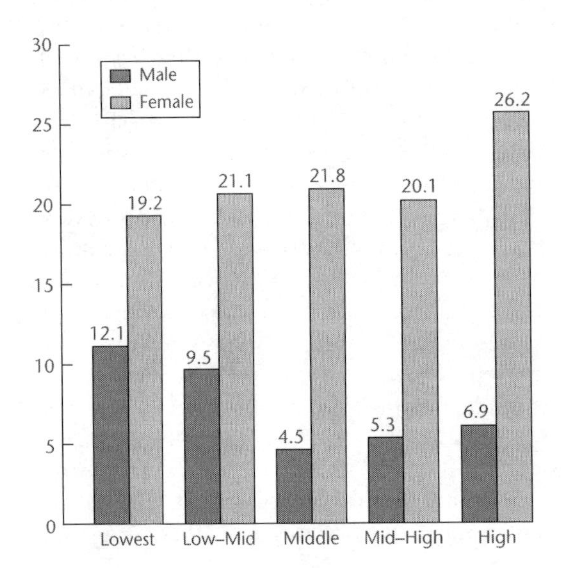

FIGURE 16.6

Percentage of Underweight Canadian Youth, by Income Level

Source: Based on Statistics Canada (1998).

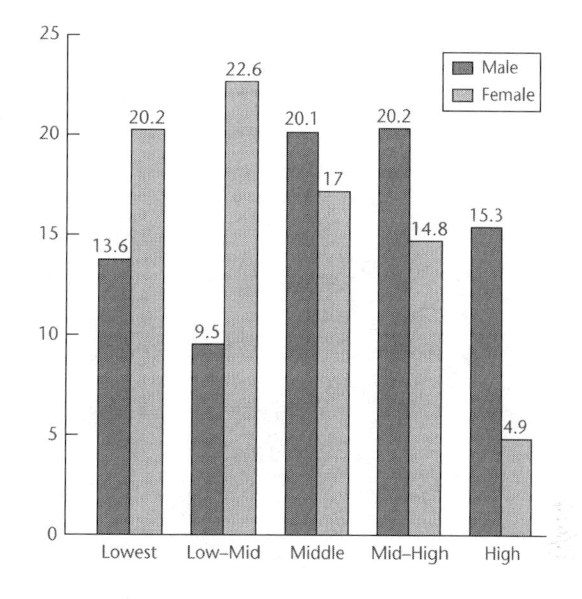

FIGURE 16.7
Percentage of Overweight Canadian Youth, by Income Level

Source: Based on Statistics Canada (1998).

in Western societies (Bordo, 2004; Dolan, 1991; Nasser, 1988). Significantly, hospitalization rates for eating disorders in girls under age 15 increased by 34 percent from 1987 to 1999 (CIHI, 2005).

The findings for young men are more difficult to understand in an affluent country like Canada, but perhaps poor young males simply lack access to an adequate diet by virtue of their poverty, especially given how much, in general, developing young males need to eat. Certainly, the National Organization on Poverty in Canada has argued that the dietary demands of male children are greater than those for their female counterparts and it is conceivable that poor young males, as well, suffer poor diets as a result of their privation.

Lastly, in this figure, it is apparent that the malady of insufficient weight is much more prevalent amongst young females than males; this finding is consistent with research that analyzes anorexia and bulimia in the context of constructed images of femininity and social value (Bordo, 2004; Crisp et al., 1999; Showalter, 1997; Findlay, 1996).

Figure 16.7 illustrates the condition which would appear to be the corollary of anorexia and bulimia but is, at a very core level, a manifestation of the same type of social value we place on body type and size. Health Canada has declared obesity to be a national health problem and has essentially created a national stigma scrutinizing those who are overweight. The results here indicate quite clearly that if you isolate the two poorest income levels of adolescents, young women are substantially more overweight than their male counterparts. At the high end of the income spectrum, however, the opposite is true; young men have higher rates of obesity than young women.

Explanations for these trends were explored in research conducted at McGill University which investigated obesity amongst children and youth in Montreal. The conclusions from this research directed attention to higher levels of fat intake and lower levels of micro-nutrient intake amongst poor families (Johnson-Down et al., 1997). The general socio-medical conclusion is that a general trend toward obesity in children and youth in Canada is more pronounced in more disadvantaged children than it is in their wealthier counterparts (LeBlanc, 2003; Starfield et al., 2001; Yip et al., 1993), and that the unhealthy dietary habits learned early in life tend to persist into adulthood (LeBlanc, 2003; Clarke & Lauer, 1993). It is interesting that the findings from the National Population Health study in Figure 16.7 show the low income/poverty effect for young females only. If the effect of poor diets in children is manifested in adolescents and adults, we would expect the class effect to apply to young males as well as females.

In light of the foregoing discussions, the question arises as to how body image and body size come to preoccupy youth to a point where weight control leads to self-injurious behaviours like anorexia and bulimia at one extreme, and obesity at the other. What we are investigating, in essence, is how a generation of adolescents comes to orient themselves primarily to body image as a source of validation and identity. It is important to acknowledge, as well, that this pathogenic preoccupation with body weight and image filters down to children. The "sickness of body image" starts at a very early age, a fact which was confirmed by the Jacobs Institute of Women's Health in 1997 when it reported that 40 percent of third-grade girls said they were dieting to lose weight. By the fifth grade, the figure had increased to 75 percent (Mosley, 1997).

EATING DISORDERS AND SEXUALITY

Despite the profusion of medical research based on the psycho-pathology of eating disorders – from research based primarily on the taxonomy of psychiatric disorders and eating disorders, to the psychological search for connections between eating disorders and personality characteristics – we are still faced with the historical question of why youth only now are engaging in eating behaviours which are injurious. The first and most obvious response to this query is that the social value that we place on thinness and youth is so strong, and of course, so closely tied to the merchandising of "body image enhancing products" that youth grow up orienting their lives to "**beauty norms**." But, more importantly, modern society creates the equation between social and personal value and beauty, and children and youth are extremely vulnerable to the inadvertent and subliminal conveyors of this message. Feminist authors generally contend that thinness is a patriarchal/political economic construction that sets tyrannical cultural expectations for girls and women. As I argue in the next section, the tyranny of body image is becoming as oppressive for young men as it is for young women.

Popular critic Naomi Wolf (1990) has argued that diet, cosmetic, fashion, and plastic surgery industries conspire to keep women unsure of themselves and their physicality, and as a result "in their place." Youth, more so than others, buy into the "beauty myth" and place themselves at risk by engaging in self-destructive behaviours such as **anorexia nervosa** and **bulimia**. Anorexia nervosa is characterized by extreme weight loss and a pathological fear of becoming fat, while bulimia is distinguished by binge eating and then purging either through vomiting or laxative use. In either case, medical researchers argue that victims of the disorders are already troubled people who are unfortunately influenced by popular culture images of the ideal body. However, while medicine studies the relatively uncommon "pathological cases" of obsession with weight, there is increasing evidence that a large proportion of all youth, especially female youth, are preoccupied with weight to the point that they put themselves at risk through inadequate eating or purging or through the use of diet pills (Saul, 2003). Importantly, eating disorders have increased significantly over time; hospitalization rates in Canada for eating disorders in girls under age 15 increased by 34 percent from 1987 to 1999 (CIHI, 2005). Currently, Canada estimates suggest that 1.5 percent of young women have serious cases of bulimia and another 1 percent have anorexia nervosa; it is also estimated that in Ontario, 27 percent of girls 12–18 years old are engaged in severely problematic food and weight behaviour (Jones et al., 2001). In the United States, the cultural obsession with body image is similar to that in Canada: 80 percent of girls between grade three and six feel bad about their bodies and 70 percent are on diets (Saul, 2003). What we are experiencing, as a result, is less of an eating disorder epidemic and more of a normative youth commitment to weight control based on popular culture body images. In fact, the reality may be that "women with bulimia and anorexia are...taking cultural standards of female beauty (or even acceptability) to their natural – if extreme – conclusion" (Saul, 2003, p. 146).

A harsh example of the influence of popular culture has been documented by the Harvard Medical School anthropology professor Anne Becker (Shin, 1999) who has studied eating habits in Fiji in the wake of the introduction of television in 1995. Her findings, based on a 1998 survey and historical work on Fijian society, determined that a sudden increase in eating disorders amongst young girls in Fiji coincides and may be linked to the introduction of television and access to American shows such as *Melrose Place*, *ER*, and *Xena, Warrior Princess*. In her survey, Becker found that 74 percent of Fijian girls reported "being too fat," and 15 percent reported they had vomited to control weight. As Becker also reports, this is in a historical/cultural context in which "robust, well-muscled" body types are the norm and in which dieting and purging are unknown. She concludes that television is a pathogen and that Western ideals of physicality and body image are like a plague.

In response to critics like Wolf, more psychologically-oriented critical theorists like Showalter (1997) and Shorter (1994) blame the media, clinics, doctors, and charismatic healers for constructing a public panic over a series of decades that culminated in a real epidemic of eating disorders as potential patients "bought into" the hype. Showalter especially argues that a mass publicity campaign spread the news of this modern condition to every young woman in the Western world, with the result that these young women react accordingly in a true psychosomatic fashion by manifesting the behaviours of the constructed disease (Showalter, 1997; Shorter, 1994). In fact, Groesz et al. (2002) did a meta-analysis of the extant research on media influences on adolescents' images of themselves and their propensity to obsession with weight and made a very strong argument that, especially for participants under 19 years of age, body image deteriorates with exposure to media images of stereotypically thin women.

While theories of popular culture are important and are intuitively interesting, they do make some rather broad leaps of faith regarding the immediate impact that the entertainment and advertising industries have on personal conduct. They also stop short of tying images of men and women to the broader historic-cultural forces that shape the ways that society views men and women as distinct, sexualized beings.

Several decades ago, Michel Foucault (1980) argued that modern society is characterized by the "deployment of sexuality." In essence, he suggested that sex has become so sublimated and mysterious that a proliferation of discourses has resulted as a consequence of the uncertainty of sexuality. The more we repress sex, the more we crave to know about it, especially among the disciplines of medicine, science, and, of course, pop psychology. His work seems appropriate here as it helps us understand the seemingly overwhelming concern with body image. Body image is about sexuality, about understanding the mystery of sex at an organizational/professional level and at a personal level. Adolescents, but especially young women, are largely defined – and define themselves – as sexual beings. If sexuality is the fundamental defining characteristic of the "normal" (and abnormal) person, then a preoccupation with the trappings of sexuality are understandable. To appear conventional (i.e., attractive), young people fulfill the mandate of a sexualized society by engaging in "grooming conduct." While anthropologists might argue that this is normal sexual conduct for the human animal, a more insightful Foucauldian-based analysis would contend that repressed sexuality is a modern invention that has lead us to explore, at length, the mysteries and deviances of sex. The legitimate speakers in this discourse of sex are, of course, science and medicine, but more and more commonly, popular culture in the forms of pop psychology, fashion, and celebrity are having their voices heard. Further, it is no surprise that young people engage in "body image activity" by using the inventions of science and medicine as legitimate techniques of self-development. Many of the substances that youth choose to control weight and to foster a certain body image are produced by pharmaceutical companies and the industry of medicine as legitimate means of corrective sexuality. The next section on sports and legitimate drugs is an apt example of how this works.

THE PATHOLOGY OF ATHLETICS

A 1993 study of anabolic steroid use in sports in Canada indicated that 83,000 Canadians between the ages of 11 and 18 use steroids, constituting 2.8 percent of all youth in this age category and 4.3 percent of all male youth (Melia, Pipe & Greenberg, 1996). American research around the same time period indicated higher incidences ranging from 5–10 percent of adolescent boys (Eliot & Goldberg, 1996). More current research indicates levels of steroid use of approximately 5 percent for boys and 1 to 2 percent for girls overall (Field et al., 2005; Cafri & Thompson, 2006), and much higher use for youth athletes, especially for those involved in football, wrestling, bodybuilding, and weightlifting (Bahrke et al., 2000). Furthermore, dangerous drugs such as ephedrine, prohormones, and **creatine** are becoming more common amongst young athletes in their quest for athletic and physical excellence, and all of these drugs have been shown to have dangerous side effects. Interestingly, drugs such as steroid precursors, ephedra, and growth hormone have no documented effects on body mass and strength (Calfee & Fadale, 2006).

However, the prevalence of steroid use still overwhelms other types of diet and bodybuilding drugs, despite the rather general knowledge that steroids have severe long-term consequences for health. Taking anabolic steroids can lead to heart problems, depression, severe aggressive behaviour, sex-organ problems in both men and women, and several forms of cancer. In short, continued steroid use can lead to premature death as evidenced by several high-profile cases including American football star Lyle Alzado, major league baseball batting champion Ken Caminiti, and World Wrestling Federation star Rick Rude.

Steroid and other performance enhancing drugs used by Western youth illustrates one of the fundamental dangers of contemporary athletics. The "succeed at all costs" mentality has become so pervasive in sports, especially amongst youth, that coaches instruct within this paradigm (Bigelow, 2002; Clark, 2000). So much of what coaches and other sports officials communicate to youth is an inadvertent expectation that athletic prowess and success is closely tied to body shape and body image. In essence, athletic prowess and attractiveness become conflated, and this has implications for muscle enhancement and weight control. Male youth take performance enhancing drugs to emulate popular cultural idols, mostly athletes, as evidenced by the overwhelming popularity of professional wrestling amongst young men. Female youth tend to fixate on weight control especially in the subjectively-judged sports that require a lean, youthful body for presentation – figure-skating, gymnastics, and competitive dance. Importantly, in these so-called aesthetic sports, the participant often reaches her athletic prime before puberty. In fact, obsessive weight control to keep the "child body form" amongst young female athletes has been linked unequivocally to gynecological risks such as **amenorrhea** (delayed menstruation), infertility, and osteoporosis (Anderson, 1999; Fogelholm et al., 1996; Constantini, 1994).

The conflation of athletics and aesthetics results in double jeopardy for male and female youth. Most research on steroid use amongst young men suggests that their desire to use steroids is closely associated with body dissatisfaction and body mass index – in other words, that they are preoccupied primarily with improving their body image. That young men buy into the "beefcake myth" suggests that they are, in part, as susceptible to the damaging effects of images of sex and gender in popular culture as are young women (Cafri & Berg, 2006). Many young men are willing to risk the dangers of steroid use to avoid the stigma of being small and weak. The use of steroids, however, has more complex origins than mere cosmetics. As Parks and Read argue, the increasing preoccupation with body image amongst young men (and the attendant use of muscle enhancing substances) "may induce some adolescents to participate in athletics in general, while the individual's body type may provide the impetus for selection of a particular sport" (Parks & Read, 1997, p. 594). Their research is instructive in that it illustrates that the futile struggle to obtain the perfect physique is closely tied to perceived success in athletics, which in turn is closely tied to popularity and success in school. These connections are borne out by the obvious popularity of school sports like football, and the obvious social popularity of elite high school athletes, especially males.

For young women, as mentioned previously, the connection between body obsession and sports is similar in its psychic implications but different in its physical manifestations. The traditional "female sports" are based on the aesthetics of the female body. Figure skating and gymnastics (especially rhythmic gymnastics) are typical of athletics whose presentation and form are judged as closely as or more closely than athletic prowess. These aesthetic sports create additional undue pressure on young female athletes to control weight. As mentioned before, messages of body image and performance efficiency are often communicated by coaches either directly or inadvertently within a competitive "winning" context. Geoff Gowan, President of the Coaching Association of Canada, argues that coaches at all levels have enormous influences on their athletes and that what coaches say in a casual way "may be perceived by the young athlete, particularly in a sport where body shape and weight is of immense importance, to have a significant impact. These athletes are just beginning to get conscious of the fact that there is a danger she is going to get too heavy or too big or whatever, but is also trying to please a coach" (Moser, 1994, p. B2). Kevin Spink, a sports psychologist at the University of Saskatchewan, in interviews with young athletes in aesthetic sports, found that a majority was dieting, and that their intense preoccupation with weight and body image was fostered by coaches, parents, and other competitors. The subtle pressure to attain a certain body size and shape is contained in a "discourse of competition" which is based on "body talk" as if the aesthetic body is paramount to participation (Moser, 1994).

This "gestalt of success" carries with it extraordinary risk, especially for female youth. As Spink argues, "the idea that body image affects our self-esteem is just starting to emerge....It's basically the anxiety a person feels when physique is being evaluated in any way" (Moser, 1994, p. B2). A growing body of research focuses on the actual physical risk that athletes face in organized sports. The overarching conclusion is that young athletes participating in sports in which leanness or weight gain are required are at substantially higher risk for eating disorders. One study in Norway revealed that of the 522 young females athletes studied, 22.4 percent could be classified as at risk from eating disorders and 89 percent of those at risk were diagnosed with either anorexia nervosa or bulimia. More importantly, the researchers stated that 75 percent of those young athletes, who were told by coaches that they were too heavy, used pathogenic weight control methods, including purging, dieting, water loss, extreme exercise, and amphetamine use (Sundgot-Borgen & Torstveit, 2004; Sundgot-Borgen, 1994). The dangers that this trend poses for young female athletes especially include disordered eating, amenorrhea, and osteoporosis (precipitated by gradual loss of bone density) (Anderson, 1999; DiPietro & Stachenfeld, 1997).

While the connections between eating disorders and athletics have been discussed primarily in the context of young women, it is significant that recent research is uncovering a hidden epidemic of high risk behaviours (including anorexia and bulimia) amongst male adolescents, especially those who participate in sports such as long distance running (Sundgot-Borgen & Torstveit, 2004; Parks & Read, 1997). Furthermore, weight classification sports such as wrestling, boxing, and rowing have an innocuous but dangerous risk associated with them involving short term weight loss and subsequent rapid weight gain. The athletes involved are primarily young men who use laxatives, diuretics, wear plastic heat suits, and ingest no water. In short, they do anything to rid the body of water in an attempt to make a certain weight class. The typical pattern is to lose several kilograms of weight and then to regain the weight loss through binge drinking and eating, a subtle form of bulimia. This technique, which is almost universally accepted in high school weight class sports, is potentially lethal as evidenced by the death of three college wrestlers in the United States in 1997. All three died in the midst of strenuous **weight-loss workouts** which included rapid dehydration and starvation; heart and kidney failure were the results of these workouts (Litsky, 1997).

I have included the following two figures to give the reader some sense of the extent of chemical control of body weight by teenagers in Canada. The data are based on the Saskatchewan Youth Attitude Survey of 1996, a representative sample of 2,600 youth ages 13–19 in Saskatchewan. The data present the extent of diet pill use and steroid use for males and females within age categories.

Figure 16.8 illustrates several important phenomena regarding chemical weight control. Firstly, it is clear that female youth use diet pills more than their male counterparts for all age groups do. Secondly, the overall rates of use indicate a rather marked increase

FIGURE 16.8
Percentage of Saskatchewan Youth Who Take Diet Pills, 1996

Source: Based on Saskatchewan Youth Attitude Survey (1996) (unpublished).

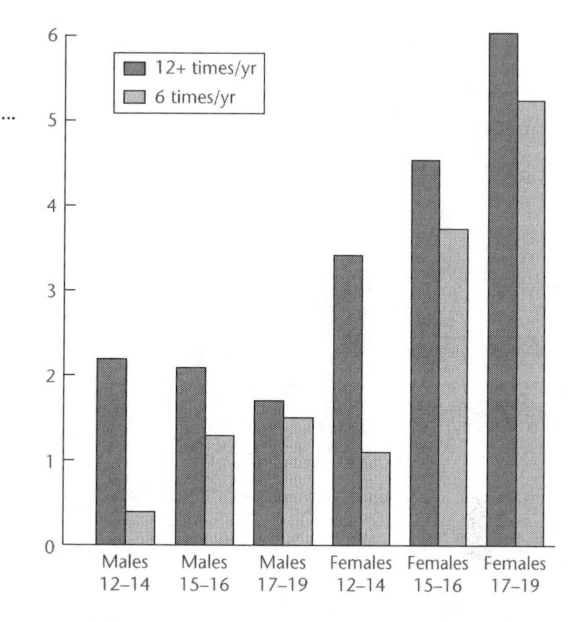

in use from the youngest to oldest age groups for girls to the extent that over 11 percent of female adolescents ages 17–19 use diet pills six or more times a year (6+5.2%). For male youth, the rates are significantly smaller than for female youth, but interestingly, as many young males use diet pills as do older male adolescents (especially those who use pills more than twelve times a year). For steroid use (Figure 16.9), as indicated previously, young males tend to be the primary users to the extent that over four percent of 17–19 year old males use steroids more than twelve times a year. Almost seven percent of this group use steroids at least six times a year. Interestingly, steroid use, although highest for oldest males, is relatively high for 12–14 year old male youth (over 3 percent use steroids more than twelve times a year). As expected, the rates for female youth are substantially less than for males, but steroid use for girls is highest in the youngest age group. Either steroid use for girls diminishes with age or we may be tapping a cohort increase in use for girls. These data are from 1996, and it may be that steroid use is becoming more common for girls; the youngest groups manifesting this cohort effect the most.

In light of this convincing data that youth are involved in the body image struggle, it is significant that the substances used by youth to their own detriment are manufactured, marketed, and advocated by adults. Although the advocacy is not overt, as indicated previously, the subtle pressure to appear "strong" and "beautiful" and to buy into the ethos of physical and occupational success, allows legitimately produced drugs like amphetamines and steroids to become part of a youth's arsenal in the fight against their physicality. Although the use of steroids and diet pills has recently acquired the status of deviant activity, new ammunition for physical improvement is constantly on the horizon. One of the new quick fixes for "underdeveloped" athletes are the amino acid based compounds like creatine and male hormone-based substances including androstenedione. These new safe "chemicals" are touted as natural compounds that can enhance muscle growth and improve body image and physical efficiency. High school age youth

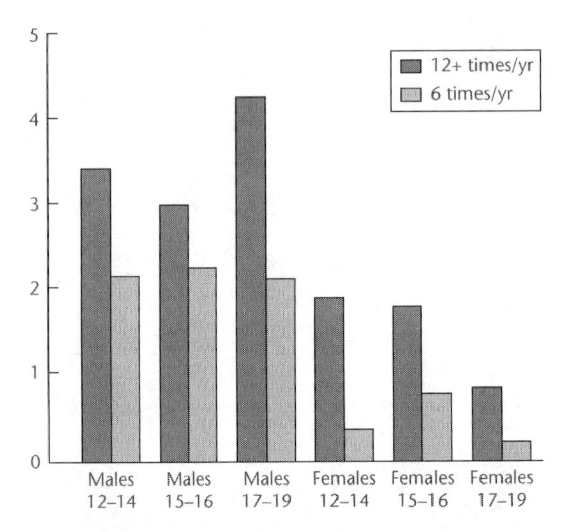

FIGURE 16.9
Percentage of Saskatchewan Youth Who Take Steroids, 1996

Source: Based on Saskatchewan Youth Attitude Survey (1996) (unpublished).

are consumers of such products (primarily creatine), especially in light of the ethos of sports and success in school, because the products are advertised as safe and natural, and because they are often used and endorsed by sports heroes. Similar products are offered for weight control that are not narcotics-based but are instead based on the "natural" suppression of appetite. While products like creatine are easy to access, there is little research regarding the long-term effects, especially on the developing adolescent body. The limited research does suggest, however, that androstendione can cause premature closure of the growth plates in youth and side effects typical of anabolic steroid use that are more pronounced in youth than in adults (Schnirring, 1998a). Furthermore, creatine, as the supplement of choice in high schools, may produce kidney failure and liver damage (Schnirring, 1998b). Such products endorse the fight against being either overweight or underweight, and function to perpetuate the **pathology of body image** for youth, especially in the context of what is defined as athletic excellence.

YOUTH AND WORK: EXPLOITATION AND INEXPERIENCE

One of the basic human rights in Canadian society is to be able to work in a safe and secure environment for adequate wages. These rights are to accrue to everyone despite social characteristics. Although we often violate this legislation, we do, however, legislate protection from labour exploitation for children. This legislative protection is based on our knowledge of how industries have historically exploited children for profit and how children and youth are being exploited throughout the world; despite the United Nations' declaration on the Rights of the Child in 1989, 250 million children worldwide still work long hours in hazardous conditions (Parker, 1997). In general, however, adolescent labour in most countries is considered a normal part of the transition to adulthood. What is rarely acknowledged, however, is that youth labour is highly exploitative; wages are generally low, benefits non-existent, and on-the-job injuries are relatively commonplace. In fact, young workers are more likely than their adult counterparts to be injured on the job, and their injuries are relatively serious (Lavallete & Cunningham,

2004; Lavalette, 2000; Dunn & Runyan, 1993). Furthermore, the industries that use youth labour (the fast food industry is a typical case in point), rarely provide the training and safety standards that are considered fundamental in the adult work world. In the United States, approximately 70 adolescents under 18 die from work related injuries per year, and about 64,000 are treated in emergency wards for on-the-job injuries. Approximately 40 percent of all work-related injuries for youth occur in the fast food preparation industry. Federal child labour regulations in the United States prohibit anyone less than 16 years of age from either cooking or baking; yet, one third of all injuries to youth in 1992 occurred amongst 14–15 year olds who were identified as cooks. In Canada, the same age minimum of 16 applies to youth who work in the general construction industry; however, in July of 1999, in Lashburn, Saskatchewan, a 15 year old boy was killed when he was trapped between the cab and the box of a truck he was operating at a tire recycling plant. The boy was alone and unsupervised, and was obviously in charge of operating heavy equipment. The negligence of management is distressing and the family's trauma is unimaginable. What is equally distressing, however, is the relative indifference paid to the incident, evidenced by Occupational Health and Safety investigators whose initial comments focused on the applicability of the age restriction to this industry and their comments in the media that "when we hear about a very young worker, it causes us some concern" (Trifunov, 1999). It is certainly reasonable to expect that regulatory officials would take a more pro-active, advocacy stance. The reality in this situation is typical of many other workplaces: underage youth are employed at sometimes less than minimum wage, are often untrained, and often unsupervised.

Many of the industries that employ youth as seasonal or "on call" employees depend on exploited labour to maximize profit (Schlosser, 2002; Reiter, 1996). The fast food industry, for example, is staffed largely by school-age employees and the turnover rate is deliberately high. In contexts like this, employers rarely spend time and money training employees in workplace safety. It is expensive to do so and somewhat futile when the employee will only be on the job for a few months (Schlosser, 2002). Disturbingly, while the types of injuries that occur amongst youth in the food service industry are "soft-tissue" injuries, the Government of Ontario is currently introducing legislation that would cut workers' compensation benefits for soft tissue injuries by deducting from the initial wage and the amount of work that the injured person could still perform while injured. As Doug Pearault, President of the Ottawa and District Injured Workers' Group argues, the most disadvantaged by this bill are young people whose wages are already so low that the wage deduction from their assessment will leave them no compensation at all (Bodnar, 1999).

The previous arguments apply to adolescents working in legal conditions. The tragedy of adolescent health and labour, however, is most apparent in the research on hidden work, primarily youth working in illegal conditions. The employment of children and youth under illegal conditions is becoming increasingly common in Canada and the United States (Basran, Gill & MacLean, 1995). This trend is undoubtedly tied to increasing rates of poverty amongst children and the increasing exploitation of immigrant labour (ILO, 2004; Human Rights Watch, 2000; Landrigan & Belville, 1993). In the United States, at least 70 percent of work related injuries occur to children and youth who are employed illegally, and their rate of injury is 10 times higher than that for children and youth employed legally. For example, in 1993, 1,500 sweat shops in the garment industry in New York City employed children between the ages of 8 and 18, where these children were exposed to "unguarded machinery, no fire exits, boilers, wiring problems, egress problems, machines too close together" (Holloway, 1993, p. 16).

The most innocuous context for illegal child and youth exploitation in North America is agriculture. In most states in the United States, agriculture is not even covered by child labour laws. In Canada, agricultural labour is covered, but the ethos of the family farm virtually dictates that child and youth labour is expected. Despite the cultural orientation toward children/youth and farm work in agriculture-based communities, the implications for children and youth are severe, deriving from both the potential for immediate accidental injury and for long-term exposure to dangerous environmental pathogens (Human Rights Watch, 2000).

On the first point, because the labour of children and youth on farms is often unpaid, or at least not part of the formal wage labour system, accidents largely go unreported unless they are either fatal or extremely severe. Nonetheless, the existing evidence suggests that Canada has one of the highest accident mortality rates in the industrialized world; in agriculture-based provinces like Saskatchewan, accidental death and injury rates for children and youth are inordinately high (Marlenga, Pickett & Berg, 2001; Glor, 1989). On the second point, the work of Basran, Gill, and MacLean (1995) is most important. The researchers surveyed Indo-Canadian migrant farm workers in the Fraser Valley in British Columbia. One of the central concerns of the study was to determine the exposure to agricultural chemicals amongst workers and their children. Approximately 50 percent of the immigrant farm workers reported bringing children with them to the fields, primarily as a consequence of a lack of daycare facilities. Like the adults, the children were exposed to pesticides and herbicides, primarily from next-day contact with treated plants and soil rather than from direct spray contact. The workers, while reluctant to report on the health effects on their own children, indicated a considerable and alarming effect on the children of other workers, to the extent that only 9 percent of all the workers surveyed suggested that children's ill-health was not related to pesticide/herbicide exposure. The authors concluded that:

> children in Surrey are being exposed to health risks, the implications of which may be quite severe, simply because there is a poverty of childcare resources in Surrey and there are simply no other options for the families of these children. (Basran, Gill & MacLean, 1995, p. 87)

STREET KIDS: THROWAWAY ADOLESCENTS

One of the central arguments in this chapter is that poverty disposes youth to relatively high health risk. In the introduction, I illustrated the connections between poverty and certain illnesses. In the two subsequent sections, I showed how both substance abuse and low-end work are related to the associations between poverty and ill health. In this section, I wish to show how living on the margins of society dramatically endangers the health of society's most marginalized youth. Schissel and Fedec (1999) conducted a study of street youth by examining the YOA files of young offenders. A subset of these data was based on young offenders who had been charged for being involved in the sex trade. The adolescents in question were primarily street youth in the City of Saskatoon; they constituted a cross section of youth who had been convicted under the Young

Offenders Act, and who were involved in the sex trade in the inner city. The following figure compares the health jeopardy for street youth involved in prostitution to young offenders who were not involved in the sex trade. As most of the literature on youth and street life suggests, prostitution is engaged in because of economic need, and the youth involved represent the most marginalized adolescents in society.

Figure 16.10 illustrates the extreme jeopardy that street youth face, especially in the context of life in the sex trade.

The two most important phenomena in this figure are the astonishing increase in health risk for youth involved in the sex trade and the absolute levels of health risk for both groups of youth. For example, 41.7 percent of female youth involved in the sex trade have been pregnant. Pregnancy not only poses a health risk for street youth as mothers it also places the fetus at risk; further, pregnancy is itself an indicator of high-risk sexual activity. This subgroup of street youth is obviously engaging in unprotected sex: "Unprotected sex is a valuable commodity in the sex trade and the highest profits are obtained from the prostitution of young girls who are willing to engage in unprotected sex" (Schissel & Fedec, 1999, p. 38). Female street youth not only run the risk of pregnancy, they are also exposed to sexually transmitted diseases and run rather extremes risks of transmitting HIV/AIDS.

Substance abuse poses an immediate risk for all youth, but is especially threatening for marginal youth. For example, of those who indicated "no involvement" in prostitution, 42 percent use drugs and alcohol and 20 percent suffer severe alcohol abuse. For youth in the sex trade, the figure increased dramatically to more than 80 percent using drugs and alcohol, and over 40 percent with severe alcohol problems. For those who are living dangerous and unpleasant lives, substance abuse may be the only reasonable form for normalizing an otherwise intolerable life situation. This is further evidenced by the self-injury indicators. Ten percent of the "no involvement" youth have severe suicidal tendencies, and over 10 percent have attempted suicide. For "involvement" youth, approximately 25 percent have severe suicidal tendencies and 25 percent have attempted suicide. Finally, while a small percentage of all youth in the study has engaged

FIGURE 16.10

Health Risks for Young Offenders, by Extent of Involvement in the Sex Trade: Saskatoon, 1996

Source: Based on Schissel and Fedec (1999), p. 48.

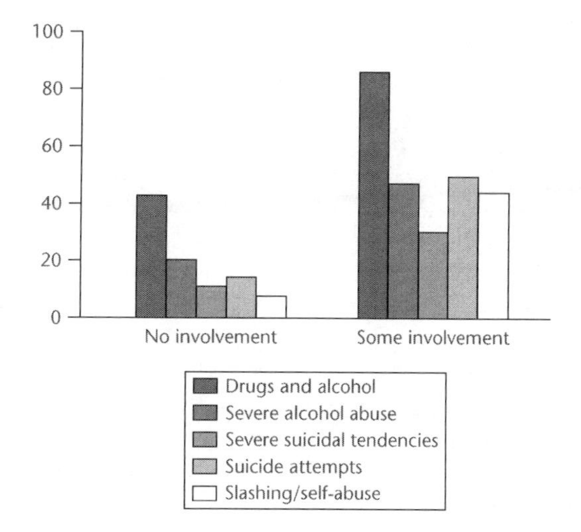

in slashing, over 40 percent of the youth in the sex trade have engaged in this form of self-abuse. The phenomenon of slashing is important in understanding the trauma of marginality. The research on slashing has argued that it is a form of emotion-masking behaviour typical of people who are in extremely traumatic life situations – exemplified by the high rates of slashing amongst women prisoners (Boritch, 2003). The alarmingly high rates of slashing amongst youth prostitutes display quite clearly the extreme psychic trauma under which they live. That even a small percentage of all the youth in this study engage in slashing is indicative of the marginal and traumatic nature of life for many young offenders. The expectation would be that slashing is non-existent in a psychically and socially healthy adolescent population.

It is clear from these data that young offenders, as typically marginal youth, are exposed to rather severe medical trauma. The risks run from substance abuse, to self-injury, to **high-risk sexuality**. For the most marginal in the society, the inner city street kid who sells herself to survive, the medical jeopardy is most startling.

I wish to illustrate further the pathology of economic and social marginality for adolescents by focusing on the social and cultural genocide that First Nations people in Canada have experienced. This protracted genocide has resulted in extreme physical and emotional jeopardy for Aboriginal youth. On January 26, 1993, six Inuit youth in Davis Inlet, Labrador, tried to commit suicide together by sniffing gasoline. Their attempt at collective death was thwarted by an addictions counselor who heard the youth declare that they wanted to die. Subsequently, fourteen youth from this small community were airlifted south for medical treatment, but the legacy of colonialization and governmental neglect remained. Ninety-five percent of the adult population of Davis Inlet was addicted to alcohol, 10 percent of the children and youth were chronic gasoline sniffers, and 25 percent of the adults had attempted suicide. Seven years later, the trauma for Davis Inlet had grown. In November of 2000, twenty Innu children were, again, airlifted to the Goose Bay treatment centre as an interim reaction to another epidemic of gas sniffing among the children. Of the 169 children (ages 10–19) living in Davis Inlet at the end of 2000, 154 have attempted gas sniffing and seventy of them are chronic sniffers. Davis Inlet is typical of Aboriginal communities in Canada that have been historically exploited, and social and economically neglected.

In his compelling book *The Dispossessed*, Geoffrey York documents how, in a matter of thirty years, Aboriginal communities in Canada went from suffering from virtually no pathologies to levels of self-damage equivalent to those in Davis Inlet. His historical argument is an indictment of economic exploitation and community disruption in Canada's Aboriginal communities; he describes how feelings of hopelessness and despair, coupled with the omnipresence of development, have lead to what could easily be considered a type of protracted collective suicide amongst Northern Aboriginal youth. The Shamattawa Crees in Northeastern Manitoba were relocated onto reserves in the 1940s, and the associated trauma and cultural dislocation are described in a contemporary community scenario which York describes as the rule and not the exception:

> Gasoline is the lifeblood of Shamattawa. It is the lifeblood of any northern Indian reserve. Without it, the Cree cannot run their skidoos or their motorboats. Without these vehicles, they cannot collect firewood to heat their homes, nor can they hunt or fish or trap to supplement their social assistance cheques.

> But Gasoline is the deadliest poison at Shamattawa. Children and teenagers sniff to gain a quick escape, a cheap and immediate high – a few minutes of euphoria in a land of poverty and misery. Their attraction to gasoline becomes irresistible. The children of Shamattawa teach each other how to inhale it. At night, they break into snowmobile gas-tanks to steal more of the precious substance, until if finally dominates their existence....Medical experts have concluded that gasoline sniffing is one of the most dangerous addictions in the world...a single inhalation can hook a child....Gasoline sniffers often become convinced that they are invincible....Once inhaled, gasoline harms the kidneys and liver, and inflicts permanent damage on the nervous system and the brain. (York, 1992, pp. 8–9)

It is clear from York's vivid description that when a people are shunted off to the margins of the society, either through socio-political neglect or through flagrant economic exploitation, the damages are extreme and filter down most dramatically to children and youth. Whether it is life on an inner city street or life in a socio-economically damaged Northern Aboriginal community, the reality is that children and youth are at extreme jeopardy and their physical and emotional sufferings follow them to adulthood. A growing body of work on the long-term damages of sexual and physical exploitation of Aboriginal children in residential schools, for example, indicates quite clearly how physical and mental injury to children and youth results in future generations of wounded and impaired adults (Quewezance & Schissel, W., 2003; Miller, 1996).

CONCLUSION

The health of children and youth in Canada can be framed within the context of certain indisputable truths. Firstly, while the United Nations has recently declared Canada to be the best country in the world in which to live, they chastised Canada for its deplorable record on child and youth poverty and for creating and sustaining Third-World conditions for Aboriginal peoples. Secondly, in 1996 UNICEF reported that Canada's teenage suicide rate is alarmingly high compared with other industrial countries. From 1979–91, suicides by young people 15–19 doubled to 13.5 percent per 100,000, ranking Canada third behind New Zealand and Finland. In 2000, suicide was the third leading cause of death amongst 15–24 year olds, and the third leading cause of death for children ages 10–14 (Miniño et al., 2002). Further, the risk factors for suicide most often are those associated with political and economic exploitation and marginality: low family income, low education, losses due to divorce, family relocation, unemployment, loss of cultural and personal identity, and social isolation. Lastly, Canada's child and youth poverty rate is second highest in the industrialized world, next to the United States, and the problem is greatest for single mothers, over 50 percent of whom live below the poverty line. The Canadian Council on Social Development in 1998 cited the highlights of their study on youth and child poverty; they concluded that child and youth poverty rates are rising, the gap between the rich and the poor is widening, and poor children and youth have fewer opportunities than before.

In light of the foregoing, we need to inquire how a country as relatively affluent as Canada arrives at a point at which children and youth are *de facto* disregarded. The problem can best be characterized as ill regard rather than disregard, which is indicated by public demands to get tougher on youth crime, to make youth more accountable in school, and, in the interests of fiscal prudence, to implement work for welfare programs in many jurisdictions. This condemnation of youth is found in most media forms and is consistent, condemning, and mostly unfounded (Schissel, 2006). We must look no further, I believe, than the way our society is structured. For the most part, Canada's success, both internationally and internally, is based on a responsible balance of payments, low interest and inflation rates, a decreasing deficit, and a healthy dollar. None of these indicators have anything to do with the real health of the society and its people. Economic growth and vitality is an adult concern in a democratic, adult-based political economy. Children and youth do not vote; they are literally and figuratively disenfranchised from all levels of democratic input. And, yet, as consumers of adult-produced goods – both legal and illicit – they comprise a fertile market. Further, as cogs in the wheels of industry, they are an easily exploited reserve army of labour, and at the extreme, are treated as the hottest commodities for sexual exploitation on the street and in residential schools. Children and youth do not count until they are needed. They, as the United Nations has implied, are not a part of Canada's political and economic society, despite our collective but seemingly empty rhetoric that they are our most valuable resource.

STUDY QUESTIONS

1. *Smoking is a considerable and increasing health risk for female youth. Why is this so, in light of growing public concern about smoking as a major health problem?*
2. *Why do relatively poor youth tend to experience certain weight-related problems and wealthier youth experience others? What explains the persistent relationships between socio-economic status and weight-related health problems among youth?*
3. *The popular perception is that athletics are very beneficial for children and youths because they contribute to both physical and emotional well-being. In this chapter, however, there is evidence that organized athletics may constitute a threat to the well-being of male and female youth. Explain the "pathology of athletics" and how adults may be held responsible for it.*
4. *Why is the basic human right to "work in a safe and secure environment" so easily and readily violated in terms of the employment of children and youth?*
5. *Many of the damaging things that happen to children and youth seem to be the result of an economic-corporate and political world engaging in "business as usual." Explain how this happens.*
6. *In an ethical world, health status should have nothing to do with the amount of wealth a person has. And, yet, socio-economic status is often related to the health and well-being of children and youth. How does one make sense of this rather obvious social injustice?*

GLOSSARY

ADHD Attention-deficit/hyperactivity disorder is a controversial condition of childhood that, in medical terms, is a developmental disorder characterized by persistent inattention and/or hyperactivity, often related to and diagnosed in the context of classroom conduct.

amenorrhea a delay in the onset of menstruation due, in part, to obsessive weight control in young women, especially in the context of organized athletics.

anorexia nervosa an eating disorder characterized by extreme weight loss and a pathological fear of becoming fat.

beauty norms the standards by which women and girls are judged on the basis of stereotypical images of thinness, youth, and beauty.

bulimia an eating disorder characterized by binge eating and then purging by either vomiting or by laxative use.

commodified looked upon by greater society in terms of economic value. Youth may be seen either as assets or liabilities, or as consumers, labourers, or sexual commodities, and exploited as such by the labour market, politics, the marketplace, and the sex trade market.

creatine an amino-acid-based compound that occurs naturally in the body but is produced artificially and used to enhance muscle growth and repair.

high-risk sexuality a general reference to sexual conduct characterized by a lack of safe-sex practices, including sexual relations with unknown partners.

pathology of body image the obsession with body image (staying thin, young-looking, athletic, and sexually attractive), which creates the conditions under which many people, especially youth, engage in self-injurious behaviour while attempting to attain the ideal body image.

slashing the phenomenon of self-injury usually occurring as a result of knife or razor blade wounds that, in many cases, are attempts to mask the trauma of living in adverse life situations, such as being in jail or "on the street."

weight-loss workouts in weight-class sports, exercise done to reduce body weight to acceptable levels. Engaged in by young male athletes in an attempt to lose weight through dehydration; accomplished by exercising in extreme conditions that generate excessive perspiration.

REFERENCES

Abernathy, T.J., Webster, G., & Vermeulen, M. (2002). Relationship between poverty and health among adolescents. *Adolescence, 37*(145), 55–67.

Anderson, J.M. (1999). The female athlete triad: Disordered eating, amenorrhea, and osteoporosis. *Connecticut Medicine, 11*(6), 647–652.

Bahrke, M.S., Yesalis, C.E., Kopstein, A.N., & Stephens, J.A. (2000). Risk factors associated with anabolic-androgenic ateroid use among adolescents. *Sports Medicine, 6*(1), 397–405.

Basran, G., Gill, C., & MacLean, B. (1995). *Farmworkers and their children.* Vancouver: The Collective Press.

Beaulne, G. (1997). *For the safety of Canadian children and youth: From injury data to preventative measures.* Ottawa: Health Canada.

Bigelow, B. (2000). Is your child too young for youth sports or is your adult too old? In J. Gerdy (Ed), *Sports in schools: The future of an institution.* New York: Teacher's College Press.

Bodnar, C. (1999, March 5). Students may hurt from new workers' comp bill. *Fulcrum Online.*

Bordo, S. (2004). *Unbearable weight: Western culture and the body.* Berkeley: University of California Press.

Boritch, H. (2003). Women in prison in Canada. In B. Schissel & C. Brooks (Eds.), *Marginality and condemnation: An introduction to critical criminology* (pp. 309–328). Halifax: Fernwood.

Breggin, P.R. (2001). *Talking back to Ritalin, revised.* Cambridge, MA: Perseus.

Breggin, P.R. (2002). *The Ritalin fact book: What your doctor won't tell you.* Cambridge, MA: Perseus.

Brownell, M.D., & Yogendran, M.S. (2001). Attention-deficit hyperactivity disorder in Manitoba children: Medical diagnosis and psychostimulant treatment rates. *Canadian Journal of* Psychiatry, 46, 264–272.

Cafri, G., van den Berg, P., & Thompson, J.K. (2006). Pursuit of muscularity in adolescent boys: Relations among biopsychological variables and clinical outcomes. *Journal of Clinical Child and Adolescent Psychology, 35*(2), 283–291.

Calfee, R., & Fadale, P. (2006). Popular ergogenic drugs and supplements in young athletes. *Pediatrics, 117*(3), 577–589.

Canadian Institute of Child Health. (1998). *The air children breathe: The effects on their health.* Ottawa: Pollution Probe and the Canadian Institute of Child Health.

Canadian Institute of Child Health. (2000). *The health of Canada's children: A CICH profile* (3rd ed.). Ottawa: Canadian Institute of Child Health.

Canadian Institute of Health Information. (2005). *Improving the health of Canadians: Canadian population health initiative.* Ottawa: Canadian Institute for Health Information.

Cassels, A. (2003). Manufacturing patients. *Ideas,* hosted by Paul Kennedy. Toronto: CBC Radio. Transcript available from ideast@toronto.cbc.ca.

Centre for Addiction and Mental Health. (1999). *Canadian profile: Alcohol, tobacco and other drugs.* Ottawa: Canadian Centre for Substance Abuse.

Chisholm, P. (1996, March 11). The ADD dilemma. *Macleans, 11,* 42–44.

Clark, Michael. (2000). Who's coaching the coaches? In J. Gerdy (Ed.), *Sports in schools: The future of an institution.* New York: Teachers' College Press.

Clarke, W.R., & Lauer, L.R. (1993). Does childhood obesity track into adulthood? *Critical Review of Food Science and Nutrition, 33,* 423–430.

Constantini, N.W. (1994). Clinical consequences of athletic Amenorrhea. *Sports Medicine, 17,* 213–223.

Crater. D., Heise, S., Perzanowski, M., Herbert, R., Morse, C., Hulsey, T., & Platts-Mills, T. (2001). Asthma hospitalization trends in Charleston, South Carolina, 1956–1997: Twenty-fold increase among black children during a 30-year period. *Pediatrics, 108*(6), 97.

Crisp A, Sedgwick, P., Halek, C., Joughin, N., & Humphrey, H. (1999). Why may teenage girls persist in smoking? *Journal of Adolescence, 22*(5), 657–672.

Diller, L. (1998). *Running on Ritalin: A physician reflects on children, society, and performance in a pill.* New York: Bantam Books.

DiPietro, L., & Stachenfeld, N. (1997). The female athlete triad. *Medicine and Science in Sports and Exercise, 29,*1669–1671.

Dolan, B. (1991). Cross-cultural aspects of anorexia nervosa and bulimia: A review. *International Journal of Eating Disorders, 10,* 67–68.

Dunn, K., & Runyan, C. (1993). Deaths at work among children and adolescents. *American Journal of Diseases in Children, 147,* 1044–1047.

Eliot, D., & Goldberg, L. (1996). Intervention and prevention of steroid use in adolescents. *American Journal of Sports Medicine, 24*(6), S46-S47.

Field, A.E., Austin, S.B., Camargo Jr., C.A., Taylor, C.B., Striegel-Moore, R.H., Loud, K.J., & Colditz, C.A. (2005). Exposure to the mass media, body shape concerns, and use of supplements to improve weight and shape among male and female adolescents. *Pediatrics, 16*(2), 214–220.

Findlay, D. (1996). The body perfect: Appearance norms, medical control, and women. In B. Schissel & L. Mahood (Eds.), *Social Control in Canada: Issues in the Social Construction of Deviance* (pp. 174–200). Don Mills, ON: Oxford University Press.

Fogelholm, M., Lichtenbelt, W., Ottenheijm, R., & Westerterp, K. (1996). Amenorrhea in ballet dancers in the Netherlands. *Medicine and Science in Sports and Exercise, 28*, 545–550.

Foucault, M. (1980). *The history of sexuality: Volume 1: An introduction.* New York: Vintage Books.

Garfinkel, P., Lin, E., Georing, P., Spegg, C., Goldbloom, D., Kennedy, S., Kaplan, A., & Woodside, D.B. (1995). Bulimia nervosa in a Canadian community sample: Prevalence and comparison of subgroups. *American Journal of Psychiatry, 152*, 1052–1058.

Glor, E. (1989). A survey of comprehensive accident and injury experience of high school students in Saskatchewan. *Canadian Journal of Public Health, 80*, 435–440.

Gracey, M. (2002). Child health in an urbanizing world. *Acta Paediatrica, 91*(1), 1–8.

Greaves, L. (1996). *Smoke screen: Women's smoking and social control.* Halifax: Fernwood.

Greenberg, M.T. (2001). The prevention of mental disorders in school-aged children: Current state of the field. *Prevention and Treatment, 4*(1), Article A.

Groesz, L.M., Levine, M.P., & Murnen, S.K. (2002). The effect of experimental presentation of thin media images on body satisfaction: Meta-analytic review. *International Journal of Eating Disorders, 31*(1), 1–16.

Hagan, J., & McCarthy, B. (1998). *Mean streets: Youth crime and homelessness.* Cambridge: Cambridge University Press.

Health Canada. (2000). *Youth smoking in Canada.* Ottawa: Canadian Tobacco Use Monitoring Survey.

Holloway, M. (1993). Hard times: Occupational injuries among children are increasing. *Scientific American, 269*, 14–16.

Hotton T., & Haans, D. (2004). Alcohol and drug use in early adolescence. *Health Reports, 15*(3), 9–19.

Human Rights Watch (HRW). (2000). *Fingers to the bone: United States failure to protect child farmworkers.* New York: Human Rights Watch.

International Labour Organization. (2002). *A Future without child labour.* Geneva: International Labour Office.

International Obesity Task Force. (2006). *Overweight and obesity.* Atlanta, GA: Center for Disease Control. Retrieved on June 15, 2006 from http://www.iotf.org/popout.asp?linkto=http://www.cdc.gov/nccdphp/dnpa/obesity/.

Johnson-Down, L., O'Loughlin, J., Koski, K., & Gray-Donald, K. (1997). High prevalence of obesity in low income and multiethnic schoolchildren: A diet and physical activity assessment. *Journal of Nutrition, 127*(12), 2310–2315.

Jones, J.M., Bennett, S., Olmsted, M.P., Lawson, M.L., & Gary, R. (2002). Disordered eating attitudes and behaviours in teenaged girls: A school-based study. *Canadian Medical Association Journal, 165*(5), 547–552.

Keyes. L.M., & Goodman, S.H. (2006). *Women and depression: A handbook for the social, behavioral and biomedical sciences.* New York: Cambridge University Press.

Kutcher, S. et al. (1996). Mental health concerns of Canadian adolescents: A consumer's perspective. *Canadian Journal of Psychiatry, 41*, 5–10.

LaGrange, T.C., & Silverman, R. (1999). Low self-control and opportunity: Testing the general theory of crime as an explanation for gender differences in delinquency. *Criminology, 37*, 45–91.

Landrigan, P., & Belville, R. (1993). The dangers of illegal child labor. *American Journal of Diseases in Children, 147*, 1029–1030.

Lavalette, M. (2000). Child employment in a capitalist labour market: The British case. In Bernard Schlemmer (Ed.), *The exploited child* (pp. 214–230). London: Zed Books.

Lavalette, M., & Cunningham, S. (2004). Globalization and child labour: Protection, liberation, or anti-capitalism? In R. Munck (Ed.), *Labour and globalisation: Results and prospects*. (pp. 181–205) Liverpool: Liverpool University Press.

LeBlanc, C.M. (2003). The growing epidemic of child and youth obesity: Another twist? *Canadian Journal of Public Health, 94*(5), 329–331.

Litsky, F. (1997, December 19). Collegiate wrestling deaths raise fears about training. *New York Times*, C7.

Livingston, K. (1997, Spring). Ritalin: Miracle drug or cop-out? *The Public Interest*, 3–18.

Males, M. (1996). *The scapegoat generation: America's war on adolescents*. Monroe, ME: Common Courage Press.

Males, M. (2000). *Framing youth: Ten myths about the next generation*. Monroe, ME: Common Courage Press.

Marlenga, B., Pickett, W., & Berg, R.L. (2001). Agricultural work activities reported for children and youth on 498 North American farms. *Journal of Agricultural Safety and Health, 7*(4), 241–252.

McCreary Centre Society. (1994). *Adolescent health survey: Street youth in Vancouver*. Burnaby, BC: McCreary Centre Society.

McIntyre, L., Walsh, G., & Connor, S. (2001). *A follow-up study of child hunger in Canada*. Ottawa: Human Resources Development Canada.

Melia, P., Pipe, A., & Greenberg, G. (1996). The use of anabolic-androgenic steroids by Canadian students. *Clinical Journal of Sport Medicine, 6*(1), 9–14.

Miller, J.R. (1996). *Shingwauk's vision: A history of Native residential schools*. Toronto: University of Toronto Press.

Miniño, A.M., Arias, E., Kochanek, K.D., Murphy, S.L., & Smith, B.L. (2002). Death: Final data for 2000. *National Vital Statistics Reports, 50*(15). Hyattsville, MD: National Center for Health Statistics.

Morbidity and Mortality Weekly Report. (1996, August). Asthma mortality and hospitalization among children and young adults – United States, 1980–1993. *American Family Physician, 54*, 777.

Moser, D. (1994, December 15). Eating disorders in sports. *Regina Leader Post*, A3.

Mosley, B. (1997). Striking the balance. *Women's Sport and Fitness, 19*, 29.

Mustard, C.A., & Roos, N.P. (1994). The relationship of prenatal care and pregnancy complications to birthweight in Winnipeg, Canada. *American Journal of Public Health, 84*(9), 1450–1457.

Muszynski, A. (1994). Gender inequality and life chances: Women's lives and health. In B.S. Bolaria & R. Bolaria (Eds.), *Women, medicine, and health* (pp. 57–72). Halifax: Fernwood.

Nasser, M. (1988). Culture and weight consciousness. *Journal of Psychosomatic Research, 32*, 73–77.

Newacheck, P., Hung, Y.H., Park, M.J., Brindis, C., & Irwin, Jr., C. (2003). Disparities in adolescent health and health care: Does socio-economic status matter? *Health Services Research, 38*(5), 1235–1252.

Nichols, M. (1999, January 11). The obesity epidemic. *Macleans* (pp. 54).

Northcott, H.C. (1991). Health status and health care in Canada: Contemporary issues. In B.S. Bolaria (Ed.), *Social issues and contradictions in Canadian society* (pp. 178–195). Toronto: Harcourt Brace Jovanovich.

Oen, K., Fast, M., & Postl, B. (1995). Epidemiology of juvenile Rheumatoid Arthritis in Manitoba, Canada. 1975–1992: Cycles in incidence. *Journal of Rheumatology, 22*(4), 745–750.

Offord, D.R. et al. (1989) Ontario child health study: Summary of selected results. *Canadian Journal of Psychiatry, 43*, 483–491.

Parks, P., & Read, M. (1997). Adolescent male athletes: Body image, diet, and exercise. *Adolescence, 32*(127), 593–602.

Parker, D.L. (1997). *Stolen dreams: Portraits of working children*. Minneapolis: Lerner Publications.

Popper, C.W. (2002). Child and adolescent psychopharmacology at the turn of the millennium. In S. Kutcher (Ed.), *Practical child and adolescent psychopharmacology* (pp. 1–37). Cambridge: Cambridge University Press.

Quewezance, H., & Schissel, W. (2003). Damaged children and broken spirits: A residential school survivor's story. In B. Schissel & C. Brooks (Eds.), *Marginality and condemnation: An introduction to critical criminology* (pp. 175–192). Halifax: Fernwood.

Rainwater, L., & Smeeding, T.M. (2003). *Poor kids in a rich country: America's children in comparative perspective*. New York: Russell Sage Foundation.

Reiter, E. (1996). *Making fast food: From the frying pan into the fryer*. Montreal: McGill University Press.

Rees, A. (1998, June 30). Ritalin 25: North Okanagan hot pot. *Vancouver Province* (pp. A6).

Saul, J.M. (2003). *Feminism: Issues and arguments*. Oxford: Oxford University Press.

Schissel, B. (1995). Degradation, social deprivation and violence: Health risks for women prisoners. In B.S. Bolaria & R. Bolaria (Eds.), *Women, minorities and health* (pp. 287–300). Halifax: Fernwood.

Schissel, B. (1997). *Blaming children: Youth crime, moral panics, and the politics of hate*. Halifax: Fernwood.

Schissel, B. (2006). *Still blaming children: Youth conduct and the politics of hate*. Halifax: Fernwood.

Schissel, B., & Fedec, K. (1999). The selling of innocence: The gestalt of danger in the lives of youth prostitutes. *Canadian Journal of Criminology, 41*(1), 33–56.

Schlosser, E. (2002). *Fast food nation: The dark side of the all-American meal*. New York: Harper Perennial.

Schnirring, L. (1998a). Androstenedione et al: Nonprescription steroids. *The Physician and SportsMedicine, 26*(11), 15–18.

Schnirring, L. (1998b). Creatine supplements face scrutiny: Will users pay later? *The Physician and Sportsmedicine, 26*(6), 15–23.

Senthilselvan, A. (1998). Prevalence of physician-diagnosed Asthma in Saskatchewan, 1981–1990. *Chest, 114*(2), 388–92.

Shin, L. (1999, May 31). Fiji TV: Wrong images? *Newsweek* (pp. 70).

Shorter, E. (1994). *From the mind into the body: The cultural origins of psychosomatic symptoms*. New York: The Free Press.

Showalter, E. (1997). *Hystories: Hysterical epidemics and modern media*. New York: Columbia University Press.

Snell, C. (2005). *Peddling poison: The tobacco industry and kids*. Westport, CT: Praeger.

Starfield, B. et al. (2002). Social class gradients in health during adolescence. *Journal of Epidemiology and Community Health, 56*(5), 354–361.
Statistics Canada. (1998). *National population health survey, 1996–1997.* Ottawa: Minister of Industry.
Statistics Canada. (2003). *Health indicators* (1). Catalogue No. 82221XIE.
Sundgot-Borgen, J. (1994). Risk and trigger factors for the development of eating disorders in female elite athletes. *Medicine and Science in Sports and Exercise, 26*, 414–419.
Sundgot-Borgen, J., & Torsfveit, M.K. (2004). Prevalence of eating disorders in elite athletes is higher than in the general population. *Clinical Journal of Sport Medicine, 14*(1), 25–32.
Trifunov, D. (1999, July 13), Dead worker's family not interested in blame. *Saskatoon Star Phoenix*, A13.
Triggle, D. (2005). Vaccines, Viagra, and Vioxx: Medicines, markets, and money – when life-saving meets life-style. *Drug Development Research, 64*, 90–98.
Trypuc, J.M. (1994), Gender based mortality and morbidity patterns and health risk. In B.S. Bolaria & R. Bolaria (Eds.), *Women, medicine and health* (pp. 73–88). Halifax: Fernwood.
United States Department of Justice. (2005). *Ritalin – DEA evaluation.* Dallas, TX: Greater Dallas Council on Alcohol and Drug Abuse. Retrieved on May 19th, 2007 from http://www.gdcada.org/statistics/ritalin/dea.htm.
Virani, A. (2004). Anti-depressants and the risk of suicide in children and adolescents: What's the link? *Child and Adolescent Psychopharmacology, 9*(4), 1–6.
Votta, E., & Manion, I. (2004). Suicide, high-risk behaviors, and coping style in homeless adolescent ales. *The Journal of Adolescent Health, 34*(3), 237–243.
Webber, M. (1992). *Street kids: The tragedy of Canada's runaways.* Toronto: University of Toronto Press.
Wolf, N. (1990). *The beauty myth.* Toronto: Vintage Books.
Woo, P., & Wedderburn, L.R. (1998). Juvenile chronic arthritis. *The Lancet, 351*, 969–73.
Yip, R., Scanlon, K., & Trowbridge, F. (1993). Trends and patterns in height and weight of low-income U.S. children. *Critical Review of Food Science and Nutrition, 33*, 409–421.
York, G. (1992). *The dispossessed: Life and death in Native Canada.* Toronto: Little Brown and Company.

17

WELL-BEING AT MID-LIFE: DETERMINANTS OF PREVENTIVE HEALTH

LYNN M. MEADOWS University of Calgary

INTRODUCTION

Preventive health has the powerful potential to reduce health care costs and delay or prevent the onset of established chronic disease. At mid-life, there are a multitude of measures that can be taken, both by health care professionals and laypeople, that can make a difference to the health and well-being of those in mid-life. In order for this potential to be realized, a broad determinants of health perspective is needed to situate efforts aimed at prevention and well-being in the context of people's day-to-day lives.

Mid-life is often seen as a time of transition, opportunity, and challenge. For some, it is also a time of "heightened reevaluation and reorientation" (Klohnen, Vandewater & Young, 1996, p. 431). Those reevaluations and reorientations may involve turning points that are aimed at making the most of the second half of lives. While individuals have some agency in their decisions and actions, well-being is also influenced by the mechanisms through which the determinants of health influence ongoing health. In considering health at mid-life, a broad rather than a narrow view on health and well-being is preferable.

There is no single biological marker or life event that thrusts one into middle age. While definitions vary in the literature, for the purposes of this chapter, mid-life will be defined as between 40 and 65 years of age. Literature on health and mid-life is generally focused on the beginning of bodily "decline," when hormone levels drop, physiological functions begin to fail, mental acuity wanes, and the resulting inevitable deterioration of health occurs for both men and women (Boul, 2003; Green, Thompson & Griffiths, 2002; Lachman, 2004; O'Brien & Edwards, 2002).

From a demographic perspective, mid-life is a time when those having children have usually had them, or are either planning or hoping to have them soon. Parents of people in mid-life are aging, or may have passed away. Career transitions or beginnings can occur at mid-life, and for others, retirement and post-retirement decisions are being considered. Medically, both women and men are more susceptible to disease related to aging, family history, and cumulative exposure to risk factors.

In a chapter in the third edition of this text, Dickinson and Kosteniuk (2002) presented information about the leading causes of death in Canada and various factors that either contribute to well-being or are detriments to realizing well-being. Information that summarizes the epidemiological view of morbidity and mortality, although applied to slightly different age groups than the one considered here, generally highlights causes of death from malignant cancers, diseases of the circulatory system, accidents and adverse events, and "all other causes" as the underlying causes of mortality at mid-life. Morbidity at ages 45–64 is attributed to a number of high profile diseases, such as heart disease, diabetes, obesity, stroke, the beginnings of osteoporosis and arthritis, and the omnipotent cancers associated with reproduction such as breast, ovarian, and prostate.

In this chapter, however, a different perspective is taken. Using a combination of social determinants of health and **population health promotion** approaches, the seemingly more mundane and often taken for granted factors that contribute to health and well-being in our daily lives at mid-life are examined. A typical disease-based biomedical model is aimed at identifying diseases, discovering their underlying etiology, and then treating and hopefully curing the disease. Here we discuss the complex contexts of well-being and health, focusing on the determinants of health that affect our well-being throughout our lives. Their interactions spin a web that influences health beginning before we are born, and maybe the degree of well-being at mid-life. Understanding the environments in which agency and structure combine to affect health related outcomes requires a willingness to explore well-being as a multifaceted entity, one that is physical, emotional, spiritual, and mental. To better understand well-being at mid-life requires consideration of the broad range of health determinants – from bench to bedside to backyard, planning to policy to prevention, all within the societal contexts in which we live our lives.

This chapter begins with background information that frames the context in which mid-life and well-being are discussed. In this section, brief summaries of the social determinants of health, population health, the lifecourse, life choices, and life chances are presented. This is followed by material that explores prevention and preventive health at mid-life, through a bio-medical lens and in our everyday lives, including through turning points. References and examples from research are presented throughout.

FRAMING THE CONTEXT OF MID-LIFE HEALTH AND WELL-BEING

The Social Determinants of Health

In contrast to a disease oriented examination of health and well-being, the twelve factors currently listed as determinants of health (Public Health Agency of Canada, 2003) will be the focus of this discussion. These health determinants are:

- Gender
- Culture
- Income and social status
- Healthy child development
- Biology and genetic endowment
- Physical environment
- Employment and work conditions

- Personal health practices and coping skills
- Education
- Health services
- Social support networks
- Social environments

Although we have gained important insight into the meaning and correlates of health from past research, there continues to be a need for a greater understanding of the processes through which people seek and attain health and well-being, and the contexts in which health and well-being occur. Mid-life is a time at which the range of determinants of health whose effects may cumulate over time may affect one's well-being. For example, early exposure to environmental toxins, both chemical and emotional, may manifest themselves through cardiac disease or immune system related disease (Corin, 1994). At a social level, risk associated with stresses related to employment, balancing demands of busy lives, migration, and limited resources can negatively affect well-being on a day-to-day basis.

Population Health

A population-based approach to health requires an ecological lens and an understanding that the world comprises complex systems (Green, Richard & Potvin, 1996; Robertson, 1998). Context, locality, and health are intertwined to affect the health of populations (Robertson, 1998; Frohlich & Potvin, 1999a; Frohlich, Potvin, Chabot & Corin, 1999b; Frohlich, 2000; Frohlich, Corin & Potvin, 2001): "A broad population health perspective requires us to examine with a critical eye...the conditions of life and work that damage the health of our communities" (Frank, 1995, p. 164). A population health approach focuses on the entire population and recognizes the importance of investigating the health disparities in populations (Robertson, 1998; Frohlich et al., 1999a; Frohlich et al., 1999b; Frohlich, 2000; Frohlich et al., 2001; Health Canada, 2005). Population health recognizes that health is influenced by factors from social systems to individuals. This approach also supports upstream investment in health (e.g., at a preventive level), bases decisions on evidence, and sees citizens as part of the process (Vollman, Anderson & McFarlane, 2004a).

Lifecourse as an Approach to Aging

"Lifecourse" is a sociological term that is used to describe life stages in social and cultural contexts (Backett & Davison, 1995). A lifecourse approach acknowledges the fluidity of the interaction between people and their environment, and the social and cultural contexts of biological change (Backett & Davison, 1995; Cummings & Melton, 2002; Melton, III, 2000). There is a tendency for professionals (e.g., health care providers) and people in their everyday lives (i.e., laypeople) to place "emphasis on the existence of a set of structurally defined, but culturally experienced life stages" (Backett & Davison, 1995, p. 629). That is, we all have ideas about what people should do, how they look, and their health, often based on past experiences or people we know. As Ballard, Elston, and Gabe (2005) and others note, aging is visible and the distinctions between the public and private sides of aging further create a dynamic among perceptions of what mid-life is, how mid-life "feels," and how mid-life looks (Howell & Beth, 2002; Ogle & Damhorst, 2005). Given that both laypeople and those professionals involved in practice, policy, and planning bring these perspectives to their work and care, making explicit how these biases affect those at mid-life is especially important.

The differences in experiences of mid-life become especially salient when one examines how different cohorts experience this life stage (Evandrou & Glaser, 2002). For instance, Hunt (2002) notes the variability in experiences in professional employment, family structure, marital status, retirement and other socio-economic variables between women born as little as twenty years apart. Without an understanding of the range of social and cultural perspectives of people in the professional and popular sectors, efforts aimed at well-being, health, and prevention will continue to be less than optimal.

Life Choices and Life Chances

In an earlier version of this text, Bolaria and Bolaria (2002) highlighted the importance of the difference between life choices and life chances. These two terms are often misused by those unfamiliar with the determinants of health and well-being, and who use the blanket term **lifestyle** to either praise or critique people whose well-being is seen as compromised by unwise choices and practices. It is not uncommon to hear politicians and others blame people's health on individuals rather than determinants of health, and to suggest that those making seemingly poor choices should have health card debits or other limits to health resources. Traditional lifestyle-based health advice focuses on a micro level and individual people, and assumes that those living an unhealthy lifestyle are doing so by choice. However, as Bolaria and Bolaria finely illustrate, lack of formal education that affects literacy, low income that forces food choices, housing and employment environments, and other factors at a structural or societal level may make what seem like "personal" choice the only choice. Bolaria and Bolaria explain that lifestyle is strongly mediated and influenced by life choices that place individuals and their agency in a context of social and structural institutions. Thus, the advice to, "Stop smoking or cut down," has a highly differential meaning to preventive health advice for someone trying to dampen hunger pangs with a mooched cigarette, and "Keep physically active by walking every day" is unthinkable to someone who earns(ed) her living, either now or in the past, on a prostitution stroll.

Bolaria and Bolaria also note that, "Life choices are shaped by life chances" (2002, p. 447). The lifecourse access to material resources and the social and cultural environments in which we live throughout our earlier years influence our health and well-being significantly at mid-life. The exhortation to "Stop being poor and if you have to be poor be so for only a short time" (Raphael, 2004a, p. 12) is only partly tongue in cheek. Strong evidence suggests that early access to nutrition, education, employment, and knowledge make a difference to health outcomes at mid-life (Evans, 1994; Raphael, 2004b). For example, those with lower education are less likely to question treatment decisions in the case of illness or disease; poor nutrition caused by the expense of purchasing fresh foods and milk in the North; the easy availability of fast food and huge portion sizes; and the growing restrictions on traditional sources of food for Inuit, First Nations, and other people who grow, hunt, or fish for their food sources mean that their choices are restricted by their (un)natural environment, as well as policy that influences food prices and access to resources.

EMPIRICAL EXAMPLES OF THE DETERMINANTS OF HEALTH AND PREVENTION

Prevention

Prevention, especially at mid-life, is as under-examined as it is complicated as a health issue. Prevention or preventive health addresses issues that may lead to chronic disease, injury, or infectious disease further downstream in the lifecourse. Primary prevention (stopping an adverse health event before it happens) strategies often begin early in life (Vollman, Anderson & McFarlane, 2004b). For example, drinking milk and other calcium-rich liquids, and eating calcium-rich foods in childhood builds strong teeth and bones, and consuming adequate amounts of calcium and doing weight bearing exercise contribute to the strength and density of bones during youth and young adulthood, and are preventive measures that can help lower the risk of developing **osteopenia** or **osteoporosis** at mid-life and beyond. At mid-life however, there are still compelling opportunities to take action for primary prevention and especially focus on secondary prevention (e.g., prevent further incidents of injury or illness, such as a second low energy fracture, or the establishment of chronic disease such as osteoporosis). Sometimes these prevention strategies are as simple as walking more, carrying groceries, or taking a vitamin supplement.

Prevention must address complicated factors such as the rhetoric regarding lifestyle and the realities of life choices as they are influenced by circumstances in which people at mid-life experience their day-to-day lives. These contextual variables are not often addressed or taken into account within the health care system, where prevention is often anchored. Arguably, these factors could be addressed both within and outside that system, but currently are not addressed at optimal levels in either.

In addition, gender, the central stratifying characteristic in our society, is often overlooked as an important determinant of health. Important gender differences and similarities that affect health are often instead treated as **gender neutral** or even **gender blind**; it would be preferable instead to examine health and wellness in the context of prevention from a lifecourse perspective and explicitly recognize cohorts that are multidimensional.

Biomedical Prevention

From a biomedical perspective, the Canadian Task Force on the Periodic Health Exam (CTFPHE) (Dubey & Glazier, 2006) has generated age-specific recommendations for preventive health during the periodic health exam (commonly known as the "annual physical"). At mid-life, these include screening for colorectal cancer (after age 49), sexually transmitted infections, cholesterol (after age 49), diabetes (after age 39), bone mineral density (if at risk), and mammography (ages 50–69 every two years) and cervical cancer (sexually active until age 69) for women. Recommendations also suggest that these patients be asked about seat belt and helmet use, personal safety from domestic violence, sun exposure, alcohol and drug use, lifestyle and nutrition, as well as smoking status (Preventive Care Checklist Form©, Dubey, Mathews, Glaziers & Iglar, 2004).

These investigations and maneuvers are aimed at prevention of common threats to life, morbidity, or day-to-day well-being. In order for many prevention-related activities to take place, people must be easily identified as eligible or appropriate candidates (Backett & Davison, 1995) for these investigations. In the case of periodic health exams, the age of the patient should be the cue; however, initiation of other preventive health measures is not so obvious.

In addition to clinical practice guidelines and checklists, health professionals and laypeople alike use cultural systems of explanation to make judgments and decisions about who is at risk for disease or accident, and therefore may require screening. This lay epidemiology complements the research on etiology and distribution of chronic disease that is used by health care professionals (Backett et al., 1995). For example, laypeople can readily identify candidates for a heart attack, describing them as "big fat wheezy blokes" or "a walking heart attack waiting to happen" (Davison, Smith & Frankel, 1991). Yet, people may not recognize the same conditions within themselves. That is, although people at mid-life may be aware of the epidemiological statistics they read in various information sources about who is at risk for what, these population health level risks are mediated by laypeople's own experiences, those of friends and family, and their own information sources. Ideas such as skinny people having low cholesterol or fat people being happy or elderly women with dowager's humps being the only people at risk for osteoporosis are common examples. At mid-life, as with other stages in the lifecourse, people base decisions about whether or not to take vitamins, exercise, and perform other health related choices on their evaluation of personal risk (Lauritzen & Sachs, 2003; Vollman et al., 2004a).

Prevention in Everyday Life

Formal medical attention to preventive health usually occurs during a medical encounter focused on a periodic health exam. Prevention in everyday life, however, occurs on an ongoing basis. Lives at mid-life are usually busy: women and men are balancing the demands of careers, children at home, parents who are aging, volunteer work, and the after-effects of immigration, urbanization, or migration across the country, among other factors. Yet, at a time in the lifecourse when many expect to be planning for retirement, some are facing job loss, enduring jobs that are replete with stress, and struggling with food insecurity or re-establishing themselves and their families in a new homeland. And often, these experiences are in tense contrast with the rhetoric of our land being one of plenty and prosperity fuelled by a cult of individualism. At the same time, ongoing media and government reports bombard us with visions of physician shortages, research illustrates long wait lists for medical services (McGurran & Noseworthy, 2002; Noseworthy, McGurran & Hadorn, 2003), and the consequences of government deficits and program cuts to resources that support well-being abound.

Several sub-populations of mid-life Canadians experience health and well-being in a context that has subtle yet important layers of influence. For example, in a study of women living in rural environments, women spoke of not wanting to "bother busy physicians" with "small health problems" (Meadows, Thurston & Berenson, 2001).

Although the women were quick to ensure their family members saw a physician when needed, their own health conditions were often minimized and unattended. It was only when they experienced an acute health incident or when the gradual culmination of multiple health problems impeded their "busyness" that women finally made time to visit a physician. Otherwise, their existing health problems like chronic indigestion, aches and pains, headaches, sore feet, broadening waistlines, feeling down in the dumps, and other minor concerns were relegated to a "when I have time" pile. In spite of the mass media and direct to consumer advertising that suggests that mid-life for women is all about menopause (erectile dysfunction and prostate cancer for men), menopause was seldom mentioned by women in the rural health study or other studies that have focused on determinants of health.

Employment and Working Conditions

Sources of stress at mid-life that may be risk factors in one sub-population may actually be preventive or positive mediating factors in another sub-population. In a study of developmentally disabled women, the subjects reported that their work environment was also their social environment and a source of both social and emotional support (Sonpal-Valias, Luterbach & Meadows, 1999). These women looked forward to going to their job every day, took pride in what they accomplished there, and saw employment as a source of support far beyond the economic remuneration. There is no reason to expect the experience to be different for men in the same situation. Their experience stands in stark contrast to many urban, middle-class women in a different study who discussed stress in their employment environment (Meadows & Thurston, 1999; Meadows, 2002). While seemingly economically privileged through their middle-class status, these women spoke of strain and conflict in employment relations, fears that their skills would not keep up with an evolving workplace, and labeled stress as both ubiquitous and detrimental to their health. Women described "The typical situation where you have no control and a lot of people to report to and the rules are carved in stone even if they don't make any sense and that kind of thing" (Meadows, 2002). Other issues that were sources of stress were job security and post-retirement financial situations, with one woman noting she "didn't want to end up like a bag lady on the streets" (Meadows, 2002). Men too face these issues at mid-life, and are also affected by the need to constantly upgrade skills, the limitations of seasonal work, and in some cases, a changing physical environment that affects traditional sources of livelihood such as hunting and fishing. As people progress through mid-life, the passing of time is also marked: "When you're 45 you don't think about age and your health as much as you do when you're hitting 50" (Meadows, 2002).

Income and Social Status

Income from employment is often closely linked to **social status**. Most careers are well established by the onset of mid-life. Those that require many years of advanced training – for example, some medical professions or advanced degrees, such as Doctor of Philosophy (PhD) – may mean that careers are established somewhat later, or that having children is delayed. In the case of those who migrate to Canada at mid-life, particularly those with advanced skills or degrees, the challenges of re-establishing their credentials in another country can mean significant changes to their former social status. Thus, at mid-life, a foreign-trained family physician may find himself driving taxis or being a porter in a hospital. A pediatrician may find herself working as a part-time research assistant and pursuing a Masters or nursing degree (Basran & Zong, 1998). At the same time, cultural norms from their homeland related to gendered roles and children's behaviour are challenged and disrupted. Women are often more employable than men when first arriving in Canada, especially in the service sector, so may become the family breadwinner.

Re-credentialing may take many years, especially when it requires further certification, examinations, or residencies for medical specialties. In the meantime, the individuals going through this process are usually family members, often living in economic and status conditions that are limited compared to what they experienced in their homelands. The daily and relentless stress of status loss, defending one's quest for employment, and adapting to reduced social support can affect mental, physical, and emotional health. Among those long resident in Canada, shifts in domains of economic prosperity, seasonal employment, and corporate downsizing expose many others to sources of stress and compromised immune systems. The toll on families, whether through either welcome or unwelcome changes to gender roles, economic organization, or discretionary time, in turn influence well-being through changes in social status, social support, and environment. There is growing evidence that persistent stress can negatively impact our immune system, potentially creating lower levels of resistance to infections and increasing risk for diseases such as chronic fatigue, fibromyalgia, and depression (McEwen, 1998).

Prosperity can also have its adverse influence on health. The sociological literature (Strickland, 1992; Papanek, 1973) illustrates the concept of the two person career. In this circumstance, one spouse is formally in the workplace while the other spouse supports the career through childcare, housekeeping, managing the employed spouse's personal life, and doing the Goffmanian backstage work of maintaining their social status through conspicuous consumption and front stage display of their status through their home, activities, and appearance (Goffman, 1959). The work of status maintenance can be hard work – chauffeuring children to and from school, multiple lessons, play dates, and sports – and can be experienced as very demanding and stressful to those involved. Women in a recent study noted that they were expected to entertain children and adults, take their children to lessons, and remain fit enough to be able to engage in various sports such as tennis and hiking that were the norm in their group (Meadows, Thurston & Vollman, 2005b). Well-being can suffer from this lifestyle as well, as unstructured time is rare, conspicuous consumption a must, and busyness is heightened by long days of endless activity.

Subtle workplace morés are also influential in our quest for well-being. There is an increase in the amount of time both men and women are working (Aronsson, Gustafsson & Dallner, 2000; Rones, Ilg & Gardner, 1997). Sociological explanations for the increase in work vary and include changing workplace expectations, personal achievement, avoidance of home and family life, and the accumulation of wealth and material goods (Aronsson et al., 2000; Brett & Stroh, 2003; Dew, Keefe & Small, 2005; Gerson, 2004). Working longer hours impacts psychological and physical health, as well family and social relationships (Aronsson et al., 2000; Sparks, Cooper, Fried & Shirom, 1997). Furthermore, working more hours affects the amount of time available to dedicate to prevention and to attend to regular health checkups.

Life Choices and Life Chances for Prevention

In spite of repeated calls by those in government at all levels for people to take responsibility for their lives and health through their lifestyles, there is ample evidence in determinants of health and research that life choices and life chances are a limiting factor to this naïve demand. At mid-life, many of the determinants of health may be beyond the control of individuals. There is little one can do about pre-natal or childhood factors such as growing up with low socio-economic status. Lack of employment choices may mean that unsafe or insecure employment conditions must be tolerated in order to generate income. Workplace related injury may occur when warning signs and safety materials are in a format or language that is inaccessible to workers (Thurston & Verhoef, 2003).

Exhortations to change one's lifestyle to maintain health and prevent the onset of disease take an individual and reductionist view of the determinants of health. For example, statements that having children early is a protective factor for breast cancer are of little help to those trying to conceive at mid-life after putting children on hold for a career, or due to fertility difficulties. Suggesting men and women get more exercise through walking ignores the realities of communities without walkways or rural areas that are unsafe due to a lack of roads or roaming dogs. For those balancing family, career, and the general demands of increasingly busy lives, joining a gym may be either unaffordable or inaccessible, and walking for half an hour may be impossible without respite care for their dependents.

Community-Based Wish Lists for Well-Being

A recent study in Alberta (Meadows et al., 2005b) asked women's communities across the province to identify priorities for women's health. The results did not focus either on specific diseases or the oft noted shortages of medical personnel. Rather, women in all geographic locations and socio-economic circumstances consistently highlighted issues related to communication, knowledge, and being partners in their health as their concerns. For example, although there is more than ample rhetoric and statistics suggesting shortages of family physicians across Canada, women did not request more family physicians but more physicians who talked with them rather than at them, and had or took the time to establish communication. People at mid-life are generally eager to understand more about their health so that they can be active participants in their own care and decisions. Trying to schedule time for a periodic health examination is as challenging for people at mid-life as it is for office staff in physician's offices. People juggling busy careers, family demands, and the multi-tasking that is becoming commonplace cannot always schedule appointments months ahead of time, or squeeze out the time that is needed for consultations and testing. Thus, although from an epidemiological perspective, mid-life women and men should be worried about heart disease, stroke, diabetes, and other high profile threats to health, the assumption that such concerns are central to those at mid-life remains, at a population health level, an assumption rather than a reality.

Candidacy for Prevention

Finally, another consideration in prevention at mid-life is the issue of candidacy – who is seen by whom as at risk, and how that risk is acted upon. As previously noted, physicians are armed with guidelines that suggest who should be screened and when. Family history and exposure to risks are also considerations. But one very important factor is the cultural perspective of laypersons and professionals that guide decisions about risk. In a recent study of women who experienced low energy extremity fractures at mid-life there was considerable variation in follow up related to prevention. For some women, the advent of a fracture was placed firmly in the realm of accident, and unlikely to occur again. Family physicians may or may not have been aware that their patients suffered a fracture, and at times a bone mineral density test in the normal range was taken as evidence that no future investigation was needed. In some cases, neither the woman who had the fracture nor her attending physicians saw her as a candidate for future fracture risk. Thus, important opportunities for upstream prevention of secondary fragility fractures were missed (Meadows, Mrkonjic, Petersen & Lagendyk, 2004a; Meadows, Mrkonjic & Lagendyk, 2005a).

Turning Points and Prevention

A turning point can be defined as "The observable moment when...there is a definite change in direction....This is a change of fortune; what Aristotle described as peripeteia, or reversal. It is the equivalent of reaching a peak and beginning the descent beyond."[1] At mid-life, turning points may not be identifiable single instants in time, but they are certainly the culmination of processes of reevaluation, priority setting, and often decisions about how to live the second half of one's life. Turning points may be coincident with either birth or death, and at mid-life turning points may be either positive or negative in consequence. They often mark a reorientation or adaptation. A turning point may also occur with a lifecourse change: becoming, for example, a parent or a grandparent. It may also occur in a nanosecond through a personal injury, accident, or the onset of an acute health incident for oneself or for someone close. People at mid-life with both children and parents may have experiences related to what is often called the sandwich generation (Chisholm, 1999; Nevidjon, 2004; Schlesinger & Raphael, 1993). They may be part of a process of diminishing life choices or deteriorating quality of life.

Turning points may also provide opportunities for attending to prevention that will reduce current and future risks to well-being. Past research has demonstrated the differences in reaction to heart attacks among those younger than 65 and those 65 and older. People in the younger group express surprise, apprehension about future risk, concerns about healing quickly to return to work, and questions about rehabilitation issues. Older people in post-retirement years are more likely to talk about having a heart attack (or stroke) as part of the inevitable breakdown of the body as they age (Wright & Meadows, 1999). While a jolting experience, a cardiac event at mid-life may provide an important opportunity to investigate underlying health and management using a number of medical and non-medical treatments, for example, pharmaceutical products, changes in diet, or information about what constitutes heart healthy eating.

Mid-life is often a time when predisposing factors, including family and personal histories, for various health conditions come to light, sometimes through turning point events. For example, the occurrence of a fragility or low energy extremity fracture (e.g., from a standing height or similar trauma (Kanis & Pitt, 1992; Seeman, 2002)) should trigger follow-up to investigate underlying bone architecture, and can be a turning point for women at mid-life (Meadows & Mrkonjic, 2003; Meadows et al., 2005a; Meadows,

Mrkonjic, O'Brien & Tink, 2007). The fracture can alert mid-life women to the need for taking preventive action in terms of their bone health. At mid-life, early signs of compromised bone density and strength might be addressed through diet (ensuring sufficient calcium and Vitamin D) or regular weight bearing exercise (walking instead of driving, carrying groceries), thus slowing or preventing established chronic disease in the form of osteoporosis. In order for prevention to occur, the fractures must be recognized as markers for further investigation at both the system and institutional levels; this recognition must be combined with individual recognition and knowledge of risk factors, so that appropriate preventive action takes place at every level.

In recent research with First Nations communities, some women described turning points in their lives when they became grandmothers, in some cases at relatively early ages (Meadows, Thurston & Lagendyk, 2004b). Women often noted that becoming a grandmother provided the motivation they needed to make deliberate life changes (Meadows et al., 2004b). Women were generous in sharing their experiences of discrimination, the effects of residential schools on their generation, their search for education, and their experiences with personnel in health care professions. Some women talked in detail about turning their lives around through deliberate decisions to improve their lives and health, and those of their communities. These life changes might include dealing with past abuse, getting treatment for substance abuse, making personal decisions to seek out healthier food, encouraging healthy child development in their grandchildren, supporting their own children in learning to become good parents, and being a conduit for reclaiming traditional cultural practices for their communities.

Women at mid-life were actively becoming agents of change in their communities, and tired of the same old stories and lack of response from formal and traditional institutions (Meadows et al., 2004b). Women in other studies have also spoken of wanting to be there for their grandchildren, of the need to be well to play with them and be part of their lives, and sometimes of even injuring themselves through doing activities that "weren't age appropriate" (Meadows et al., 2004a).

Finally, mid-life turning points which can have significant effects on well-being can occur through having an elderly independent parent become frail or dependant, or through losing one's employment or source of income. New federal policies provide a "compassionate care benefit" or employment insurance benefits to care for a parent or spouse in palliative care (Human Resources and Skills Development Canada (HRSDC), 2004). This short term bandage is certainly an improvement from depending on employer-specific rules on compassionate leave, but does not address the stress and work of either arranging care or personally caring for an aging or frail parent or partner. Arrangements for respite care for the affected individual are gradually becoming available. Yet, the effect on well-being of dealing with financial and economic issues, housing and long term care decisions, and squeezing that into already full schedules cannot be underestimated.

The effects of a personal injury can also force a turning point. In a study of mid-life women with fractures, some women reported losing jobs due to the fracture, while others had to hire locums to run their businesses (Meadows et al., 2005a). Others had to depend on family for assistance in the activities of daily living: "So we called my Mom and Dad and they came down and they stayed with us for the next $3^1/_2$ weeks – I don't know what I would have done without them." Finally, the forced inactivity during the recovery period resulted in some women making major life changes, facing past traumas and stresses head on, and for some engendered applied diligence to preventing future fractures.

Awareness of the potential for prevention at the level of broad understanding at this stage in the lifecourse, and the consequences of ignoring prevention for curative resources, needs to be pushed into the view of policy- and decision-makers, and program planners sooner rather than later.

DISCUSSION

The mid-life years bring changes that are the natural consequence of aging, yet these years also bring opportunities for prevention aimed at reducing threats to health and well-being. Identifying the determinants of health is only part of the task. Research continues to be needed to add to what is already known about the mechanisms through which the determinants of health affect day-to-day well-being. Greater understanding of these mechanisms – as simple as broadening the focus of what needs attention at mid-life – will contribute to coordinated and effective health interventions. More research is needed to raise awareness of less well known issues of poor health, such as bone and joint disease, nutrition, and gaps in knowledge needed for health literacy. To widen the lens through which well-being at mid-life is viewed, the concepts of health and prevention must expand to incorporate a determinants of health perspective and population health promotion.

Prevention requires vigilance. It also requires system level support and the acknowledgement that upstream investments in health and well-being are as important as curative medicine focused on fighting disease. Understanding how agency and structure combine to affect health related outcomes requires a willingness to explore well-being as a multifaceted entity, one that is physical, emotional, spiritual, and mental. Research and policy, as well as funding and resources, must take into account the broad array of realities in which mid-life Canadians live and experience health, including our local environments, our nation as a whole, and with a determinants of health approach that includes a spectrum from bench to bedside to backyard.

The mechanisms through which the determinants of health affect mid-life people's day-to-day well-being range from seemingly individually chosen personal practices and coping skills, to the larger structural cultural context surrounding health. It is apparent that there is continuing tension between individual actions, health at a population health level, and the larger context in which health and well-being are pursued. In making the factors in daily lives that either support or stand in the way of focusing on prevention more explicit, it becomes clear that the determinants of health are intricate, interrelated, and infinitely important if we are to understand and foster well-being for women and men.

CONCLUSION

A population health promotion approach to the determinants of health at mid-life reminds us that a complex issue is being tackled. Men and women at mid-life have a myriad of health statuses. Their earlier lives have exposed each individual to circumstances and experiences that influence their current and future health status. We are encouraged to make explicit the mechanisms that foster and maintain disparities in health, reminded that the health of populations cannot be understood solely with reductionist approaches, and challenged to insist that resources are well invested to maintain well-being and prevent disease and illness. At mid-life, major health issues are much more than issues of morbidity and mortality; they are pleas for health knowledge, excellence in communication around health, and attention to the broader determinants of health.

STUDY QUESTIONS

1. *Why are epidemiological (statistical) summaries of morbidity and mortality causes for people at mid-life insufficient to explain their causes of poor health?*
2. *What is the difference in focus between the traditional population health and the newer population health promotion approach? (Students will have to search for discussions in Vollman et al. (2004) or the Health Canada website for this information.)*
3. *Why is health and well-being at mid-life an important part of the lifecourse to examine?*
4. *Using medical journals such as* CMAJ *and* Canadian Family Physician, *identify the major threats to health at mid-life over the past five years. Compare these health risks to those presented over a seven day content analysis of health issues related to mid-life health in the* Globe and Mail *and your local newspaper.*

FIGURE 17.1
Source: Mike Baldwin (1999). Distributed by Universal Press Syndicate. www.cornered.com

5. *Search the current medical and sociological literature for examples of men's perspectives and experiences of health that complement those in this article on women's health. Discuss similarities and differences.*
6. *Please comment on this cartoon from a determinants of health perspective, assuming that the person is around age 60.*

GLOSSARY

gender blindness the inability to perceive that different gender roles and responsibilities are held by men and women, leading to different effects on men and women of development policies, programs, and projects.

gender neutrality the assumption that gender does not make a difference to health, health outcomes, daily life, or the stratification of society and its institutions. This assumption is acted upon by treating everyone, women and men, as the same, thereby putting gender blindness into practice.

lifestyle a way of living reflected in identifiable patterns of behaviour based on an individual's choices, and influenced by the individual's personal characteristics, their social interactions, and socio-economic and environmental factors.

osteopenia a clinically identified decrease in bone mineral density that is a precursor condition to osteoporosis. A bone mineral density (BMD) test is used for evaluation.

osteoporosis a chronic condition characterized by low bone mass and micro-architectural deterioration of bone leading to increased bone fragility and an increase in risk of fracture after minimal trauma (Affenito & Kerstetter, 1999).

population health promotion putting into action the principles of population health. In population health, the complex interplay of the determinants of health are acknowledged, the focus is on health at the level of populations rather than individuals, upstream investment in health is encouraged, multiple strategies (including collaborations across sectors) are practiced, citizens are engaged in the process, and there is increased accountability for health outcomes (see Vollman et al., 2004).

social status the "standing," honour, and/or prestige attached to one's position in society. Note that social status is influenced by social position, but one can have several social positions, but only one social status. Weber talks about social status as defined by people who are grouped together because of similarities in culture. They have a "common lifestyle and viewpoint of the world, and...identify one another as belonging to a group" (Collins, 1985, p. 88).

REFERENCES

Affenito, S.G., & Kerstetter, J. (1999). Position of the American Dietetic Association and Dietitians of Canada: Women's health and nutrition. *Journal of the American Dietetics Association, 99*, 738–751.

Aronsson, G., Gustafsson, K., & Dallner, M. (2000). Sick but yet at work. An empirical study of sickness presenteeism. *Journal of Epidemiology and Community Health, 54*, 502–509.

Backett, K.C., & Davison, C. (1995). Lifecourse and lifestyle: The social and cultural location of health behaviours. *Social Science and Medicine, 40*, 629–638.

Ballard, K., Elston, M.A., & Gabe, J. (2005). Beyond the mask: Women's experiences of public and private ageing during midlife and their use of age-resisting activities. *Health (London), 9*, 169–187.

Basran, G.S., & Zong, L. (1998). Devaluation of foreign credentials as perceived by visible minority professionals. *Canadian Ethnic Studies/Études Ethniques au Canada, 30*, 6–23.

Bolaria, B.S., & Bolaria, R. (2002). Personal and structural determinants of health and illness: Lifestyles and life choices. In B.S. Bolaria & H.D. Dickinson (Eds.), *Health, illness and health care in Canada* (3rd. ed., pp. 445–459). Toronto: Thomson Nelson.

Boul, L.A. (2003). Men's health and middle age. *Sexualities, Evolution & Gender, 5*, 5–22.

Brett, J.M., & Stroh, L.K. (2003). Working 61 plus hours a week: Why do managers do it? *Journal of Applied Psychology, 88*, 67–78.

Chisholm, J.F. (1999). The sandwich generation. *Journal of Social Distress and the Homeless, 8*, 177–191.

Corin, E. (1994). The social and cultural matrix of health and disease. In R.G. Evans, M.L. Barer, & T.R. Marmor (Eds.), *Why are some people healthy and others not? The determinants of health of populations*. New York: Aldine de Gruyter.

Cummings, S.R., & Melton, L.J. (2002). Epidemiology and outcomes of osteoporotic fractures. *Lancet, 359*, 1761–1767.

Davison, C., Smith, G.D., & Frankel, S. (1991). Lay epidemiology and the prevention of paradox: The implications of coronary candidacy for health education. *Sociology of Health and Illness, 13*, 1–19.

Dew, K., Keefe, V., & Small, K. (2005). "Choosing" to work when sick: Workplace presenteeism. *Social Science & Medicine, 68*, 2273–2282.

Dickinson, H.D., & Kosteniuk, J.G. (2002). Health status in Canada. In B.S. Bolaria & H.D. Dickinson (Eds.), *Health, illness and health care in Canada* (3rd ed.) (pp. 37–52). Toronto: Thomson Nelson.

Dubey, V., & Glazier, R. (2006). Preventive care checklist form. Evidence-based tool to improve preventive health care during complete health assessment of adults. *Canadian Family Physician, 52*, 48–55.

Dubey, V., Mathews, R., Glaziers, R., & Iglar, K. (2004). Preventive care checklist form for average-risk, routine female health assessments. *The College of Family Physicians of Canada*. Retrieved on April 1, 2007 from http://www.cfpc.ca/local/files/Communications/Health%20Policy/Preventive%20Care%20Checklist%20Form/English/Female_Preventive_Care_ChecklistForm.pdf.

Evandrou, M., & Glaser, K. (2002). Changing economic and social roles: The experience of four cohorts of mid-life individuals in Britain, 1985–2000. *Population Trends*, Winter (110), 19–30.

Evans, R.G., et al. (Eds.). (1994). *Why are some people healthy and others not? The determinants of health of populations*. New York: Aldine De Gruyter.

Frank, J.W. (1995). Why "population health"? *Canadian Journal of Public Health, 86*, 162–164.

Frankel, S., Davison, C., & Smith, G.D. (1991). Lay epidemiology and the rationality of responses to health education. *British Journal of General Practice, 41*, 428–430.

Frohlich, K.L. (2000). *The collective lifestyles framework: A contextual analysis of social practices, social structure and disease* (Rep. No. T00–02). Montreal: Université de Montreal.

Frohlich, K.L., Corin, E., & Potvin, L. (2001). A theoretical proposal for the relationship between context and health. *Sociology of Health & Illness, 23*, 776–797.

Frohlich, K.L., & Potvin, L. (1999a). Collective lifestyles as the target for health promotion. *Canadian Journal of Public Health, 90*, S11–S14.

Frohlich, K.L., Potvin, L., Chabot, P., & Corin, H. (1999b). Health promotion through the lens of population health: Toward a salutogenic setting. *Critical Public Health, 9,* 211–222.

Gerson, K. (2004). The morality of time: Women and the expanding workweek. *Dissent, 51,* 53–56.

Goffman, E. (1959). *Presentation of self in everyday life.* New York: Doubleday.

Green, E.E., Thompson, D., & Griffiths, F. (2002). Narratives of risk: Women at midlife, medical "experts" and health technologies. *Health, Risk & Society, 4,* 273–286.

Green, L.W., Richard, L., & Potvin, L. (1996). Ecological foundations of health promotion. *American Journal of Health Promotion, 10,* 270–281.

Health Canada. (2005). Population health approach. *Public Health Agency of Canada.* Retrieved on August 24, 2006 from http://www.phac-aspc.gc.ca/ph-sp/phdd/.

Howell, L.C., & Beth, A. (2002). Midlife myths and realities: Women reflect on their experiences. *Journal of Women & Aging, 14,* 189–204.

Human Resources and Skills Development Canada (HRSDC). (2004). *A New employment insurance benefit – compassionate care benefit.* Retrieved on August 26, 2006 from http://www.hrsdc.gc.ca/en/cs/comm/hrsd/news/2004/040106.shtml.

Hunt, K. (2002). A generation apart? Gender-related experiences and health in women in early and late mid-life. *Social Science & Medicine, 54,* 663–676.

Kanis, J.A., & Pitt, F.A. (1992). Epidemiology of osteoporosis. *Bone, 13 Suppl 1,* S7–S15.

Klohnen, E.C., Vandewater, E.A., & Young, A. (1996). Negotiating the middle years: Ego-resiliency and successful midlife adjustment in women. *Psychology and Aging, 11,* 431–442.

Lachman, M.E. (2004). Development in midlife. *Annual Review of Psychology, 55,* 305–331.

Lauritzen, S.O., & Sachs, L. (2003). Normality, risk and the future: Implicit communication of threat in health surveillance. *Sociology of Health & Illness, 23,* 497–516.

McEwen, B.S. (1998). Protective and damaging effects of stress mediators. *New England Journal of Medicine, 338,* 171–179.

McGurran, J., & Noseworthy, T. (2002). Improving the management of waiting lists for elective healthcare services: Public perspectives on proposed solutions. *Hospital Quarterly, 5,* 28–32.

Meadows, L.M. (2002, April). Conceptualizing wellness: Insight from the WHEALTH study. In *Invited keynote address,* 8th Annual Qualitative Health Research Conference. Banff, AB.

Meadows, L.M., & Mrkonjic, L. (2003). Breaking – bad news: Women's experiences of fractures at midlife. *Canadian Journal of Public Health, 94,* 427–430.

Meadows, L.M., Mrkonjic, L., & Lagendyk, L. (2005a). Women's perceptions of future risk after low-energy fractures at midlife. *Annals of Family Medicine, 3,* 64–69.

Meadows, L.M., Mrkonjic, L., Petersen, K.M.A., & Lagendyk, L. (2004a). After the fall: Women's views of fractures in relation to bone health at midlife. *Women & Health, 39,* 47–62.

Meadows, L.M., Mrkonjic, L.A., O'Brien, M.D., & Tink, W. (2007). The importance of communication in secondary fragility fracture treatment and prevention. *Osteoporosis International, 18,* 59–66.

Meadows, L.M., & Thurston, W.E. (1999, November). *Social determinants of health: Perceptions of 3 groups of midlife women.* In NAPCRG '99 27th Annual Meeting, San Diego, CA.

Meadows, L.M., Thurston, W.E., & Berenson, C. (2001). Health promotion and preventative measures: Interpreting messages at midlife. *Qualitative Health Research, 11*, 450–463.

Meadows, L.M., Thurston, W.E., & Lagendyk, L.E. (2004b). Aboriginal women at midlife: Grandmothers as agents of change. *Canadian Woman Studies, 24*, 159–165.

Meadows, L.M., Thurston, W.E., & Vollman, A.R. (2005b). *Alberta women's health: Identifying and prioritizing the agenda through practice, research and community consultations*. Final report to Women's Health Bureau. Calgary, Alberta.

Melton, L.J., III (2000). Who has osteoporosis? A conflict between clinical and public health perspectives. *Journal of Bone and Mineral Research, 15*, 2309–2314.

Nevidjon, B. (2004). Managing from the middle: Integrating midlife challenges of children, elder parents, and career. *Clinical Journal of Oncology Nursing, 8*, 72–75.

Noseworthy, T.W., McGurran, J.J., & Hadorn, D.C. (2003). Waiting for scheduled services in Canada: Development of priority-setting scoring systems. *Journal of Evaluation in Clinical Practice, 9*, 23–31.

O'Brien, C.S., & Edwards, K. (2002). Alice in menopauseland: The jabberwocky of a medicalized middle age. *Health Care Women International, 23*, 325–343.

Ogle, J.P., & Damhorst, M.L. (2005). Critical reflections on the body and related sociocultural discourses at the midlife transition: An interpretive study of women's experiences. *Journal of Adult Development, 12*, 1–18.

Papanek, H. (1973). Men, women, and work: Reflections on the two-person career. *American Journal of Sociology, 78*, 852–872.

Public Health Agency of Canada (2003). What determines health? *Public Health Agency of Canada*. Retrieved on September 4, 2006 from http://www.phac-aspc.gc.ca/ph-sp/phdd/determinants/index.html

Raphael, D. (2004a). Introduction to the social determinants of health. In D. Raphael (Ed.), *Social determinants of health: Canadian perspectives* (pp. 1–18). Toronto: Canadian Scholars' Press.

Raphael, D. (Ed.). (2004b). *Social determinants of health: Canadian perspectives*. Toronto: Canadian Scholars' Press.

Robertson, A. (1998). Critical reflections on the politics of need: Implications for public health. *Social Science & Medicine, 47*, 1419–1430.

Rones, P.L., Ilg, R.E., & Gardner, J.M. (1997). Trends in hours of work since the mid-1970s. *Monthly Labor Review, 120*, 3–14.

Schlesinger, B., & Raphael, D. (1993). The women in the middle: The sandwich generation revisited. *International Journal of Sociology of the Family, 23*, 77–87.

Seeman, E. (2002). Pathogenesis of bone fragility in women and men. *Lancet, 359*, 1841–1850.

Sonpal-Valias, N., Luterbach, L., & Meadows, L.M. (1999, April). *Health of women with disabilities in mid-life*. In The Alberta Association of Rehabilitation Centres Initiative '99 – Values, Voices & Visions, Calgary, AB.

Sparks, K., Cooper, C., Fried, Y., & Shirom, A. (1997). The effects of hours of work on health: A meta-analytic review. *Journal of Occupational and Organizational Psychology, 70*, 391–408.

Strickland, W.J. (1992). A typology of career wife roles. *Human Relations, 45*, 797–811.

Thurston, W.E., & Verhoef, M.J. (2003). Occupational injury among immigrants. *Journal of International Migration and Integration, 4*, 105–124.

Vollman, A.R., Anderson, E.T., & McFarlane, J.M. (2004a). *Canadian community as partner*. Philadelphia: Lippincott Williams & Wilkins.

Vollman, A.R., Anderson, E.T., & McFarlane, J.M. (2004b). Epidemiology, demography, and community health. In *Canadian community as partner* (pp. 28–57). Philadelphia: Lippincott Williams & Wilkins.

Wright, B., & Meadows, L.M. (1999, November). *Assessing quality of life in the frail elderly population.* In North American Primary Care Research Group, 26th Annual Meeting, Montreal, Quebec.

ENDNOTE

1. Definition from "Basic Glossary of Literary Terms" available at http://members.fortunecity.com/fabianvillegas2/drama/glossary-t.htm#point

18

Aging, Health, and Health Care: From Hospital and Residential Care to Home and Community Care

MARGARET J. PENNING University of Victoria

KRISTINE VOTOVA University of Victoria

INTRODUCTION

Like the other industrialized nations, Canada has an "aged" population that is continuing to age.[1] At the beginning of the 20th century, just 5 percent of Canadians were aged 65 years and older (Norland, 1994). Today, approximately 13 percent of the population is aged 65 and over (Statistics Canada, 2005). As a result, within the next decade or so, adults aged 65 and over will begin to outnumber children aged 15 and younger (Statistics Canada, 2005). It is estimated that by 2031, almost one quarter (23%) of the nation's population will be aged 65 and over, and almost one half of the older adult population will be aged 75 and over (Bélanger & Dumas, 1998). The oldest of the old, those aged 85 years and older, represent the fastest growing age group, and are expected to represent 4 percent of the total Canadian population by 2041 (Lindsay, 1999).

Individual and population aging are causes for celebration – more and more people are living longer and healthier lives. Yet, they are not without their challenges as well. Health and health care invariably emerge as major areas of concern when discussing an aging population, both from an individual and from a social perspective. In particular, one often hears of concerns regarding the impact of population aging on health care utilization and costs. There is no doubt that an aging population will have a major influence on the health care needs of the population and the demands imposed on the Canadian health care system. However, aging, health, and illness are situated within given social, political, and economic contexts, and it is ultimately these factors and not demography that determine how health and old age are defined and dealt with in a society (see Gee, 2000).

This chapter focuses on the nature and implications of the social construction of health and aging in the Canadian health care context. It argues that historically, these constructions have tended to reflect the application of biomedical criteria, resulting in the **medicalization** of the health and health care issues associated with aging. This is consistent with the primary focus of the Canadian health care system on the treatment and cure of acute conditions by physicians, largely within acute-care hospital settings. Yet, in many ways, older adults and the health needs they present remain marginal to this system. Consequently, they not only often find themselves considered to be inappropriate and problematic users of the primary publicly funded health care system, but also among the main recipients of a secondary, more privately focused system of health care.

THE SOCIAL CONSTRUCTION OF HEALTH AND AGING

Whether we view old age as a time of health or of illness and disease depends, to a large extent, on how these constructs are defined and assessed. In the not too distant past, many of the biological changes associated with old age (e.g., decreases in vision, hearing, and mobility) were considered natural and normal accompaniments of aging. However, with the ascendance of scientific medicine in the late 19th and early 20th centuries, they were gradually redefined as diseases (Brown, 1996). Increasingly, health came to be defined by using biomedical criteria, and was consequently equated with the absence of disease or pathology. Aging, in turn, tends to be constructed as a medical problem – as a biological process involving inevitable and progressive physical and cognitive decline, disease, and ill health (Stahl & Feller, 1990).

With its focus on the treatment and cure of disease, the **biomedical model** is oriented primarily toward acute rather than chronic disease. However, while acute conditions (those characterized by a specific onset and limited duration) tend to decline in later life, chronic conditions (or diseases that persist over time and tend not to be curable) become more prevalent. About 80 percent of older adults today report having one or more chronic condition, with some of the most prevalent of these being arthritis and rheumatism, hypertension, heart disease, and diabetes (Lindsay, 1999). Importantly, having these conditions is related not only to age but also to broader social determinants of health such as gender, ethnicity, race, poverty, and social inequality (Wilkinson & Marmot, 2003). For example, women and those with lower education and income report the greatest number of chronic conditions (Statistics Canada, 2002). However, these are not necessarily major causes of mortality. In Canada, the major causes of mortality in later life include cardiovascular disease, cancer, respiratory diseases, accidents, diabetes, and diseases of the digestive system (Statistics Canada, 2004).

While the biomedical perspective equates health with the absence of disease, other perspectives define health more broadly and in positive rather than negative terms. One of the most often cited definitions is from the World Health Organization (WHO), which some years ago conceptualized health as "a state of complete physical, mental and social well-being and not merely the absence of disease or infirmity" (WHO, 1958, p. 459). Following from these broader definitions, health status has also been assessed in terms of levels of functioning and self-assessments of mental, physical, and social well-being that may or may not correspond with one another. For example, not all **chronic illnesses** necessarily or automatically result in reductions in functioning, as reflected in restrictions on people's abilities to engage in major activities of daily living (i.e., at home, at work, at school, in social life, and in sports and leisure).

The picture that emerges from looking at the health status of older adults more broadly differs from that developed solely on the basis of information regarding the presence or absence of disease. For example, although functional **disability** also increases with age, older adults report relatively good health, being active, functioning autonomously, and feeling good about themselves and their lives. Therefore, despite the fact that most report having one or more chronic conditions, research evidence indicates that less than one half (40%) of older (aged 65+) people living in the community (i.e., not in residential or institutional care) report experiencing any activity limitations or disabilities (including problems in such areas as mobility, agility, hearing, seeing, speaking, and memory) as a result (Statistics Canada, 2002). A similar proportion report experiencing difficulties with basic personal care activities such as eating, bathing, dressing, and personal mobility (Lindsay, 1999). Even fewer (about 15%) experience severe disabilities (Norland, 1994), including Alzheimer's Disease (which affects 6–8 percent of those aged 65 and over), a major source of cognitive impairment and memory loss in later life (Canadian Study of Health & Aging [CSHA], 1994). It is therefore apparent that chronic conditions do not necessarily imply high levels of disability among older adults.

Self-assessments of physical and mental health tend to be even better. In general, research findings suggest that when older adults are asked to describe their health compared to that of other people their own age, approximately three quarters state that they are in good to excellent health (Lindsay, 1999). Although self-reports and assessments of health are often discounted as not providing valid representations of health, research evidence also reveals that self-reports are often equal to or better than physician evaluations for predicting various outcomes, including mortality (see Ferraro & Farmer, 1999). Similarly, subjective assessments of psychological health or well-being tend to be very positive in nature and often are more positive than those reported by younger adults.

Overall, these findings suggest that while old age tends to be socially constructed as a time of illness and disability, with health conceptualized broadly, the older population as a whole emerges as having relatively good health. Moreover, where health-related needs are evident, they tend to be in terms of chronic rather than acute conditions.

THE HEALTH CARE SOLUTION

The social construction of old age as a time of illness and disability has implications not only for attitudes regarding aging and old age, but also for the way we deal with the health-related needs of the older population – for the health policies and services we develop, how they are structured, where they are delivered, and by whom.

In general, biomedically defined problems are accompanied by biomedically oriented solutions. Historically, therefore, Canada has structured its health care system with a primary focus on the treatment and cure of acute conditions – on the delivery of health care services that are primarily medical in focus, physician-dominated, and delivered in physicians' offices or in acute care hospital settings. In 1957, for example, the *Hospital Insurance and Diagnostic Services Act* was introduced, providing coverage for acute hospital care for the entire Canadian population. In 1966, a comparable national insurance plan for physician services (the *Medical Care Act*) was established. In 1984, the *Canada Health Act* brought the two together to provide universally available, publicly insured access to physician and acute hospital care based on need rather than ability to pay for services (i.e., a system known as medicare). But other forms of care, corresponding with broader definitions of health and needs for chronic rather than acute care, are not similarly covered.

The distribution of public and private expenditures on health provides evidence of this focus. In 2000, for example, total expenditures on health care in Canada totaled

$95 billion, of which over 70 percent went to cover the costs of physician, hospital, and pharmaceutical services (32% to hospital care, 25% to salaries for physicians and other health professionals, and 15% to drugs). Less than 10 percent went to fund other health care institutions (e.g., nursing homes, psychiatric hospitals), while 18 percent went to cover all other expenditures. This includes **home care** as well as public health services and other expenditures, such as building costs, equipment, and administration (Canadian Institute for Health Information, 2001).

Acute Physician and Hospital Care

Given the social construction of health and aging in biomedical terms, and a health care system structured to provide biomedically focused services, it comes as no surprise that older adults are major consumers of physician and other medical services, and that health expenditures tend to be higher for older than younger age groups (Cheal, 2000). Although those aged 65 and over represent about 13 percent of Canada's total population, they also account for about 43 percent of total health care expenditures (CIHI, 2001).

Physicians are major providers of care and also serve as gatekeepers, controlling access to services within our health care system. According to the 1998–99 Canadian National Population Health Survey (Statistics Canada, 2001), 89 percent of community-dwelling older adults in Canada reported having contacted a physician at least once during the previous year. About the same proportion (87%) reported having used one or more medications (prescription and nonprescription) or other health products in the previous month. Overall, older adults appear to account for about one quarter of all physician billings for care, and use about 40 percent of all prescription drugs (Barer, Evans & Hertzman, 1995). Physician service utilization has also increased over the past two decades, largely through greater use of specialist services. In fact, while general and family practitioner (GP/FP) service utilization appears to have decreased in recent years, the opposite has been reported with regard to specialists (Barer et al., 2004). According to Watson et al. (2005), GPs appeared to be increasingly focusing on less time-consuming (younger) patients while referring more complex (older) patients to specialists. It should be noted that while access to GPs is under the control of individual patients, this is not the case with regard to specialist services, which generally require referral from other physicians. This has implications for arguments concerning older adult population responsibility for increasing health care costs.

Acute care hospitals also play a primary role in the biomedical approach to health; they serve as repositories for the latest medical technologies and places where health care professionals control the treatment process (Brown, 1996). Approximately one fifth of all older adults have spent at least one night in hospital during the previous year. They account for about one third of all hospital stays and, because they tend to be in hospital longer than younger individuals, they also account for about one half of all days spent in hospitals (CIHI, 2001). In 1996–97, the average hospital stay amongst those aged 65 and over was 17 days compared to 9 days among those aged 45–64, 7 days among those aged 35–44, and 6 days among those who less than 35 years of age (Statistics Canada, 1999).

Not only are older adult hospitalization rates relatively high, but they have also continued to increase since the introduction of nationally insured hospital services. For example, between 1961 and 1992, as per capita use of hospitals decreased for all other age groups, there was a 23 percent increase in use evident among those aged 75 and older (Bergman et al., 1997). In 1960, those aged 65 and over accounted for 13 percent of all hospital admissions and 29 percent of all days spent in hospital (Nair, Karim & Nyers, 1992). This increased to 33 percent of admissions and 60 percent of days in hospital by 1995–96 (CIHI, 2001; Health Canada, 1999).

Increases in hospital utilization do not appear to reflect increases in the proportion of older adults in the population (i.e., population aging – see Cheal, 2000). Instead, they appear to be due to changes in how older adults are treated by the health care system. This includes more intensive service provision and an increasing concentration of hospital care on meeting the health care needs of a relatively small segment of the older adult population: those who are very old, those recovering from the effects of strokes, and those who are dying (see Barer, Evans & Hertzman, 1995). Findings reported by Hertzman et al. (1990) indicate that 80 percent of the increase in hospital occupancy rates observed for older adults between 1969 and 1987 occurred in extended care and rehabilitation units (rather than in hospital units devoted to acute care), suggesting that older adults in hospital "were recovering from strokes and cardiac conditions, suffering from senile dementia or awaiting placement elsewhere" (Northcott & Milliken, 1998, p. 98). Similarly, a recent study conducted in Manitoba found that from 1991/92–1999/2000, 40 percent of all acute care hospital days were used by 5 percent of patients who had long stays. About two thirds of these patients were aged 75 and over, and many were awaiting transfer to another type of care (i.e., nursing home care, home care, chronic care) (DeCoster, Bruce & Kozyrskyi, 2005).

Somewhat paradoxically, however, the biomedicalization of aging also appears to be accompanied by a lack of interest and expertise on the part of the medical community in dealing with the largely chronic health problems of an aging population (Forbes, Jackson & Kraus, 1987). Whereas chronic conditions typically require a greater orientation toward care rather than cure, the biomedical model generally directs attention to issues of cure. It has been suggested that conditions like arthritis, diabetes, emphysema, and chronic pain may challenge medical professionals' faith in the abilities of scientific medicine by offering little likelihood of cure while bringing their own abilities into question (Klein et al., 1982). Consequently, the amount of time spent by physicians in medical encounters with older patients is often less than that spent with younger patients, even though older patients present more problems.

Older adults may also be considered inappropriate candidates for curative treatments. For example, some research evidence indicates that differential treatment options may be available for older and younger adults. A recent study of the effects of age on the care of people hospitalized with congestive heart failure in Alberta (Cujec et al., 2004), found that older patients received less therapy (including diagnostic procedures, surgical procedures, prescriptions for specific drugs) than those in younger age groups despite representing the vast majority (85%) of patients studied, and despite their longer stays in hospital. There is also evidence indicating that while the proportion of women with congestive heart failure increases with age, older adults and especially older women with cardiac disease tend to be treated less aggressively (Alder et al., 2002; Cujec et al., 2004; Demers, 1998). Similarly, a study conducted by Ganz (1992) reports that older women with breast cancer (the vast majority of such patients) are less likely to be offered breast conserving surgery as a treatment option during the early stages of cancer than are younger women. Findings suggest that physicians tend to support the idea of rationing services and treatments for those considered too old to benefit from them (Kirkey, 1992), or else they assume incorrectly that older patients will be harmed rather than benefit from treatment (Williams, 1996).

Taken together, findings of this nature suggest that while we define old age as a time of disease and seek to treat it within the context of a biomedically oriented health care system, we also construct disease in old age as a problem not entirely appropriate for biomedical intervention. In this way, the old would appear to occupy a unique (and marginal) position in the modern health care system. The fact that chronic rather than **acute illness** tends to prevail in later life suggests a mismatch between the health care needs of an aging population and the health care system available to meet those needs.

Long-Term Residential and Community-Based Care

Although the primary focus of the health care system has been on acute care, the major health-related needs of many older adults are for services that will enable them to cope with chronic conditions and the functional disabilities that result from them – thus, long-term rather than acute care. Prevailing approaches to long-term care range from chronic hospital and nursing home care at one end of the continuum through formal community-based care, and informal and self-care at home at the other. However, while acute hospital services are publicly funded and, in principle at least, universally available to those in need regardless of their ability to pay, no directly comparable system of national health insurance exists to cover non-hospital-based long-term care services (that is, either residential or community-based care). Instead, long-term care remains much more heavily oriented toward the private sphere, with the responsibility and costs of care often borne directly by the recipients themselves.

Like acute-care hospitals, chronic-care hospitals provide medical and nursing services, and are therefore included in the provisions of Canada's public health insurance system. However, while care is provided at no cost to patients if delivered in acute-care hospitals, this is not necessarily the case in chronic-care hospitals. Many are privately owned and operated on a for-profit basis. For example, in 1990, while 365 Canadian hospitals (29.4%) were privately owned and operated, most were long-term care hospitals that collected fees from patients for the services provided (Lassey, Lassey & Jinks, 1997). Currently, most provinces also require that patients contribute to the costs of their care through income-based co-payments (to cover room and board costs) within these facilities (Deber & Williams, 1995, p. 301).[2] Interestingly, some provinces have introduced similar charges for patients with long stays (e.g., 60 days or more) in acute-care hospitals. In Ontario, for example, a Chronic Care Co-payment (up to $48.69 per day or $1,480.99 per month depending on income levels) is charged to patients in regular acute care hospitals who are awaiting placement in a chronic care hospital or long-term care facility (Ontario Ministry of Health and Long-Term Care, 2006).

However, most long-term care is not hospital-based but, rather, is provided in other residential care settings (e.g., nursing homes, special care, or **assisted living** homes) or in people's own homes in the community. These services do not come under the provisions of the public health insurance program. Instead, they are covered by programs such as the Canada Assistance Plan and the Extended Health Care Services Program.[3] As a result, they fall within the domain of social welfare programs rather than the health care system. This means that they are viewed quite differently by the state. As Deber and Williams note:

> At their best, Canada's social programs embody a principled social commitment to enrich the lives of Canadians who for some reason (e.g., aging, disability) need external support to maintain their dignity, independence and quality of life. At their worst, they embody the belief, descended from Victorian Poor Laws, that individuals and their families bear responsibility for their own welfare, and that those who require external support are, in most cases, the victims of their own misfortune. This policy framework would imply that the state should provide only the most minimal assistance, and provide that as a last resort. Accordingly, throughout most of the country's history, services for seniors and those with disabilities, to the extent they were available, were provided primarily on a local basis...as part of the "public welfare" system.... There was relatively little direct involvement by federal or provincial governments. (1995, p. 299)

Consequently, unlike physician and hospital-based programs, which are generally publicly funded (with private insurance prohibited for any services covered by provincial plans), formal long-term care programs (including residential, community, and home-based programs) have developed under the auspices not only of the public sector but also the private for-profit and private not-for-profit sectors, resulting in a diversity of systems and models of care across as well as within provinces. Guarantees of universality, comprehensiveness of services, portability, and so forth, as well as restrictions on private ownership, user fees, and extra-billing that apply to acute care services, do not apply to long-term care.[4]

LONG-TERM RESIDENTIAL CARE

In the early part of the 19th century, care of chronically ill older adults was in the hands of family or, for those with sufficient financial resources, also in the hands of privately hired help. In either case, it was generally provided at home. There was little alternative to the poorhouse for those without family or financial resources. In the dawn of the 21st century, much appears unchanged. The long-term care of older chronically ill and disabled adults often remains in the hands of family. Those with sufficient financial resources are also able to access privately paid services, which now include both community-based and residential care. Currently, those lacking such resources may also be able to access some level of publicly funded community-based care. However, the vast majority of governmental funding for long-term care goes to support the care provided in nursing homes and other residential care facilities. Those without family and other resources are the most likely to find themselves in such facilities.

Like most other health services, long-term residential care is funded by the federal government. Provincial governments assume primary responsibility for establishing policies and regulations, with regional health authorities assuming increasing responsibility for actual service delivery in most provinces. Consequently, no uniform or coherent policy exists in Canada to regulate standards of accommodation, funding arrangements, quality, and standards of care and instead, considerable variation exists across as well as within provinces (Berta et al., 2006). The same diversity is evident in terms of ownership. In 1988, almost one half (48.7%) of all long-term-care facilities in Canada were privately owned and operated on a for-profit basis. However, because for-profit facilities tend to be smaller in size than either non-profit or public facilities, the greatest proportion (48.9%) of long-term-care beds (and thus, of residents as well) was in public care facilities. This appears to be changing. For example, in Ontario in 1988, 57 percent of long-term care facilities in the province were privately owned and operated for a profit (Greb et al., 1994). From 1996–2002, approximately 62 percent of long-term care facilities in the province were proprietary (for-profit) (Berta, Laporte & Valdmanis, 2005). As well, an increasing number now operate as part of chains (Baum, 1999). The remainder is government owned (17.4%) or is operated by non-profit lay or religious organizations (14.1%) (Berta et al., 2005). The proportion of long-term care beds operated on a for-profit basis also increased from 56 percent in 1996/97 to 59.6 percent in 2001/02, while government-owned beds decreased from 26.3 percent to 22.6 percent (Berta et al., 2005). Similar changes appear to be underway in other provinces. In British Columbia, reductions in residential care facilities and beds from 2001–2004 are reported to have been accompanied by "a dramatic six-fold increase in corporate investment in residential care and assisted living facilities" in that province (Cohen et al., 2005, p. 7). According to these authors, "Over 90 percent of net residential bed closures since 2001 have been in the not-for-profit sector, while proportionately more of the new residential and assisted living openings have been in the for-profit sector" (Cohen et al., 2005, p. 25).

While provincial governments generally provide some funding for the care of those assessed as eligible, because long-term care is not considered to be *medically necessary*, residents can also be charged user fees to cover the costs of their care (Jacobs, Mills & Hollander, 1997). In each province, at least some residents of long-term care facilities are required to contribute to the overall cost of their care, with the level of co-payment often dependent upon the level of care and personal ability to pay (based on income or assets). The nature and extent of the co-payment varies. In the Atlantic provinces, residents are "income and asset tested and may have to pay up to the full cost of care, or an amount which is capped that is considerably more than the room and board costs of care" (Hollander & Walker, 1998). In other provinces, residents may pay up to a fixed cost to cover the costs of the room and board component of care (i.e., accommodation, meals). In British Columbia, for example, those with state-supported or public pension income only (i.e., Old Age Security, Guaranteed Income Supplement) are required to pay an amount equivalent to 85 percent of this income to cover the costs of their care. Those with income beyond this level are required to contribute an amount up to the average board and room cost for the province (Cohen et al., 2005).

Currently, a minority of older adults is in long-term residential care at any given point in time. In 2001, 9.2 percent of women and 4.9 percent of men aged 65 and over were residents in such facilities. Nevertheless, the likelihood of residential care placement also increases with age. In 1996, very few persons (2.1%) aged 65–74 were being cared for in nursing homes and related settings. However, this increased to 8.9 percent of those aged 75–84 and 33.8 percent of those aged 85 and over (Lindsay, 1999). As a result, the proportion of older adults who will spend some time in a facility of this type at some point in their lives appears considerably higher. This is because residents tend not to remain in such facilities very long: the median length of stay tends to be approximately two years

(CIHI, 2000). Residence also varies by gender and socio-economic status. Two thirds of long-term care facility residents are women, reflecting the combined realities of differential longevity, age- and gender-based poverty, higher levels of chronic illness, and disability among women, as well as their lesser access to informal community-based supports (CIHI, 2001). Research findings indicate that in addition to the influence of health problems (and especially cognitive impairment), age, gender, and socio-economic status, social factors such as living alone and being without a spouse or other informal caregiver also influence the likelihood of being in long-term residential care (St. John et al., 2002).

Overall, such findings suggest that it is the very old, women, and those with lesser access to social and economic resources who are the most likely recipients of this more privately focused and market-driven form of long-term care.

COMMUNITY-BASED HOME CARE SERVICES

Home care services encompass personal health, supportive, and therapeutic services provided in the home or community setting, and are designed to enable those who are "incapacitated in whole or in part, to live at home, often with the effect of preventing, delaying or substituting for long-term care or acute care alternatives" (Health Canada, 1999). They were first introduced in Canada during the 1950s as pilot programs and, at that time, tended to offer medical services only, primarily as a means of shortening hospital stays. However, in the 1970s, home health care services were more formally introduced as a means of potentially limiting the number of people requiring long-term residential care (Chappell, 1994). At that time, it was also argued that home care needed to be considered a basic form of health care in its own right (and not only as a substitute for institutional care), and that the types of services offered needed to be broad and include a wide range of personal health and supportive services necessary to maintain or help "persons with health and/or social needs related to physical or mental disability, personal or family crises or to illness of an acute or chronic nature" (Health and Welfare Canada, 1975, p. 13, cited in Chappell, 1994, p. 239).

Responsibility for home care, like other health services, rests with the provinces and territories. However, unlike physician and hospital services, they are not covered by national health insurance. Consequently, home care policies, services, and the ways in which they are delivered vary a great deal from one province or territory to the next (Coyte, 2000; Coyte & McKeever, 2001). In some, they are administered and delivered as part of a provincial health care program. In others, they are regionally or locally administered. Some provinces (e.g., Newfoundland and Labrador, Prince Edward Island, and Ontario) require physician referral, especially for access to professional services (e.g., nursing, physiotherapy), thereby preserving the gate-keeping function of the physician as well as the dominance of the biomedical approach. Others also have age restrictions (e.g., limiting access to those aged 65 and over) and income restrictions.

As with long-term residential care, the private health care sector is more heavily involved in home care than in either medical or hospital services. Across the country, home care services are delivered by both public and private sources, and on both a proprietary and not-for-profit basis (Aronson et al., 2004). Most provinces currently offer a mix of publicly and privately funded services. While more medically oriented services (e.g., nursing, therapeutic services) are often delivered by publicly funded program staff, supportive health services (e.g., personal care, homemaking assistance, meal preparation, transportation services) are often contracted out. In British Columbia, for example, professional services (including assessment, case management, nursing, rehabilitation services) are provided directly by government. All other services are purchased from for-profit or not-for-profit agencies external to government (Hollander & Pallan, 1995). Most programs also involve user fees, usually assessed on a sliding scale depending upon income (Chappell, 1994).

Currently, all provincial and territorial plans cover home support services (such as homemaking, personal care, meal services), and home nursing care (Ballinger, Zhang & Hicks, 2001). Some plans also offer therapeutic services (physiotherapy; occupational, speech, and respiratory therapy), medical equipment and supplies, minor home repair and home maintenance, social services (such as friendly visiting services), as well as respite and palliative care. While respite care is designed to give family members a break from the demands of caregiving, palliative care is end-of-life care aimed at pain and symptom control for older adults who are in the advanced stages of life-threatening illness. Although palliative care is offered in a variety of settings including long-term care facilities, hospitals or, in some cases, hospices, the trend is increasingly toward care in the home. Who pays for palliative care depends upon where the care is administered.

Home care appears to be one of the fastest-growing programs in the health care system (Williams, 1996), particularly when percentage increases in funding (rather than actual dollars) are taken into account. It has also attained prominence in government policy documents and rhetoric, where it is often presented as an inexpensive and therefore attractive alternative to increasingly costly physician, hospital, and long-term residential care. The 1990s saw extensive review and restructuring of the Canadian health care system, a process initiated in response to growing governmental concern over the current and future costs of health care as well as the system's effectiveness and efficiency. Home care, along with other community-based services, assumed a central role in the new health care system that was being envisioned during this period. As noted by Chappell:

> The rhetoric provides a vision of a new health care system which is truly a health and not simply a medical care system....[W]e would see a redistribution of dollars from medical and institutional care to a broader base of community health services....[It] promises to bring care closer to home and to shift decision making and the power base from...professionals to the individual whose health is affected. (1995, p. 25)

This new vision led to recommendations that home care become part of Canada's publicly insured and universally accessible health care system (National Forum on Health, 1997). To date, however, formal community-based home care has not emerged as a major component of Canada's universal health care system. Instead, it remains politically and economically secondary and subordinate to the more medical components of the health care system. Despite recent increases in funding, home care accounts for only a small proportion (4% in 1997–98) of total national public health care spending (Health Canada, 1998). As well, recent increases in funding have not necessarily been accompanied by increases in the number of people receiving such care. Figures for community care are difficult to access, particularly when it comes to privately paid services. However, according to the National Population Health Survey (Statistics Canada, 1998), about 10 percent of adults aged 65 and over reported receiving publicly funded or subsidized formal home care services in the preceding year. Approximately 5 percent received homemaker or home help services. Fewer received home nursing care (3.9%); help with personal care activities such as bathing, dressing, or getting in and out of bed (3.2%); and meal preparation or meal delivery services (1.7%).

Research recently conducted in British Columbia points to declines in the number of older adults receiving publicly funded or subsidized home care services (including home support services and home nursing care), as well as the extent of care received in recent years (number of hours or visits) (see Cohen et al., 2005). Those most likely to rely on these services are those with high levels of chronic illness and disability, older elderly women, those without access to informal sources of support, and those with lower levels of income (Coyte & McKeever, 2001; Penning & Chappell, 1996). Evidence of service reductions together with decisions to shift from publicly to privately funded care will therefore have a disproportionate impact on these groups (Williams et al., 2001).

COMMUNITY-BASED SELF- AND INFORMAL CARE

A common perception within contemporary Western societies such as ours is that responsibilities for health and health care are primarily vested in formal and largely state-supported bureaucratic structures, which have taken over the private roles and responsibilities of self, family, and community (with the latter all too willingly backing away from their traditional personal, familial, and community obligations). However, research evidence indicates that this is not the case. Instead, formal services, whether delivered in residential care facilities or community settings, provide only a small fraction of the overall care that older adults and other people receive. Today, as in the past, the vast majority of long-term care continues to be either self-administered or provided by family members, friends, and others in the community, frequently acting within the context of a largely "hidden health care system" (Levin & Idler, 1981).

Unlike the past, however, the current context is also one in which health and health care are being commodified within an increasingly profit-driven health care marketplace (Coburn, 2004; Navarro, 2002). Older adults and other health service users are being encouraged to consume in the name of health, lifestyle, and independence, as well as to "shop for services" and pay privately for care that enables independent living for as long as possible. Patterns of consumption are perhaps most evident in the domain of self-care.

> Self-care includes a broad range of activities that individuals engage in to promote health, prevent disease, limit illness and disability, and restore health (Dean, 1981). The form of self-care and the activities associated with it depends in large part on the health of the older adult, with well older adults more likely to use broader treatment options and emphasize health promotion activities (e.g., dietary practices, exercise programs), and less well older adults more likely to engage in self-care in response to illness (e.g., self-treatment, therapeutic services). Research on self-care in response to chronic illness and disability suggests that it, rather than either informal or formal care, represents the single most dominant mode of care. (Stoller, 1998)

Further, as disability levels increase, self-care activity also increases, particularly for personal care tasks such as bathing and dressing; self-care activity is gradually supplemented by formal and Informal sources of care (Penning et al., 1998). Health information provided through the Internet and other media encourages individuals to be "informed patients" who take personal responsibility for their health (Lupton, 1997). We see this manifested in various trends, including an increased number of illness-specific support groups (Gottlieb, 2000) and greater use of complementary and alternative medicine (CAM). Twelve percent of Canadians aged 50 and older used at least one form of CAM in 2000, with chiropractic being the most common, followed by massage and acupuncture (Votova, 2003). Pain and comorbidity (i.e., having more than one chronic illness) appear to be consistent predictors of CAM use (Astin et al., 2000), implying that the biomedical model is not meeting the chronic care needs of older adults. Health beliefs also influence CAM use, albeit to a lesser extent (Votova & Wister, forthcoming). While older adults currently use CAM less often than middle-aged and younger adults do, CAM use among older adults is expected to increase as younger generations who are more familiar with their use and who may have less faith in medical care carry their current health consumption patterns into old age.

Evidence amassed over more than two decades now confirms that informal resources, particularly family members, are major sources of care, providing an estimated 75–85 percent of all the long-term care received by older adults, including those with relatively high levels of chronic illness and disability (Penning & Keating, 2000). Typically, formal services are accessed only as a last resort and usually in conjunction with, and secondary to, informal care, not as a replacement for it (Penning & Keating, 2000; Tennstedt, Harrow & Crawford, 1996).

An emphasis on self-care locates responsibility for long-term care on older adults themselves and particularly, on the shoulders of those most likely to experience chronic illness and long-term disability. Similarly, an emphasis on informal care situates responsibilities for care of older adults within the private domains of family and, within family, on the unpaid labour of women (Chappell & Penning, 2005). The vast majority (70% or more) of informal caregivers are women, particularly older wives and middle-aged adult daughters. Some argue that this has created a "sandwich generation" of mostly middle-aged women pressed by the demands of caring for an older relative(s) at the same time as caring for children of their own. According to the 2002 General Social Survey, women spend an average of twenty-nine hours per month providing care to an older relative, more than double that of the thirteen hours per month that their male counterparts contribute (Statistics Canada, 2002). Furthermore, the vast majority of adult child caregivers is in the paid labour force, with almost one half reporting reduced work hours, a change in work schedule, or lost income due to the competing demands of being employed and providing care for older relatives (Armstrong & Armstrong, 2003; Fast, Williamson & Keating, 1999). This suggests that the work-related and other costs of caregiving (e.g., lost career mobility, fewer retirement benefits, lost leisure, and financial, physical, social, and emotional stress) also accrue disproportionately to women.

CONCLUSION

This chapter has focused on the implications of the social construction of health and aging in accordance with the biomedical model using a political economy lens. It has noted that chronic rather than acute conditions tend to prevail in later life and require a focus on long-term *care* rather than short-term *cure*. Yet, the Canadian health care system has been structured with a primary focus on short-term acute medical and hospital care. Long-term care remains secondary and continues to be structured more as a private responsibility, to be assumed by individuals and their families, than collectively in the context of public institutions. It is also an area increasingly targeted for private for-profit investment and service delivery.

The Canadian health care system is often cited as an example of an equitable if not ideal system, one that "embodies the collectivist principle that the community has responsibility for the welfare of its members" (Clark, 1998, p. 159). Yet, evidence indicating that it is the very old, women, and those with limited economic and social resources who are the least likely to have their needs met in this system and among those most likely to be required to assume private responsibilities for care (either by paying for it or by providing it themselves) while often having the fewest resources available for doing so, would seem to challenge generalized claims regarding equity.

Nevertheless, it appears that the emphasis on private responsibilities for care may well increase rather than decrease in the near future as Canada and other industrialized countries seek ways to reform their health care systems in response to concerns regarding increased costs of health care, the increased demands for care posed by an aging population, and the need to participate in the new global economy. Contrary to fears that an aging population will drain the health care system, research indicates that it is the construction of aging as a medical problem, inappropriate servicing, and a focus on individual rather than social determinants of health that are more problematic than the absolute number of older adults needing health care services. Community-based services such as home care are being widely touted as inexpensive alternatives for acute and long-term hospital and residential care (Taylor, 1990; Williams, 1996). Yet, there are concerns that while the restructuring of health care has resulted in reduced funding for health care and, therefore, in hospital and hospital bed closures, declines in admission rates, and shortened hospital stays, sufficient additional resources are not being transferred to the community care sector to allow it to offer the needed services (Chappell, 1995). Instead, those in need of care are being viewed as health care consumers and encouraged to access the private spheres of self-, family, and market-based options for care.

STUDY QUESTIONS

1. *Outline the biomedical model of health. What are the limitations of this model for an understanding of the health and health care issues faced by an aging population?*
2. *Who are the major beneficiaries of the biomedical approach to health and health care? Why?*
3. *Given evidence indicating a lack of interest by the biomedical community in dealing with the chronic health problems of older adults, how can evidence pointing to the increasing intensity of hospital care for older adults in recent years be explained?*
4. *Discuss the likely implications of changing the focus of Canada's health care system toward community-based (self-, informal, and formal) care. Are they likely to differ depending upon such factors as age, gender, and social class?*

GLOSSARY

acute illness illness characterized by sudden onset and limited duration (e.g., appendicitis, influenza).

adult daycare a program that typically provides personal care, health care, and recreational services in a group setting and on a half- or full-day basis.

assisted living a model of housing in which a person lives somewhat independently (e.g., in apartment units) but receives assistance with meals, basic housekeeping, personal health care, and opportunities for social interaction. Also known as Supportive Housing.

biomedical model a model that regards health as being the absence of disease and therefore focuses on the biological determinants of disease (thereby ignoring broader social, environmental, and other influences).

chronic illnesses illnesses that develop and persist over time and are unlikely to be cured (e.g., arthritis, cancer, diabetes, heart disease).

disability a restriction or lack of ability to perform the regular activities of daily life (e.g., work roles, housework, personal care).

home care an array of services provided to individuals who are incapacitated so as to enable them to live at home. Services vary but can include personal care (assistance with bathing, dressing, grooming), meal preparation, household cleaning, transportation, therapeutic care, the administering of medications, and other treatments.

medicalization a social process that "consists of defining a problem in medical terms, using medical language to describe a problem, adopting a medical framework to understand a problem, or using a medical intervention to 'treat' it" (Conrad, 1996, p. 139).

REFERENCES

Alder, D.A., Naylor, C.D., Austin, P.C., & Tu, J.V. (2002). Biology or bias: Practice patterns and long-term outcomes for men and women with acute myocardial infarction. *Journal of the American College of Cardiology, 39,* 1909–16.

Armstrong, P., & Armstrong, H. (2003). Thinking it through: Women, work and caring in the new millennium. In. K. Grant et al., (Eds.), *Caring for, caring about.* Aurora: Garamond Press.

Aronson, J., Denton M., & Zeytinoglu, I. (2004). Market-modeled home care in Ontario: Deteriorating working conditions and dwindling community capacity. *Canadian Public Policy, 30*(1), 111–125.

Astin, J.A., Pelletier, K.R., Marie, A., & Haskell, W.L. (2000). Complementary and alternative medicine use among elderly persons: One-year analysis of a Blue Shield Medicare supplement. *Journal of Gerontology: Medical Sciences, 55A*(1), M4–M9.

Ballinger, G., Zhang, J., & Hicks, V. (2001). *Home care estimates in national health expenditures.* Ottawa: Canadian Institute of Health Information.

Barer, M.L., Evans, R.G., & Hertzman, C. (1995). Avalanche or glacier? Health care and the demographic rhetoric. *Canadian Journal on Aging, 14*(2), 193–224.

Barer, M.L., Evans, R.G., McGrail, K.M., Green, B., Hertzman, C., & Sheps, S.B. (2004). Beneath the calm surface: The changing face of physician-service use in British Columbia, 1985/86 versus 1996/97. *Canadian Medical Association Journal, 170*(5), 803–807.

Baum, J.A.C. (1999). The rise of chain nursing homes in Ontario, 1971–1996. *Social Forces, 78*(2), 543–583.

Bélanger, A., & Dumas, J. (1998). *Report on the demographic situation in Canada, 1997.* Ottawa: Minister of Industry. (Statistics Canada cat. no. 91–209-XPE).

Bergman, H., Béland, F., Lebel, P., Contandriopoulos, A.P., Tousignant, P., Brunelle, Y., Kaufman, T., Rodriguez, R., & Clarfield, M. (1997). Care for Canada's frail elderly population: Fragmentation or integration? *Canadian Medical Association Journal, 157*(8), 1116–1121.

Berta, W., Laporte, A., & Valdmanis, V. (2005). Observations on institutional long-term care in Ontario: 1996–2002. *Canadian Journal on Aging, 24*(1), 71–84.

Berta, W., Laporte, A., Zarnett, D., Valdmanis, V., & Anderson G. (2006). A pan-Canadian perspective on institutional long-term care. *Health Policy,* in press.

Brown, A.S. (1996). *The social processes of aging and old age* (2nd ed.). Upper Saddle River, NJ: Prentice-Hall.

Canadian Institute for Health Information: CIHI. (2001). *Health care in Canada.* Ottawa: Canadian Institute of Health Information.

Canadian Study of Health and Aging: CHSA. (1994). The Canadian study of health and aging; Study methods and prevalence of dementia. *Canadian Medical Association Journal 150,* 899–913.

Chappell, N.L. (1994). Health care in Canada. In D.G. Gill & S.R. Ingman (Eds.), *Eldercare, distributive justice and the welfare state* (pp. 233–254). Albany: State University of New York Press.

Chappell, N.L. (1995). Policies and programs for seniors in Canada. *World Review of Sociology, 1,* 17–35.

Chappell, N.L. & Penning, M.J. (2005). Family caregivers: Increasing demands in the context of 21st century globalization? In Johnson, M. et al. (Eds.)., *The Cambridge handbook of age and aging* (pp. 455–62). Cambridge: Cambridge University Press.

Cheal, D. (2000). Aging and demographic change. *Canadian Public Policy, 26* Suppl, S109–S122.

Clark, P.G. (1998). Moral economy and the social construction of the crisis of aging and health care: Differing Canadian and U.S. perspectives. In M.M. Minkler & C.L. Estes (Eds.), *Critical gerontology: Perspectives from political and moral economy* (pp. 147–167). Amityville, NY: Baywood.

Coburn, D. (2004). Beyond the income inequality hypothesis: Class, neo-liberalism, and health inequalities. *Social Science and Medicine, 58,* 41–56.

Cohen, M., Murphy, J., Nutland, K., & Ostry, A. (2005). *Continuing care renewal or retreat? BC residential and home health care restructuring 2001–2004.* Vancouver, BC: Canadian Centre for Policy Alternatives.

Conrad, P. (1996). Medicalization and social control. In P. Brown (Ed.), *Perspectives in medical sociology* (2nd ed., pp. 137–162). Prospect Heights, IL: Waveland Press.

Coyte, P. (2000). *Home care in Canada: Passing the buck.* Toronto: University of Toronto Home Care Evaluation and Research Centre.

Coyte, P.C., & McKeever, P. (2001). *Submission to the Standing Committee on Social Affairs, Science and Technology.* Toronto: Home and Community Care Evaluation and Research Centre, University of Toronto.

Cujec, B., Quan, H., Jin, Y., & Johnson, D. (2004). The effect of age upon care and outcomes in patients hospitalized for congestive heart failure in Alberta, Canada. *Canadian Journal on Aging, 23*(3), 255–267.

Dean, K.J. (1981). Self-care responses to illness: A selected review. *Social Science and Medicine, 15A,* 673–687.

DeCoster, L., Bruce, S., & Kozyrskyi, A. (2005). Use of acute care hospitals by long-stay patients: Who, how much, and why? *Canadian Journal on Aging, 24* Suppl. 1, S97–S106.

Deber, R.B., & Williams, A.P. (1995). Policy, payment and participation: Long-term care reform in Ontario. *Canadian Journal on Aging, 14*(2), 294–318.

Demers, M. (1998). Age differences in the rates and costs of medical procedures and hospitalization during the last year of life. *Canadian Journal on Aging, 17*(2), 186–196.

Fast, J.E., Williamson, D.L., & Keating, N.C. (1999). The hidden costs of informal eldercare. *Journal of Family and Economic Issues, 20*(3), 301–326.

Ferraro, K.F., & Farmer, M.M. (1999). Utility of health data from social surveys: Is there a gold standard for measuring morbidity? *American Sociological Review, 64*(2), 303–315.

Forbes, W.F., Jackson, J.A., & Kraus, A.S. (1987). *Institutionalization of the elderly in Canada.* Toronto: Butterworths.

Ganz, P.A. (1992). Treatment options for breast cancer: Beyond survival. *New England Journal of Medicine, 326*(17), 1147–1149.

Gee, E.M. (2000). Population and politics: Voodoo demography, population aging and Canadian social policy. In E.M. Gee & G.M. Gutman (Eds.), *The overselling of population aging: Apocalyptic demography, intergenerational challenges, and social policy* (pp. 5–25). Don Mills, ON: Oxford University Press.

Gottlieb, B.H. (2000). Self-care among older adults. *Canadian Journal on Aging, 9* Suppl, 32–57.

Greb, J., Chambers, L.W., Gafni, A., Goeree, R., & LaBelle, R. (1994). Interprovincial comparisons of public and private sector long-term care facilities for the elderly in Canada. *Canadian Public Policy, 20*(3), 278–296.

Health Canada. (1998). *Public home care expenditures in Canada, 1975–76 to 1997–98.* Ottawa: Minister of Public Works and Government Services.

Health Canada. (1999). *Statistical report on the health of Canadians.* Ottawa: Federal, Provincial, and Territorial Advisory Committee on Population Health.

Hertzman, C., Pulcins, I.R., Barer, M.L., Evans, R.G., Anderson, G.M., & Lomas, J. (1990). Flat on your back or back to your flat? Sources of increased hospital services utilization among the elderly in British Columbia. *Social Science and Medicine, 30*(7), 819–828.

Hollander, M.J., & Pallan, P. (1995). The British Columbia Continuing Care system: Service delivery and resource planning. *Aging: Clinical and Experimental Research, 7*(2), 94–109.

Hollander, M.J., & Walker, E.R. (1998). *Report of continuing care organization and terminology.* Ottawa: Minister of Public Works and Government Services Canada.

Jacobs, P., Mills, C., & Hollander, M. (1997). Financing long-term care in Canada. *Health Care Management, 3*(1), 101–115.

Kirkey, S. (1992). MDs back rationing of care: Survey. *Saskatoon Star Phoenix,* p. A14.

Klein, D., Najman, J., Kohrman, A., & Munro, C. (1982). Patient characteristics that elicit negative responses from family physicians. *Journal of Family Practice, 14*(5), 881–888.

Lassey, M.L., Lassey, W.R., & Jinks, M.J. (1997). *Health care systems around the world.* Upper Saddle River, NJ: Prentice-Hall.

Levin, L.S., & Idler, E.L. (1981). *The hidden health care system: Mediating structures and medicine.* Cambridge, MA: Ballinger.

Lindsay, C. (1999). *A portrait of seniors in Canada* (3rd ed.). Catalogue No. 89–519-XPE. Ottawa: Statistics Canada.

Lupton, D. (1997). Consumerism, reflexivity and the medical encounter. *Social Science and Medicine, 45*(30), 373–381.

Nair, C., Karim, R., & Nyers, C. (1992). Health care and health status: A Canada-United States statistical comparison. *Health Reports, 4*(2), 175–183.

National Forum on Health. (1997). Canada health action: Building on the legacy. Volume I. The final report. Ottawa: Health Canada.

Navarro, V. (2002). Neoliberalism, globalization, unemployment, inequalities and the welfare state. In V. Navarro (Ed.), *The political economy of social inequalities: Consequences for health and quality of life* (pp. 33–119). Amityville, NY: Baywood Publishing.

Norland, J.A. (1994). *Profile of Canada's seniors.* Ottawa: Statistics Canada (cat. no. 96–312E).

Northcott, H.C., & Milliken, P.J. (1998). *Aging in British Columbia. Burden or benefit?* Calgary: Detselig Enterprises.

Ontario Ministry of Health and Long-Term Care. (2006). Chronic care co-payment 2004. Retrieved on January 24, 2006 from http://www.health.gov.on.ca/english/public/pub/chronic/chronic.html.

Penning, M.J., & Chappell, N.L. (1996). *Home support services in the Capital Regional District: Client survey.* Final report submitted to the Capital Regional District, Department of Health, Victoria, BC.

Penning, M.J., Chappell, N.L., Stephenson, P.H., Rosenblo, L., & Tuokko, H.A. (1998). *Independence among older adults with disabilities.* Final report submitted to the National Health Research and Development Program, Health Canada, Ottawa.

Penning, M.J., & N.C. Keating. (2000). Self, informal and formal care. *Canadian Journal on Aging, 19* Suppl, 58–100.

St-John, P.D., Montgomery, P.R., Kristjansson, B., & McDowell, I. (2002). Cognitive scores, even within the normal range, predict death and institutionalization. *Age and Ageing, 31*(5), 373–378.

Stahl, S.M., & Feller, J.R. (1990). Old equals sick: An ontogenetic fallacy. In S.M. Stahl (Ed.), *The legacy of longevity* (pp. 21–34). Newbury Park, CA: Sage.

Statistics Canada (1998). Home care in Canada. *Health Reports, 10*(1), 29–37. Catalogue No. 82–003-XIE. Ottawa: Statistics Canada.

Statistics Canada. (1998). National population health survey. Public use micro data files. Ottawa: Statistics Canada.

Statistics Canada. (1999). A portrait of seniors in Canada, 3rd edition. Catalogue No. 89–519-XPE. Ottawa: Statistics Canada.

Statistics Canada. (2002). A profile of disability in Canada, 2001. Catalogue No. 89–577-XIE. Ottawa: Statistics Canada.

Statistics Canada. (2002). The sandwich generation. *Perspectives on Labour and Income, 5*(9). 75–001-XIE. Ottawa: Statistics Canada.

Statistics Canada. (2004). Deaths, 2002. Catalogue No. 84-F0211-XIE. Ottawa: Statistics Canada.

Statistics Canada. (2005). Population projections for Canada, provinces and territories, 2005. Catalogue No. 91–520-XIE. Ottawa: Statistics Canada.

Stoller, E.P. (1998). Dynamics and processes of self-care in old age. In M.G. Ory & G.H. DeFriese (Eds.), *Self-care in later life* (pp. 24–61). New York: Springer.

Taylor, M.G. (1990). *Insuring national health care: The Canadian experience.* Chapel Hill: University of North Carolina Press.

Tennstedt, S., Harrow, B., & Crawford, S. (1996). Informal care vs. formal services: Changes in patterns of care over time. In M.E. Cowart & J. Quadagno (Eds.), *From nursing homes to home care* (pp. 71–91). New York: Haworth Press.

Votova, K. (2003). *Complementary and alternative medicine use among older adults: The role of health beliefs.* Unpublished master's thesis, Simon Fraser University, Vancouver, BC.

Votova, K., & Wister, A.V. (Forthcoming). Complementary and alternative medicine use among older adults: The role of push-pull health belief structures.

Watson, D., Heppner, P, Reid, R., Bogdanovic, B., & Roos, N. (2005). Use of physician services by older adults: 1991/92 to 2000/2001. *Canadian Journal on Aging, 24* Suppl. 1, S29–S36.

Wilkinson, R., & Marmot, M. (2003). *Social determinants of health: The solid facts* (2nd ed.). Copenhagen, Denmark: World Health Organization.

Williams, A.M. (1996). The development of Ontario's home care program: A critical geographical analysis. *Social Science and Medicine, 42*(6), 937–948.

Williams A.P., Dever, R., Baranek, P., & Gildiner, A. (2001). From Medicare to home care: Globalization, state retrenchment, and the profitization of Canada's health care system. In P. Armstrong, H. Armstrong, & D. Coburn (Eds.), *Unhealthy times: Political economy perspectives on health and care in Canada* (pp. 7–30). New York: Oxford University Press.

World Health Organization (WHO). (1958). *The first ten years of the WHO*. Geneva: World Health Organization.

ENDNOTES

1. According to the United Nations, a country is considered "young" if less than 4 percent of its population is aged 60 or over, "youthful" if 4–6 percent is aged 60 and over, "mature" if 7–9 percent is aged 60 or over, and "aged" if 10 percent or more of its population is aged 60 and over.
2. The rationale for this requirement for co-payment in hospital settings appears to be that it will discourage patients from remaining in hospital settings (acute or chronic) when they could instead be moved to other (less costly) long-term care facilities.
3. The first was established in 1966 as a federal-provincial program to share the cost of developing social welfare programs and, therefore, providing limited resources to cover such things as homemakers and adult daycare services. The second was established in 1977 to provide provinces with some support for the development of nursing homes, home care, adult residential care, and ambulatory health care services.
4. Canada's public health care insurance program was founded on five principles: universality of coverage (i.e., coverage for all Canadians), accessibility of services, comprehensiveness of services, portability (from one province or region to another), and public administration (on a non-profit basis and without the involvement of the private sector).

PART 6

ENVIRONMENT, WORK, AND HEALTH

There is growing and persuasive evidence that social determinants of health such as income, education, employment status, food security, workplace, and environment play an important part in the health status of individuals and populations. Lifestyles and behaviour patterns have minor impact compared to social and economic factors.

Work, workplace health and safety standards, and physical and social environments have greatly influence health outcomes and morbidity and mortality rates. Two readings in this section address these issues.

In Chapter 19, S. Harris Ali points out that rather than separate issues, environmental and health issues are intimately related. He argues that these issues can only be analyzed in their social, political, and economic contexts, and understood in terms of a "tragedy of the commons." Such a perspective, he argues, highlights the important relationship between the state, industry, and society in the origin and management of environmental health risks.

Ali provides a brief historical account of environmental concerns, giving recognition to the pioneer work in 1962 with the publication of *Silent Spring* by Rachael Carson. He then presents an examination of how environmental regulations are established through two conventional approaches – epidemiology and toxicological risk assessment. The establishment of environmental regulations and management of risks exemplify initial attempts to deal with these risks. More recently, those who advocate and lobby for a clean, safe, and healthy environment often employ the notion of the "precautionary principle" in public policy and lobby for alternative ways to establish health regulations through activities such as those found in the environmental justice movement and popular epidemiology. The environmental justice movement arose out of the recognition that environmental risks are unevenly distributed in society. Popular epidemiology arose as a response to the perceived limitations of traditional epidemiology, risk assessment, and public health regulatory activities. Ali notes that these developments highlight the complexity of dealing with environmental health problems as the stakeholders are numerous, and that to effectively address the problem requires going beyond the technical solutions. The social context of environmental health problems must be considered. Furthermore, environment must no longer be thought of as a "luxury issue" but as an issue intimately connected to public health and human survival.

Robert Storey, in Chapter 20, turns to the relationship between work and health, occupational health and safety issues, and the Canadian workers' compensation system. He argues that workplace health and safety is a social, economic, and political problem of significant proportions. First and foremost, this is revealed by the toll in human lives resulting from workplace fatalities and injuries. The economic cost associated with medical care alone runs into billions of dollars. Workers' compensation boards cover only those costs which are deemed to be directly associated with a person's workplace. All other costs for injuries and diseases whose etiology cannot be definitely determined and linked to work are shouldered by the injured worker and the society as a whole.

Storey points out that while workers faced health hazards in pre-industrial forms of work, it is generally recognized that work became more hazardous with the onset of industrial capitalism in England. The rise of industrial capitalism in Canada in the late 19th century brought with it many of the same health and safety problems that characterized its rise in England and elsewhere. The initial regulatory efforts produced factory acts and workmen's compensation legislation to protect workers. These were weak and voluntary and did not cover the great majority of workplaces and workers. These statutes were directed at "dangerous trades" mostly performed by men; women, as domestic workers and garment workers at home, were not covered. The gender bias shown in these early provisions remains, to some extent, in the contemporary context.

The voluntary essence of occupational health and safety and workers' compensation remained in place for quite some time. Storey points out that it was only during the sixties and seventies, along with various social movements, the protests of industrial and public sector workers, and the appearance of illness in large number of workers (particularly in radium and asbestos mining), that occupational health and safety issues were brought into the forefront. Canadian workers during this time made numerous gains and saw some important changes in occupational health and safety and workers' compensation laws. But the focus remained primarily on illness and disease amongst male workers in the primary and industrial sectors. It was not until the eighties and later that white collar and office work, fast food service work, and grocery work were finally being recognized as potentially unhealthy and dangerous work. In addition, increased work expectations contribute to elevated stress levels that can have severe consequences for workers' health. Storey notes that some of the workplace hazards "spill over" into the broader environment and endanger the health of workers' families and communities.

While the provisions of health and safety legislation and employer's responsibilities have expanded, full compliance with these regulations and provisions remains in contention. Storey notes that employers across the country have opposed recent developments and even want a "pushback" in workers' compensation injuries covered and the amount of compensation paid to injured workers. The workers and the trade unions continue to resist these alterations in occupational health and safety and the workers' compensation system. These struggles are a continuous reminder to workers and the trade unions to remain vigilant in safeguarding the gains made in occupational health and safety. These developments point to the social, economic, and political significance of occupational health and safety and workers' compensation systems.

19

ENVIRONMENTAL HEALTH AND SOCIETY

S. HARRIS ALI York University

INTRODUCTION

Although often portrayed as separate issues, environmental and health issues are intimately related. Examples of this interconnection are abundant and a cursory look at a newspaper on any given day will reveal stories covering a wide range of problems involving the interrelationship of health and the environment. To review just a few, you may find stories on: the closing of public beaches due to high bacterial levels; smog and air pollution leading to breathing problems for urban dwellers; boil water alerts for rural dwellers; U.V. warnings urging people not to stay out in the sun too long because of the thinning ozone layer; chemical contamination of water supplies due to industrial accidents; the onset of disease outbreaks caused by microbes spread through the air, water, soil, or food chain; and so on.

In this chapter, we will investigate how many environmental health issues can only be analyzed if the social and political economic contexts in which these issues are embedded are understood first. Toward this end, we will begin with a very brief historical account of the rise of modern environmental concern and see how this is related to many of the health issues that we confront today. To further our sociological understanding in this direction we will then consider how many environmental health issues may be theoretically understood in terms of one of the basic foundational precepts of environmental sociology, namely the "tragedy of the commons." In particular, such a perspective will highlight the important relationship between the state, industry, and society in the origin and management of environmental health risks. This will be followed by a brief examination of how environmental health regulations are established via two conventional approaches – epidemiology and toxicological risk assessment. Finally, we shall see how the management of environmental health risks is a political process and how those who advocate for a clean, safe, and healthy environment often employ the notion of the "precautionary principle" by actively pursuing and lobbying for alternative ways to establish environmental health regulations through social movement activities such as those found in the Environmental Justice movement and Popular Epidemiology.

PUBLIC CONCERN ABOUT THE ENVIRONMENT AND HEALTH

Arguably, one of the most significant influences that inspired the modern-day environmental movement was the 1962 publication of *Silent Spring*. In this book, former marine biologist Rachel Carson describes in compelling detail the devastating environmental and health impacts of the synthetically produced chemical DDT. Indiscriminately used soon after the Second World War for the control of a wide range of insect pests (notably mosquitoes involved in malaria transmission), Carson compiled scientific evidence that indicated that DDT was widespread in the environment and in the food chain. She also wrote of the harmful effects of this pervasive chemical. What perhaps enabled the book to resonate so widely with the general public was Carson's depiction of a future scenario that was quite feasible and supported by the scientific findings of the day. In the preface, entitled "A Fable for Tomorrow," Carson vividly describes a typical American town that becomes enveloped by an eery silence. The previously vibrant town has become a barren desolate landscape in which no signs of nature or life, from the songs of birds, to the splashing of fish and frogs, to even the playful voices of children could be heard – all silenced by the insidious effects of synthetic chemicals in the environment. The publication of *Silent Spring* inspired numerous political and social reactions as environmental movements arose to protect the environment from chemical contamination and to demand the need to regulate industry. In response, the chemical industry formalized their own efforts to counter the claims made by the burgeoning environmental movement, and the tensions between environmental and industrial interests soon became entrenched.

Just as *Silent Spring* helped contribute to a new public awareness that human health was threatened by unchecked human intervention in nature, another major event that contributed to the adoption of this new type of consciousness was the famous photograph of the planet Earth taken from outer space during the first lunar landing in 1969. With this photograph, for the first time, we, as human beings, were able to view our home from a unique vantage point, outside our usual terms of reference. The depiction of our "big blue marble" suspended in the vast emptiness of space brought into vivid focus the finite and fragile qualities of the physical/material basis that supports our lives and with that, the realization of the need to preserve that "life support system" (or **carrying capacity**) through environmental protectionism (WCED, 1987). With this came the acute realization that the Earth (i.e., the environment) had to be protected if human health and well-being were to be maintained.

The emphasis on the urgent need to protect the environment was further bolstered by the release of the Limits to Growth report in 1972. Prepared by Massachusetts Institute of Technology (MIT) researchers, and commissioned by a group of European industrialists, business advisers, and civil servants collectively known as the Club of Rome, the report presented different future scenarios based on the results of inputting a large number of different variables into a computer model. Using data from 1900–1970 and extrapolating to the year 2100, the report concluded that industrial growth could not keep going the way it was presently going, because that would lead to societal collapse based on major food shortages, the depletion of natural resources, and an excessive amount of pollution and chemical contamination. The release of this report, as well as the oil crisis in 1972, served to heighten public awareness of the environmental issues throughout the seventies. It was also during this period that we saw the rise of various environmental acts, legislation, and government bodies such as the federal and provincial Ministries of Environment.

More than a decade later, another influential report was released, this time by the United Nations World Commission on Environment and Development. Entitled *Our Common Future*, this report introduced the influential notion of sustainable development as "development that meets the needs of the present without compromising the ability of future generations to meet their own needs" (1987, p. 8). In trying to address the tensions between industry and environmentalists that was coming to a boil over the course of the previous decades, the notion of sustainable developed proffered a possible solution by formally attempting to bridge together concerns about environmental protection with continued industrial growth. The urgency to adopt such an approach became even more compelling shortly thereafter as evidence mounted for two environmental problems of a worldwide scope, both of which could be attributed to industrial activities of the modern day – the thinning ozone layer due to **CFCs** and global warming due to **greenhouse gases**.

THE TRAGEDY OF THE COMMONS

The view that the life-supporting capabilities of the Earth were being threatened by increasing impacts of human activities, particularly industrial activities, has been referred to as a neo-Malthusian perspective. Writing in the early 1800s, Robert Thomas Malthus presented an analysis in which he argued that since the human population grows geometrically (i.e., exponentially), while natural resources grow linearly, at some point soon, population growth will outpace the growth of food needed to feed the ever increasing number of people. He then came to the gloomy conclusion that, as a result, human misery will be an inevitable part of life in the future because the Earth will no longer be able to provide subsistence for the population.

A similar type of argumentation was developed much later by Garret Hardin in an influential article published in the journal *Science* in 1968. In this article, Hardin essentially argues that serious problems arise because the sustainability of the commons – that is, that which is owned equally by everyone in the community, such as common land, the air we breathe, and the water we drink – is threatened because of what Hardin describes as the inherent human drive to maximize utility based on rational but selfish considerations. Let us consider Hardin's argument through the example of a common area in which a number of sheep owned by different individuals can freely graze. Here, the commons is the grazing land that is owned by all. Let us assume for the sake of simplicity that each individual shepherdess owns an equal number of lambs. At some point, an equilibrium will be reached when the amount of grass consumed by the sheep will be exactly the amount that can grow back to feed the sheep (i.e., be replenished so as to sustain the integrity of the commons). However, one shepherdess may feel that by adding an additional animal to her personal herd she will be able to make more money for herself, and only herself (based on the assumption of maximum utility and rational self-interest). This individual does realize that adding this additional animal will result in overgrazing, whereby the commons is threatened as the sustainable equilibrium is disrupted (a negative consequence). But, at the same time, she realizes that this negative consequence will be shared with all the other shepherdesses in the community. From a rational self-interest point of view, she has much to gain individually because the profits of having the extra animal in her personal herd will fall to her and her alone. The costs/consequences, on the other hand, will be shared with all others in the community. In a sense, this individual is getting a *free ride* – she is profiting at other people's expense. Now, what will happen if all the other shepherdesses think like this? A significant problem will arise because the common land will quickly be destroyed. The moral here then is very similar to the fable in which a greedy individual, in his quest to secure more and more golden eggs, literally kills the goose that lays the golden eggs, thereby destroying the source of golden eggs once and for all. In a similar light, the *over-exploitation* of the Earth's resource will undermine the ability of the Earth to maintain its life-support functions, which we as human beings depend upon for our survival.

In more formalistic language, the environmental costs that are shared by community are known as **externalities** because they are treated as if they are external to the system. Let us now consider a more familiar example with reference to the industrial capitalist system. Say that an industrial capitalist is producing some commodity, but a by-product of the manufacturing process is a toxic particulate that leaves the factory through a smoke stack. These dangerous chemicals are then carried through the air and are deposited in the surrounding air, water, and soil, as well as in the lungs of people residing close to the factory. Who assumes the costs of the environmental clean up of the water, air, and soil, and the health costs of those made ill by the toxic chemicals? Who assumes the economic benefits of manufacturing commodities but not the costs of the environmental cleanup? The capitalists argue that these externalities are somebody else's problem, not theirs. So, if the pollution they produce makes people outside the factory sick, then the government should do something about cleaning up the pollution, and the government should pay for the medical bills of the sick people through the welfare state.

In this example, the commons is represented by the surrounding air, water, and soil, and the costs of the environmental consequences of polluting the commons are shared by the community (and/or the state as will be discussed momentarily). In other words, the costs of industrial manufacture are externalized. The same is true for the associated health care costs. The industrial capitalist thus receives a *free ride* because the profits of industrial manufacturing accrue to the private industrialist, but the costs of the contaminated commons are *externalized* onto the general public (and the state). Currently, environmental economists have developed various techniques to "internalize" these costs in an attempt to end the free ride (for example, tradable pollution permits, the polluter pays principle, tax disincentives, etc.) but a discussion of these goes beyond the scope of the present chapter.

For the sake of clarification, note that our previous example involving the grazing of common land involved a *subtraction* of natural resources from the commons (i.e., grasslands), whereas the latter example deals with an unwanted *addition* to the commons (i.e., pollution); but in either case, we are dealing with externalities that destroy the commons and the free rider problem. It should also be noted that externalities may take many different forms, such as the costs of cleanup and treatment of sewage, household garbage, nuclear waste, various synthetic chemicals, and so on – all of which, it should be recalled, have important consequences for human health. Second, as will now be discussed, societal attempts to deal with externalities quickly become political issues involving environmental health issues associated with risk management and environmental justice.

A TOXIC CULTURE

Ulrich Beck (1992) contends that we live in a "risk society" where the *unanticipated* side effects or *unintended* consequences and externalities of the industrialization process are brought to the political forefront. Beck argues that in the past (from the Second World War to around the seventies) there was tacit societal tolerance for the production of negative externalities, because such consequences were rationalized and justified as the "costs of progress," and therefore accepted within the logic of the political economic context of the day. In contrast, with the contemporary proliferation of **environmental risks** of potentially global impact, such approval has increasingly become politically problematic, and the logic of risk production has become questioned by the general public.

The need to confront the externalities of the industrial age is especially noteworthy with respect to chronic toxicity, where harmful health effects occur because of low-dose exposures over long periods. Studies have shown that today, virtually every living human being to some degree carries what is known as a toxic body burden. **Body burden** refers to the **bioaccumulation** of toxic substances in the body (Steingraber, 1997). Such substances enter the body through various routes – inhalation, ingestion, and skin absorption – and through various sources – food, air, water, and soil. Many of the chemicals that persist in the body are fat soluble and as such, body fat is considered an especially sensitive indicator of exposure to environmental contaminants – particularly those referred to as **Persistent Organic Pollutants (POPs)**. Since human breast milk is about three percent fat, POPs tends to concentrate here and it has been found that 99 percent of the breast milk sampled in the United States contained one such class of chemicals – poly-chloro-biphenyls (PCBs) – which were widely used in the recent past as coolants in electrical transformers (Milly & Leiss, 1997). In fact, studies have shown that about one of every four samples taken from mothers contained PCB concentrations exceeding the legal limit (2.5 parts per million); significantly, commercial formula is pulled from the shelves when it contains levels above 2.5 parts per million (Steingraber, 1997). Or, to put it another way: roughly 25 percent of all U.S. breast milk was too contaminated to be bottled and sold as a food commodity. Moreover, the highest levels of PCBs in fat and milk were found amongst those living in the Arctic regions where the chemical is carried by wind currents and concentrates in the food chain through bioaccumulation (NRTEE, 2001). The extremely high concentrations of PCBs in the Indigenous peoples of the North also raise questions of environmental equity: why should this group of individuals, who had and have little to do with industrial production in the South, have to bear the environmental health externalities of the South? This is just one example of living in what is referred to as a toxic culture.

Hofrichter (2000) defines a toxic culture as one in which social arrangements encourage and excuse the deterioration of the environment and human health. The emergence of a toxic culture is based on an unquestioned production of hazardous substances as well as the presence of dangerous technologies, substandard housing, chronic stress, and exploitative working conditions. How did such circumstances come to prevail? Let us attempt to seek answers to this question by considering the relationship between industries, the state, and the environment and health movements – particularly with respect to the issue of how environmental health regulations are established.

ENVIRONMENTAL HEALTH REGULATIONS

Environmental health regulations specify the legally permitted amount of dangerous chemicals that industry may dispose of in the commons, or the amount to which people may be exposed. These regulations are specified in various Acts such as: the Canadian Environmental Protection Act, the Pest Control Products Act, the Food and Drugs Act, the Hazardous Products Act, the Fertilizers Act, the Fisheries Act, and the Feeds Act, as well as the occupational health and safety acts of various provinces. The regulations themselves are determined through the activities of government ministries such as Environment Canada, Health Canada, or the Pesticide Management Regulatory Agency which is made up of experts from these two ministries, in addition to Agriculture Canada and Natural Resources Canada. The specific regulation for each chemical (or class of chemical) is based on the results obtained from epidemiological or toxicological risk assessment analyses (a third method, the **clinical control trial** is used exclusively for drugs, whereas the former methods are used for toxic substances). Each of these methods poses certain problems when used to establish environmental health regulations, not the least of which, as we shall see, is the political dimension involved in what at first sight appears to be a purely technical process.

EPIDEMIOLOGY

Epidemiology may be generally defined as the study of the incidents and distribution of disease/illness in the population; as such, it relies somewhat heavily on the analysis of statistics, particularly the frequencies related to particular health outcomes and exposures. Epidemiological techniques involve observational studies of humans to gather and analyze data in order to determine whether a particular health outcome arises due to exposure to certain factors – often called risk factors. Risk factors may include concentrations of various environmental carcinogens (in the case of establishing environmental health regulations), as well as other influences such as cardiovascular risk factors (e.g., cholesterol, body fat) or certain risk behaviours (smoking, alcohol consumption).

One of the most common measures used in certain types of epidemiological studies is known as **Relative Risk**, and it is defined as the ratio of the risk of developing the disease amongst those exposed compared to the risk of the developing the disease amongst those not exposed.

Despite the various successes of conventional epidemiology, the use of epidemiological analysis in studying environmental health problems has met with resistance by some members of the environmental health community (Needleman, 1997; Tesh, 2000; Wing, 2000). The main reason is that from a technical standpoint, the Relative Risks obtained are often low for environmental exposures – typically less than two – and they do not often attain statistical significance (that is, from a statistical perspective, the obtained Relative Risk figure could be the result of chance) (Pekkanen & Pearce, 2001). Low Relative Risks are then used by certain industrial and state interests to dismiss the need to investigate environmental health problems. Critics argue, however, that low Relative Risks are obtained because of the nature of environmental health problems. That is, *involuntary* exposure to toxic chemicals, such as the situation amongst residents living in a highly industrialized area, occurs over long periods of time, while the exposures themselves occur at low concentrations. Furthermore, this type of prolonged, low concentration exposure tends to vary between individuals within a given area, thereby lowering the calculated Relative Risks. Such situations are very different from *acute exposure* circumstances, such as a chemical explosion in a factory, that are normally studied by epidemiologists.

TOXICOLOGICAL RISK ASSESSMENT

Toxicological risk assessment is perhaps more widely used than epidemiology for the establishment of environmental health regulations and is applied to various products and processes, including: pharmaceuticals, consumer products, cosmetics, biological agents, radiation, industrial chemicals, food additives, pesticide residues, and air, water, and soil pollutants.

The conventional method followed in conducting risk assessments is given by a framework presented in the U.S. National Research Council's (1983) *Risk Assessment in the Federal Government: Managing the Process* (commonly referred to as the "Red Book"). The heart of the framework for the establishment of environmental health regulations may be considered the phase known as dose-response assessment. Here the goal is to obtain a mathematical equation that expresses the relationship between exposure – which is defined in terms of the amount exposed or the *dose* – and the number of cases where adverse effects develop (this is the *response*).

The data for the Dose-Response equation comes from laboratory experiments where different groups of animals are exposed to different doses; after a certain period of time, the animals are examined to detect the presence of cancerous tumours (or other adverse health effects). Notably, the animals are exposed to very high doses of the substance in order to ensure that that an adverse effect develops within the given time allotted for the experiment. In relation to cancer in particular, the *latency period* – the period between exposure and onset of the disease – may be quite long (for some forms of cancer in humans it may be between 10–30 years; e.g., lung cancer). This, however, results in the need to mathematically extrapolate from the high doses that were administered to the test animals to the low doses that human beings are usually exposed to in the environment, which in turn introduces an uncertainty in the applicability of the results to the human situation. To help compensate for this uncertainty in high to low dose, as well as the uncertainties due to the different metabolic processes and lifespan of animals versus humans, a safety factor is introduced when establishing a regulatory level. The mathematical analysis of the dose-response relationship is done to identify a threshold dose-exposure level where adverse effects manifest only once this threshold level is exceeded. In other words, an ostensibly "safe" level of exposure is determined, and this level is used to establish the regulation (with the safety factor incorporated).

Although epidemiology and risk assessment appear to be purely technical, and therefore politically neutral exercises, they are not. Part of this lack of neutrality has to do with the working assumptions adopted in researching a particular case. Consequently, the results of the risk assessment can be manipulated by taking out certain factors from consideration or putting others in, thereby biasing the results toward a particular conclusion favoured by political or industrial interests. For example, although one risk assessment revealed that there were certain health impacts from a herbicide (dacthal) found in Oregon drinking water, a subsequent risk assessment was conducted by the U.S. Environmental Protection Agency to eliminate a certain factor in the model – a factor that took into account the fact that children would be drinking the water (as opposed to only adults). When this factor was eliminated, the results of the risk assessment revealed no health impacts (O'Brien, 2000).

RISK MANAGEMENT

Risk Management deals with the social aspects of establishing environmental health regulations, especially the process through which a regulatory agency sets the standards and decides what action to take based on the results of the risk assessment and epidemiological analyses. These types of decisions are often quite difficult and contentious because good risk management practice requires the combining of technical information about risk with political, economic, legal, ethical, and other considerations (Leiss & Chociolko, 1993).

In setting environmental health regulations, the state agency (for example, Environment Canada or Health Canada), as part of the government, finds itself caught between several competing interests and must make an immediate decision on the basis of a great deal of technical uncertainty – a situation referred to as the **regulator's dilemma** (Bodansky, 1991). On the one hand, the government feels that it has to ensure the protection of the public health and environment as demanded by environmental groups and many members of the general public. On the other hand, the political elites often have a long-standing arrangement with industrial elites (Clement, 1975) in terms of tax and environmental concessions of various sorts. When it comes to question of the level at which a particular regulatory standard should be set, industry and the environmentalists often have very divergent views. Industries do not normally support the introduction of stringent environmental standards because they will have to change their industrial processes/practices and invest in environmental technologies to meet these standards; and they consider these actions (and the costs associated with them) as unnecessary and a threat to their profitability and survival. Recall that under the present industrial capitalist system, the industrial capitalist is getting somewhat of a "free ride" when it comes to polluting the commons and they would like to maintain that situation, but the imposition of strict environmental regulations begins to erode this "free ride." On the other hand, environmental health activists believe that the standards should be made more stringent in order to protect the environment and public health. Hence, the competing pressures – industry for lax or no standards at all versus the environmental lobby's pressure for stricter standards. Under such competing forces, the government is faced with what is referred to by Habermas (1975) as a "**legitimation crisis.**" That is, the government is put in a difficult position where it may not be seen as legitimate and will therefore not be able to establish sufficient commitment or sense of authority to govern. In the case of environmental health regulations, if the government appears to favour industry too much, it will lose its legitimacy in the eyes of the public and will therefore likely face a difficult time retaining power over the next election. If the state is seen to favour the environmental lobby too much, it will lose the financial backing of industry (see also Poulantazas (1980) on the "**relative autonomy of the state**" for a more general discussion of the role of the state in society).

Despite certain reservations, private industry does generally support the use of risk assessment in establishing regulations – especially, as we will see, in light of the other possibilities. One reason that risk assessment finds industrial support is that risk assessment, by essentially directing attention to the question of *how much* of a chemical is allowed to enter the commons, in effect permits a certain level of environmental contamination. This diverts attention away from questions such as the necessity of producing toxic substances in the first place; this diversion also tends to include dismissing the need to consider more massive changes to the industrial process to eliminate toxic by-products altogether through preventive engineering and the redesign of the industrial process. Second, risk assessment gives the impression that industry is being "scientific" about environmental health issues and if regulatory disputes occur, industry is in a position to hire their own counter-experts to critique the risk assessments done by government. Furthermore, disputes and legal appeals over the government risk assessment may go on for many years, thus allowing industry to carry on business as usual in the meantime.

THE PRINCIPLE OF PRECAUTIONARY ACTION

The principle of precautionary action (or more commonly, the precautionary principle) refers to the idea that if an activity or substance is suspected to threaten human health or the environment, precautionary measures should be taken, *even if* a cause-effect relationship has not yet been scientifically established (Raffensperger & Tickner, 1999). The logic is one based on the sentiment that it is better to "be safe than sorry." In a real sense, the precautionary principle captures the rationale behind sustainable development because the latter involves a future orientation – that is, that no harm come to future generations because of any actions taken today. As such, sustainable development, like the precautionary principle, is based on the notion of foreseeing and forestalling environmental health problems with an emphasis on the anticipation of environment and health problems, and taking action before the problems occur. So, for example, based on correlational evidence, if there is some suspicion that exposure to a particular substance leads to cancer, even if a cause-effect relationship has not yet been established, the substance should be banned on the basis of the rationale of the precautionary principle (similar arguments have been made for genetically modified food, genetic engineering, nanotechnologies, global warming, the loss of biodiversity, and so on).

Advocates of the precautionary principle contend that a major failing of conventional risk management processes is that currently the burden of proof is on those who wish to stop or prevent some environmental health risk producing activity or product, rather than on those who promote it (Tesh, 2000). They argue that with the adoption of the precautionary approach, there needs to be a shift in the onus of proof from those affected by the risks to those producing the alleged risks. That is, with the precautionary principle, those who are developing the technology or chemical substance must be the ones who prove that there is no reasonable threat to environment and health. They should be the ones who are to prove that the emissions, chemical, or technology are "harmless." And it is only if they can demonstrate this to the public should approval go ahead for the manufacture of the product in question. In this light, it should not be up to the government or environmental groups to prove that there is harm.

Critics of the precautionary principle argue that in implementing the precautionary principle, one may unnecessarily forgo the benefits of the substance, product, activity, etc. because there may in fact be no cause-effect relationship. Thus, the benefits are said to be lost for no good reason. However, in considering such an argument what should be kept in mind is the free-rider phenomenon, as well as who receives the benefits and who bears the risks. In this light, the management of risk via risk assessment processes should not be thought of as simply a politically neutral technical process.

ALTERNATIVES ASSESSMENT

One way to incorporate the precautionary principle in risk management and environmental health policy is through alternatives assessment (O'Brien, 1999). Proponents of alternatives assessment argue that the guiding logic of risk assessment is misguided because it does not ask the "right" question; rather it is obsessed with the question of how much (i.e., what dose) is acceptable to the public. The question of how much suspected poison is acceptable precludes any consideration of the option that no suspected poison is at all acceptable.

With alternatives assessment the fundamental questions to be asked are: "Is this potentially hazardous activity necessary?" and "What less hazardous options are available?" The focus then changes from issues related to "What amount of risks are acceptable?" to "What options do we have for avoiding risks altogether?" Once identified by lay individuals and experts, the alternatives can be ranked by all stakeholders according to short and long term environmental criteria; then, after the alternatives are ranked, only those alternatives that reveal more, rather than less, precaution should be seriously considered, in particular the identification of those options in which the toxic chemical or risk producing activity is neither produced nor pursued. Examples of alternatives assessment include: the consideration of alternative methods of providing a service or manufacturing a product in which no toxic by-products are produced, such as alternative ways of dry-cleaning (in which halogenated solvents are not used or alternative technologies based on environmentally friendly engineering practices such as Design For Environment are used) (Graedel & Allenby, 1996). Other options include Industrial Ecology (Shrivastava, 1995) and Preventive Engineering (Vanderburg, 2000), where technology substitutions in the manufacturing process are incorporated to eliminate externalities altogether (e.g., pollution prevention technologies) or the by-products that are produced (i.e., externalities) are reincorporated into the industrial cycle as inputs for other processes. The organic farming movement provides another illustration of alternatives assessment. By considering alternatives to chemical pesticides and fertilizers, including such techniques as crop rotation, tilling, mulching, and cover crops, accepting some losses due to pests, breeding plants for pest resistance, and restoring the biological health of soils, organic farming represents a less toxic alternative.

THE ENVIRONMENTAL JUSTICE MOVEMENT

An integral element of the toxic culture is the fact that environmental risks are unevenly distributed within society – they are disproportionately found in areas occupied by minorities and the poor. In a landmark study, Robert Bullard (1990) found a statistically significant correlation between the location of toxic landfill sites and African-American neighbourhoods in Houston. That is, African-Americans were disproportionately exposed to negative environmental health impacts. This led to charges of environmental racism, that is, that environmental laws, regulations, and enforcement (including land use decisions) were seen to be discriminatory because they target communities on the basis of minority status by allowing polluting industries to be preferentially established in those areas. Since then, however, historical studies of siting decisions have led to the conclusion that sites may or may not have been selected because of racial prejudice alone, but also because of other factors, such as social class. Thus, a site may have been chosen to host a hazards-producing facility because: (1) the area was economically depressed and those in the area would be more willing to accept a potentially hazardous facility for the jobs and tax revenues for the town it promised; or (2) the people in the area were, or were perceived to be, politically less able to resist siting (Anderson et al., 1994). Regardless of the reasons, the outcome is one of an uneven distribution of environmental health risks. The need to address such inequities gave rise to what has become known as the *environmental justice movement* which has drawn attention to the racial and social class disparities in environmental health (Bryant & Mohai, 1992).

The victims of these environmental decisions feel that the government is favouring economic growth over protection of its citizens. This they see as an *injustice*, and they feel that the government is taking advantage of the local community's lack of resources to pursue economic growth at their expense. The environmental justice movement has emerged as a response to such injustice. As the movement has matured, it has expanded its mandate to consider how environmental health problems are connected to concerns of *social justice* (Szasz, 1994). As such, environmental hazards, economic impoverishment, and racial discrimination are not considered separate in the environmental justice movement. Further, in the context of the environmental justice movement, the concept of the "environment" has expanded in scope to include all life conditions in which people live, work, and play. The notion of environmental justice has therefore come to incorporate *all* life and death issues, including joblessness, abusive police practices, lack of health care, decent housing, and equitable education. And by drawing upon the assistance of labour unions, tenants' associations, and civil rights and community groups, the environmental justice movement has been involved with a diversity of issues such as: the problems of hazardous wastes, groundwater contamination, industrial pollution, and workplace safety. For example, lead is known to cause neurological problems and learning disabilities in children, and children living in low-income and inner city public housing have been found to suffer the most from lead poisoning (Mielke, 1999). The environmental justice movement would conceive of poisoning from lead in the paint of older homes or the lead present in the soils of homes in high traffic areas, not only as environmental health issues, but also as educational and housing issues.

POPULAR EPIDEMIOLOGY

Popular epidemiology is a form of participatory inquiry into the community environmental health problems that arose as a response to environmental justice concerns. It involves not only lay efforts to uncover these problems, but the organized political reaction as well. Popular epidemiology can be seen in such recent films as *Erin Brokovitch* and *A Civil Action*, both of which depict the active involvement of lay individuals in identifying a local chemical contamination problem that was the result of an **environmental corporate crime** (Cable & Benson, 1993; Capek, 1993; Ali, 2002a, b). These films also reveal the role of popular epidemiology in legal arguments made in what have come to be known as **toxic tort** cases.

Popular epidemiological efforts arose as responses to the perceived limitations of traditional epidemiology, risk assessment, and public health regulatory activities – notably, the tendency to exclude the concerns of victims and lay individuals in dealing with environmental health issues. In this light, risk assessment and conventional epidemiology are seen as being elitist, technocratic, and undemocratic. Popular epidemiology is therefore a social movement that calls for greater public participation in environmental health issues, including in-depth collaboration between members of the grassroots environmental groups and the technical experts (such as public health officials), as well the adoption of strategies involving politics and the courts in order to address the health/disease problem (Brown & Mikkelsen, 1990).

Typically, the popular epidemiology movement is initiated by members of the community who start to make lay observations concerning health effects in their area. For example, in the case of chemical contamination in Woburn, Massachusetts (which was the case covered in the film *A Civil Action*), Ann Anderson noticed that when she was taking her son for leukemia treatment in the local hospital, there were other children in the waiting room suffering from the same disease. In talking with other parents in the waiting room, she started to suspect that there might be some common underlying cause for this cancer. Further discussions with neighbours about the poor quality of water in the area (that led to bad taste, foul smells, and the discolouring of household laundry) led to a hypothesized connection between contaminated water and leukemia. To investigate her hypothesis, Anderson, with the help of the local minister, started to map out who in the neighbourhood had cancer and they found that a cluster of cancer cases was clearly evident.

Armed with this lay research, community members approached government officials (usually public health officers) to look for answers but were often rebuked and given little support with their research being dismissed as being "unscientific." Consequently, victims feel violated on two levels. First, because of the contamination itself, and second, because their sense of social justice is violated by the social reaction to their problems. In response, community members organize their efforts by forming a local grassroots group that engages in various activities such as: writing letters to regulatory agencies, demanding public hearings on the issue, staging demonstrations at the regulatory offices, picketing in front of the companies suspected of contaminating the area, and organizing rallies, protests, and marches to convince and educate others of the environmental injustices being committed.

As the movement has matured, popular epidemiology has been extended to encompass a critique of public policy, scientific discourse, and the limits of medical research itself, particularly the tendency of conventional epidemiological approaches to separate biophysical factors (i.e., exposure – disease) from social factors that need to be considered in the more effective analysis of environmental health problems. Along with this critique comes a conscious refocusing on the structural basis of the causes of health problems in the community, and the unequal distribution of environmental health risk, particularly in reference to traditional epidemiology's tendency to account for patterns of health problems in terms of lifestyle rather than community exposures to environmental hazards (Novotony, 1998).

CONCLUSION

The production of externalities, such as toxic pollution, POPs, CFCs, and greenhouse gases, threaten the ability of our planet to sustain human life in general and maintain human health in particular. By destroying the air we need to breathe, the water we need to drink, the atmosphere we need to protect us from harmful radiation, and the soil we need to grow food, we can see that environmental and health issues are in actuality two sides of the same coin.

Public recognition of the social origin of environmental health risks (and especially the role of the free rider problem in the production of such risks) has led to the politicization of such issues in modern times; we now are starting to realize that such problems are of such great importance to our overall survival that they can no longer be ignored. The establishment of environmental regulations and the management of environmental risks exemplify initial attempts to deal with these risks. More recently, other attempts, such as the implementation of the precautionary principle in public policy and opportunities for social movement activities to be involved in risk management activities, have been pursued – particularly in relation to issues involving the unequal distribution of environmental health risks. In particular, such attempts bring to the fore the complexity of dealing with environmental health problems, as evidenced by the fact that the primary stakeholders dealing with such problems are numerous – industry, the state, the public, and social movement actors. Further, such attempts highlight the fact that in order to address environmental health problems effectively, a technical solution is not enough; the social context must be also considered.

In the future, we will undoubtedly face new health problems such as: **endocrine disruption** (Colborn et al., 1997; Krimsky, 2000), **new and emerging diseases** (Ali, 2004; Levy & Fischetti, 2003; Garrett, 1994), and **multiple chemical sensitivity** (Kroll-Smith & Floyd, 1997). The environment plays a critical role in all of these. As such, it is clear that the environment should no longer be thought of as a "luxury issue" marginalized to the lower echelon of the political agenda. Rather, the environment should now be recognized as an issue intimately connected to both public health and human survival. That is, the protection of the environment is equivalent to the protection of human health, and for this reason alone the environmental issue should be placed closer to the top of the political agenda.

STUDY QUESTIONS

1. *Explain how environmental issues and health issues are two sides of the same coin.*
2. *Explain how the concepts of the toxic culture and the risk society can be used in the study of environmental health problems. In your answer, pay particular attention to the relationship between industry, the state, and the public.*
3. *Discuss how the precautionary principle can be used to critique the ways in which environmental health regulations are currently established. How can the precautionary principle be used to develop alternative approaches to the establishment of such regulations?*

4. *Discuss the ways in which social movements, such as the Environmental Justice Movement and Popular Epidemiology, have linked environmental health issues to larger issues related to social justice and a broader critique of industrial capitalist society.*
5. *Ulrich Beck notes the following:*

> *The environmental problem is by no means a problem of the world surrounding us. It is a crisis of industrial society itself, deeply rooted in the foundations of its institutions and with considerable political resonance. Threats are produced industrially, externalized economically, individualized juridically, legitimized scientifically, and minimized politically. (1995, p. 140)*

Develop an argument for or against the above statement with reference to the management of environmental health risks in contemporary society.

GLOSSARY

bioaccumulation the process through which the concentration of synthetic chemicals in the body increases over time because of environmental exposures (see also body burden).

body burden the sum total of all synthetic chemicals in the body due to environmental exposures from all routes of entry (inhalation, ingestion, and dermal absorption) and all sources (food, air, water, workplace, home, and so on). For example, 177 different organo-chlorine residues can be found in the body of an average middle-aged North American male (Steingraber, 1997).

carrying capacity the carrying capacity represents the critical limit or threshold potential for the earth to support the human population. In other words, it is a measure of the maximum level of stress that the Earth's ecosystems can withstand in order to continue as a stable life-sustaining system in equilibrium.

CFCs chlorofluorocarbons (CFCs) are a group of synthetic chemicals containing atoms of carbon, chlorine, and fluorine. They are used in aerosol sprays, blowing agents for foams and packing materials, solvents, and in refrigerants. They have been found to be chemically active in the atmosphere and thereby implicated in the process of ozone layer depletion. CFCs were banned by the 1987 Montreal Protocol.

clinical control trials research experiments in which people are divided into two groups – an experimental group that is given a drug or treatment, and a control group that is given an inactive substance (called a placebo). The two groups are then compared to determine statistically whether the drug or treatment is effective in treating the disease or ailment.

endocrine disruption refers to certain synthetic chemicals (i.e., endocrine disruptors) in the environment that interfere with the normal functioning of the hormonal systems of the body. Notably, endocrine disruptors in extremely minute concentrations are known to have negative effects on the hormonal systems. That is, low levels of exposure may lead to greater adverse health effects than high doses.

environmental corporate crime an environmental problem results from the disruption of an ecosystem, while an environmental corporate crime occurs when this disruption is the direct result of a company or corporation engaging in some illegal production process or activity. One example is midnight dumping, where a company will arrange for a truck to come to a factory to pick up drums of toxic waste that are subsequently dumped on some remote site in the middle of the night.

environmental risks threats to human health that arise from, or are transmitted through the air, water, soil, and/or food chains.

externalities formally, an externality results when a decision (for example, to pollute the atmosphere) causes costs or benefits to individuals or groups other than the person making the decision. In other words, the decision-maker does not bear all of the costs or reap all of the gains from his or her action.

greenhouse gases the greenhouse effect is an atmospheric phenomenon that is caused by the addition of greenhouse gases into the atmosphere, thus causing global warming. Greenhouse gases include (as water vapour): carbon dioxide (from the burning of fossil fuels and deforestation), CFCs, and methane.

legitimation crisis a legitimation crisis occurs when the general public questions a particular social institution as being just and valid. Consequently, there is a lack of sufficient commitment on the part of members to a particular social institution for that organization to function effectively. Notably, governments that lack legitimation often rely on repression to continue their rule (which is very inefficient).

multiple chemical sensitivity a syndrome that results from chronic low level exposure to synthetic chemicals, particularly those in the living and working environments such as: pesticides, perfumes and other scented products, fuels, food additives, carpets, building materials, and so on. Symptoms include: difficulty breathing, sleeping, and/or concentrating; memory loss; migraines; nausea; abdominal pain; chronic fatigue; aching joints and muscles; and irritated eyes, nose, ears, throat, and/or skin. The doses that are alleged to cause this syndrome are so low according to conventional toxicological measures, that the medical profession denies the existence of this syndrome as such; thus, this syndrome is a contested disease that is surrounded by a great deal of controversy between those affected and the medical profession.

new and emerging diseases refers to those infectious diseases that have newly appeared in a population or that have been known for some time but are rapidly increasing in incidence or in geographic range. Examples of emerging infectious diseases include: HIV/AIDS, SARS, Lyme disease, *E. coli* O157:H7, hantavirus, Ebola, the Marburg virus, and Lassa Fever.

persistent organic pollutants (POPs) chemical substances that persist in the environment and bioaccumulate through the food web (see bioaccumulation and body burden). In particular, they are known to be carried by wind currents to remote locations where they accumulate in the environment.

regulator's dilemma environmental regulators often need to take action to either prevent or avoid the potential for damage to the environment and human health in the face of considerable uncertainty, an unquantifiable degree of ignorance, and inherent indeterminacies. Thus, the dilemma they face is to make a regulatory decision without sufficient information.

relative autonomy of the state a perspective which assumes that the state functions in a limited but independent way to maintain and stabilize capitalist society. If the state is seen to cater to industrial interests then it will lose legitimacy in the eyes of the voting public; if it caters too strongly to the interests of the environmental lobby, it risks losing the financial support of industry. In establishing environmental health regulations, the state therefore tries to balance these competing interests while at the same time ensuring the continued functioning of capitalist society.

Relative Risk mathematically, the Relative Risk is a ratio of two risks. From the 2 x 2 Disease-Exposure Table below we can define two types of risk based on the number of people in each of the cell categories.

	Disease Develops	Disease Does Not Develop
Exposed to Chemical in the Environment	a	b
Not Exposed to Chemical in the Environment	c	d

Risk of the disease in those exposed: a/(a+b)

Risk of the disease in those not exposed: c/(c+d)

The Relative Risk is the ratio of the above two risks: $\frac{a/(a+b)}{c/(c+d)}$

If the calculated Relative Risk is greater than one, this suggests that the exposure is associated with a certain disease or health outcome (although a statistical test still would need to be completed to determine whether this association was unlikely to occur purely by chance). Thus, for example, a Relative Risk of two suggests that exposure leads to twice the risk for those exposed compared to those not exposed. If the Relative Risk is equal to one, then there is no association between exposure and the disease/health outcome at all; that is, exposure does not create any additional risk. Finally, if the Relative Risk is less than one, this implies that exposure has a protective effect, meaning that exposure leads to a decreased risk of getting the disease – this is the sort of result that drug manufacturers would like to attain in their clinical control trials. As examples, consider the Relative Risk for smoking and lung cancer is 10.7; for smoking and gastric ulcers it is four.

toxic tort a tort is an injury to a person's bodily integrity, financial situation, or other interest caused by another person's negligence or carelessness. A toxic tort is a tort caused by contact with a harmful substance.

REFERENCES

Ali, S.H. (2002a). Disaster and the political economy of recycling: Toxic fire in an industrial city. *Social Problems, 49*(2), 129–149.

Ali, S.H. (2002b). Dealing with toxicity in the risk society: The case of the Hamilton plastimet fire. *The Canadian Review of Sociology and Anthropology, 39*(1), 29–48.

Ali, S.H. (2004). A socio-ecological autopsy of the *E. coli* O157:H7 outbreak in Walkerton, Ontario, Canada. *Social Science and Medicine, 58*(12), 2601–2612.

Anderton, D.L., Anderson, A.B., Oakes, J.M., & Fraser, M.R. (1994). Environmental equity: The demographics of dumping. *Demography, 31*(2), 229–48.

Beck, U. (1992). *The risk society: Towards a new modernity*. London: Sage.
Beck, U. (1995). *Ecological enlightenment: Essays on the politics of the risk society*. Trans. M. Ritter. New Jersey: Humanities Press.
Bodansky, D. (1991). Scientific uncertainty and the Precautionary Principle. *Environment, 33*(7), 4–5 & 43–44.
Brown, P., & Mikkelsen, E.J. (1997). *No safe place: Toxic waste and leukemia, and community action*. Berkeley: University of California Press.
Bryant, B., & Mohai, P. (1992). *Race and the incidence of environmental hazards*. Boulder, CO: Westview Press.
Bullard, R. (1990). *Dumping in Dixie: Race, class and environmental quality*. Boulder, CO: Westview Press.
Cable, S., & Benson, M. (1993). Acting locally: Environmental injustice and the emergence of grass-roots environmental organizations. *Social Problems, 40*(4), 464–477.
Capek, S. (1993). The "environmental justice" frame: A conceptual discussion and an application. *Social Problems, 40*(1), 5–24.
Carson, R. (1962). *Silent spring*. Boston: Houghton Mifflin.
Clement. W. (1975). *The Canadian corporate elite: An analysis of economic power*. Toronto: McClelland and Stewart.
Colborn, T., Dumanoski, D., & Myers, J.P. (1997). *Our stolen future: Are we threatening our fertility, intelligence and survival? – A scientific detective story*. New York: Penguin.
Garrett, L. (1994). *The coming plague: Newly emerging diseases in a world out of balance*. New York: Penguin.
Gibbs, L. (2002). Citizen activism for environmental health: The growth of a powerful new grassroots health movement. *Annals of the American Academy of Political and Social Science, 584*, 97–109.
Graedel, T.E., & Allenby, B.R. (1996). *Design for environment*. New Jersey: Prentice Hall.
Habermas, J. (1975). *The legitimation crisis*. Translated by Thomas McCarthy. London: Heinemann.
Hardin, G. (1968). The tragedy of the commons. *Science, 162*, 1243–1248.
Hofrichter, R. (2000). *Reclaiming the environmental debate: The politics of health in a toxic culture*. Cambridge, MA: The MIT Press.
Krimsky, S. (2000). *Environmental endocrine hypothesis and public policy*. In S. Kroll-Smith, P. Brown, & V.J. Gunter (Eds.), *Illness and the environment: A reader in contested medicine* (pp. 95–107). New York: New York University Press.
Kroll-Smith, H.H. (1997). *Bodies in protest: Environmental illness and the struggle over medical knowledge*. New York: New York University Press.
Leiss, W., & Chociolko, C. (1993). *Risk and responsibility*. Montreal: McGill-Queen's University Press.
Levy, E., & Fischetti, M. (2003). *The new killer diseases: How the alarming evolution of germs threatens us all*. New York: Three Rivers Press.
Mielke, H.W. (1999). Lead in the inner cities. *American Scientist, 86*, 62.
Milly, P., & Leiss, W. (1997). Mother's milk: Communicating the risks of PCBs in Canada and the Far North. In D. Powell & W. Leiss (Eds.), *Mad cows and mother's milk: The perils of poor risk communication* (pp. 182–209). Kingston: McGill-Queen's University Press.
Needleman, C. (1997). Applied epidemiology and environmental health: Emerging controversies. *American Journal of Infection Control, 25*(3), 262–274.
Novotony, P. (1998). Popular epidemiology and the struggle for community health in the environmental justice movement. In D. Faber (Ed.), *The struggle for ecological*

democracy: Environmental justice movements in the United States (pp. 137–158). New York: Guilford Press.

NRTEE (National Round Table on the Environment and Economy). (2001). *Managing potentially toxic substances in Canada*. Ottawa: Renouf Publishing.

O' Brien, M.H. (2000). When harm is not necessary: Risk assessment as diversion. In R. Hofrichter (Ed.), *Reclaiming the environmental debate: The politics of health in a toxic culture* (pp. 113–133). Cambridge, MA: MIT Press.

O' Brien, M. (1999). Alternatives assessment: Part of operationalizing and institutionalizing the precautionary principle. In C. Raffsensperger & J. Tickner (Eds.), *Protecting public health and the environment: Implementing the precautionary principle* (pp. 207–219). Washington, DC: Island Press.

Pekkanen, J., & Pearce, N. (2001). Environmental epidemiology: Challenges and opportunities. *Environmental Health Perspectives, 109*(1), 1–5.

Poulantzas, N. (1980). *State, power, socialism*. London: New Left Books.

Raffensperger, C., & Tickner, J. (1999). *Protecting public health and the environment: Implementing the precautionary principle*. Washington, DC: Island Press.

Shrivastava, P. (1995). Ecocentric management for a risk society. *Academy of Management Review, 20*(1), 118–137.

Steingraber, S. (1997). *Living downstream: A scientist's personal investigation of cancer and the environment*. New York: Vintage Books.

Szasz, A. (1994). *Ecopopulism: Toxic waste and the movement for environmental justice*. Minneapolis: University of Minnesota Press.

Tesh, S.N. (2000). *Uncertain hazards: Environmental activists and scientific proof*. Ithaca, NY: Cornell University Press.

U.S. National Research Council. (1983). *Risk assessment in the federal government: Managing the process*. Washington, DC: The National Academies Press.

Vanderburg, W.H. (2000). *The labyrinth of technology: A perspective technology and economic strategy as a way out*. Toronto: University of Toronto Press.

WCED (World Commission on Environment and Development). (1987). *Our common future*. Oxford: Oxford University Press.

Wing, S. (2000). Limits of epidemiology. In S. Kroll-Smith, P. Brown, & V.J. Gunter (Eds.), *Illness and the environment: A reader in contested medicine* (pp. 29–45). New York: New York University Press.

20

"Don't Work Too Hard": Health and Safety and Workers' Compensation in Canada

ROBERT STOREY McMaster University

INTRODUCTION

"Don't work too hard" is a familiar farewell phrase used by friends and acquaintances. No doubt most people employ this well-worn saying without much thought. Given its ubiquitous usage, though, it must have some meaning related to how the role and place of work is perceived in contemporary societies. It could mean, for example, that we should not work too hard because, after all, work is not that important – so why expend undue energy performing the obligatory tasks associated with earning a living? While some who employ this colloquialism may attach this meaning to it, there are others who believe work to be an integral component of their lives and who derive sizable chunks of their personal identities from the daily expenditure of their **labour power**. Hence, this phrase would not contain that meaning for them. Or, it could be a sincere admonishment to take care because people can, and do, get injured and hurt at work. This is certainly what is intended when you are about to get behind the wheel of a car and you are told to "drive carefully."

While there may be other associations with this phrase, it is probably the case that the one least likely to be on the minds of the people issuing this departing slogan is the last one enumerated above. To researchers and workers active in the field of workplace health and safety, this is a highly lamentable situation. Why is it, they wonder, that there are national, well-funded advertising campaigns about road safety when more people are injured and killed at work annually than on roads and highways (Canada, 2000)? Indeed, according to Canadian government reports, three workers are killed on the job every day in Canada. Someone is injured on the job every nine seconds! Further, there is a workplace injury every 19 seconds that results in that worker having to take time away from work. And, if we calculate the number of workplace deaths that stem from accidents and disease, we have a figure that is not only tragically high, it is also one which gives Canadian workplaces the dubious distinction of placing first amongst all advanced industrial/post industrial economies (Osberg & Sharpe, 2003, p. 29).

In short, health and safety is a major – albeit largely invisible – workplace issue (Barab, 2006). It is, thus, a social, economic, and political problem of significant proportions.

There is, it bears repeating, first and foremost, the toll in human lives – lives that are taken away via work-related fatalities; lives altered fundamentally due to an accident or disease; the diminishment of the lives of those left to grieve and remember family members and close friends (Seith, 2005). There are also the "costs" to society associated with lost productivity, the medical care required by injured and sick workers, and, importantly, the intangible loss of human talents and energies. To be sure, workers' compensation systems across the country are required to pay for the medical costs of injured workers whose claims they have accepted. In 1998, for example, "compensation payments and reimbursements by workers' compensation boards of various costs directly related to occupational injury totaled $4.65 billion. When indirect costs are included, workers' compensation board payments cost the Canadian economy $9.3 billion" (Canada, 2000, p. 10). Critically, these compensation systems costs refer only to those injuries and diseases deemed to be directly associated with a person's workplace. But, what of those injuries, illnesses, and diseases such as **repetitive strain injury** (RSI), chronic pain, stress, and many forms of cancer that are not compensated because their etiology cannot be definitively determined? It is the public and personal health care systems that pay for medical care in these cases. In the end, it would seem that it is injured workers and society as a whole that shoulder most of the human and economic costs that are part of, and flow from, the ongoing "assault on the worker" (Reasons, Ross & Patterson, 1981).

THE DESTRUCTION OF LABOUR POWER

There is little doubt that some forms of work have always been dangerous and unhealthy. In a book published in the year 1700, an Italian doctor, Bernardino Ramazzini, wrote about the dangers and diseases associated with specific occupations. "The mortality of those who dig minerals is very great," he wrote, "and women who marry men of this sort marry again and again. According to Agricola, at the mines in the Carpathian Mountains, women have been known to marry seven times." Interestingly, Ramazzini was also among the first to note the impact on the body of repetitive motions: "The maladies that affect the clerks," he believed, "arise from three causes: first, constant sitting; secondly, incessant movement of the hand and always in the same direction; and thirdly, the strain on the mind...The incessant driving of the pen over paper causes intense fatigue of the hand and the whole arm because of the continuous...strain on the muscles and tendons" (Quoted in Dembe, 1996, p. 27).

So, pre-industrial forms of work, including working in the fields planting and harvesting, were likely to harm those performing those labours. It is generally recognized, however, that work became more hazardous with the onset of industrial capitalism. In *Capital*, Karl Marx's (1906) sustained critique of the rise and consolidation of industrial capitalism, we find lengthy and vivid descriptions of how the arrival of factory production, complete with steam-powered machinery, fundamentally altered the relationship between workers and their jobs. Capitalists, Marx wrote, were keenly interested in getting maximum returns on their investments in buildings and technology. In the context of 19th-century English society, this was accomplished by introducing machinery to speed up and subdivide labour, to increase the pace of production, and to draw out the length of the working day. It also involved the systematic employment of women and young children who worked as long and as hard as male workers but who received less in wages. As Marx relates, of the plentiful number of investigations into the conditions of work in this period, many fastened on the plight of working children.

Mr. Broughton Charlton, county magistrate, declared as chairman of a meeting held at the Assembly Rooms, Nottingham, on the 14th of January, 1860,

> that there was an amount of privation and suffering among that portion of the population connected with the lace trade, unknown in other parts of the kingdom, indeed, in the civilized world.... Children of nine or ten years old are dragged from their squalid beds at two, three, or four o'clock in the morning and compelled to work for a bare subsistence until ten, eleven, or twelve at night; their limbs wearing away, their frames dwindling, their faces whitening, and their humanity absolutely sinking into a stone-like stupor, utterly horrible to contemplate... (Marx, 1906, p. 268)

Workers vigorously protested what they perceived to be the inherent dangers of factory production. Skilled workers, for example, formed **craft unions** both to protect the integrity of their jobs and as vehicles of cultural and political protest. Over the course of the 19th century, these protests, while failing to alter in any fundamental way either the course or the nature of capitalist industrialization, did result in the English Parliament passing a series of **Factory Acts** aimed at regulating workplaces and thereby improving the health and safety of workers.

Events in Canada took a similar course. As Eric Tucker (1990) has outlined, the rise of industrial capitalism in Canada in the late 19th century brought with it many of the same ills and dangers that had characterized its rise in England and elsewhere. Tucker provides a *Palladium of Labor* report of the death of "Charles Kirkwood, an employee at a Hamilton rolling mill":

> No person witnessed the accident; but from the positioning which he was last seen alive, and that in which his body was afterwards found, it is supposed, that when the whistle blew for the men to go to work, he got up from a bench on which he was asleep, and being in a dazed and almost unconscious state, fell into the ponderous fly-wheel, where his head was torn from his body and instantly ground into atoms. (Tucker, 1990, p. 27)

In this instance, a combination of indignant voices – trade unionists, middle class reformers, and a smattering of politicians, championed the cause of factory reform. Beginning in the mid-1880s with Quebec, and followed closely by Ontario, Canadian workers secured Factory Acts that bore a strong resemblance to those passed in England, particularly in their major **paternalistic** purpose of limiting the working days – and employment opportunities – of women and children (Tucker, 1990; Hurl, 1988). Further limitations related to regulatory provisions that did not cover the great majority of workplaces (and thus workers), while their enforcement measures (encapsulated in the form of a purposefully understaffed inspectorate whose modus operandi was education over prosecution) proved utterly unable to attend to the growing set of dangers attendant to the consolidation of mechanized factory production.

It was, in fact, the increasingly visible incongruence between the regulatory provisions of the provincial factory acts and the rising incidence of accidents and injury that created the volatile context for the next major development in workplace health and safety in Canada: workmen's compensation laws. As Michael Piva (1975) relates in his account of the coming of workmen's compensation legislation in Ontario in the 1910s, mechanized factories were turning out more products, but in the process they were also churning out more injured workers. Along with other social, economic, and political developments that were generating heightened levels of critique and protest, this carnage of industrial production prompted governments and business groups in Ontario and across the country to search for measures that would help restore industrial and political calm. In the case of Ontario, the path chosen was the appointment in 1910 of the province's chief justice, Sir William Meredith, to head a Royal Commission mandated to investigate systems of workmen's compensation in place elsewhere around the world. In 1913, Meredith submitted his report, complete with a draft bill, wherein he argued that the establishment of a modern workmen's compensation system was imperative as workers injured while at their jobs deserved a form of recompense that both acknowledged their changed employment opportunities, and that would help them maintain their dignity and economic independence (i.e., they would not become dependent on their communities and the state). But, according to Meredith, there were moral as well as economic and political reasons for passing such a law:

> In these days of social and industrial unrest it is, in my judgment, of the gravest importance to the community that every proved injustice to any section or class resulting from bad or unfair laws should be promptly removed by the enactment of remedial legislation....That the existing law inflicts injustice on the workingman is admitted by all. From that injustice he has long suffered, and it would, in my judgment, be the gravest mistake if questions as to the scope and character of the proposed remedial legislation were to be determined, not by a consideration of what is just to the workingman, but of what is the least he can be put off with... (Meredith, 1913, pp. 17–18)

The 1915 Ontario Workmen's Compensation Act, and the other provincial acts that followed, were historic victories for workers in Canada. In contrast to years and decades gone by, workers were now assured of some financial compensation if they were injured on the job. They no longer had to undergo the arduous and mostly futile process of proving the liability of their employers in unfriendly courts of law (Risk, 1981). Yet, there were immediate and long-term drawbacks. For, as injured workers quickly discovered, first, the sums they received were far less than what was actually needed to provide for themselves and their families, and, second, in instances of permanent disability, the payments did not match the extent of disability nor last as long. Moreover, as with the provincial Factory Acts, not all workers were covered by workmen's compensation legislation. Indeed, as these statutes were directed at the so-called "dangerous trades" (e.g., those performed almost exclusively by men) women, working as domestics (the largest employment category for women in this period) and as garment workers in their homes or the homes of their employers (e.g., "**sweatshops**") were not covered. Hence, the title "Work*men's* Compensation Act" was not a misnomer. And, finally, as cumbersome and as hostile as the courts had been to injured workers, that avenue was now permanently closed to them. In accepting guaranteed compensation, workers had been forced to give up their right to sue their employers. This was the "historic compromise" of workmen's compensation in Canada.

THE TIMES ARE A 'CHANGIN'

Economic forces and political frameworks congruent with a private enterprise market society thus shaped the day-to-day reality, as well as the regulatory framework, of workplace health and safety that emerged in the first decades of the 20th century. As Eric Tucker (1988) has argued, government initiatives directed at making the workplace safe and healthy were co-terminus with making the workplace "safe for capitalism." In other words, any state forays into the relationship between worker and machine and workers and their employers, would be defined by a steadfast respect for the sanctity of private property and the unfettered operation of market forces. Health and safety and workers' compensation laws and regulations would be passed; but, their effectiveness would depend on the workplace parties working together, voluntarily, to achieve this goal.

The voluntary essence of occupational health and safety and workers' compensation laws would remain in place during the five decades following the First World War. To be sure, as the 1970s appeared on the horizon, some of the particulars of the factory acts and workmen's compensation acts had undergone change, elaboration, and expansion. Nevertheless, their underlying assumptions and fundamental operative principles and practices remained largely intact.

But, to paraphrase Bob Dylan's 1960s protest song, "the times they [were] a changin'." There were, of course, the changes that would flow from the highly visible and powerful social movements of this era: civil rights, women's, anti-Vietnam War, student, and environmental movements. But, alongside these rising currents were the protests of industrial and public sector workers regarding demands for union representation (and greater union democracy), and for greater attention to their safety and health. With regard to the latter, the first to gain prominence were hard rock miners in the Appalachian mountains of West Virginia, and textile workers in North Carolina. After 20–30 years of working in dusty coalmines and textile mills, workers from these industries were sick and dying – long before their time. Doctors who assisted these workers diagnosed them with advanced fibrosis (a thickening and scarring) of the lung – conditions termed "black" lung from the injection of black coal dust, and "brown" lung from breathing in miniscule particles of cotton (Judkins, 1986; Smith, 1987; Derickson, 1998). Singly or in small groups, these workers had been unsuccessful in getting their respective compensation boards to recognize their conditions. Indeed, it was only when they formed coalitions with progressive unionists, doctors, medical researchers, and state politicians that they achieved their goals. Moreover, according to Alan Derickson (1998), the mobilization of miners around workmen's compensation for black lung disease was ultimately responsible for the passage, by the United State's Federal Government, of the 1969 Coal Mine Health and Safety Act. Further, as Charles Noble (1986) argues, it was the political and moral pressure of the black, brown, and "white" (asbestos) lung movements that forced the Republican administration of Richard Nixon to pass the 1970 Occupational Health and Safety Act.

The appearance of widespread occupational disease among U.S. miners, textile, and asbestos workers should not have come as a surprise. There had been dramatic examples of occupational illness and disease in previous decades. For example, in the late 1910s and 1920s in the state of New Jersey, young female radium dial painters became sick and started to die. Investigations discovered that these workers had ingested radium through the practice of "lippointing" the brushes they used to paint the radium onto the dials of military instruments (Clark, 1997). In the 1920s through the 1930s, thousands of miners in the United States and Canada came down with silicosis from working in mines or in foundries (Cherniack, 1980; Rosner & Markowitz, 1991; Finkelstein, 1990). But, two processes combined to make the 1960s and early 1970s different. First, the incidence of occupational disease was no longer isolated to a few clusters. Rather, occupational disease was becoming an issue among Canadian workers from coast to coast: from asbestos workers in Baie Verte, Newfoundland (Leyton, 1975; Tatatryn, 1979), to coke oven workers at steel mills in Ontario, to smelter workers in British Columbia. Second, the presence of illness and disease amongst workers was known both to employers and government ministries – but not to the workers themselves (Tatatryn, 1979; Markowitz & Rosner, 2002; Levenstein et al., 2002).

Perhaps the most dramatic example of this situation took place in Elliot Lake, Ontario, home to important sources of radium mined largely for the purposes of supplying the U.S. military. While miners in Elliot Lake were aware of their relatively poor health (Tataryn, 1979), they did not know the true state of their situation until early 1974 when a union representative, attending a radium mining conference in France, listened to a presentation from an Ontario Ministry of Health official that reported on a study of Elliot Lake uranium miners that showed elevated rates of cancer. Upon hearing of this study, Elliot Lake miners went out on a wildcat strike, both to mark their outrage at not having been informed, and to support their demands for change. According to Ed Vance, a miner at Elliot Lake at this time, the anger of the miners was directed both at the company, and, as importantly, at the government:

> To come back with a study that was presented at that conference from the Ministry of Health Ontario. Jan Muller was the author of that study. To show that 41 of us had **died** compared to the general population where only 13 should have died from lung cancer. **We weren't even aware we were being studied. They deliberately kept us ignorant. There is no other way to describe it.** Government has a responsibility and in this case they failed to keep the workers advised. They failed to warn the workers of their work environment. And, they were part of that conspiracy. (Elliot Lake, 1985)

The events at Elliot Lake drew widespread media coverage and public sympathy. So, too, did revelations that asbestos workers at a Johns-Manville plant in Scarborough, Ontario, were also sick and dying at alarming rates. The dangers of exposure to asbestos had long been known. Indeed, the Ontario government had been monitoring exposures at plants across that province since the late 1950s. Dr. Irving Selikoff's (1964, 1965) research on asbestos disease amongst American shipyard workers had sent shockwaves through the asbestos industry in the mid 1960s – resulting in the Johns-Manville company declaring bankruptcy in the face of lawsuits filed by tens of thousands of former and current employees (Brodeur, 1973, 1985). Yet, the relationship between exposure to asbestos and illness, disease and cancer, was not known amongst Johns-Manville employees in the Scarborough plant. Johns-Manville officials knew it, however. In a directive to management in 1948, not long after the plant had started operations, Johns-Manville's medical director wrote the following about the situation in the Scarborough plant:

> It must be remembered that although these men have the X-ray evidence of asbestosis, they are working today and definitely are not disabled from asbestos. They have not been told of this diagnosis, for it is felt that as long as the man feels well, is happy at home and at work, and his physical condition remains good, nothing should be said. When he becomes disabled and sick, then the diagnosis should be made and the claim submitted *by the company.* The fibrosis of this disease is irreversible and permanent and so that eventually compensation will be paid to each of these men. But as long as the man is not disabled, it is felt that he should not be told of his condition so that he can live and work in peace and the Company can benefit by his many years of experience. Should the man be told of his condition today there is a very definite possibility that he would become mentally and physically ill, simply through the knowledge that he has asbestosis. (Selikoff, 1979, p. 93)

The tragic developments at Elliot Lake and Johns-Manville served the purposes of putting occupational *health* on trade union and political agendas. From the mid-1970s forward, trade union officials made it clear to employers and governments across the country that change in occupational health and safety and workers' compensation laws was imperative – and, change was not long in coming. In 1972, Saskatchewan passed the first modern occupational health and safety act. Ontario followed later in the decade (Walters, 1983; Storey, 2005). Among the important changes brought about by the new laws was the enshrinement of three basic worker rights: the right to know about the substances they worked with; the right to participate, through joint health and safety committees, in maintaining and improving the safety and health conditions of their workplaces; and, third, the right to refuse work they considered dangerous. Dubbed the "three Rs" by Robert Sass, the architect of the Saskatchewan law, these rights went beyond any that Canadian workers had heretofore secured and enjoyed in that they encroached – or seemed to encroach – on management's right to manage their workplaces as they desired. Under the various occupational health and safety laws, especially in the case of the right to refuse, workers could actively, and within the law, challenge their employers' production methods and equipment and not be disciplined and/or terminated for doing so – as they could be in other areas of management-labour relations. In effect, to varying degrees Canadian workers had been written into the occupational health and safety regulatory frameworks of their respective provinces and there was now hope that great improvements would follow as a matter of course (Storey & Tucker, 2006). After all, workers and unionists stated, no one else understood the operation of steel mills, mines, automotive assembly lines, textile factories, etc., better than the workers themselves. The times, it seemed, had changed.

THE GENDER OF SAFETY AND DISEASE

As the previous discussion outlined, the appearance of large numbers of workers with illness and disease added "health" to the safety concerns of workers, unions, employers, and state officials. Somewhat inevitably, the focus was on the illness and disease exhibited by male workers in the primary and industrial sectors. Canada was, after all, a nation that made its money and paid its bills largely via the felling of trees; the catching of fish;

the mining of coal, nickel, and asbestos; the making of iron and steel; the assembly of cars, fridges, stoves, etc. If anyone thought to wonder about the health and safety hazards associated with office and white collar work more generally, the conclusion was that such work was both healthy and safe. Indeed, such perceptions found their way into the provincial occupational health and safety acts in that their provisions were concerned with, and pertained almost exclusively to, the primary/industrial workforce. In concrete terms, this meant that many white-collar office jobs were not covered by the laws. In some instances, like university professors and community college instructors, their exclusion came as a result of requests by these very groups who, at this historical moment, did not see their workplaces as dangerous and/or did not associate their work and lives with those of working class, primary, and industrial workers.

However, the decisions about which workplaces and industries to include/exclude were also underpinned by a view that conflated office work with "women's work," and, as neither was either unhealthy or dangerous, there was little or no need to bring them under statutory umbrellas. It was not long, however, before this benign view of office work was actively being deconstructed. Two of the first critics of this view were Jeanne Stellman and Mary Sue Henifin, whose book *Office Work Is Dangerous To Your Health* (1983), laid bare the not so hidden hazards of office work, such as poorly designed furniture and work spaces, poor lighting, noise, and fire safety. Stellman and Henifin's concerns regarding visual display terminals (VDTs) were taken up in the Canadian context by union occupational health and safety activist, Bob DeMatteo. In his pamphlet *Terminal Shock* (1981), DeMatteo wrote that prolonged exposure to the radiation emanating from VDTs put women workers at risk of miscarriage. Further, DeMatteo pointed to the growing evidence that prolonged use of VDTs created problems relating to eye strain, headaches, and stress from the increased pace of work, and musculoskeletal injuries from repeated motions. So, too, as Stellman and Henifin and other researchers observed, the new energy efficient office buildings (e.g., buildings with windows that did not open) were compounding other health and safety problems, such as the vapours given off by photocopy machines and carpets via the re-circulation of the same air within the buildings. By the mid- to late 1980s, a new phrase had entered the health and safety lexicon: "**sick building syndrome**" (Murphy, 2006).

Two processes were thus coming together in the mid- to late 1980s in Canadian occupational health and safety. First, office work, which had always existed alongside industrial production, was finally being understood as potentially dangerous and unhealthy. Second, changes in the economy and the structure of work – both increasingly synonymous with the shift to a post-industrial economy and flexible work – were creating an additional set of health and safety hazards. The smokestacks and blast furnaces might be crumbling either through old age or via well-placed sticks of dynamite, but their replacement – the information age office – was not as pristine as advertised.

FLEXIBLE PRODUCTION – FLEXIBLE BODIES?

In the 18th and 19th centuries, miners took canaries into the mines with them. They did so not to listen to their pretty song, but rather to serve as a warning signal regarding the presence of deadly gases. That is, if they could no longer hear the song of the canary, it was time to get out of the mine.

For some researchers, a new warning sign has emerged in the last two decades of the 20th century in the form of hidden chronic aches and pains they argue are closely associated with the new information technologies, or, more particularly, the ways in which these new technologies are utilized in contemporary workplaces. Placed under the umbrella term of **musculoskeletal disorders** (MSDs), such injuries actually predate the arrival of the information age into our workplaces. Allard Dembe, in his book *Occupation and Disease: How Social Factors Affect the Conception of Work-Related Disorders* (1996), shows how social factors such as financial compensation, labor activism, economic instability, environmental concerns, cultural stereotyping, medial attention, marketing efforts, military conflicts, political actions, and economic costs can combine to either facilitate or obstruct the recognition of occupational disease. Dembe provides the examples of "cumulative trauma disorders" of the hands and wrists (e.g., telegraphists' cramp and **carpal tunnel syndrome**) and "back pain" as illustrations of how the role of medical experts can have a determinative influence on if, when, and how an occupational disease becomes generally recognized as such. In the case of carpel tunnel syndrome, Dembe highlights the role of Dr. George Phalen, of Cleveland, Ohio. Beginning in the early 1950s, Phalen insisted that the cause of carpel tunnel syndrome was not occupational. In 1957, he wrote the following about 37 cases of carpal tunnel syndrome he had observed in his practice:

> We believe that spontaneous compression neuropathy of the median nerve in the carpal tunnel is not an occupational disease. Often repeated, forceful grasping movements might cause some tenosynovitis of the flexor tendons in the carpel tunnel, but this is certainly not a common finding... it is true that almost every patient in our series described an aggravation of symptoms after strenuous use of the hands, and the symptoms were almost always worse in the dominant hand. None of these patients, however, consistently did an excessive amount of work with the hands. (p. 70)

According to Dembe, the critical rationale behind Phalen's refusal to see carpal tunnel syndrome as work-related lay in the fact that most of his patients were women. In Phalen's view, women did not do the type of work – either in the paid labour market or in the home – that would precipitate this condition. As Dembe relates, Phalen's influence in the North American and European medical and research communities was such that his views were dominant, thereby holding back the recognition of carpal tunnel disease as occupationally related for at least two decades.

Much the same story can be told about back injuries. As Dembe recounts, doctors and workers' compensation officials were highly suspicious of workers who presented them with back pain. From the 1910s through to the 1980s, these highly influential officials held that such injuries either did not exist in the great majority of cases, or that the worker was exaggerating the extent of the injury and the pain in order to secure higher workers' compensation benefits. Because they could not "see" the injury either with their naked eye or via x-rays, it did not exist. Hence, the injury was either the result of aging or it was a fabrication. This was certainly the view of some Ontario workers' compensation board officials and medical experts in the 1960s and 1970s. A construction boom in Ontario had produced a small explosion in injuries to construction workers – including injuries of the lower back. When these workers – overwhelmingly Italian men who were recent immigrants to Canada – attempted to secure compensation for these injuries, they were roundly suspected of either exaggeration or malingering. While doctors and workers' compensation board officials held these views about most workers with injured backs, they were deeply suspicious in the case of Italian construction workers, stating that "Mediterranean people had weak backs" or were culturally predisposed to complain and exaggerate. Such views became known to the Italian community in Toronto in the early 1970s when it was revealed that a University of Toronto psychiatrist, Dr. Ian Hector, had authored a workers' compensation assessment of an Italian worker, Guiseppe Pulera, wherein he stated that Pulera was "a poorly acculturated Italian without any useful occupational skills" (Peter Rosenthal, 2003).

MSDs, then, were present in the workforce before the advent of the computer and the arrival of the information age. Indeed, back injuries have been first among workers' compensation claims since the middle of the 1970s. This is not to deny, however, that the proliferating number of jobs characterized by highly repetitive motions through short distances – keyboarding, scanning food products in supermarkets, sewing the same article of clothing, electronics and automobile assembly, etc.—have served to produce more numerous and/or different types of MSDs. One such "new" injury is Repetitive Strain Injury (RSI). According to Statistics Canada (2003), "[o]ne out of every 10 Canadian adults had a repetitive strain injury (RSI) serious enough to limit their normal activities in 2000/01":

> Most repetitive strain injuries affected the upper body. About 25% were in the neck or shoulder. Another 23% occurred in the wrist or hand, followed by the back (19%) and then the elbow or lower arm (16%). The remaining 17% involved a lower extremity or unspecified body part. (p. 1)

The report also indicates that women and men have different manifestations of RSI:

> Men were more likely than women to have hurt their arm, leg or back. In contrast, a higher percentage of women than men reported injuries to their neck, shoulder or hand. These differences are likely attributable to the types of activities each sex undertakes. (p. 2)

The "[l]east likely to be injured were people in management," the Statistics Canada report continued: "Men and women who worked in sales or service; trades, transport or equipment operating; farming, forestry, fishing or mining; and processing, manufacturing or utilities had high odds of reporting an RSI, compared with those in management. This was particularly true for women in traditionally male-dominated occupations" (p. 2).

Despite these alarming figures, however, RSI is a contentious issue around the world. Andrew Hopkins (1989), for example, has shown how the emergence of RSI related injuries amongst women workers in Australia in the 1980s was met with skepticism and hostility by medical researchers, employers, and the government. Indeed, according to Hopkins, the overwhelmingly negative reception to an "epidemic" of RSI amongst Australian women workers was informed by the view that women's work was not hazardous and that women were likely to exaggerate their symptoms (as was the case with carpal tunnel syndrome). Penny Kome (2006) writes of a similar reaction amongst medical practitioners and researchers and workers' compensation boards in Canada.

IT ALL ADDS UP TO – STRESS!

MSDs seem to be just the tip of the iceberg. Over the past decade, reports coming back from Canadian workplaces on the health and well-being of Canadian workers conjoin into one word: stress. While stress has always been understood as an integral and inevitable part of one's life, occupational health and safety researchers point to the increasing levels of stress exhibited by a broad range of workers in contemporary societies. In the 1950s, this research focused on the white-collar male and/or the high-powered executive who, it was assumed, confronted a sizable number of stressors in the course of any given work day. It was stressful, for example, to make investment decisions concerning large sums of money, or regarding what to manufacture, or how many employees were required to make their products. The image of the dynamic, yet stressed-out white, male executive, however, has been replaced by that of the lesser-skilled production worker who, rather than being burdened with making critical decisions, is the subject of those decisions. Moreover, this person is no longer male, but female – it is women who tend to staff those jobs most associated with generating stress: high responsibility, low authority.

This view of which jobs are the most stressful has been developed and popularized by Robert Karasek and Tores Theorell (1990). Their "job strain model" posits that stress is created in workers when the controls they have over their jobs are less than are required to actually perform their jobs. Hence, workers are stressed and hypertension is experienced when they find themselves "working very fast," "working very hard," and "not having enough time to get the job done." Most recently, this model has been complemented by John Siegrist's (1996) "effort-reward imbalance model" which attempts to measure the impact of labour markets on health. In this model, a worker is at risk if their high efforts at work go unrewarded or are not accorded the rewards anticipated by the worker. The anticipated rewards are what one would expect: money, social approval, job security, and career opportunities – in other words, the essential ingredients of a "good job."

These models have now been "tested" by numerous researchers in the Canadian context. Reaching back into the industrial age, Lewchuk and Robertson (1998) conducted an intensive study aimed at determining the emotional and physical health of auto workers at four automotive assembly plants in Ontario. Their conclusions paralleled those of Karasek and Theorell in that the majority of the workers they sampled told them that they could do little or nothing to alter the pace of work. In short, they had low autonomy and control, with workers in the newer, "leaner" plants emphasizing this condition more so than workers in the older assembly plants. With regard to the "health" of these workers, the report concludes that while their findings contained interesting and important variations with respect to skilled versus unskilled workers (skilled workers reporting higher levels of emotional health than assembly line workers), and male versus female auto workers (women workers reported marginally less emotional health), the overall conclusion of the researchers was clear: traditional, and especially newer forms of work organization (e.g., **lean production** methods) had an adverse effect on the health of auto workers.

Other researchers have taken these stress and health models into the health care and service sectors. In a series of publications, Donna Baines (2005, 2006) has shown how front line care workers in psychiatric and home care contexts display high levels of stress stemming from increased levels of violence coming primarily from their patients. According to Baines, while this potential for violence has always been present in such difficult settings, the rise in violent incidents is directly associated with the process of deinstitutionalization of psychiatric patients (a positive step in Baines's view) without the necessary and critical resources required for proper care. So, too, nurses have been the subject of studies probing the relationship between their state of health and the changing nature of their jobs in a globalizing world. Linda Hall and Diana Kiesners (2005), for example, use Seigrist's effort-reward imbalance model in a study of hospital nurses. In their interviews, the nurses spoke of how, with an added patient load, and, critically, more patients who are seriously ill, they had less and less time to actually tend to their patients. As one interviewee stated:

> You have to start asking questions right off the bat. While you're bathing them you're asking them who they live with, where they live, how they are getting home. You have to. You don't have time to say, "Okay, now we'll discuss your ileostomy." While you're making the bed you're saying "Oh, the ostomy nurse – do you know if she's booked to come in on Tuesday to discuss the type of prosthetics that you're going to need and give you the forms for the doctor to sign to have it paid for?" (p. 2487)

The authors also note that some nurses reported that basic hygiene and housekeeping – such as "bed and baths" – were becoming compromised because of lack of time and overwhelming nursing workload. The study concludes on a worrisome note:

> The nurses' narratives suggest that multiple factors constitute the nurses' work environment and their experiences and perceptions of it. Issues which surfaced repeatedly in the interviews related to changing needs of hospitalized patients in today's health care system and the associated workload, the widespread shortage of nurses, and the imbalances this creates for nursing work. A crucial finding is the extent to which the nurse is impacted by the inadequacy of care they are able to provide. The narratives outline a tremendous burden of guilt and the over commitment that nurses bear when factors in the work environment prevent them from providing complete, quality care. Nurses are experiencing frustration and stress that is impacting their work life, family, and home life, personal health, and possibly patient outcomes. (p. 2482)

With an expanding service sector, the front line now extends well beyond "good" service public sector jobs like nursing. Indeed, with the contraction of the public sector that has proceeded apace with the coming to power of neo-liberal political parties intent on downsizing the role of government, the growth in services is primarily in the private sector. Unfortunately, to use the other half of a phrase we have utilized earlier, a great number of these jobs tend to be the "bad" ones. That is, they are likely to offer little in the way of economic or intrinsic rewards – regardless of the effort put in by the worker. Jobs at the lower end of the service hierarchy are low paid, offer little avenue for decision-making or creative autonomy, present minimal opportunity for upward mobility, and are primarily part-time. They are the core group in the growing cadre of contingent workers with precarious – and often unsafe and unhealthy – forms of employment.

To date, we know little about the health and safety conditions of such "bad" private sector service jobs. The reasons for this lack of knowledge are many, but two can be highlighted. First, service work is, relatively speaking, a new employment sector and it has taken some time for researchers to come to grips with its permanence and growing importance. Second, and more significantly, the service sector has always been the preserve of women workers and, as with office work, it has not been considered worthy of research: after all, as it was women's work, it could not be dangerous or unhealthy. Of course, not everyone has understood service work in this fashion. Some researchers, such as Karen Messing (1998), have attempted to mount research projects into the health and safety dimensions of "women's work." They have, however, been unsuccessful in doing so. As Messing points out in her book, *One-Eyed Science*, however, such applications have been regularly turned down because the reviewers and funders did not consider the research to be either as relevant or as important as research into the health and safety conditions of men's work. Not surprisingly, then, there is very little substantive research to draw on when it comes to the service sector.

Research findings that do exist, however, uncover some troublesome issues. Stuart Tannock (2001), in an insightful analysis of young men and women working in fast food and grocery stores, relays the many concerns these workers have for their health and safety – all of which add up to stress. "Accidents, injuries and attacks are a common part of young fast-food and grocery workers' lives," Tannock writes; "Teenagers and young adults working in these industries, who expect to have long lives ahead of them, often worry that their jobs, which are supposed to be meaningless, stop-gap places of employment, will have lasting and detrimental effects on their bodies and future life activities" (p. 54). For the fast food workers in this study, the most common injuries included "burns from the splashing or spilling of hot shortening; cuts, back, head and knee injuries caused by slipping and falling; and back injuries caused by lifting heavy loads" (p. 54). According to Tannock, burns were so frequent that the workers "had come to accept them as part of the job" (p. 54). Further, as in other accounts of service sector jobs (Hochschild, 2003), these young servers are obliged to put up with the verbal and sometimes physical abuse of customers: "'I've had customers threaten my life,' says one cashier in disbelief, 'because I didn't give them a breast instead [of the chicken leg that is regularly part of a special mean package]'" (p. 54). Another fast food worker nearly had an eye permanently damaged when an angry and drunk customer punched the glass window in the drive-through, sending pieces of the shattered glass into the person's eyes. Other fast food workers told Tannock of being robbed.

Grocery store workers also spoke of "customer attacks, burns, cuts, and falls" (p. 54). Moreover:

> Workers who have been in their jobs for extended periods of time also face cumulative injuries: repetitive stress injuries in arms and wrists; back, hip, knee and foot ailments that workers attribute to working standing up for long stretches of time and to the pounding caused by walking on concrete supermarket floors; and back and knee injuries caused by repeated heavy lifting. One twenty-four-year-old checker I interviewed, for example, had been working part time or full time at a grocery check stand for six years. Three years before our interview, she had lost four months of work because of tendonitis in her right shoulder. Although she was back on the job, she continued to feel pain and numbness in her shoulder and arm, as well as aches down her back. Her shoulder movement is now restricted – she is no longer able to braid her own hair. (p. 55)

As can be seen from these accounts, the injuries and the consequent aches and pains associated with fast food and grocery store work are strikingly similar to those found among workers in primary and industrial employment. There are two important differences, however. First, these are young and vulnerable workers in jobs not highly prized by society. One of the consequences of this indifference is that little or no pressure is generated to make changes, thus leaving these workers vulnerable and unable to effectively challenge unsafe and unhealthy conditions. In short, they report being unable to exercise their rights to know and refuse work they believe to be unsafe (Gray, 2002). Second, there is the vital addition of the customer in the service employment relationship who, in too many instances, becomes a source of emotional and/or physical abuse leading to increased stress among Tannock's study participants and service workers more generally.

Clearly, as the research previously outlined indicates, service work can be dangerous to the health and safety of those people who do these types of jobs. Indeed, it could be argued that these jobs, with their precarious employment relationships, are the occupational health and safety shock troops of the post-industrial economy. In Canada, as elsewhere, they are staffed in the great majority by young women and men, recent immigrants, and racialized minorities (Jackson, 2005). They are, thus, highly reminiscent of the type of workers who took on the dirtiest and most dangerous jobs in Canada during the first industrial revolution of the late 19th and early 20th centuries. Yet, even as we shift our gaze to those women and men who labour behind desks, over fast food counters, and in malls selling clothes, music, and cell phones, we need to recall that in certain areas of Canada extracting minerals, felling trees, fishing, and manufacturing still matter and that the labour processes associated with them are still hazardous. In 1992, 26 miners at the Westray Mine in Nova Scotia were buried and died underground after a buildup of methane gas and an errant spark from an underground digger combined to produce an explosion (Comish, 1993; Cobb, 1994; Glasbeek & Tucker, 1999). And, then, as the new millennium approached, readers of newspapers across the country were shocked to learn of hundreds of new cases of asbestosis among men who had worked at Holmes Foundry in Sarnia, Ontario (Smith, 2001; Keith et al., 2004). So, too, even as service work has been on the rise, steelworkers, auto workers, rubber workers, and textile workers have continued to get injured and killed on the job. They remain our most dangerous and unhealthy forms of work. Moreover, the communities where these industries have operated continue to live – and die – from their environmental legacies. There is a growing list of documented cases of asbestos-related disease among family members of Holmes Foundry workers. Tragically, family members came into contact with asbestos fibres in washing clothes or via the wind that blew the asbestos dust into their backyards and open kitchen windows. So, too, the residents of Frederick Street in Sydney, Nova Scotia, are experiencing elevated rates of cancer (Barlow, 2000). Frederick Street borders the abandoned and highly toxic tar ponds of the now defunct Sydney Steel Company. Finally, there are now serious questions being raised about the relationship between industrial pollution and breast cancer (Davis, 2002).

WHAT IS TO BE DONE?

In raising the question of "what is to be done," we return to the thorny issue of laws and regulations. In the minds of the families and friends of the 26 dead Westray miners, one of the more positive outcomes of this tragedy is the passage of legislation – Bill C-45, wherein it is stated that "Everyone who undertakes, or has the authority, to direct how another person does work or performs a task is under a legal duty to take reasonable steps to prevent bodily harm to that person, or any other person, arising from that work or task." Under this law, those deemed to be responsible can be prosecuted under charges of "criminal negligence" if it is determined that they willfully or recklessly disregarded their health and safety responsibilities. (Heretofore, violations of occupational health and safety acts were civil, not criminal, offences. For the most part, they remain so.) This legislation, which came into effect in March 2004, was the product of a sustained struggle by survivors of the dead miners and the United Steelworkers of America – the union that was attempting to organize the miners at the time of the explosion. For some of the surviving family members, Bill C-45 has brought some resolution to their anger and sadness. For others, it is too little, too late. Regardless of their feelings, it remains the case for all that no piece of legislation can bring their husbands, sons, brothers, and friends back to life.

Already it seems evident that Bill C-45 will be used only in exceptional circumstances such as serious injury, rampant incidence of occupational disease, and/or fatalities. Regulation of occupational health and safety will be left, as it has been since the 1970s, to the various provisions of the provincial occupational health and safety acts. With regard to those Acts, although they were perceived to be marked improvements over what was in existence at the time, it was not long before important cracks in these frameworks began to appear. Workers' rights to know and participate depended on the effectiveness of **joint health and safety committees**. However, by the mid- to late 1980s, an Ontario Ministry of Labour survey found that a large number of workplaces did not yet have committees, that these committees did not meet regularly or at all, that management officials sometimes chose the worker representatives, and that worker representatives did not feel that the committees were very effective (O'Grady, 2000). Moreover, the word coming from the shop floor was that employers were not willing to share important information regarding the composition of chemicals, solvents, compounds, etc., they considered to be patented parts of their production processes. In Ontario, the frustrations of workers at de Havilland and McDonnell Douglas, two aerospace companies employing thousands of workers in Toronto, boiled over when their respective employers failed to act on their complaints regarding chemicals workers believed to be dangerous (Smith, 2001). In this instance, it took a wildcat strike of these workers to bring their employers to the bargaining table. According to Cathy Walker (2000), the national director of health and safety for the Canadian Auto Workers Union (CAW), the strikes at these aerospace giants were "the absolute critical thing" that lead to the passage in 1988 of legislation – Workplace Hazards Material Information System (WHMIS) – that placed stronger obligations on employers to provide their employees with information on the substances utilized in production processes. So, too, WHMIS mandated worker training in health and safety processes and practices for all workers in all workplaces.

Employers across the country opposed these developments – not simply because they meant more regulations to contend with, but because they also wrote workers and unions into the regulatory processes in more involved and defined ways (Sass, 1998). For the same reasons, they also opposed amendments to occupational health and safety acts that broadened their coverage to include office and service sector workers. In the early 1990s, this opposition was transformed into an open pushback. An integral part of this employer campaign has been the promotion of self-regulation of workplace health and safety through what have been termed management health and safety systems (Nichols & Tucker, 2000). Under these systems, health and safety becomes the sole responsibility of management – employees follow the rules and procedures as prescribed by management. If they do so, proponents of these systems believe, there will be no or very few accidents. If accidents do occur under such systems, they would, naturally, be the responsibility of the worker her/ himself.

Blaming the victim is not a novel approach to explaining workplace accidents. Turn-of-the-20th century studies of workplace accidents held that up to 95 percent of all accidents were the result of thoughtless or careless worker behaviour (Eastman, 1910). The revival of such ideas in the mid 1990s in Canada has been congruent with the rise and consolidation of neo-liberal ideologies that place the individual at the centre of social, economic, and political analysis. In terms of occupational health and safety, these ideas have informed employer support for management health and safety systems and for government initiatives with regard to bolstering the emphasis on **internal responsibility systems**. Indeed, as these ideas and their associated practices have taken hold, occupational health and safety regulators across the country have reinforced their preferences for education and persuasion rather than prosecution (Storey & Tucker, 2006).

While these developments within occupational health are significant, it is the area of workers' compensation that has witnessed the most profound alterations. Dating from the late 1970s, Canadian employers complained about what they contend were prohibitively high costs of workers' compensation. Specifically, they argued that the benefits paid to injured workers were too generous, thus minimizing any incentive for these workers to return to their jobs. So, too, they have stated that the types of injuries and diseases being covered by workers' compensation boards are too broad (i.e., they are paying for injuries and diseases whose origins are not workplace based).

Stress and chronic pain lie at the centre of these latter complaints. Over the course of the 1980s and early 1990s, injured workers and their advocates had been pressuring workers' compensation boards to recognize claims based on stress and chronic pain that they claimed did, in fact, emanate from the workplace. That such efforts met with some success is evidenced in the attempts of provincial governments to halt and reverse these trends. In the mid 1990s in Ontario, for example, the newly-elected Conservative government of Mike Harris quickly turned its attention to "reforming" the workers' compensation system. A key component of their reform package was their stated intent to de-list stress and chronic pain as compensable injuries and diseases.

As one might expect, there was sustained opposition to such changes in Ontario and elsewhere – including Nova Scotia where in 1996, the governing party had terminated payments for chronic pain even if it was shown that the source of the pain was the workplace. The law was immediately challenged by two injured workers from Nova Scotia. Over time, they were joined by injured worker groups and unions from across Canada. Ultimately, the challenge wound its way to the halls of the Supreme Court of Canada where, in a unanimous ruling in October 2003, the Supreme Court struck down the contentious regulation. According to Chief Justice Charles Gonthier, the regulation harmed the dignity of those workers suffering from chronic pain by questioning its veracity. Justice Gonthier continued:

> Chronic pain sufferers are thus deprived of recognition of the reality of their pain and impairment as well as of a chance to establish their eligibility for benefits on a footing equal with others. This message clearly indicates that, in the Nova Scotia Legislature's eyes, chronic pain sufferers are not equally valued as members of Canadian society. (Gonthier, 2003, p. 22)

As with the mid-1980s struggles of injured workers in Ontario, the ruling of the Supreme Court was a clear victory. Other issues remain, however. Katherine Lippel's (1995) research into the Quebec workers' compensation system has revealed the discriminatory fashion in which compensation officials handle stress claims from women and men. In short, the claims made by women are more likely to be dismissed, Lippel argues, because compensation and appeals board officials either do not find the condition to be work-related or they hold to the view that women exaggerate their levels of distress. In a further study, Lippel (2003) found the Quebec compensation board utilizing various methods of surveillance to covertly monitor the day-to-day activities of injured workers officials believed were defrauding the system. As Martha McCluskey (1998) underlines in her study of workers' compensation reform in the United States, however, the real purpose of such initiatives is not to find worker abuse. After all, she recounts, research into abuse of workers' compensation systems in the United States reveals pervasive *employer* not worker abuse. Rather, McCluskey writes that the real purpose of such campaigns is to draw workers' compensation recipients into the anti-welfare discourse. It is, in effect, part of the broader neo-liberal exercise to render efficiency arguments synonymous with moral judgments about who deserves to be covered by workers' compensation.

Finally, there are concerns about policies and practices implemented by workers' compensation boards across Canada that are designed to get injured workers back to work. Studies of these programs are still few in number (Eakin, 2003, 2004; Injured Workers Participatory Group, 2001), but they uniformly conclude that government and employer desires to lower workers' compensation costs result in injured workers being pressured to return to work before they are fully healed. Further, it is claimed by injured worker groups (Women of Inspiration, 2005) that associated retraining programs are not working: they are "training" injured workers either into low paying jobs or into jobs that do not exist. Canadian and U.S. studies (Gunderson, 2000; Azaroff, 2004) point as well to vigorous claims management on the part of employers whereby workers injured on the job are encouraged to come to work and do "light duties" until they have recovered. In this way, compensation claims are not filed and employer annual compensation assessments are not affected. In light of these findings, researchers question the claims of compensation boards across the continent that declining injury rates mean that the health and safety of workers is improving.

CONCLUSION

As it turns out, the old phrase "hard work never killed anyone" is fallacious in at least two important ways. First, and quite simply, hard work does injure and kill some who perform it. Hard work in steel mills, auto companies, forests, mines, in the fields, on roads, and in smoke-filled bars, does kill. It can kill immediately, over time via disease, or it can slowly diminish a worker's vitality. Meg Luxton and June Corman (2001), in their book on Hamilton steelworkers and their families, quote a recently retired steelworker who, while never experiencing a serious accident in all of his time at the Steel Company of Canada's main Hilton Works plant in that city, spoke of how the job wore him down:

> It's like you're just worn away. The day-to-day work leaves you tired each day, but then you rest and you're fine for the next days. But, year after year it kind of builds up and gets harder. And everyone has an accident that leaves them just a little bit not so great. Most of us have had lots of small things over years and they all add up. After a lifetime at Hilton Works, most of the life in you has been sucked dry. (p. 80)

Second, the work does not have to be physically "hard" to kill. Office work, especially in this era of almost continual restructuring, has meant that fewer workers – from middle management to the rank and file office clerk – are doing both their own jobs and parts of others'. While some management consultants have transformed this new reality into an invocation to "work smarter, not harder," most workers experience "lean" and "flexible" production systems as work intensification. As research evidence indicates, increased expectations at work roll over into elevated rates of stress. And, again as we have seen, excess stress can have severe consequences for a worker's health. Moreover, those who work in service employment confront threatening working conditions in the form of potentially violent behaviour from customers. As Margaret Keith (2001) and her colleagues demonstrate, such issues are at play in casinos, as are hazards associated with noise and second-hand smoke. Finally, with work restructuring and thoroughgoing change in labour markets, many of these less physically demanding jobs are defined by employment insecurity that, in turn, generates negative impacts on workers that cover the distance from the office door to the kitchen table (Lewchuk et al., 2006). Moreover, their time on the job is made still more perilous with employers rarely investing the time and resources to educate and properly train "here today, gone tomorrow," "just-in-time" employees. Finally, as Richard Sennett (1998) warns, employers no longer place much value on what their employees accomplished for them last year, last month, last week, or even yesterday. Rather, they judge an employee on what she/he can do for the company today. According to Sennett, this ever-steeper gradient of expectations, when taken in conjunction with the obliteration of recognition of past achievements, leaves workers without a firm or coherent sense of themselves. A person's character is corroded, Sennett claims, when they have to prove themselves every working day.

There is, as there was in Karl Marx's time, resistance to these invasive alterations in occupational health and safety and workers' compensation systems. Trade unions in Canada, the United States, and in Europe have been successful in forcing governments to ban asbestos, to lower exposure limits to toxic substances, and in the case of British Columbia, to develop and implement **ergonomic** standards aimed at rectifying some of the causes of MSDs. Worker activism has also led to the establishment of February 28 as International RSI day (the first RSI day was February 29, 2000, as it was the only non-repetitive day of the year), and April 28 as the annual Day of Mourning for workers killed or injured on the job. Such initiatives, while perhaps more symbolic than real in their importance, serve the purpose of reminding workers – especially young workers – that they are not invincible and that the pains they feel in their bodies may come from their jobs. As such, they may help give more resonance to the old phrase "Don't work too hard!"

STUDY QUESTIONS

1. *What are the basic assumptions that underlie occupational health and safety legislation in Canada?*
2. *The passage of workers' compensation laws in the early 1910s in Canada gave workers injured on the job a guarantee that they would receive some money for their injury. At the same time, workers had to give up their right to sue their employer. Do you think this was the right thing to do? Should this be changed?*
3. *Modern day occupational health and safety acts give workers the right to refuse work they believe is unsafe. Think about your own work history. Have there been instances where you thought the work you were doing was unsafe? Did you refuse to work? If so, what happened? If not, why not?*
4. *Do you know anyone who suffers from stress or chronic pain? Do they believe that it comes from their work? If so, what do they say is the source/cause of the stress and chronic pain? If you were an employee in a workers' compensation board, would you give them compensation? Why? Why not?*
5. *Are there any particular dangers that confront young workers in Canadian workplaces?*
6. *Are the health and safety and workers' compensation issues confronted by workers in manufacturing any different from those faced by workers in the service sector?*

GLOSSARY

carpal tunnel syndrome a painful condition of the hand and fingers caused by compression of a major nerve where it passes over the carpal bones through a passage at the front of the wrist, alongside the flexor tendons of the hand.

Craft Unions organizations of skilled workers such as electricians, carpenters, printers, etc.

ergonomics according to the Canadian Centre of Occupational Health and Safety, ergonomics is the study and process of "matching the job to the worker and product to the user." It focuses on how work affects workers. Ergonomic hazards include repetitive and forceful movements, vibration, temperature extremes, and awkward postures that arise from improper work methods and improperly designed workstations, tools, and equipment.

Factory Acts occupational health and safety laws passed by provincial governments in the late 19th and early 20th centuries. They are the historical forerunners of modern day occupational health and safety acts.

internal responsibility systems the modern occupational health and safety acts passed in the 1970s were based on the premise that the workplace parties, i.e., the workers, unions (if there was a union present), and employers, had a mutual interest in making workplaces safe and healthy, and hence should not really depend on external enforcement in the form of Ministry of Labour inspectors. The internal responsibility system which comprised the right to know, the right to participate, and the right to refuse unsafe work, was said to be sufficient.

joint health and safety committees a workplace committee with an equal number of employee and management representatives. Their mandate is to regularly inspect the workplace and make recommendations for change.

labour power according to Karl Marx's understanding, a worker did not sell his/her labour to an employer. Rather they sold their labour power or their ability to work. The amount of labour power expended and purchased is always intangible, and thus open to potential conflict between workers and their employers.

lean production according to its advocates, lean production is about reorganizing the workplace via the establishment of teams, the elimination of waste, the reduction of inventories, etc., so that companies can attain maximum efficiency and productivity. According to critics, however, lean production is characterized by large-scale outsourcing (contracting out) of parts and final assembly to companies where workers receive low wages and their employment is insecure. Other differences are in technical developments, such as the ease of making products (simple designs, fewer parts, quick assemblies). The most important feature is work intensification.

musculoskeletal disorders an umbrella term for a wide range of injuries such as low back pain, joint injuries, repetitive strain injuries, carpal tunnel syndrome, etc.

paternalistic a personal, political, or employment relationship based upon unequal social and economic power where the party with the greatest degree of power acts in ways that they assume are in the best interests of the person, party, or worker with the lesser amount of power.

repetitive strain injury injuries to soft tissues, muscles, bones, joints, and ligaments said to be the result of performing the same or highly similar motions through a relatively short distance.

Sick Building Syndrome one of the results of the energy crisis of the 1970s was the construction of airtight buildings, the reorganization of workspaces into open plans, and the use of new materials such as plastics, solvents, drywall, adhesives, and the like. Not long after, workers, principally women, began complaining of respiratory problems and headaches. These and other symptoms are known as sick building syndrome.

sweatshops turn-of-the-20th century small, unsafe, and unhealthy factories or other establishments where primarily women and children made items of clothing.

REFERENCES

Azaroff, S., et al. (2004). Wounding the messenger: The new economy makes occupational health indicators too good to be true. *International Journal of Health Services, 34*(2), 271–303.

Baines, D. (2005). Criminalizing the care work zone? The gendered dynamics of using legal and administrative strategies to confront workplace violence. *Social Justice, 32*(1), 132–150.

Baines, D. (2006). Staying with people who slap us around: Gender, juggling and violence in paid (and unpaid) care work. *Gender, Work and Organization, 13*(3), 129–151.

Barab, J. (2006). Acts of God, acts of man: The invisibility of workplace death. In V. Mogensen (Ed.), *Worker safety under siege: Labor, capital, and the politics of workplace safety in a deregulated world* (pp. 3–16). Armonk, NY: M.E. Sharpe.

Brodeur, P. (1973). *Expendable Americans*. New York: Viking.

Brodeur, P. (1985). *Outrageous misconduct: The asbestos industry on trial*. New York: Pantheon.

Cherniack, M. (1996). *The Hawk's Nest incident: America's worst industrial disaster*. New Haven, CT: Yale University Press.

Clark, C. (1997). *Radium girls: Women and industrial health reform, 1910–1935*. Chapel Hill: University of North Carolina Press.

Cobb, D. (1994). *Calculated risk: Greed, risk and the Westray tragedy*. Halifax: Nimbus.

Comish, S. (1993). *The Westray tragedy: A miner's story*. Halifax: Fernwood.

Davis, D. (2002). *When smoke ran like water: Tales of environmental deception and the battle against pollution*. New York: Basic Books.

DeMatteo, B. (1981). *The hazards of VDTs*. Toronto: Ontario Public Service Employees Union.

Dembe, A. (1986). *Occupation and disease: How social factors affect the conception of work-related disorders*. New York: Yale University Press.

Derickson, A. (1998). *Black lung: Anatomy of a public health disaster*. Ithaca, NY: Cornel University Press.

Eakin, J., et al. (2003). "Playing it smart" with return to work: Small workplace experience under Ontario's policy of self-reliance and early return. *Policy and Practice in Health and Safety, 1*(2), 19–41.

Eakin, J. (2004). The discourse of abuse in return-to-work: A hidden epidemic of suffering. In C. Peterson & C. Mayhew (Eds.), *Occupational health and safety: International influences and the 'new' epidemics*. New York: Baywood: 159–174.

Eastman, C. (1910). *Work accidents and the law*. New York: Arno.

Finkelstein, M. (1980). A review of aluminum prophylaxis against Silicosis. *Occupational Health in Ontario, 1*, 22–26.

Firth, M., Brophy, J., & Keith, M. (1997). *Workplace roulette: Gambling with cancer*. Toronto: Between The Lines.

Glasbeek, H., & Tucker, E. (1999). Death by consensus at Westray? In C. McCormick (Ed.), *The Westray chronicles: A case study in corporate crime* (pp. 71–96). Halifax: Fernwood.

Gonthier, Charles, Nova Scotia (Workers' Compensation Board) v. Martin; Nova Scotia (Workers' Compensation Board) v. Laseur, [2003] 2 S.C.R. 504; 2003 SCC 54.

Gray, G. (2002). A socio-legal ethnography of the legal right to refuse dangerous work. *Studies in Law, Politics & Society, 24*, 133–169.

Gunderson, M. (2000). Workers' compensation in the new world of work. In M. Gunderson & D. Hyatt (Eds.), *Workers' compensation: Foundations for reform* (pp. 27–57). Toronto: University of Toronto Press.

Hall, L.M., & Kiesners, D. (2005). A narrative approach to understanding the nursing work environment in Canada. *Social Science and Medicine, 61*, 2482–2491.

Hochschild, A. (2003). *The managed heart: Commercialization of human feeling*. Berkeley: University of California Press.

Hopkins, A. (1989). The social construction of repetitive strain injury. *Australian/New Zealand Journal of Sociology*, 25(2), 239–259.

Human Resources Development Canada. (2000). *Work safety for a healthy future: Statistical analysis occupational injuries and fatalities*. Ottawa.

Hurl, L. (1988). Restricting child factory labour in late nineteenth century Ontario. *Labour/Le Travail, 21*, 87–121.

Injured Worker Participatory Research Project. (2001). *Making the system better: Injured workers speak out on compensation and return to work issues in Ontario*. Toronto.

Jackson, A. (2005). *Work and labour in Canada: Critical issues*. Toronto: Canadian Scholar's Press.

Judkins, B.M. (1986). *We offer ourselves as evidence: Towards workers' control of occupational health*. New York: Greenwood Press.

Karasek, R., & Theorell, T. (1990). *Healthy work: Stress, productivity, and the reconstruction of working life*. New York: Basic Books.

Keith, M., & Brophy, J. (2004). Participatory mapping of occupational hazards and disease among asbestos-exposed workers from a foundry and insulation complex in Canada. *International Journal of Occupational and Environmental Health, 10*, 144–153.

Keith, M., Cann, B., Brophy, J., Hellyer, D., Day, M., Egan, S., Mayville, K., & Watterson, A. (2001). Identifying and prioritizing gaming workers' health and safety concerns using mapping for data collection. *American Journal of Industrial Medicine, 39*(1), 42–51.

Kome, P. (2006) The 10 percenters: Gender, nationality, and occupational health in Canada. In V. Mogensen (Ed.), *Worker safety under siege: Labor, capital, and the politics of workplace safety in a deregulated world* (pp. 143–56). Armonk, NY: M.E. Sharpe.

Levenstein, C., DeLaurier, G.F., & Dunn, M.L. (2002). *The cotton dust papers: Science, politics, and power in the "discovery" of byssinosis in the U.S.* Amityville, NY: Baywood.

Lewchuk, W., & Robertson, D. (2000). *The healthy workplace index and the Canadian automobile industry*. McMaster University, Labour Studies and Canadian Automobile Workers Union.

Lewchuk W., de Wolff, A., & King, A. (2006). The Hidden Costs of Precarious Employment: Health and the Employment Relationship. In L. Vosko (Ed.), *Precarious employment: Understanding labour market insecurity in Canada*. Montreal: McGill-Queen's University Press, 141–162.

Leyton, E. (1975). *Dying hard: The ravages of industrial carnage*. Toronto: McClelland and Stewart.

Lippel, K. (1995). Watching the watchers: How expert witnesses and decision-makers perceive men's and women's workplace stressors. In K. Messing (Ed.), *Invisible: Issues in women's occupational health* (pp. 265–91). Charlottetown, PE: Gynergy.

Lippel, K. (2003). The private policing of injured workers in Canada: Legitimate management practices or human rights violations? *Policy and Practice in Health and Safety, 1*(2), 97–118.

Luxton, M., & Corman, J. (2001). *Getting by in hard times: Gendered labour at home and on the job*. Toronto: University of Toronto Press.

Marowitz, G., & Rosner, D. (2002). *Deceit and denial: The deadly politics of industrial pollution*. Berkeley: University of California Press; New York: Milbank Memorial Fund.

Marx, K. (1906). *Capital, Vol 1. A critique of political economy*. New York: Modern Library.

McCluskey, M.T. (1998). The illusion of efficiency in workers' compensation "reform." *Rutgers Law Review, 50*(3), 657–941.

Meredith, W. (1913). *Final report on laws relating to the liability of employers to make compensation to their employees for injuries received in the course of their employment which are in force in other countries, and as to how far such laws are found to work satisfactorily*. Toronto: Queen's Printer, 17–18.

Messing, K. (1998). *One-eyed science: Occupational health and women workers*. Philadelphia: Temple University Press.

Murphy, M. (2006). *Sick building syndrome and the problem of uncertainty*. Durham, NC: Duke University Press.

Nichols, T., & Tucker, E. (2000). Occupational health and safety management systems in the United Kingdom and Ontario, Canada: A political economy perspective. In K. Frick (Ed.), *Systematic occupational health and safety management: Perspectives on an international development* (pp. 285–309). Amsterdam: Pergamon.

Noble, C. (1986). *Liberalism at work: The rise and fall of OSHA*. Philadelphia: Temple University Press.

O'Grady, J. (2000). Joint health and safety committees: Finding a balance. In T. Sullivan (Ed.), *Injury and the new world of work* (pp. 162–97). Vancouver: University of British Columbia Press.

Osberg, L., & Sharpe, A. (2003). *An index of well-being for OECD countries*, Ottawa: Centre for the Study of Living Standards.

Piva, M. (1975). The workmen's compensation movement in Ontario. *Ontario History, 67*, 39–56.

Ramazzini, B. (1700). *The diseases of workers*. (W.C. Wright, Trans.). New York: Hafner.

Reasons, C., Ross, L., & Patterson, C. (1981). *Assault on the worker: Occupational health and safety in Canada*. Toronto: Butterworths.

Risk, R.C.B. (1981). "This nuisance of litigation": The origins of workers' compensation in Ontario. In D.H. Flaherty (Ed.), *Essays in the history of Canadian law, vol. II* (pp. 418–91). Toronto: Osgoode Society.

Rosenthal, Peter, interview with author, July 7, 2003.

Rosner, D., & Markowitz, G. (1991). *Deadly dust: Silicosis and the politics of occupational disease in twentieth-century America*. Princeton, NJ: Princeton University Press.

Sass, R. (1998). The limits of workplace health and safety reform in liberal economies. *New Solutions, 3*(1), 31–40.

Seith, E. (2005, December 27). Work killed my wife. *The Glasgow Herald*, p. 13.

Selikoff, I. (1964). Asbestos exposure and neoplasia. *Journal of the American Medical Association, 188*, 22–26.

Selikoff, I. (1965). The occurrence of asbestosis among insulation workers in the United States. *Annals New York Academy of Science, 132*, 139–155.

Sennett, R. (1998) *The corrosion of character: The personal consequences of work in the new capitalism*. New York: W.W. Norton.

Siegrist, J. (1996). Adverse health effects of high effort/low reward conditions. *Journal of Occupational Health Psychology, 1*, 27–41.

Smith, B.E. (1987). *Digging our own graves: Coal miners and the struggle over black lung disease*. Philadelphia: Temple University Press.

Smith, D. (2000). *Consulted to death: How Canada's workplace health and safety system fails workers*. Winnipeg: Arbeiter.

Statistics Canada. (2003, August 12). Repetitive strain injury. *The Daily*: 1–4.

Stellman, J., & Henefin, M.S. (1983). *Office work can be dangerous to your health*. New York: Pantheon Books.

Storey, R. (2005). Activism and the making of occupational health and safety law in Ontario, 1960s–1980. *Policy and Practice in Occupational Health and Safety, 1*, 41–68.

Storey, R., & Tucker, E. (2006). All that is solid melts into air: Worker participation and occupational health and safety regulation in Ontario, 1970–2000. In V. Mogensen (Ed.), *Worker safety under siege: Labor, capital, and the politics of workplace safety in a deregulated world* (pp. 157–85). Armonk, NY: M.E. Sharpe.

Tannock, S. (2001). *Youth at work: The unionized fast-food and grocery workplace*. Philadelphia: Temple University Press.

Tatatryn, L. (1979). *Dying for a living: The politics of industrial death.* Ottawa: Deneau.
Tucker, E. (1988). Making the workplace "safe" for capitalism: The enforcement of factory legislation in nineteenth century Ontario. *Labour/Le Travail, 21*, 45–85.
Tucker, E. (1990). *Administering danger in the workplace: The law and politics of occupational health and safety regulation in Ontario, 1850–1914.* Toronto: University of Toronto Press.
Tucker, E. (2003). Diverging trends in worker health and safety protection and participation in Canada, 1985–2000. *Relations Industrielles/Industrial Relations, 58*(3), 395–426.
Vance, E. (1985). *Elliot Lake.* Toronto: Workplace Health and Safety Centre.
Walker, C. (2000). Interview with author, December 1, 2000.
Walters, V. (1983). Occupational health and safety regulation In Ontario: An analysis of its origins and content. *Canadian Review of Sociology and Anthropology, 20*(4), 413–434.

PART 7

CURRENT ISSUES AND PUBLIC POLICY

The health care system, like all social institutions, is constantly in a state of flux. The source of this flux is changing social needs and political and economic interests. Policymakers attempt to anticipate and respond to these changing needs and interests; the chapters in this part of the book examine ways in which evolving needs and interests are reflected in current policy debates and health care practices.

Mental health is a perennial policy problem. In Chapter 21, Dickinson and Graham argue that this is so because debate in this area is characterized by disagreement over the nature of the problem to be solved, and as a result, there is disagreement about how best to solve it. They show, through a review of the literature, that the mental health domain is populated by a number of distinct groups with distinct and irreconcilable understandings of the nature of mental disorders and of how best to deal with them. Medical professionals and others maintain that mental disorders are mental illnesses that should be treated like other illnesses. Nonmedical health professionals, such as psychologists and social workers, maintain that mental disorders are really reflections of underlying psychosocial problems of living, not illnesses. Finally, members of the psychiatric consumer or psychiatric survivor movement maintain that whatever the true nature of the problem, its treatment and management are the prerogative of those with the problem, not some professional group. Dickinson and Graham conclude that although current mental health policy initiatives recognize at least some of these contending approaches to the problem, their resolution is by no means assured.

Drug therapies are an essential and growing part of Canada's health care system. Lexchin and Wiktorowicz, in Chapter 22, highlight the contradiction between the public good and private profit, especially in the pharmaceutical industry. They show that the unusually high profits of the pharmaceutical industry are the result of industry-state relations, the research activities of drug companies, the price of drugs, and the industry-promoting activities of physicians in their prescribing behaviours. Lexchin and Wiktorowicz argue that when the drive for profits and the needs of health care consumers conflict the pursuit of profits prevails.

Lexchin and Wiktorowicz's chapter raises profound ethical problems. Storch, Rodney, and Starzomski pick up on this theme in Chapter 23. They maintain that ethical issues are inherent in all health care decisions, whether the issues are clinical decisions, institutional decisions, or policy-level decisions. At the level of clinical decision making, the common ethical question concerns quality of life. Quality of life issues are particularly thorny due to the fact that the concept is rather vague and relative to people's positions and preferences. The issue is further complicated by the question of who should make quality-of-life assessments and who should pay for them.

Some of the contemporary clinical decisions that Storch and her colleagues address are end-of-life decisions, transplantation and organ donation decisions, genetics and genetic testing decisions, and institutional-level decisions. Resource allocation decisions, in particular, are also inherently ethical decisions. Whether resources are made available for a kidney dialysis program or a mental health program for the elderly directly affects the quality of life of those involved and raises the question of equity.

The authors go on to describe the ways in which ethical issues, both clinical and institutional, are currently addressed in Canada. This discussion is followed by speculation regarding future ethical concerns and issues in the context of Canadian health care. The authors conclude that the challenge is to develop the motivational, institutional, and procedural means to enable ethical decision making at all levels of the health care system.

Chapter 24, by Smith and Fiddler, which aptly includes in its title "Making the Gift of Life," addresses the significance of blood supply and the regulatory role of the state to ensure its safety from pathogens. The significance of blood supply is clear when one considers that the Canadian Blood Services (CBS) supply every year enough blood and blood products for well over half a million transfusions for a wide range of medical conditions. If collected blood carries pathogens, the recipients are at risk of contamination, unless such contaminants are detected and eliminated from the blood supply. This risk was highlighted in the 1970s and 1980s when two deadly viruses were found in the blood supply – Human Immunodeficiency Virus (HIV) and Hepatitis C (HCV) Virus. The consequences were far-reaching because thousands of people were infected worldwide and in Canada. This public health crisis raised the issues of accountability and the role of the state in regulating blood collection and setting regulatory standards to ensure a safe blood supply.

Smith and Fiddler offer an overview of the tainted blood scandal and discuss the regulatory consequences. They provide a brief history of CBS and its current management and discuss key findings from the Krever inquiry regarding contamination of the Canadian blood supply. Smith and Fiddler then take a critical look at risk management practices now in place and the roles played by various stakeholder groups and regulatory bodies in creating the regulatory structures that ensure the safety of the blood supply in Canada. They conclude with a discussion of the moral consequences of the regulatory structures, and the emergence of a precautionary culture where public policy decision makers face denouncement and are even held criminally responsible for risk to public health. The preoccupation with safety can also affect the blood supply because of the emergence of new diseases and the exclusion of donors who may pose a threat to the blood supply with the consequence that the risk management experts may face an unenviable dilemma – the safer they make the blood supply the more the risk of scarcity of safe transfusable blood.

Bolaria and Bolaria, in Chapter 25, provide an overview of the debate on the relative importance of personal and structural determinants of health and illness. Specifically, their focus is on lifestyles and life chances. They argue that both the biomedical-clinical paradigm and the lifestyles approach tend to neglect the social-structural context of individuals' lives and that the singular focus on lifestyles ignores the social and material bases of lifestyles and health and illness. The literature indicates that lifestyles are shaped by life chances and socioeconomic inequalities produce social variability in health status.

Chapter 25 concludes with a discussion of policy implications of the individualistic and structural perspectives concerning health promotion. Whether the policies and programs target individuals and their harmful lifestyles or target social conditions and inequalities depends upon the analysis of the sources of health problems. In conclusion, the authors emphasize the importance of research on social behaviour and the lifestyle choices individuals make within the social-structural constraints of their lives because such an investigation would make a significant contribution to the structure-agency debate in sociology.

21

Mental Health Policy in Canada: What's the Problem?

HARLEY D. DICKINSON University of Saskatchewan

PAUL J. GRAHAM University of Saskatchewan

INTRODUCTION

There is a growing recognition that despite its strength, our health care system has a number of weaknesses. One its the most significant weaknesses is that it is not primarily a health care system at all, but rather an illness care system. As such, it is a more or less effective means for dealing with acute injuries and illnesses but it is less adequate as a solution to the chronic and degenerative health problems that currently predominate in Canada. Among the "new" health problems, mental health ranks high (Epp, 1986). As a consequence, considerable attention has been devoted to developing mental health policy in Canada (Epp, 1988).

The scope of the problem is substantial. It has been estimated that 20 percent of the Canadian population (that is, one in five) suffer from mental health problems; of these, two percent suffer from severe **mental illnesses** (Cochrane, Durbin & Goering, 1997, p. 1). Data from the Canadian Community Health Survey, collected in 2002, reveal that 12.2 percent of Canadians will experience a major depressive episode over their lifetime, and 4.8 percent will do so annually (Patten et al., 2006, p. 86). In addition, both the number of persons and the proportion of the population receiving treatment have increased over time, although the nature and location of treatment has changed dramatically (Randhawa & Riley, 1996).

The assessment of those receiving mental health services in hospitals has changed in Canada, leading to indications of a decrease of in-patient hospital stays. Initially, between 1960 and 1976, the number of beds in mental hospitals was reduced from 47,633 to 15,011. At the same time, the number of beds in psychiatric wards in general hospitals increased from 844 to 5,836 (Cochrane, Durbin & Goering, 1997, p. 1). Between the late 1960s and the early 1980s, mental disorder rose from the fifth to the leading cause of in-patient treatment in general hospitals (Blishen, 1991, pp. 36–38).

Since then, however, current use of separation rates from both psychiatric and general hospitals in Canada shows a decrease. The CIHI defines a separation as a "departure of an inpatient from hospital, either due to a discharge or death" (CIHI, 2005, p. C-2). Administrative records, based on hospital separations, are used to

FIGURE 21.1

Hospital Separation Rate for Mental Illness by Type of Hospital 1994–95 to 2002–03*

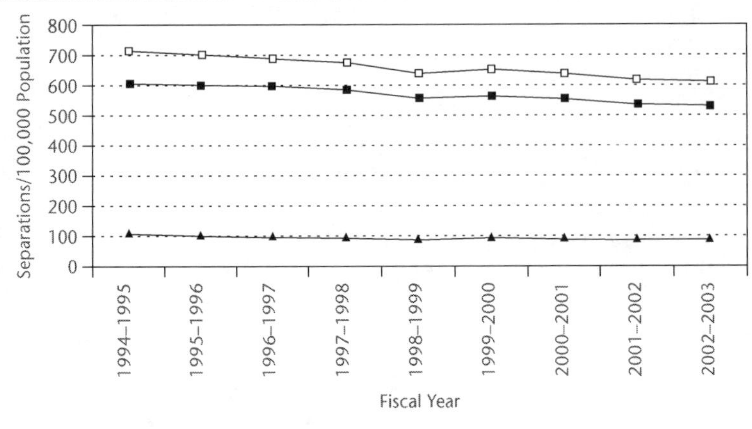

*Crude rates based on the number of separations per 100,000 population. Population counts based on Statistics Canada's population estimates for 2002.

Source: HMHD, CIHI 2005.

FIGURE 21.2

Average Length of Stay for Mental Illness by Type of Hospital 1994–95 to 2002–03

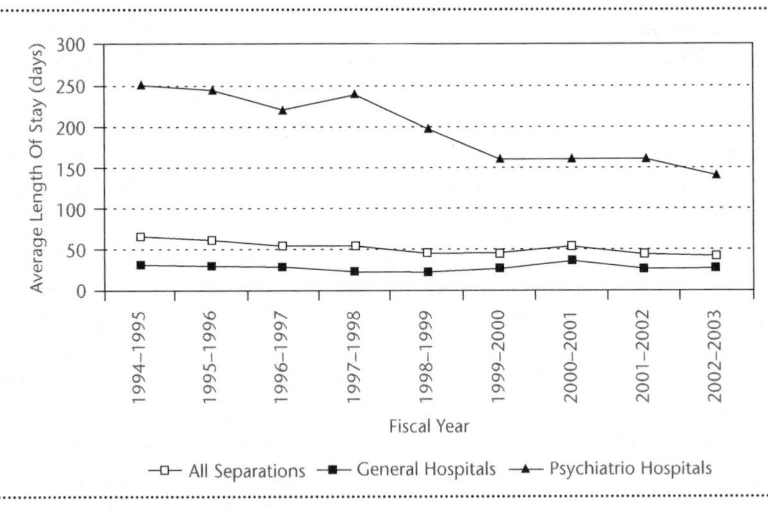

Source: HMHDB, CIHI 1994–2003.

provide statistics on either increases or decreases in utilization of hospital services (i.e., separation rates). The CIHI have recently reported a decrease in the number of mental health services utilized in hospitals. This may be explained as the result of the refinement of psychiatric medications and the development of community-based services which have contributed to a decrease in the numbers that receive psychiatric care in hospitals (CIHI, 2005, p. v). As Figures 21.1 and 21.2 show, both the numbers of individuals receiving treatment and their duration times in hospitals have decreased.

Many people, however, are never admitted to hospital for treatment of their mental health problems. In Ontario, more than half of all psychiatric patients are treated in primary care settings, and the family physician is most often the source of help (Lin & Goering, 2000; Rhodes et al., 2006). Across Canada it is estimated that family physicians manage 80 percent of all mental health problems (Health Edition Online, 2001). In addition, in Ontario, about 30 percent of all family physicians' patients experience some psychosocial or psychiatric problem. Other studies show that 50–75 percent of persons who could benefit from mental health services never seek help (Lin & Goering, 2000).

In addition to people who do seek help from physicians for mental health problems, there are those who only seek help from various non-medical mental health professionals, or who receive informal help from family, friends, or other volunteers, or who receive no help or services. This last category of people contributes to the growing homeless populations that characterize contemporary urban societies (Hardin, 1993).

In Ottawa, Canada, the issue of the relationship between homelessness and mental illness has been addressed via outreach services. The Psychiatric Outreach Team (a multidisciplinary team) of the Royal Ottawa Hospital works with the homeless, those at risk of homelessness, those who suffer from persistent severe mental illness, and those who use emergency shelters, rooming houses, etc. (Royal Ottawa Health Care Group, 2002). A recent review of the literature on outreach programs shows attention to conceptual and clinical issues, as well as the special needs of this population, but there exists very few innovative service models (Farrell et al., 2005, p. 738).

It is difficult to know the total cost of mental health problems. Specifically, measurement of direct and/or indirect costs provides various results depending on methodology. The costs associated with non-institutional treatment are additional to these. It is also estimated that direct hospital costs are at least matched by various indirect costs, including the costs associated with lost productivity, unemployment, and the personal suffering and reduced quality of life experienced by the mentally disordered and their families (Bland, 1988, p. 1).

It has been estimated that the cost of hospital days alone exceeded one billion dollars in Canada in 1978. Since then, hospital costs for mental disorders have increased (Bland, 1988, p. 1). A Health Canada study published in 1997, charting the economic burdens of illness, estimated that in 1993 the cost of mental health for both direct and indirect costs was $7.83 billion (Moore et al., 1997, pp. 10–11). A similar study analyzing 1998 data indicates a slightly higher figure of approximately $7.87 billion (Health Canada, 2002, pp. 6–7). However, a 2001 re-evaluation of mental health costs, building on the 1993 study but using the 1996/97 National Population Health survey, resulted in a drastic 71 percent increase in estimated costs to $14.4 billion for 1998 (Stephens & Joubert, 2001, p. 22). There is an obvious difficulty in assessing mental health costs in Canada.

International data reveal the serious crisis in cost management. American estimates place them at more than $136 billion (Health Beat, 1992, p. 20). Schizophrenia alone in the United States, based on 2002 data, reveals an estimated cost of $62.7 billion (Wu et al., 2005, p. 1125). Data from Europe show that mental health costs can take up 3 to 4 percent of GDP (European Commission, 2005, p. 4). Most recently, however, a systematic review commissioned by the World Health Organization (WHO) compared the costs of mental health internationally (Hu, 2006). For example, the total cost for schizophrenia for Taipei, China, was evaluated in 1994 as costing $562 million US currency (Hu, 2006, p. 8). The only African data comes from Kenya and shows a total cost of $0.205 million for mental illness (Hu, 2006, p. 9). Although much data is compared, this study clearly reveals the incomplete and sometimes outdated state of data that is available worldwide on mental illness.

The existing mental health care system seems to be overwhelmed and incapable of effectively dealing with these problems. The reasons for this are the subject of debate.

In this chapter, we briefly overview some of the main dimensions of disagreement; the chapter consists of two main sections. In the first section, we briefly describe how various solutions to the problem of mental disorders follow from the different ways in which the problem is defined. The second section briefly outlines a number of common themes and trends present in current mental health policy debates. The central argument is that current policy initiatives undertaken within a health promotion policy framework reflect an attempt to establish an accommodation between differing and potentially incompatible definitions of the problem while at the same time containing costs.

THE SOCIOLOGY OF MENTAL ILLNESS AND MENTAL HEALTH

One problem that all societies must solve is what to do with individuals who engage in socially disruptive forms of deviant behaviour. The first and arguably the most important steps are to define the problem. The way in which a problem is defined determines the type of solution that is implemented. If, for example, troublesome behaviours are defined as criminal, legal solutions will be devised; if a problem is seen as biological in nature, medical solutions will be developed; and if the problem is seen to be spiritual in origin, a religious solution will be developed. If there is uncertainty concerning the nature of the problem there will also be uncertainty concerning the nature of the solution to be applied to it – and uncertainty is dominant in the area of mental disorder.

In Western societies, the solution to the problem of what to do with individuals labeled deviant has evolved through a series of steps from religious, to legal, to medical forms of management and control (Conrad & Schneider, 1980; Freidson, 1970; Kittrie, 1972; Manning, 1989; Scull, 1982, 1983). The medicalization of social control is generally thought to have taken place between the ends of the 18th and 19th centuries.

During that time period, the form of deviance previously known as madness or insanity came increasingly to be understood as mental illness, and the asylum, later renamed the mental hospital, came to be the principal source and form of treatment (Conrad & Schneider, 1980; Foucault, 1973; Scull, 1982, 1983, 1991). The confinement of the mentally ill in mental hospitals remained the dominant solution to the problem until the 1960s. Since then, there has been a marked demise of the mental hospital as the principal means and location for managing mental illness, and there has occurred a corresponding rise in various community-based alternatives, including treatment in general hospitals. Although there is general agreement that this transformation heralded a major change in the nature and organization of **psychiatry,** there is little agreement concerning either the causes or consequences of those changes.

A number of different accounts of this transformation have been proposed (Busfield, 1986; Cohen, 1985; Dickinson, 1989; Ralph, 1983; Scull, 1983). Although it is not possible here to review them all, I will provide a brief sketch of the main aspects of the differing descriptions and explanations of the transition from asylum to community psychiatry.

The first, and probably most popular, account of the transformation is the "march of medical science" story (Cohen, 1985). According to this account, advances in modern medical science resulted in the discovery of new and true knowledge about the nature and causes of mental illness. The new scientific understanding of mental illness replaced the ignorance, superstition, and myths of previous generations, and led to new forms of medical treatment that replaced the old treatment regimes that were discredited as ineffective at best and brutally inhumane at worst.

Central to this account is the claim that modern medical science demonstrated that "madness" and "insanity" were really "mental illnesses." Given this claim, it followed that mental illness should be treated in the same way, and in the same locations, as all other illnesses. In this regard, the mental hospital was seen as an obstacle to the humane and effective medical management of the mentally ill (Goffman, 1961). Mental hospitals were more like prisons than hospitals, and their radical reform was seen as imperative. From this point of view, the transition from mental hospital to community psychiatry was essentially a triumph of science and humanitarian concern, the final realization of which was made possible by the discovery of powerful psychotropic drugs in the 1950s. To the extent that proponents of this rather celebrationist history acknowledge that there are problems with community psychiatry, said problems are generally considered to be the result of inadequate resources; based on this belief, it is believed that more resources will solve the problems faced by community psychiatry.

Another, more critical, explanation argues that the demise of the mental hospital and the rise of community psychiatry is best understood as the substitution of one form of social control for another which is neither more humane nor more scientifically justified than that which preceded it (Scull, 1983; Ralph, 1983). From this perspective, the transition from mental hospital to community psychiatry is best understood in political and economic terms. Scull (1983), for example, claims that in the post-World War II period, a growing fiscal crisis of the state resulted in efforts to reduce costs. As a result, the state began to divest itself of responsibility for the institutional care or control of various deviant populations, especially the mentally ill. Thus, the emptying of the mental hospitals, a process he termed **decarceration,** was driven by economic and political imperatives, not the progressive and humanitarian advances of medical science.

Despite the differences between the "march of medicine" and the critical "fiscal crisis" perspectives for understanding the development of community psychiatry, they both share the view that the object of treatment, or mistreatment, is the same, namely, mental illness and the mentally ill.

The claim that the domain of psychiatry is mental illness, however, has not gone unchallenged. Indeed, Szasz (1972, p. 12) has proclaimed that mental illness is a myth, and that psychiatric "treatment," especially involuntary treatment, is best understood, not as the application of medical science to the treatment of mental illness, but rather as a form of torture. This view, variously expressed, is termed **anti-psychiatry.**

Anti-psychiatry shares with the critical "fiscal crisis" perspective the belief that the primary function of psychiatric diagnosis and treatment is the social identification, classification, and control of deviance. Anti-psychiatrists agree that persons diagnosed and treated as mentally ill have problems, but they disagree about the nature of those problems.

Szasz (1972), for example, argues that the problems currently being diagnosed and treated as medical problems by **psychiatry** are really **psycho-social** problems in living. Conceived of in this fashion, it follows that individuals suffering from such problems should not be labeled as mentally ill, nor should they be treated by psychiatrists. Rather, they should be helped to solve their problems in living by those more suited to doing so, namely social workers, psychologists, or other non-medical psychotherapists.

Another branch of the anti-psychiatry movement argues that even this position is wrong. Laing and Esterson (1964), for example, argue that persons labeled as mentally ill, are neither ill nor are their putative problems in living the primary problem. Rather, the so-called mentally ill are responding to an insane and maddening social reality in a sane and rational fashion. From this perspective, the problem is not the individuals who refuse to conform to social demands and expectations, but rather the health-destroying and soul-deforming demands of modern social institutions, particularly the bourgeois family and the capitalist economy. Those who are diagnosed as mentally ill are really reacting against the demands of family and economy by embarking on a journey of individual growth and personal development. Thus, from this perspective, madness is seen as an act of resistance and psychiatrists are seen as the storm troopers of society's reaction. The role of the radical, anti-psychiatric therapist in this rebellion against conformity and oppression is to aid and abet the rebels in their emancipatory journey through madness.

Despite the obvious and substantial differences between these two versions of anti-psychiatry, they do share a common component – they both reserve a privileged position for the professional, non-medical therapist. Recent efforts to accommodate anti-psychiatry into mainstream mental health care is still a contested issue (Hopton, 2006; Cresswell, 2005). An alternative perspective on the appropriate role of professionals in the definition of mental health problems and their solutions is provided by the mental patient's/ consumer's rights movement.

The mental patient's/consumer's rights movement emerged in its contemporary forms alongside the rise of community psychiatry. The culmination of efforts to medicalize psychiatry resulted in many of the mentally ill being given the same rights as other patients. These rights include the right to informed consent, the right to receive adequate treatment in the least restrictive environment, the right to refuse treatment, and various other protections against involuntary detention and treatment.

The extension of these rights to the mentally ill fundamentally altered the nature of the doctor-patient relationship. In most cases, psychiatric patients were empowered relative to psychiatrists, and came to have a greater say in the definition of their problems and the determination of solutions. This empowerment of patients was further advanced in the context of the anti-psychiatry movement. This rejection of medical dominance was encouraged by various non-medical mental health professions as part of their own struggles to achieve professional autonomy in the context of newly emerging community psychiatry (Dickinson, 1989). One consequence of the competing claims concerning the nature of the problem and the most appropriate solution to it was that patients/clients came to have a choice of treatments available to them, and consequently came to act more as consumers than patients. Today, the Canadian Mental Health Association prefers the term "consumers" (CMHA, 2006).

The presumed sovereignty of the consumer, however, is frequently limited by a number of factors, including the fact that the consumerist ethic is often mediated through advocacy/support groups that are not controlled by those with mental health problems. Many mental health advocacy groups, for example, are dominated by the families of those with mental health problems, and/or various professional interests. This creates a potential for a conflict of interests between those who propose to speak for and define the needs of the service consumers, and the service consumers themselves.

Recognition of this conflict of interests has contributed to the emergence of another branch of the anti-psychiatry movement generally referred to as the **mental patient's liberation movement** or **psychiatric survivor's movement** (Burstow & Weitz, 1988; Chamberlin, 1990; Olsen, 1993). This movement maintains that professionally provided mental health services, whether medical in nature or not, are oppressive forms of social control. It must be pointed out, however, that the psychiatric survivor's movement, at least as it has evolved in Canada since the 1970s, is not homogenous either in terms of membership or ideologies (Olsen, 1993; Trainor et al., 1997).

Chamberlin (1990, p. 323) notes that, despite the lack of organizational and ideological unity, the movement is held together by its common commitment to a twofold mission, namely, the development of self-help alternatives to professionally provided treatment, and the securing of full citizenship rights for individuals labeled "mentally ill." In practical terms, proponents of the anti-psychiatry perspective endorse the empowerment of service consumers in defining and resolving their problems.

Sociologists have contributed to these debates in a number of ways. Sociological analyses have focused on class and gender differences in the prevalence and incidence of mental disorders, as well as class and gender differences in forms of treatment. There is an inverse relation between social class and the probability of being diagnosed with a mental disorder (Faris & Dunham, 1939; Hollingshead & Redlich, 1958; Leighton et al., 1963; Srole et al., 1962). In terms of gender differences, women are more likely to be diagnosed with mental disorders than men (Chesler, 1972; Dohrenwend & Dohrenwend, 1976; Gove & Tudor, 1973; Showalter, 1985). The correlations between gender and mental disorder, and social class and mental disorder are well established (Randahawa & Riley, 1996). There is some debate, however, over the explanation of these relationships.

Social selection theories have been developed specifically to explain the inverse relationship between social class and mental disorder. They maintain that low class position is a consequence of mental disorder, not a cause. There are two variants of this approach. The **downward drift hypothesis** suggests that people with mental disorders are unable to function effectively in occupational and other social roles. Over time, this results in a downward drift into the lower social classes. A variant on this view suggests that it is not so much that mentally disordered individuals drift down into the lower social classes; rather, their mental disorders limit their ability to achieve upward social mobility. As a result, in each generation, the mentally disordered are left behind and over time tend to be over-represented in the lower classes. Both types of social selection theories accept the validity of psychiatric diagnoses.

Social causation theories, on the other hand, to a greater or lesser extent, reject medical explanations of mental disorder and deny that mental illness, as illness, exists. Rather, like Szasz, these theorists tend to understand mental disorder in terms of various **psycho-social problems with living**.

The social stress theory, for example, explains the correlation of class and gender with diagnosed mental disorder in terms of differential exposure to, and experiences of, stress.

It is suggested that women and members of other marginalized groups experience greater stress in their lives and this, in turn, is manifested as higher rates of mental disorders. The higher levels of stress are related to a general condition of social powerlessness that is experienced more concretely as overcrowded housing, broken homes, poverty, boring and dangerous work, and frequent and prolonged periods of unemployment.

Langer and Michael (1963) were among the first to demonstrate that members of the lower classes experienced greater stress than members of the higher social classes. They and others (see Kessler, 1979) found, however, that at any given level of stress, members of the lower classes also cope less well than members of the higher classes. This has given rise to the notion that class differences in the rate of mental disorders are not a result of the shear magnitude of stress experienced, but rather, these differences reflect inequalities in the resources and coping skills available to members of the lower classes compared to others.

Kohn (1977) has argued that this is at least partly the result of class-based differences in the form and content of socialization. He maintains that the structural conditions of lower class life, and the marginalization and disempowerment characteristic of it, are reflected in a lower class consciousness that is expressed as a form of passive fatalism and deference to authority.

In contrast, individuals in the higher classes occupy social positions that enable them to make consequential decisions. Occupying positions that provide at least relative degrees of power and autonomy gives rise to individuals who become more skilled and competent in terms of identifying and mobilizing the resources and supports needed to help them solve problems or to change the circumstances that give rise to problems. This relative resource richness helps explain why higher class persons are less often diagnosed with mental disorders.

The societal reaction approach, or **labeling theory,** focuses on the reaction of society to the behaviour of individuals, not on the individual's behaviour itself. Thus, rather than seeing mental disorder as an illness that has causes within the mind or body of the individual, labeling theory understands the diagnosis of mental illness to be a social label attached to individuals who exhibit deviant behaviour or communication patterns. According to labeling theory, these labels come to be accepted by individuals as core elements of their identities and ultimately as important determinants of their social status (Scheff, 1984). An empirical study using a modified version of Scheff's labeling theory found that labeled patients preformed a set of beliefs about the meaning of being mentally ill prior to receiving treatment which in turn affected their behaviour in social groups (Link et al., 1989, p. 419). This study in turn has been much cited throughout the various literatures evaluating stigma, stigmatization, and/or self-stigma which can be considered a subfield of labeling theory (Teachman et al., 2006; Stewart et al., 2006; Rusch et al., 2006; Mueller et al., 2006; Lee et al., 2006).

The class and gender patterns are explained by labeling theorists as a reflection of the fact that psychiatry tends to be a profession made up mostly of middle class, white males. The associated cultural characteristics and biases of psychiatrists, it is thought, predispose them to evaluate the mental health of members of the lower classes, racial minorities, and women unfavourably. This is because the normal behaviours of women and members of the lower classes and racial minority groups are understood as deviant from the point of view of middle class, white, male professionals.

It is obvious from the foregoing that there is much disagreement concerning the nature and causes of the problem of mental disorder. It is, consequently, also the case that there is much disagreement and uncertainty about how to solve the problem. To briefly summarize, we have seen that the mental health field is characterized by a number of distinct groups, each with different conceptions of the nature of the problem and the most appropriate solution to it. These groups are:

- Medical professionals and others who maintain that the problem is really mental illness that should be treated like every other illness.
- Non-medical professionals such as social workers, psychologists, and other types of psychotherapists who maintain the problem is really various types of psycho-social problems in living that require their therapeutic assistance for its correct identification and solution.
- Psychiatric consumers/survivors who maintain that whatever the true nature of the problem is, those suffering from it should be primarily responsible for its definition and solution.

This brief overview of some of the relevant sociological literature reveals that available research findings are ambiguous, providing support for all the various positions. In the following section, we show that current policy initiatives can be understood as efforts to accommodate these incompatible perspectives and interests, while at the same time responding to demands for cost containment.

CURRENT POLICY PROPOSALS AND DEVELOPMENTS

In Canada, mental health, like health in general, is a provincial responsibility. Each province, therefore, is developing its response to the problems of mental health relative to its own circumstances. Despite this, mental health policy in all jurisdictions is developing within the health promotion framework and consequently is characterized by a number of common themes and trends. These include an increased emphasis on mental health promotion and the prevention of mental disorders, the protection of human rights and freedoms, a greater emphasis on community care, and concern for the coordination of service planning and delivery (Epp, 1988, 1986; Health and Welfare Canada, 1990, p. 169; Macnaughton, 1992; Nelson et al., 1996; Commission on the Future of Health Care in Canada, 2002; Senate of Canada, 2006). The balance of this chapter examines these themes and some of the contradictions embedded within and between them.

Mental Health Promotion and Prevention of Mental Disorders

The promotion of mental health as a policy objective presupposes a definition of mental health. There is, however, no widely accepted definition. For that reason Health and Welfare Canada proposed the following:

> Mental health is the capacity of the individual, the group and the environment to interact in ways that promote subjective well-being, the optimal development and use of mental abilities (cognitive, affective and relational), the achievement of individual and collective goals consistent

with justice and the attainment and preservation of conditions of fundamental equality. (Epp, 1988, p. 7)

An important aspect of this definition is that mental health is not defined as the absence of mental illness. Thus, mental health and mental illness are not seen as lying at opposite poles on a single continuum. Rather, it is suggested that they lie on separate continuums. Thus, mental disorders are conceptualized as existing on a continuum with maximal mental disorder at one pole characterized by the greatest severity, frequency, and range of psychiatric symptoms, and absence of mental disorder at the other pole, characterized by freedom from psychiatric symptoms (Epp, 1988, p. 9).

Mental health, on the other hand, is seen as lying on a continuum with optimal mental health at one pole and minimal mental health at the other. Optimal mental health exist where individual, group, and environmental factors work together effectively to ensure subjective well-being, optimal development and use of mental abilities, the achievement of goals consistent with justice, and conditions of fundamental equality. Minimal mental health, at the other pole, is characterized by subjective distress, impairment or underdevelopment of mental abilities, failure to achieve goals, destructive behaviours, and entrenchment of inequalities caused by contradictory interactions between individual, group, and environmental factors (Epp, 1988, p. 8, Figure 2).

Given this conceptualization, the absence of psychiatric symptoms in itself does not imply optimal mental health. Similarly, the presence of mental disorders, or psychiatric symptoms, does not preclude the possibility of mental health. Rather, "mental disorder may be regarded as one of several possible obstacles" to the achievement of mental health (Epp, 1988, p. 8).

The promotion of mental health, therefore, is the same for all individuals regardless of whether or not they suffer from mental disorders. It involves minimizing or eliminating barriers to the achievement of empowering interactions between individuals, groups, and the environment (Epp, 1988, p. 9). These interventions can be aimed either at individuals or they can be directed toward altering social and organizational structures and policies.

Conceptually and practically, the prevention and treatment of mental disorders is distinct from the promotion of mental health, although in a number of aspects they intersect (Nelson et al., 1996). As we have seen, there is much debate about the underlying causes of many of the major mental illnesses/disorders. There is, however, an emerging consensus that they result from the interaction between biological, developmental, and/or psycho-social factors and "can – in principle, at least – be managed using approaches comparable to those applied to physical disease (that is prevention, diagnosis, treatment and rehabilitation)" (Epp, 1988, p. 8).

Despite this emergent consensus concerning the multifactor causes of mental disorders/illnesses, little is currently done in the way of primary prevention, that is, prevention of the onset of mental disorders (Nelson et al., 1996). Secondary prevention, or the prevention of relapse through the management of symptoms, has been facilitated by "pharmacological and other modalities" (Epp, 1988, p. 8), although there is still considerable controversy concerning both the effectiveness and appropriateness of chemotherapy and other forms of treatment directed toward symptom management. Currently, therefore, attention is being given to tertiary prevention, that is, the prevention or minimization of the degree of disability associated with mental disorders. In more concrete terms, tertiary prevention is directed toward minimizing the need for expensive in-patient and residential forms of treatment. Tertiary prevention efforts, whatever their focus, attempt to identify and mobilize resources in the form of self-help or mutual-aid, and to minimize reliance on expensive professional services whenever possible.

Like current efforts to prevent mental disorders, mental health promotion practices are based on the ideal of consumer involvement and empowerment. As we have seen, however, not all stakeholders understand the nature of the problem and the most appropriate approach to its solution in the same way. This has led to the two "blind alleys" of mental health policy debate: "exclusive reliance on medical treatment technologies on the one hand, and anti-professionalism and exclusive reliance on individual initiative or volunteer action on the other" (Epp, 1988, p. 10).

Problem recognition is a first step toward its resolution. The above quotation makes it clear that policy-makers recognize the existence of two approaches to the problem of mental health/illness, namely the medical and the anti-professional, anti-psychiatric approach. The distinctions and potential conflicts between the medical and the non-medical professional models, however, are not as clearly recognized. Without concrete proposals for how proponents of the contending positions are to co-operate, calls for various stakeholders to work together may be dismissed as hopelessly naïve, or worse, as an effort to obscure continued forms of psychiatric oppression or professional dominance behind an ideological façade of co-operative partnership (Boudreau, 1991b). The current emphasis on human rights and freedoms in mental health policy deliberations may be intended to forestall the latter interpretation.

Protecting Human Rights and Freedoms

The protection of human rights and freedoms has been a perennial concern relative to the social management and control of madness/mental illness. Over the last two centuries, the power to define and treat the mad/mentally ill has alternated between the state delegation of power to the medical profession and the legal profession. The rationale for a medically dominated system is that early diagnosis and treatment are argued to be necessary for effective cures. The rationale for a legally structured system is twofold. In the first instance, it is intended to be a means to protect society from the mentally ill and the mentally ill from themselves. In the second instance, it is a means to protect the mentally ill from unjust and inappropriate confinement and treatment (Hardin, 1993).

This second objective rose to prominence in the face of recent attempts to demonstrate the truth of the claim that mental illness is really an illness that should be treated like every other illness. As a result of the successful medicalization of psychiatry there emerged a growing recognition of the right of mental patients to informed consent, to refuse treatment, and to be treated in the least restrictive setting and manner possible. This impetus to mental patients' rights also, paradoxically, received impetus from the anti-psychiatry movement that maintains, as we have seen, that mental illness is a myth and that the system of medically dominated diagnosis and treatment was itself a violation of human rights.

These general factors contributed to a growing consensus that patients/consumers should have a significant say, if not a veto, in defining the nature of their problems and the nature of the most appropriate solution(s) to them. Consumer participation in these processes is currently seen as an effective means to protect their rights and freedoms (Health and Welfare Canada, 1990, pp. 173–174).

The forces that contributed to an emphasis on consumer participation as a means of ensuring the protection of individual rights and freedoms were given further impetus with the adoption of the Canadian Charter of Rights and Freedoms in 1982. In 1987, a draft *Uniform Mental Health Act* was prepared (Uniform Law Conference, 1987). The draft Act, although it has no legal status, was intended to serve as a guide for the legislative incorporation of the requirements of the Charter of Rights and Freedoms into provincial and territorial legislation.

Despite the fact that there is an increasingly explicit commitment to consumer empowerment and participation in the mental health field a contradiction remains. It resides in the fact that mental health policy and practice has a dual function: it is intended both to provide care and treatment to those in need, and it is intended to protect others from mentally disordered individuals who may be dangerous. Indeed, in the 1987 model mental health act, the protection of society and the terms and conditions for providing involuntary treatment to those considered dangerous are the dominant concerns (Health and Welfare Canada, 1990, pp. 173–74).

It is obvious that the provision of involuntary examination, custody, care, treatment, and restraint is inevitably going to be in conflict with the principle of consumer control and voluntary participation. In legal terms, this contradiction can be expressed as a conflict between society's right to provide involuntary treatment in order to protect its members and the individual's right to refuse unwanted treatment.

Recent efforts to resolve this contradiction have resulted in the introduction of mandatory community treatment orders. These orders enable the courts to require individuals to take their medications and to appoint someone, often a physician, to ensure that they do so. It is generally thought that many individuals caught in the revolving door of hospitalization-release-hospitalization could have that cycle broken if they would stay on their medications while in the community. Community treatment orders are an attempt to prevent re-hospitalization. Thus, they are part of the tertiary prevention efforts mentioned above.

Community Care

The emphasis on community care is often interpreted to mean the establishment of a more "balanced" configuration of institutional (i.e., in-patient and other residential treatment services) and community-based (i.e., out-patient and non-residential) services and supports of various types. More specifically, it refers to a further reduction in the use of long-term residential care facilities and expensive in-patient services in general hospitals.

The fact that the majority of mental health care costs are associated with the provision of general hospital-based treatment and care is taken as indicative of the failure of the 1960s and 1970s **deinstitutionalization** movement (Lurie, 1984; Simmons, 1990; Trainor et al., 1992). It is important to note, however, that during the first phase of the development of community psychiatry, the substitution of general hospital based in-patient treatment services for mental hospital services was seen as a major advance toward community psychiatry (Dickinson, 1989; Tyhurst et al., 1963).

The current commitment to reduced in-patient services is accompanied by the recognition that a range of housing alternatives is required "in order to provide for people at various levels of individual functioning, while allowing the appropriate degrees of professional supervision and personal autonomy" (Health and Welfare Canada, 1990, p. 170).

It is explicitly stated that the service users are to have a central role in developing and coordinating community psychiatric services (Health and Welfare Canada, 1990, p. 170). It is also made explicit that the satisfaction of those needs will involve the coordinated identification, use, and development of various "informal and natural support networks with respect to care and rehabilitation efforts" (Health and Welfare Canada, 1990, p. 170).

The identification and mobilization of these informal community-based resources for the provision of care and rehabilitation services in addition to being indicative of a respect for patient rights, also signal a commitment to "least cost" solutions and constitute a mainstay in mental health policy. Assuming no new resources will be made available, this goal can only be achieved by reallocating resources from the medically dominated hospital sector to the non-medical community mental health care system. Thus, it seems likely that putting community care into practice will neither be easy nor free of conflict. Recognition of these potential difficulties underpins a commitment to co-ordination in service planning and delivery.

COORDINATION OF SERVICE PLANNING AND DELIVERY

Accurate identification of needs is the foundation of service planning and delivery. It is generally believed that once needs are accurately identified, rational decisions can be made concerning the (re)-allocation of mental health resources, both financial and human. Related to this is the proposition that accurate assessment of needs, especially at the individual level, allows for the development of individualized service delivery plans. This is deemed essential both for minimizing the possibility of unnecessarily institutionalizing individuals and inadvertently creating dependence, and for reducing the risks for individuals falling between the cracks in an uncoordinated system.

The priority currently given to co-ordination in policy planning and service delivery is at least partly a response to these general concerns. More specifically, it is a response to widespread criticism of the initial phase of the deinstitutionalization movement of the 1960s and 1970s. A problem with that first phase of community psychiatry was that it over-emphasized efforts at deinstitutionalization, which in practice often amounted to little more than depopulation of the old asylums. The depopulation of asylums, which was made possible as a result of the successful medicalization of psychiatry (Dickinson, 1989; Dickinson & Andre, 1988), was roundly criticized because it failed to adequately establish community-based services and resources. This failure had a number of consequences, all of which are considered to be negative. These consequences are referred to in various ways, but they generally include "ghettoization" and trans-instutionalization.

The ghettoization of the mentally ill is considered to be a result of the abandonment of discharged patients into a community setting that is neither equipped nor willing to provide necessary services and supports for them (Dear & Wolch, 1987; Scull, 1983). A consequence of this lack of adequate community mental health services is that discharged mental patients, who usually have few resources or money, tend to drift toward low rent inner city neighbourhoods. Increasingly, those with mental disorders contribute to the growing population of homeless that are a ubiquitous and distressing feature of contemporary societies.

The problems associated with "ghettoization," magnified by cutbacks to welfare and social services, and increasing levels of apparently permanent unemployment and underemployment, are a crucible for crime. The mentally ill are both victims and offenders. A consequence of this is that many discharged mental patients are caught up in the criminal justice system. This is often referred to as the criminalization of mental illness, and it is an aspect of **trans-institutionalization.**

Trans-institutionalization is the process of shifting individuals with mental disorders from one institutional setting to another without solving the problem that motivated their discharge from mental hospitals in the first place. Indeed, most analysts agree that trans-institutionalization exacerbates the problem because individuals end up in institutional settings even less well equipped to provide appropriate services and support than were the old mental hospitals. For example, it is also seen to be a problem for the aged mentally disordered who, it is frequently maintained, are often simply drugged and warehoused in long-term care facilities.

Another area of concern is the prevalence of mental illness amongst the prison population. Internationally, data reveal high levels of mental illness in prison populations. The U.S. Department of Justice released data showing that in 2005, over 50 percent of inmates had a mental health problem (James & Glaze, 2006, p. 1). The *Lancet* reviewed prison population health literature to assess the worldwide numbers; the results were striking. Although only a review of the available literature, Fazel and Danesh discovered that one in seven prisoners have some form of mental illness or disorder (Fazel & Danesh, 2002, p. 548). A similar review of the literature, in order to retrieve models of prison health care, reveals serious mental health problems the world over for prisoners (Watson et al., 2004, pp. 122–123). Mental health problems are not only more prevalent in prison populations than in the general population, but they are also increasing (Watson et al., 2004).

In Canada, there is no consensus on the prevalence of mental disorders in prison populations. A report by the British Columbia mental health advocate estimated that 32 percent of inmates in BC correctional facilities have some type of mental disorder (*Star Phoenix*, 2000). Some general estimates range anywhere from 16–67 percent (Zapf, 2004, p. 285). Prison assessment at time of imprisonment reveals that 14 percent of inmates have had some prior psychiatric/psychological treatment (Griffiths, 2007, p. 297). Additionally, the 2005 report of the federal Office of the Correctional Investigator discovered a 61 percent increase in diagnosis of mental health problems from 1997 to 2004 (Griffiths, 2007, p. 297).

The issue of prisoner diagnosis of mental health presents an especially poignant set of problems in regards to trans-institutionalization. On the one hand, if a majority of prisoners have mental health problems, which clearly is the case, then incarceration in prison appears *prima facie* to be the inappropriate environment for treatment. Indeed, the Canadian Mental Health Association (CHMA) released a news item on their website on November 4th, 2005, titled simply "Sub-Standard Treatment of Mentally Ill Inmates is Criminal: Experts" (CHMA, 2005). On the other hand, there would undoubtedly be political pressure for the majority of prisoners to remain incarcerated in a prison environment due to a supposed risk assessment to society, or a sense of being "soft on crime" as voiced by a general public – an undoubtedly unpopular position at election time for politicians wishing to resolve this issue. Institutions, such as prisons, are thus forced to compensate by employing treatment programs hoping to manage the ever growing critical mass of mentally ill within their charge (Anonymous, 2004).

In an effort to avoid and correct these problems, decentralization and regionalization have been enthusiastically embraced as means for coordinating mental health program planning and development. The anticipated advantages of decentralization and regionalization are twofold; it is hoped they will enable the identification of location specific service delivery needs, and that they will facilitate the creation of local commitment to the mobilization and reallocation of resources within the communities most directly affected. This last point is particularly important in light of the commitment to self-care and mutual-aid as essential elements in the health promotion framework (Epp, 1986, 1988).

The commitment to decentralization and regionalization is expressed in varying degrees in different provinces, but generally it entails a transfer of at least some executive and fiscal responsibility to new administrative structures. This transfer of power is seen to have both positive and negative effects. On the positive side, it is argued to be an extension of democratic decision-making into new areas of community life. On the negative side, it is argued that it simply results in the transfer of difficult and divisive resource allocation decisions to local communities. Both of these have the consequence of politicizing decisions at the community level, and thereby intensifying the struggle for control of available resources.

The nature of the membership of the regional planning and administrative bodies which are proposed and emerging in various forms and with various degrees of autonomy across the country is important if the hopes for increased democratization are to be achieved. There are a number of "stakeholders," or vested interests in the mental health field. They do not all share a common definition of the nature of the problems to be solved nor do they share a common vision of the most appropriate solutions to be applied (Boudreau, 1991a, 1991b, 1987; Dickinson, 1989; Dickinson & Andre, 1988; White & Mercier, 1991). Furthermore, it is not apparent that any consensus can be reached on these issues.

Attempts to skirt these issues by selective participation in planning and administration of mental health services will undermine the legitimacy of these new initiatives and consequently their likelihood of success. Sensitivity to this potential problem is crucial given the importance to the health promotion framework of securing individual, family, and community participation in the planning and provision of services, as well as support for those with mental health problems and mental disorders.

CONCLUSION

This chapter focused on the problem definition components of current policy initiatives in the mental health field and their relationship to the proposed reforms of mental health service systems. We argued that lack of consensus about the nature of mental health problems contributes to the institutionalization of contradictions at the level of service delivery.

More specifically, we argued that current policy initiatives appear to be directed toward establishing a compromise between three conceptions of the problem to be solved and the best way to solve it. Despite the laudable intentions behind these policy proposals, it is not clear that they can be effectively put into practice in the form of a comprehensive and integrated mental health care services system. The problem is that the various stakeholders, including both medical and non-medical professional interests and the non-professional interests of service users and their advocates, do not necessarily agree on the nature of the problem, nor do they agree on the nature of the best solution to it. Current policy initiatives, therefore, may have the unintended consequence of locking proponents of conflicting positions into a system of perpetual conflict. Thus, rather than being the solution to existing problems, current initiatives may simply be creating new ones.

STUDY QUESTIONS

1. *Identify and discuss the relationships between the three main approaches to defining the problem of mental disorders/health presented in this chapter.*
2. *What are the four main issues common to mental health policy debates and reforms currently taking place in Canada?*
3. *Outline and discuss the relationship between the anti-psychiatry movement and the psychiatric consumers/survivors movement.*
4. *The distinction between mental disorders and mental health problems is intended to avoid the two "blind alleys" of mental health policy debate. Outline and discuss.*

GLOSSARY

anti-psychiatry the view that psychiatry is a form of social control, not a medical specialty.

decarceration the thesis that the emptying of the mental hospitals was motivated more by economic and political interests of the dominant classes than by the interests of the mentally ill.

deinstitutionalization the process of shifting the treatment of mental illness from mental hospitals to the community in order to avoid the learned dependency and chronicity associated with long term residence in bureaucratically organized institutions.

labeling theory the theory that mental illness is a social role assumed by individuals as a result of a social labeling process, in particular the process of psychiatric diagnosis.

mental illness emotional, ideational, and behavioural abnormalities thought primarily to be caused by biochemical or neurological disorders.

mental patients' liberation/psychiatric survivor's movement the most radical branch of the anti-psychiatry movement that advocates for full citizenship rights for the mentally ill and emancipation from professional domination and control.

psychiatry the medical subspecialty that deals with the definition, classification, and treatment of mental illness.

psycho-social problems with living emotional, ideational, and behavioural abnormalities thought to be primarily the result of traumatic experiences, faulty socialization, or stressful social and personal life experiences.

downward drift hypothesis the hypothesis that the inverse relationship between social class and rates of mental illness is a result of intergenerational downward social drift caused by the fact that the mentally ill are incapable of effectively performing social roles.

trans-institutionalization the process of shifting the mentally ill from one institution to another, particularly from mental hospitals to prisons and other long-term care facilities where they receive little or no treatment.

REFERENCES

Anonymous. (2004). Appendix 4 – psychiatric in-patient programs. *Canadian Journal of Public Health, 95*(suppl. 1), s60–s61.

Bland, R.C. (1988). Prevalence of mental illness. *Annals of the Royal College of Physicians and Surgeons of Canada, 21*, 89–93.

Blishen, B.R. (1991). *Doctors in Canada: The changing world of medical practice*. Toronto: University of Toronto Press, in association with Statistics Canada.

Boudreau, F. (1987). The vicissitudes of psychiatric intervention in Quebec. In E.M. Bennett (Ed.), *Social intervention, theory and practice* (pp. 295–323). Lewiston, NY and Queenston, ON: The Edwin Mellen Press.

Boudreau, F. (1991a). Stakeholders as partners? The challenges of partnership in Quebec mental health policy. *Canadian Journal of Community Mental Health, 10*, 7–28.

Boudreau, F. (1991b). Partnership as a new strategy in mental health policy: The case of Quebec. *Journal of Health Politics, Policy and Law, 16*, 307–329.

Burstow, B. & Weitz, D. (Eds.) (1988). *Shrink resistant: The struggle against psychiatry in Canada*. Vancouver: New Star Books.

Busfield, J. (1986). *Managing madness: Changing ideas and practices*. London: Unwin Hyman.

CIHI (Canadian Institute for Health Information). (2005). *Hospital mental health services in Canada 2002–2003*. Ottawa: CIHI.

Chamberlin, J. (1990). The ex-patient's movement: Where we've been and where we're going. In D. Cohen (Ed.), *Challenging the Therapeutic State: Critical Perspectives on Psychiatry and the Mental Health System*, special issue of *The Journal of Mind and Behavior, 11*(3&4), 323–336.

Chesler, P. (1972). *Women and madness*. New York: Avon Books.

CMHA (Canadian Mental Health Association). (1978). *Women and mental health in Canada: Strategies for change*. Toronto: CMHA.

CMHA (Canadian Mental Health Association). (2005). *Sub-standard treatment of mentally ill inmates is criminal: Experts*. Retrieved February 12, 2006 from http://www.cmha.ca/bins/content_page.asp?cid=6–20–21–965–773&lang=1.

CMHA (Canadian Mental Health Association). (2006). *Questions and answers*. Retrieved March 17, 2006 from http://www.cmha.ca/bins/content_page.asp?cid=6–20–23–45.

Cochrane, J., Durbin, J., & Goering, P. (1997). *Best practices in mental health reform*. Discussion Paper prepared for the Federal/Provincial/Territorial Advisory Network on Mental Health. Ottawa: Health Canada.

Cohen, S. (1985). *Visions of social control: Crime, punishment and classification*. Cambridge: Polity Press.

Conrad, P., & Schneider, J. (1980). *Deviance and medicalization: From badness to madness*. St. Louis, MO: Mosby Co.

Commission on the Future of Healthcare in Canada. (2002). *Building on values: The future of healthcare in Canada*. Saskatoon: Commission on the Future of Healthcare in Canada.

Cresswell, M. (2005). Psychiatric "survivors" and testimonies of self-harm. *Social Science & Medicine, 61*(8), 1668–1677.

Dear, M., & Wolch, J. (1987). *Landscapes of despair: From deinstitutionalization to homelessness.* Princeton: Princeton University Press.

Dickinson, H.D. (1989). *The two psychiatries: The transformation of psychiatric work in Saskatchewan, 1905–1984.* Regina: Canadian Plains Research Centre.

Dickinson, H.D., & Andre, G. (1988). Community psychiatry: The institutional transformation of psychiatric practice. In B.S. Bolaria & H.D. Dickinson (Eds.), *The Sociology of Health Care in Canada* (pp. 295–308). Toronto: Harcourt Brace Jovanovich.

Dohrenwend, D.P., & Dohrenwend, B.S. (1976). Sex differences in psychiatric disorder. *American Journal of Sociology, 81,* 1447–54.

Epp, J. (1986). *Achieving health for all: A framework for health promotion.* Ottawa: Health and Welfare Canada.

Epp, J. (1988). *Mental health for Canadians: Striking a balance.* Ottawa: Health and Welfare Canada.

European Commission. (2005). *Improving the mental health of the population: Towards a strategy on mental for the European Union.* Brussels: European Communities.

Faris, R., & Dunham, W. (1939). *Mental disorders in urban areas.* Chicago: University of Chicago Press.

Farrell, S.J. (2005). Taking it to the street: A psychiatric outreach service in Canada. *Community Mental Health Journal, 41*(6), 737–746.

Fazel, S., & Danesh, J. (2002). Serious mental disorder in 23,000 prisoners: A systematic review of 62 surveys. *The Lancet, 359,* 545–550.

Foucault, M. (1973). *Madness and civilization: A history of insanity in the Age of Reason.* New York: Vintage Books.

Freidson, E. (1970). *Profession of medicine: A study in the sociology of applied knowledge.* New York: Harper and Row.

Goffman, E. (1961). *Asylums: Essays on the social situation of mental patients and other inmates.* New York: Anchor Books.

Gove, W.R., & Tudor, J. (1973). Adult sex roles and mental illness. *American Journal of Sociology, 77,* 812–35.

Griffiths, C.T. (2007). *Canadian criminal justice: A primer* (3rd ed.). Canada: Thomson Nelson.

Hardin, H. (1993, July 22). Uncivil liberties. *Vancouver Sun,* A15.

Health and Welfare Canada. (1990). *Mental health services in Canada, 1990.* Ottawa: Health and Welfare Canada.

Health Beat. (1992). Research for mental disorders gets shortchanged. *Natural Health: The Guide to Well-Being,* May/June, 20.

Health Canada. (2002). *Economic burden of illness in Canada, 1998.* Ottawa: Minister of Government Works and Government Services Canada.

Health Edition Online. (2001). Psychotherapy. *February 23, 2001: Miscellany.* Retrieved on August 25, 2007 from http://www.healthedition.com/viewarticle.cfm?id=1880.

Hollingshead, A., & Redlich, F. (1958). *Social class and mental illness.* New York: John Wiley and Sons.

Hopton, J. (2006). The future of critical psychiatry. *Critical Social Policy, 26*(1), 57–73.

Hu, T. (2006). An international review of the national cost estimates of mental illness, 1990–2003. *The Journal of Mental Health Policy and Economics, 9*(1), 3–13.

James, D.J., & Glaze, L.E. (2006). *Mental health problems of prison and jail inmates.* Washington, D.C.: Bureau of Justice Statistics.

Kessler, R. (1979). Stress, social status and psychological distress. *Journal of Health and Social Behavior, 20*, 259–272.

Kittrie, N. (1972). *The right to be different*. Baltimore: Penguin.

Kohn, M. (1977). *Class and conformity: A study in values* (2nd ed.). Chicago: University of Chicago Press.

Laing, R.D., & Esterson, A. (1964). *Sanity, madness and the family: Volume 1: Families of schizophrenics*. London: Tavistock Publications.

Langer, T., & Michael, S. (1963). *Life stress and mental health: The Midtown Manhattan study*. London: Free Press Glencoe.

Lee, S. (2006). Stigmatizing experience and structural discrimination associated with the treatment of schizophrenia in Hong Kong. *Social Science & Medicine, 62*(7), 1685–1696.

Leighton. D.C., Harding, J., Macklin, D., MacMillan, A., & Leighton, A. (1963). *The character of danger: Psychiatric symptoms in selected communities*. New York: Basic Books.

Lin, E., & Goering, P. (2000). *Fiscal changes for core mental health services delivered by fee-for-service physicians*. Institute for Clinical Evaluative Sciences (ICES), Atlas Reports, Uses of Health Services, Report 2. Toronto: ICES.

Link, B.G. (1989). A modified labeling theory approach to mental disorders: An empirical assessment. *American Sociological Review, 54*, 400–423.

Lurie, S. (1984). More for the mind, have we got less? In M.D. Nair, R.C. Hain, & J.A. Draper (Eds.), *Issues in Canadian social services* (pp. 166–185). Toronto: Canadian Council on Social Development.

Macnaughton, E. (1992). Canadian mental health policy: The emergent picture. *Canada's Mental Health, 40*, 3–10.

Manning, N. (1989). *The therapeutic community movement: Charisma and routinization*. London: Routledge.

Moore, R. (1993). *Economic burden of illness in Canada, 1993*. Ottawa: Minister of Government Works and Government Services Canada.

Mueller, B. (2006). Social support modifies perceived stigmatization in the first years of mental illness: A longitudinal approach. *Social Science & Medicine, 62*(1), 39–49.

Nelson, G., Prilleltensky, I., Laurendeau, M.-C., & Powell, B. (1996). The prevention of mental health problems in Canada: A survey of provincial policies, structures, and programs. *Canadian Psychology, 37*(3), 161–172.

Olsen, D. (1993, February). The movement. Unpublished paper.

Patten, S.B. (2006). Descriptive epidemiology of major depression in Canada. *Canadian Journal of Psychiatry, 51*(2), 84–90.

Ralph, D. (1983). *Work and madness: The rise of community psychiatry*. Montreal: Black Rose Books.

Randhawa, J., & Riley, R. (1996). Mental health statistics, 1982–83 to 1993–94. *Health Reports, 7*(4), 55–61.

Rhodes, A. (2006). Depression and mental health visits to physicians – a prospective records-based study. *Social Science & Medicine, 62*(4), 828–834.

Royal Ottawa Health Care Group. (2002). *Mental health information*. Ottawa. Retrieved March 15, 2006 from http://www.rohcg.on.ca/programs-and-services/factsheets/psychiatric-outreach-teams-e.cfm.

Rusch, N. (2006). Self-stigma, empowerment, and perceived legitimacy of discrimination among women with mental illness. *Psychiatric Services, 57*(3), 399–402.

Scheff, T. (1984). *Being mentally ill: A sociological theory* (2nd ed.). New York: Aldine.

Scull, A. (1982). *Museums of madness: The social organization of insanity in nineteenth-century England*. Harmondsworth: Penguin.

Scull, A. (1983). *Decarceration: Community treatment and the deviant – a radical view* (2nd ed.). Cambridge: Polity Press.

Scull, A. (1991). Psychiatry and social control in the nineteenth and twentieth centuries. *History of Psychiatry, 2*, 149–169.

Senate of Canada. (2006). *Out of the shadows at last: Transforming mental health, mental illness, and addiction services in Canada*. Ottawa: Standing Senate Committee on Social Affairs, Science and Technology.

Showalter, E. (1985). *The female malady: Women, madness and English culture, 1830–1980*. New York: Pantheon Press.

Simmons, H. (1990). *Unbalanced: Mental health policy in Ontario, 1930–1989*. Toronto: Wall and Thompson.

Srole, L., Langer, T., Michael, S., Opler, M., & Rennie, T. (1962). *Mental health in the metropolis*. New York: McGraw-Hill.

Star Phoenix. (2000, May 6). System fails mentally ill offenders, say advocates. *Star Phoenix*. B6.

Stephens, T., & Joubert, N. (2001). The economic burden of mental health problems in Canada. *Chronic Disease in Canada, 22*(1), 18–23.

Stewart, M.C. (2006). Stigmatization of anorexia nervosa. *International Journal of Eating Disorders, 39*(4), 320–325.

Szasz, T.S. (1972). *The myth of mental illness: Foundations of a theory of personal conduct*. Frogmore, UK: Paladin.

Teachman, B.A. (2006). Implicit and explicit stigma of mental illness in diagnosed and healthy samples. *Journal of Social and Clinical Psychology, 25*(1), 75–95.

Trainor, J., Church, K., Pape, B., Pomeroy, E., Reville, D., Teft, B., Lakaski, C., & Renaud, L. (1992). Building a framework for support: Developing a sector-based model for people with serious mental illness. *Canada's Mental Health, 40*, 25–29.

Trainor, J., Shepherd, M., Boyle, K.M., Leff, A., & Crawford, E. (1997). Beyond the service paradigm: The impact and implications of consumer/survivor initiatives. *Psychiatric Rehabilitation Journal, 21*(2), 132–40.

Tyhurst, J.S. et al. (1963). *More for the mind: A study in psychiatric services in Canada*. Toronto: Canadian Mental Health Association.

Uniform Law Conference of Canada. (1987). *Proceedings of the sixty-ninth annual meeting, Appendix F – the Uniform Mental Health Act*. Victoria, BC: Uniform Law Conference.

Watson, R. (2004). Prison health care: A review of the literature. *International Journal of Nursing Studies, 41*(2), 119–128.

White, D., & Mercier, C. (1991). Reorienting mental health systems: The dynamics of policy and planning. *International Journal of Mental Health, 19*, 3–24.

Wu, E. (2005). The economic burden of schizophrenia in the United States in 2002. *Journal of Clinical Psychiatry, 66*(9), 1122–1129.

Zapf, P.A. (2004). Psychological perspectives on criminality. In R. Linden (Ed.), *Criminology: A Canadian perspective* (5th ed., pp. 260–291). Toronto: Thomson Nelson.

22

Profits First: The Pharmaceutical Industry in Canada

JOEL LEXCHIN York University

MARY E. WIKTOROWICZ York University

INTRODUCTION

The pharmaceutical industry is no different from any other enterprise in a capitalist economy; the primary motivation for making drugs is profit. The Code of Conduct of the Pharmaceutical Manufacturers Association of Canada (PMAC), now called **Canada's Research-Based Pharmaceutical Companies (Rx&D)**[1], emphasizes the unique role it plays in providing prescription medicines and other services to the public (2005, p. 4). The practical ethics of the industry are summed up in a quotation from the former president of PMAC: "The pharmaceutical industry has never claimed to be motivated by altruism, but rather by profit for survival" (Garton, May 26, 1980, personal communication).

This chapter will begin by exploring the contradiction between public good and private profits, and will examine, in depth, the profitability of the pharmaceutical industry. The next four sections will analyze some of the most significant factors contributing to the profits of the industry: the relationship between the state and the industry, the research efforts of the drug companies, the prices of drugs, and, finally, how industry promotion influences prescribing.

PRIVATE PROFIT VERSUS PUBLIC GOOD

Eli Lilly and Benoxaprofen

The incompatibility between public service and private profit becomes evident when the stated ethics of the industry clash with the realities of turning a profit. One example of how drug companies put profit above health involved Eli Lilly's anti-arthritis drug benoxaprofen. In 1980, this drug was marketed in Britain under the trade name Opren.[2] Lilly organized an aggressive promotional program for Opren, and very quickly the drug was enjoying large sales. However, shortly after the drug appeared on the shelves of British pharmacies, Lilly's British subsidiary informed British health officials of the first of eight deaths resulting from suspected adverse reactions to Opren that occurred between May 1, 1981 and January 1982.

In February 1982, nine months after the first known British death, benoxaprofen was evaluated by the Canadian Health Protection Branch (HPB-since 2000, the Health Products and Food Branch, HPFB) as safe for use in Canada.[3] In its submission to the HPB,[4] Lilly did not mention the eight deaths in Britain connected to benoxaprofen and omitted other information about other studies indicating potential problems with the drug. Lilly officials did not give any of this critical information about their product to the HPB until just before reports of the deaths in Britain were going to appear in the *British Medical Journal* (Regush, 1982, pp. A-1, A-6).

Bristol-Myers Squibb and Pravastatin

Another example of industry values is the lawsuit that Bristol-Myers Squibb (BMS) launched against the Canadian Coordinating Office for Health Technology Assessment (CCOHTA – now the Canadian Agency for Drugs and Technologies in Health) in 1997. CCOHTA is an independent, non-profit body that conducts evaluations of pharmaceuticals and medical technologies. In this case, CCOHTA was assessing a group of drugs called "statins," which are used to lower cholesterol. CCOHTA's position, backed up by an extensive review of the literature and by other medical bodies, was that all of the statins were equivalent and all would reduce complications associated with heart disease. BMS was concerned that such a conclusion would have negative financial implications for its statin Pravachol (pravastatin)[5] and went to court to block the publication of CCOHTA's report. The implications of this case went beyond the one report involved. What BMS was trying to do in defense of its profits was to stop the free flow of scientific information (Connection, 1998).

Merck Frosst and Vioxx

A more recent example of how profit motive influences drug companies involved Merck Frosst and its drug Vioxx, indicated for relief of arthritic pain. In 1997, early clinical trials suggested Vioxx could lead to an increase in cardiovascular events, such as heart attacks and strokes. Merck's scientists tried to camouflage such adverse effects by excluding patients with high risk of heart disease from its large clinical trials "so any difference in the rate of cardiovascular problems between Vioxx patients and the others would not be evident" (Won Tesoriero et al., 2005, August).

A large clinical trial in 2000 confirmed patients on Vioxx had a higher risk of heart attacks and strokes compared to another drug comparator. Merck, however, resisted the United States Food and Drug Administration's (F.D.A.) attempts to add warnings to Vioxx's label. While it eventually complied, Merck ensured the warnings were buried and difficult to find (Berenson, 2005a). When the company later sought to expand Vioxx's treatment indications to colon cancer, the F.D.A. specified its clinical trials had to include cardiovascular endpoints. In the largest clinical trial, 14.6 percent of those who took Vioxx had cardiovascular problems, and 2.5 percent experienced serious consequences like heart attacks (Berenson, 2005b). Merck later withdrew the drug. While it was on the market, however, Vioxx led to thousands of heart attacks, strokes, and deaths. Such occurrences demonstrate one of the reasons drugs are regulated for safety and efficacy: industry may take greater risks than the public would find acceptable given its drive for profit (Wiktorowicz, 2003).

PROFITS IN THE PHARMACEUTICAL INDUSTRY

For over thirty years, profit levels in the U.S. pharmaceutical industry have outstripped profits in other industries by a wide margin and that gap has been growing. Based on data from *Fortune* magazine, during the 1970s, drug companies averaged 8.9 percent profit as a percentage of revenue compared to 4.4 percent for all Fortune 500 industries. In the 1980s, drug companies increased their margin by earning 11.1 percent compared to 4.4 percent for all Fortune 500 companies, and during the 1990s, the gap grew to 15.1 percent compared to just 4.1 percent (Public Citizen's Congress Watch, 2002). In the past couple of years, the pharmaceutical industry has fallen from first place in the *Fortune* rankings, but even at third place it still outpaces nearly all other industries in profitability. The profits of the Canadian subsidiaries of the multinational drug companies, while not as impressive, have generally been significantly above those for all manufacturing industries; these numbers can be seen in Table 22.1, which compares the rates of return on shareholders' equity for the period 1996–2003.

Profits as an Accounting Illusion?

The figures in Table 22.1 make it difficult to deny that there are huge profits to be derived from manufacturing pharmaceuticals. But Rx&D repeatedly claims that the high profits are an accounting illusion created by the standard accounting practice of treating **research and development (R&D)** expenditures as expenses against current income, rather than capitalizing these outlays as an investment item (1975, p. 18). However, as Gary Gereffi, professor of sociology at Duke University, makes clear, the accounting explanation of high profitability is inadequate, for several reasons (1983, p. 192).

First, such accounting bias is not confined only to the pharmaceutical industry, but is present in all "discovery-intensive" industries, such as oil and gas, and in industries with high levels of research and development expenditures. Under certain circumstances, the accounting rate of return could actually understate rather than overstate the "real" or

TABLE 22.1 *Rate of Return on Shareholders' Equity, Large Firms (Sales >$75 million) 1996–2003 (Percent)*

Year	Pharmaceutical industry (median)	All manufacturing (median)
2003	20.1	10.8
2002	20.8	11.3
2001	16.7	10.0
2000	11.4	13.1
1999	5.4	14.6
1998	4.1	13.3
1997	18.5	14.0
1996	23.5	12.2

Source: Statistics Canada. Financial Performance Indicators for Canadian Business, Vol. 1, 1996–99; Statistics Canada. Financial Performance Indicators for Canadian Business, Vol. 1, 2000–2002; Statistics Canada. Financial Performance Indicators for Canadian Business, Vol. 1, 2001–2003 (Catalogue 61-224-XCB).

economic rate of return. Second, by allowing pharmaceutical companies to treat research and development costs as a current accounting expense, the government, in effect, is granting them an indirect fiscal subsidy to encourage their risk-taking efforts. This accounting method thus serves to raise the drug firm's profitability in fact, as well as on paper.

Temin showed that even after "correcting" profits by treating research and development expenditures as an investment, the drug industry was still one of the most profitable industries around (1979, p. 445). More recent data from the United States came to the same conclusion. Even after making adjustments for differences amongst various industries, over the period 1976–87, returns in the pharmaceutical industry were 2–3 percent higher than in nonpharmaceutical firms (Office of Technology Assessment, 1993).

The High Cost of Research as a Justification for High Profits

As well as using accounting methodology as an explanation for high profits, the industry uses the high cost of research as a justification. Industry sponsored researchers claim that it costs about US $802 million to discover and bring a new drug to market; they also state that R&D costs are recovered in only one third of new products. These claims are based on the results of studies using industry supplied data (DiMasi, Hansenand & Grabowski, 2003). Light and Warburton (2005), however, refute this estimate, citing problems in the sampling on which the results depend that are never articulated by Rx&D and its member companies. The inflated estimate only considers R&D costs for **new chemical entities** (NCEs), which have been researched and developed "in house" by American-owned companies which represent only about 22 percent of new drug approvals. The sample leaves out new drugs that were developed conjointly with, or entirely by, government, non-profit institutions, and universities; drugs licensed from other companies; and newly marketed drugs that are not NCEs, such as long-acting versions of a drug, combination products, or other new formulations of existing products. Finally, while DiMasi, Hansen, and Grabowski (2003) excluded tax write-offs in their latest paper, they factored in these tax credits in one published just a few years earlier and showed that the overall R&D costs were reduced by 30 percent (Grabowski et al., 2002).

THE PHARMACEUTICAL INDUSTRY AND THE STATE

Compulsory Licensing and Patents

During the 1960s, a series of three reports all pointed out that drug prices in Canada were amongst the highest in the world. All three reports identified **patent protection** as one of the major reasons for this situation (Canada, House of Commons, 1967; Restrictive Trade Practices Commission, 1963; Royal Commission on Health Services, 1964).[6] The decision of the Liberal government of the time was to extend **compulsory licensing**[7] and allow companies to receive a license to import a drug into Canada, rather than having to manufacture it here.

BILL C-22

The industry lobbied vigorously against compulsory licensing, and with the election of Brian Mulroney and the Progressive Conservatives as a government in 1984 it found an ally. The Conservatives wanted a free trade deal with the United States, and the multinationals were able to get the American government to apply pressure in their favour (Sawatsky & Cashore, 1986).

In return for free trade with the Americans, the Conservatives produced Bill C-22 and eventually passed it in December 1987. The essence of the bill was that it gave companies introducing new drugs a minimum of seven years, and usually ten years, of protection from compulsory licensing and the introduction of **generic competition**.

BILL C-91

Bill C-22 was not all that the Americans wanted, however. One senior official in the U.S. Administration said, "We want better than that [bill] in a free-trade agreement," while to another senior official it was "barely acceptable." The U.S. Pharmaceutical Manufacturers Association was willing to support the bill but said that the U.S. industry "would like to see a similar level of protection as in Western Europe and the U.S.... Canada's out of synch" (quoted in Lewington, 1987, p. A1).

The final demise for compulsory licensing came with the passage of Bill C-91 in 1993.[8] In this case, it was Canadian eagerness to sign the NAFTA and Trade Related Aspects of Intellectual Property Rights (TRIPS) agreements that coincided with the interests of the drug industry. Although there is an argument that compulsory licensing would be theoretically possible under these agreements (Dillon, 1997), the Canadian government used them as the grounds for completely eliminating compulsory licensing.

While they were in opposition, the Liberals vehemently opposed Bill C-91. When the Liberals were elected in 1993, Dingwall became minister of health, and by 1997 his attitude was, "we are now part and parcel of the international community in terms of our commitments to NAFTA. And I don't want to raise a false expectation that with the review of Bill C-91, which is coming up in 1997, that we are going to flush the intellectual property rights which Canada has supported from day one and will continue to support" (CBC Radio, 1997).

The twenty-year patent term period is dictated by the Trade Related Aspects of Intellectual Property Rights (TRIPS) Agreement, and Canada is a signatory to this agreement as a consequence of its membership in the World Trade Organization (WTO). Two separate challenges have been launched against Canada in the WTO in recent years. The European Union (EU) complained about a provision in the Canadian patent law that allowed generic drug companies to begin testing, manufacturing, and stockpiling drugs for sale before patents expired. When Canada changed from a seventeen- to a twenty-year patent term for drugs approved after October 1, 1989, the change was not made retroactive. The United States charged that a group of about thirty drugs which was patented before October, 1989 should receive an additional three years of patent life. (The complaint by the United States did not just cover drugs, but patents on all products that were granted before October, 1989, and that were still valid.)

Canada lost the case filed by the United States (MacKinnon, 2000) and the WTO also ruled that generic companies could not stockpile drugs for sale before the patent expired (Scoffield, 2000). As a result of these decisions, in mid-2001, Canadian patent laws were amended with the passage of Bill S-17. The extension of the patent term on the thirty drugs is expected to add an estimated $40 million to Canada's prescription drug costs according to the Canadian Generic Pharmaceutical Association (CGPA), the lobbying arm of the generic industry ("Battle to repeal automatic injunctions against generic drug approvals moves to the fall," 2001). Prohibiting generic companies from stockpiling drugs until the patent expires will delay the marketing of generic products for weeks. A report prepared for the CGPA that looked at a group of thirty-four generic products estimated that each day of delay in reaching the market was associated with a cost of almost $5,500 per product (Anderson & Parent, 2001).

THE PHARMACEUTICAL INDUSTRY AND THE HEALTH PRODUCTS AND FOOD BRANCH

CLIENTELE PLURALISM

The industry has exercised its influence in the HPFB through a method of interaction, a policy network, termed **clientele pluralism** (Atkinson & Coleman, 1989). This is a situation in which the state has a high degree of concentration of power in one agency (the HPFB), but a low degree of autonomy. With respect to pharmaceuticals, in Canada, government regulation of drug safety, quality, and efficacy is almost solely the responsibility of the HPFB. But the state does not possess the wherewithal to undertake the elaborate clinical and preclinical trials required to meet the objective of providing safe and effective medications. Nor is the state either willing or able to mobilize the resources that would be necessary to undertake these tasks. Therefore, a tacit political decision is made to relinquish some authority to the drug manufacturers, especially with respect to information that forms the basis on which regulatory decisions are made.

On the other hand, Rx&D, the association representing nearly all of the multinational companies operating in Canada, is highly mobilized to assume a role in making and implementing drug policy through an elaborate committee structure, the ability to act on behalf of its members, and the capacity to bind member firms to agreements. In clientele pluralism, the state relinquishes some of its authority to private sector actors, who, in turn, pursue objectives with which officials are in broad agreement (Atkinson & Coleman, 1989).

Not only does the state turn over some of its authority, but the objectives being pursued are also often jointly developed between Rx&D and the relevant state bureaucracy, in this case the HPFB. One example of delegation of government authority to the industry is that the HPFB at times allows Rx&D to develop the first draft of a new policy. While the HPFB uses the draft as the basis from which to make revisions, it nevertheless allows industry to set the framework for policy, thereby granting it considerable influence (Wiktorowicz, 2000). Another area in which the HPFB delegates its authority to industry involves the control of promotional practices. This area has had a long and contentious history, but also a long history of cooperation between government and industry. Governments in nearly all industrialized countries, including Canada, have ceded day-to-day control over some or all aspects of pharmaceutical promotion to voluntary national industry associations. In turn, these associations have developed codes of marketing which their member companies are expected to adhere to. In Canada, promotion is regulated by two codes: one has been developed and is administered by an independent organization, the Pharmaceutical Advertising Advisory Board (PAAB); the second is the Code of Practice from Rx&D. Despite reasonable-sounding provisions, both codes suffer from serious enforcement problems (Lexchin, 1997a; Mintzes, 1998), which result in a significant amount of deceptive promotion (Lexchin, 1994).

UNDERFUNDING AND COST RECOVERY

In recent years, there has been a fundamental change in the relationship between the HPFB and the multinational pharmaceutical industry. Not only does the state still relinquish some of its authority to private sector actors, but the private sector (the drug companies) is also now the major funder of the branch of the HPFB, the Therapeutic Products Programme (TPP) (now the Therapeutic Products Directorate, TPD), that regulates the industry.

Downsizing the role of government in the regulation of pharmaceuticals reflected and resulted from the obsession with the federal deficit. The government saw nothing wrong with decreasing funding to the HPFB from $237 million in 1993–94 to $136 million in 1996–97, with a projection for 1999–2000 of just $118 million (Kennedy, 1997). As resources for the HPFB were progressively cut, the agency turned to the drug companies themselves for funds to keep operating, a process termed **cost recovery**. Companies pay an annual fee for each drug they market and fees for the evaluation of drug submissions, for licensing manufacturing establishments, and for a number of other services. Industry now contributes 50 percent of the $76 million in revenue that the TPD received in 2000 (Health Canada, 2000).

INCREASING INDUSTRY INFLUENCE

There are signs in a couple of areas that this combination of industry funding and a civil service with a bias for uncritical cooperation with industry is leading to a reorientation of HPFB policy that is even more favourable to industry than in the past. Until March 1997, government controlled advertising of over-the-counter products to consumers. All promotion through radio and television had to be pre-cleared by HPFB staff, and print advertisements were reviewed if there were complaints about them. In April 1997, those functions were turned over to a private sector agency, Advertising Standards Canada, a move that will probably lead to a loosening of standards for promotion of this set of products.

Government is not just weakening the controls over OTC promotion, however. Currently, regulations ban direct-to-consumer advertising (DTCA) of prescription drugs, but for the past few years, industry has been pushing the HPFB to give up that restriction. Merck Frosst has gone so far as to assert that the industry has a legal right to advertise prescription drugs directly to the public (Merck Frosst Canada, 1996). Health Canada has been reluctant to enforce its own regulations against DTCA. A commentary in the *Canadian Medical Association Journal* notes that "Response to complaints tends to be slow, probably reflecting Health Canada's under capacity to regulate DTCA, and, arguably, ineffectual" (Gardner, Mintzes & Ostry 2003). The authors go on to describe how a television advertisement promoting bupropion (Zyban) for smoking cessation was allowed to run for months, even though Health Canada deemed that it violated the regulations. No penalty of any type was imposed on GlaxoSmithKline, the company responsible for the advertisement (CBC-TV, Undercurrents, 2001). At the same time that Health Canada has been allowing the DTCA to proceed, it has been engaged in a project to re-examine and revise Canadian health safety legislation. As part of its review, the agency has issued a document outlining policy options for new legislation. This document lays out four options for direct-to-consumer advertising of prescription drugs; two of the four, including the one that is given the most prominence in terms of space, are favourable to DTCA (Health Canada, 2003), while none of the four actually advocates enforcing the current legislation as it is written.

FIGURE 22.1
Relationship between User Fees and Positive Decisions About New Drugs and Approval Times in Canada

Source: Lexchin, J. Relationship between pharmaceutical company user fees and drug approvals in Canada and Australia: A hypothesis-generating study. *Annals of Pharmacotherapy*, 2006, 40, pp. 2216–22.

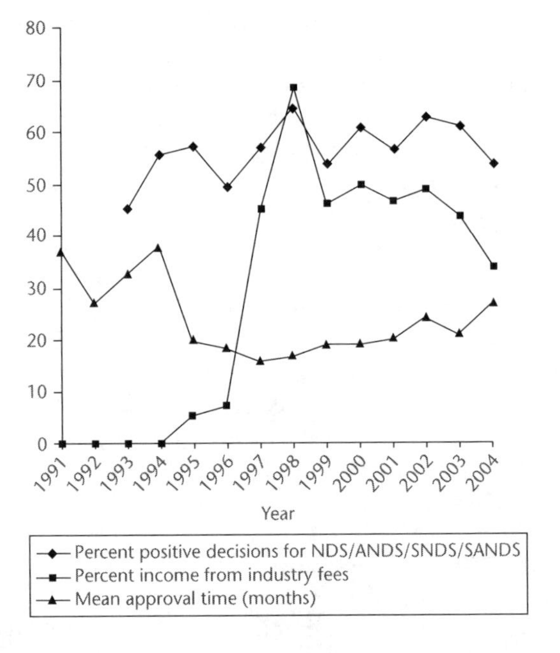

Not only has DTCA been affected by cost recovery, but there is also an association between the percent of funding of the TPD that comes from the pharmaceutical industry, how quickly drugs are approved, and what percent of applications get positive decisions. Figure 22.1 shows that as the level of industry funding rises, approval times drop and more applications receive positive decisions.

Perhaps the most revealing statement about this reorientation of the relationship between the HPFB and the industry came from Dann Michols, a former director general of the TPD. In an internal bulletin distributed to HPFB staff in February 1997, he discussed the question of who is the HPFB's client. In the context of cost recovery, he advised staff that "the client is the direct recipient of your services. In many cases this is the person or company who pays for the service." The one-page document focused on service to industry, relegating the public to the secondary status of "stakeholder" or "beneficiary" (Michols, 1997).

Research and Development

In exchange for the government passing Bills C-22 and C-91, the pharmaceutical industry agreed to increase its investment in R&D in Canada from 6.1 percent of sales (in 1988) to 10 percent. By 1997, the industry's investment in R&D was 11.5 percent of sales or $679.2 million (Cdn). Although the absolute amount has continued to increase since 1997 to almost $1.2 billion in 2004, as a percentage of sales R&D investment has been declining and is now at 8.3 percent (Patented Medicine Prices Review Board, 2005). One point that both the industry and the government neglect to mention is that these are only 60-cent dollars, owing to a 40 percent tax write-off on R&D (Department of Foreign Affairs and International Trade and Industry Canada, 1996). Therefore, the actual cost to the pharmaceutical companies is only about $620 million. The question that has yet to be answered is the value of that R&D to the scientific community and to the Canadian public.

Scientific Value of Increased R&D

The research industry conducted in Canada largely comprises clinical drug trials, which are considered the "development" aspect of R&D. An early attempt to explore the value of this research was a 1990 survey of forty key medical figures engaged in pharmaceutical research in Canada. They were happy about the availability of funding, but they also expressed a number of misgivings about drug industry funding: 90 percent foresaw a likely conflict of interest; 80 percent deemed pharmaceutical clinical research "me too" research; 75 percent saw it as "might as well" research; and 40 percent were worried about a potential delay in the publication of unfavourable results (Taylor, 1991).

Is the Canadian public getting value from the increase in R&D spending? From a review of the products that the industry has introduced since Bill C-22 passed in 1987, the answer may be no. From January 2000 to December 2004, a total of 112 **new active substances** were marketed in Canada for human use. Out of that number, only 12, or just under 11 percent, were felt to be either "breakthrough" medications or substantial improvements over existing therapies, with the rest offering moderate, little, or no therapeutic improvements (Patented Medicine Prices Review Board, 2005, Figure 2).

Moreover, since the therapeutically important drugs were not developed just for the Canadian market, they would have become available in Canada with or without the new R&D money that has been invested in Canada. Whether or not the Canadian research community was involved in the development of these drugs, and whether or not that involvement may have hastened their arrival on the market are questions that bear investigating. The answers will affect the assessment of the value of the increased R&D.

Does Industry R&D Reflect Societal Goals?

On a more fundamental level, the value of pharmaceutical R&D to Canadian society cannot be answered by counting the number of new important drugs. Are seven new drugs per year better than a government policy aimed at increasing R&D to improve agricultural output or to develop better mining technology? In what direction does Canadian society want to direct R&D? These issues were never publicly debated before Bills C-22 and C-91 were passed.

In an article in the *New England Journal of Medicine,* VanWoert stated that a representative of the U.S. Pharmaceutical Manufacturers Association confirmed that, in general, drug companies do not undertake research on relatively uncommon diseases, because drugs for them would generate insufficient profits (1978, p. 904). The same sentiments were echoed in 1980 by Joseph Williams, president of Warner Lambert, who was quoted by Gray as saying that "Our [Warner Lambert's] focus is to develop major drugs for major markets" (1981, p. 791).

Research funded by the pharmaceutical industry may leave many questions untouched. Dr. Patricia Baird, former chair of the Royal Commission on New Reproductive Technologies, noted that in the area of infertility, drug companies were only likely to fund research that would lead to a new patentable drug, ignoring topics such as behavioural factors involved in the cause and prevention of infertility (Baird, 1996). What's true in developed countries is even more evident in developing countries. Only two out of eleven of the largest pharmaceutical companies in the world are putting any money into malaria research and no company is doing any research into treatments for African sleeping sickness (Médecins sans Frontières Access to Essential Medicines Campaign, Drugs for Neglected Diseases Working Group, 2001). Do we want most of the money available for pharmaceutical research to be just narrowly directed into the development of new patentable medications, the main priority of the pharmaceutical industry, or do we also want to prioritize areas such as improving patient compliance with medications or reasons for inappropriate physician-prescribing practices?

DRUG PRICES

Effect of Generic Competition on Prices

The first generic competitor in the Canadian market typically enters at a price discount of about 25–30 percent compared with the original product; when there are four or five generic competitors, there is a difference of 50–60 percent between the brand name product and the least expensive generic version (Lexchin, 1993) (see Figure 22.1). (A subsequent study by the Federal/Provincial/Territorial Task Force on Pharmaceutical Prices (1999) extended this analysis to cover up to 1997. By the end of 1997, prices for generic drugs were, on average, only 27–37 percent below those for brand-name drugs.) Before Bill C-22, these generic equivalents of best-selling drugs would appear within five or six years after the brand name drug was marketed. Now, companies have a monopoly for about twelve years.[9] Not only is the entry of generic products delayed by about seven years, but also, by the time they appear, sales of the brand name drug are usually starting to decline and therefore the savings from the generic product are less.[10]

According to figures in the Eastman Report, in 1982, generic competition had resulted in estimated savings to the Canadian public of at least $211 million; in other words, in the absence of generic competition, Canada's drug bill would have increased from $1.53 billion to almost $1.74 billion (Commission of Inquiry on the Pharmaceutical Industry, 1985). A report produced for the Canadian Generic Pharmaceutical Association, the organization

FIGURE 22.2
Relationship between Number of Companies Marketing a Drug and Price Spread between Least Expensive and Most Expensive Versions of a Drug (number of drug preparations in parentheses)

Source: Lexchin (1993).

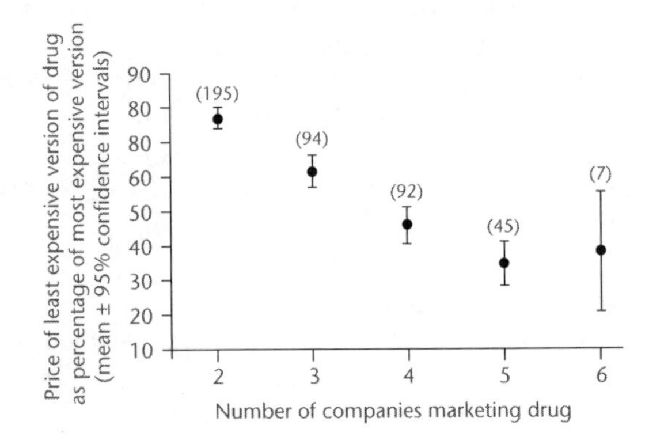

representing Canadian-owned generic companies, estimated that the cumulative costs of Bill C-91 from 1993–2000 would be $1.7 billion, and by 2010 the cumulative costs from 1993 would be $4.0 billion (Schondelmeyer, 1993).

Patented Medicine Prices Review Board

Bill C-22 established the **Patented Medicine Prices Review Board** (PMPRB), which had a mandate to set the introductory price for new patented drugs and to limit the rate of rise in the price of patented medicines to the rate of inflation. According to reports from the PMPRB, since Bill C-22 passed in 1987, the rise in the price of patented drugs at the manufacturers' level has dropped below the rate of inflation; in fact, since 1994, in most years the price of patented drugs has actually deflated (Patented Medicine Prices Review Board, 2005, Figure 27.4). The pharmaceutical industry frequently maintains that lower Canadian drug prices have nothing to do with the controls applied by the PMPRB but merely reflect the lower standard of living here compared to other industrialized countries. However, as Table 22.2 shows, there is no relationship between changes in the ratio of drug prices and the ratio of the GDP when Canada is compared to six different European countries. For example, although there was a marked drop in the ratio of drug prices for Canada to Sweden between 1997 and 2002, the GDP ratio actually increased marginally; the reverse happened when Canada was compared to the U.K. – the drug price ratio increased but the GDP ratio declined.

INTERNATIONAL COMPARISONS

The PMPRB compares Canadian prices with those in seven other countries (France, Germany, Italy, Sweden, Switzerland, the United Kingdom, and the United States) to arrive at an acceptable introductory price for new products. Comparing Canadian prices

TABLE 22.2 *Comparison of Changes in Drug Prices and GDP per Capita, Canada and Six European Countries, 1997–2002*

		France	Germany	Italy	Sweden	Switzerland	United Kingdom
1997	Drug price ratio (Canada = 100)	89.4	111.2	79.5	106.4	123.4	100.8
	GDP per capita ratio (Canada = 100)	130.6	146.4	94.3	139.2	209.6	99.0
2002	Drug price ratio (Canada = 100)	82.7	95.9	78.9	93.6	105.4	104.3
	GDP per capita ratio (Canada = 100)	127.0	136.5	89.2	140.7	196.3	95.4

Source: Lexchin, J. Canadian Drug Prices and Expenditures: Some statistical observations and policy implications. January, 2007.

with those in the seven selected countries might not tell the complete story about the cost of drugs in Canada relative to other industrialized countries, however.

Choosing a different group of countries could dramatically alter the Canadian introductory price. A study by the Australian Productivity Commission (2001, Table 3.5) showed that Canadian prices for new innovative pharmaceuticals were 9 percent higher than those in Australia and New Zealand.

High Introductory Prices

The PMPRB allows companies to price new drugs coming onto the market at the same price as the most expensive existing therapy. These high introductory prices are one reason that the cost of a prescription in Canada has risen dramatically between 1997 and 2001. Although the PMPRB regulates the price of patented medicines, it has no power over the cost of a prescription. The average price per prescription (excluding the dispensing fee) in Ontario for a non-patented medication increased 2.3 percent annually from 1997 to 2001 to a level of $22.94 in 2001. On the other hand, during the same period, patented medications went up at 6.2 percent annually to a value of $84.36 in 2001 (Green Shield, 2002). Physicians have been substituting these newer, more expensive drugs for older, less costly ones, leading to the rise in the cost of the average prescription. In Ontario, the introduction of new drugs was the second most important factor in driving the increase in provincial expenditures on prescription drugs in the period 1992/93–98/99 (Federal/Provincial/Territorial Working Group on Drug Prices, 2000).

The Value of New Drugs

If the new, more expensive medications were also more effective, then perhaps their prices could be justified, and similarly it would be understandable why they were replacing older, less expensive drugs. Elsewhere we have shown that for anti-hypertensives, anti-ulcer medications, and nonsteroidal anti-inflammatory (drugs used in the treatment of arthritis), the therapeutic gain from newly introduced drugs in these categories is marginal, but they are priced at a premium compared with older drugs (Lexchin, 1992). The adoption of these products by physicians, in the absence of a strong clinical rationale for doing so, makes a compelling case for the need to promote cost-effective therapy not only for health reasons, but also to restrain the rise in prescription prices.

THE PHARMACEUTICAL INDUSTRY AND THE MEDICAL PROFESSION

Doctors, their associations, and their journals are all prime objects of attention for the drug companies. Drugs with high introductory prices and twelve years of patent protection are no good to the companies if they are not being prescribed. Doctors are the ones who prescribe, and it is these prescriptions that translate into sales for the pharmaceutical houses. Nearly every doctor engaged in clinical medicine will prescribe, but a simple willingness to prescribe is not enough for the drug companies. In order to increase sales and profits, the industry wants and needs more from doctors. Prominent among the strategies it uses for expanding sales and profits is its encouragement of the medical profession to look first to drug therapy for medical problems. The industry tries to present an image that will make the medical profession sympathetic to the claims the industry makes for its products and willing to take the industry's side against legislation the industry sees as hostile to its interests. In short, the pharmaceutical industry needs a medical profession as an ally, a medical profession that sees the industry's goals as being harmonious with its own.

In order to achieve this alliance, the industry provides the funding (either directly or through third parties) for evening seminars accompanied by an open bar and a free meal. Drug companies help underwrite the cost of medical meetings either through purchasing booths or by sponsoring lectures, thus limiting physicians' out-of-pocket expenses. Although both the medical profession and the pharmaceutical industry have codes prohibiting paying for travel and accommodation, the companies knowingly violate these codes (Lexchin, 1999). All of these activities are sponsored by individual companies but the aim of all this largesse is not solely to sell a particular drug. The companies, and by extension the industry as a whole, are after the goodwill of the doctors. They want to establish a positive view of the industry in doctors' minds, to build and maintain the needed alliance with the medical profession.

It is eminently obvious why the drug industry wants an alliance with physicians; it is less clear why doctors should be willing to enter into such an alliance. The industry code allows it to offer items that enhance the understanding of a disease or condition (Canada's Research-Based Pharmaceutical Companies, 2005); for example, a textbook would be allowed. While the gifts that doctors receive from the industry are certainly one factor in establishing a positive doctor-industry relationship, they are probably a very minor one. It may be possible to buy the favour of some doctors, but not the vast majority. More important than such minor gift-giving is the industry's support for various projects backed by physicians, such as the organ donation program and the research funding that comes from the drug companies; but once again, these activities directly affect only a relatively small number of doctors. There are, however, interactions with the drug companies that affect, and are appreciated by, the majority of doctors. Drug company funding of **continuing medical education** is one, and personal visits from **detailers** are another (Woods, 1986).

Continuing Medical Education

Continuing medical education (CME) is the general term used for medical education that takes place after physicians start to practice. Although it can take many forms, meetings and conferences are the mainstays of CME. Nearly all forms of CME in Canada are partially or fully funded either directly or indirectly by the pharmaceutical industry. Even at conferences run by organizations such as the College of Family Physicians of Canada, the money that drug companies spend to rent booths covers a large portion of the cost of such events. Physicians have come to expect to pay relatively low costs for attending CME events because of such sponsorship.

Meetings and conferences run by universities and hospitals will almost always have rules that are supposed to ensure that the proceedings are insulated against influence by the pharmaceutical industry. Topics and speakers should be at the discretion of the individuals or groups organizing the event, not the company paying for it. Despite these precautions, however, there is evidence that biases still exist.

An analysis was performed to compare the content of two CME courses funded by two different drug companies. In both courses, the clinical effects noted for the company drug were more likely to be positive than for the non-company drugs. The few statements directly comparing the drugs usually indicated that the company drug was the better drug (Bowman, 1986). A second study looked at prescribing immediately before and six months after doctors attended three separate CME courses. In each case, prescriptions for the drugs made by the sponsoring companies went up significantly more than did prescriptions for similar drugs that were not manufactured by the sponsoring company (Bowman & Pearle, 1988).

Pharmaceutical Promotion

Doctors are prime objects of attention for the multinational subsidiaries.[11] These companies spend 16–17 percent of sales on promoting drugs to doctors, compared with about 8.3 percent on research. Multinationals account for 87 percent of the $15.9 billion in prescription drug sales in 2004 (Patented Medicine Prices Review Board, 2005); thus, spending on promotion is just over $2.2 billion per year. The companies would not spend so lavishly on promotion unless the tactic worked – the more intensively a product is advertised in journals, the greater its market share (Montgomery & Silk, 1972; Leffler, 1981; Krupka & Vener, 1985). The better physicians remember a journal ad, the more likely they are to prescribe the product (Walton, 1980; Healthcare Communications Inc., 1989).

DETAILERS

Promotion takes many forms, including journal advertising, direct mailings to doctors, posters, and sponsoring dinner meetings, but the most effective method is the use of sales representatives, or detailers – men and women who go from office to office to try to convince doctors to use their companies' products. Over 50 percent of the promotion budget is spent on salaries and expenses related to detailing. As might be expected, detailers are not objective sources of information.

Studies analyzing the quality of the information that they give have been conducted in Australia, Finland, and the United States either by audiotaping detailers' presentations (with their consent) or by having doctors fill out surveys immediately after seeing detailers. Although detailers usually mentioned the indications for their drugs, the vast majority of the time they did not spontaneously bring up prices, side effects, or contraindications. The American study found that more than 10 percent of the information given out by detailers was inaccurate (Lexchin, 1997c).

The average Canadian general practitioner sees at least one detailer per week (Strang et al., 1996) and sales representatives are family physicians' second most frequently used source for drug information (Angus Reid Group, 1991). In 2000, there were over 77,000 visits by sales representatives just to promote celecoxib (Celebrex®) alone, and almost 50,000 visits promoting rofecoxib (Vioxx®) (CBC-TV, 2002).

The faculty at McMaster University became so concerned about possible adverse educational effects of contacts between detailers and residents in the internal medicine program that these interactions were essentially prohibited during working hours in the hospital (Education Council, Residency Training Programme in Internal Medicine, 1993). An evaluation of this policy showed that when doctors who had gone through this programme went out into practice they were significantly more skeptical of sales representatives compared to residents who had not been part of the programme (McCormick, Tomlinson, Brill-Edwards & Detsky, 2001).

OVERRELIANCE ON PROMOTION

Canadian physicians frequently use various sorts of promotion as sources for drug information, even though they usually do not perceive such sources as credible (Strang et al., 1996). The problem is that studies have consistently shown that the more that doctors rely on promotion, the less rational is their prescribing (Norris, 2003). Even doctors who think that they rely on scientific literature for their knowledge can be influenced by promotional sources without being aware of it (Avorn, Chen & Hartley, 1982).

CONCLUSION

The thesis of this chapter has been that the driving force behind the pharmaceutical industry is the profit motive.

When profit and health considerations come into conflict with profit, as they did with Lilly and benoxaprofen, Bristol-Myers Squibb and pravastatin, or Merck Frosst and Vioxx, then profit wins.

Making drugs is a very profitable venture in Canada. Profit levels in the pharmaceutical industry are double those in manufacturing in general, and this level is not due to an accounting "illusion," nor is it justified by research and development costs. Profits remain high even after considering differences in accounting practices, and the high R&D costs only apply to a subset of all the new drugs that are marketed.

The high level of profits is the result of a combination of five factors: the patent system, the relationship between the industry and the HPFB, the type of R&D that the industry undertakes, drug prices, and finally, promotion to doctors.

Canada used to control drug costs through compulsory licensing, but that system was destroyed as a result of free trade deals with the United States, and later because of TRIPS and NAFTA. Because the HPFB traditionally had few resources, it existed in a clientele pluralist relationship with the industry, whereby certain functions, such as control over promotion, were turned over to the industry. In the past few years, the HPFB has had its funding cut back even further and has turned to cost recovery to fund its operations. This development has created a situation in which the industry can exercise even more control over the functions of the HPFB.

Although more pharmaceutical R&D is being done in Canada since Bill C-22 was passed, the scientific value of that research has never been systematically evaluated, and most of the products the industry brings to market do not represent major therapeutic gains. Instead, the industry directs its research efforts into areas that promise the greatest financial gain. Allowing industry goals to guide medical research is not always in the public interest.

The PMPRB has had a moderating influence on the price of patented medications, but its powers are limited, and despite the leveling off of prices, the cost of a prescription has continued to climb. Prescription prices are rising because doctors substitute newer, more expensive products for older, less costly ones. In many cases, this substitution cannot be justified, because the newer drugs are neither more effective nor any safer.

The pharmaceutical industry depends on physicians to prescribe its products, and as a result tries to form a close alliance with doctors in a variety of ways, including funding continuing medical education and spending heavily on promotion. Although there are rules in place to try to ensure that the information given out at meetings and conferences is not influenced by company sponsorship, biases still appear to exist.

One of the main reasons why doctors are switching from older, less costly products to newer and more expensive ones is because of the $2.2 billion per year that the multinational industry spends on promotion. Canadian physicians use promotion as a source of information about drugs, and the more they rely on promotion, the less rational they are as prescribers.

STUDY QUESTIONS

1. *How can the contradictions between the profit motive and the public interest be reconciled in the area of research and development?*
2. *What are the ethical implications when the interests of the public and private corporations are in competition, as may be the case with new drug approvals?*
3. *Should drug companies continue to fund the majority of the costs of continuing medical education? What would be the consequences for medical care if drug company funding were restricted and, as a result, doctors' attendance at these events declined?*
4. *Assuming that pharmaceutical promotion will continue to exist, what mechanisms could be used to ensure that it is accurate and unbiased?*
5. *Discuss whether the increase in research and development in Canada justifies the abolition of compulsory licensing.*

GLOSSARY

Canada's Research-Based Pharmaceutical Companies (Rx&D) an association that represents almost all of the multinational pharmaceutical companies operating in Canada, as well as some Canadian-owned biotechnology companies.

clientele pluralism a situation in which the state has a high degree of concentration of power in one agency, but a low degree of autonomy.

compulsory licensing granting a permit that effectively negates a patent. Theoretically, the company owning the patent on a drug would be a monopoly seller until the patent expired. However, if other companies apply for and are granted a compulsory license against a drug, they can then market their own version of that drug before the patent has expired.

continuing medical education activities doctors undertake to keep their medical knowledge up to date.

cost recovery an annual fee paid by companies to the Therapeutic Products Programme for each drug that they market and for the evaluation of new drug submissions. This money is used to fund the majority of the operating costs of the TPP.

detailers sales representatives for drug companies who visit doctors in their offices and attempt to convince physicians to prescribe their companies' products.

generic competition competition with brand name products by generics that are usually priced at least 25 percent lower.

new active substances/new chemical entities a class of new drugs, consisting of entirely new molecules that have not previously existed.

patent protection protection from competition for a period of twenty years from the date that the patent was filed.

Patented Medicine Prices Review Board an independent, quasi-judicial body created by Parliament in 1987, when Bill C-22 was passed. The PMPRB regulates the introductory price of new patented medications and the rate of rise in the price of patented medicines.

research and development/R&D the process of discovering a new drug and doing the testing necessary to bring it to market.

REFERENCES

Anderson, M., & Parent, K. (2001). *Timely access to generic drugs: Issues for health policy in Canada*. Queen's University, Kingston.

Angus Reid Group. (1991, April). *Credibility and the marketing mix*. Toronto: Angus Reid Group.

Atkinson, M.M., & Coleman, W.D. (1989). *The state, business, and industrial change in Canada*. Toronto: University of Toronto Press.

Avorn, J., Chen, M., & Hartley, R. (1982). Scientific versus commercial sources of influence on the prescribing behavior of physicians. *American Journal of Medicine, 73*, 4–8.

Baird, P.A. (1996). Funding medical and health-related research in the public interest. *Canadian Medical Association Journal, 155*, 299–301.

Battle to repeal automatic injunctions against generic drug approvals moves to the fall. (2001). *CDMA Viewpoint,* 1,6.

Berenson, A. (2005, July 20). At Vioxx trial, a discrepancy appears to undercut Merck's defense. *New York Times*. Retrieved on September 3, 2007 from *http://www.nytimes.com/2005/07/20/business/20vioxx.html?ex=1133499600&en=e47bc262490b69ab&ei=5070.*

Berenson, A. (2005, August 21). For Merck, Vioxx paper trail won't go away. *New York Times*. Retrieved on September 3, 2007 from http://www.nytimes.com/2005/08/21/business/21vioxx.html?ex=1133499600&en=b4906bc7e6c53b82&ei=5070.

Bowman, M.A. (1986). The impact of drug company funding on the content of continuing medical education. *Mobius, 6*, 66–69.

Bowman, M.A., & Pearle, D.L. (1988). Changes in drug prescribing patterns related to commercial company funding of continuing medical education. *Journal of Continuing Education, 8*, 13–20.

Canada, House of Commons. (1967). *Second (final) report of the special committee of the House of Commons on drug costs and prices*. Ottawa: Queen's Printer.

Canada's Research-Based Pharmaceutical Companies (Rx&D). (2005). *Innovation our passion: Better health our mission*. Retrieved on September 3, 2007 from *http://www.canadapharma.org/Industry_Publications/Code/CodeOfConductEN_Jan2005_updatedMay.pdf.*

CBC Radio. (1997, January 25). Drug patent law. *The House*.

CBC-TV – Undercurrents. (2001, February 4). *The battle over a drug ad*, Transcript, Canadian NewsDisc.

CBC-TV – Disclosure. (2002). *Targeting doctors.* Graph: top 50 drugs by promotional dollars. Retrieved on December 1, 2005 from http://www.cbc.ca/disclosure/archives/0103_pharm/resources.html.

Commission of Inquiry on the Pharmaceutical Industry. (1985). Report. Ottawa: Supply and Services Canada.

Connection. (1998). Spotlight: BMS vs. CCOHTA. *Connection, 1.*

Department of Foreign Affairs and International Trade and Industry Canada. (1996). *The case for investing in Canada: Assessing excellence in Canadian pharmaceutical research and development.* Ottawa.

Dillon, J. (1997, March 4). *On feeding sharks: Patent protection, compulsory licensing, and international trade law.* A study prepared for the Canadian Health Coalition.

DiMasi, J.A., Hansen, R.W., & Grabowski, H.G. (2003). The price of innovation: New estimates of drug development costs. *Journal of Health Economics* 22, 151–185.

Education Council, Residency Training Programme in Internal Medicine. (1993). Development of residency program guidelines for interaction with the pharmaceutical industry. *Canadian Medical Association Journal, 149,* 403–404.

Federal/Provincial/Territorial Task Force on Pharmaceutical Prices. (1999). *Study 6: Prices of generic-to-brand name prescription drugs in five provincial drug plans 1990–1997.* Retrieved on December 1, 2005 from http://www.pmprb-cepmb.gc.ca/english/View.asp?x=124&mp=68.

Federal/Provincial/Territorial Working Group on Drug Prices. (2000). *Cost driver analysis of provincial drug plans: Ontario 1992/93–1998/99.* Ottawa.

Gardner, D.M., Mintzes, B., & Ostry A. (2003). Direct-to-consumer prescription drug advertising in Canada: Permission by default? *Canadian Medical Association Journal, 169,* 425–8.

Gereffi, G. (1983). *The pharmaceutical industry and dependency in the third world.* Princeton: Princeton University Press.

Gottlieb, S. (2002, May 4). Drug companies maintain "astounding" profits. *British Medical Journal, 324,* 1054.

Grabowski, H., & Vernon, J. (1990). A new look at the returns and risks to pharmaceutical R&D. *Management Science, 36,* 804–821.

Grabowski, H., Vernon, J., & DiMasi, J.A. (2002). Returns on research and development for 1990s new drug introductions. *Pharmacoeconomics, 20*(Supplement 3), 11–29.

Gray, C. (1981). The pharmaceutical industry: Promoting research in the 80's. *Canadian Medical Association Journal, 124,* 787–792.

Green Shield. (2002). *Analysis of drug claim costs 1997–2001.* Toronto.

Health Canada. (2000). Departmental performance. Ottawa, 2000. Retrieved on March 25, 2005 from http://www.tbs-sct.gc.ca/rma/dpr/99–00/hc-sc/hc9900dpr02_e.asp

Health Canada. (2003a). *Health protection legislative renewal: detailed legislative proposal.* Ottawa.

Healthcare Communications Inc. (1989). *The effect of journal advertising on market shares of new prescriptions.* New York: Association of Independent Medical Publications.

How the industries stack up: Most profitable industries. (2005, April 18). *Fortune,* F-28.

Kennedy, M. (1997, September 15). Fears raised over cuts to health protection. *Montreal Gazette,* p. A1.

Krupka, L., & Vener, A. (1985). Prescription drug advertising: Trends and implications. *Social Science and Medicine, 20,* 191–197.

Leffler, K. (1981). Persuasion or information? The economics of prescription drug advertising. *Journal of Law and Economics, 24,* 45–74.

Lewington, J. (1987, August 13). Drug-patent bill not enough to satisfy U.S. on free trade. *The Globe and Mail,* p. A1.

Lexchin, J. (1992). Prescribing and drug costs in the province of Ontario. *International Journal of Health Services, 22,* 471–487.

Lexchin, J. (1993). The effect of generic competition on the price of prescription drugs in the province of Ontario. *Canadian Medical Association Journal, 148*(1), 35–38.

Lexchin, J. (1994). Canadian marketing codes: How well are they controlling pharmaceutical promotion? *International Journal of Health Services, 24,* 91–104.

Lexchin, J. (1997a). Enforcement of codes governing pharmaceutical promotion: What happens when companies breach advertising guidelines? *Canadian Medical Association Journal, 156,* 351–357.

Lexchin, J. (1997b). Consequences of direct-to-consumer advertising of prescription drugs. *Canadian Family Physician, 43,* 594–596.

Lexchin, J. (1997c). What information do physicians receive from pharmaceutical representatives? *Canadian Family Physician, 43,* 941–945.

Lexchin, J. (1999). Following the rules in marketing. *Canadian Medical Association Journal, 161,* 685–686.

Light, D.W., & Warburton, R.N. (2005). Extraordinary claims require extraordinary evidence. *Journal of Health Economics, 24,* 1030–1033.

MacKinnon, M. (2000, September 19). WTO rejects patent law appeal. *The Globe and Mail,* p. B10.

McCormick, B.B., Tomlinson, G., Brill-Edwards, P., & Detsky, A.S. (2001). Effect of restricting contact between pharmaceutical company representatives and internal medicine residents on post training attitudes and behavior. *Journal of the American Medical Association, 286,* 1994–1998.

Medecins Sans Frontieres Access to Essential Medicines Campaign, Drugs for Neglected Diseases Working Group. (2001). Fatal imbalance: the crisis in research and development for drugs for neglected diseases. Geneva.

Merck Frosst Canada Inc. (1996, July 17). Direct-to-consumer advertising of prescription pharmaceuticals: A Merck Frosst position paper on how to use comprehensive patient information to deliver improved, cost-effective health outcomes.

Michols, D. (1997, February). Drugs and medical devices. *Programme Quality Initiative Bulletin, 2.* Ottawa: Health Protection Branch.

Mintzes, B. (1998, July). *Paper tiger or toothless tabby? Regulation of prescription drug promotion in Canada.* Health Policy Research Unit Discussion Paper Series (HPRU 98:6D). Vancouver: University of British Columbia.

Montgomery, D., & Silk, A. (1972). Estimating dynamic effects of market communications expenditures. *Management Science, 18,* B485–B501.

Norris, P. (2003). What impact does pharmaceutical promotion have on behaviour? World Health Organization/Health Action International Drug Promotion Database. Retrieved on December 1, 2005 from http://www.drugpromo.info/read-reviews.asp?id=4.

Patented Medicine Prices Review Board. (1995, October). Decision on patent dedication. *Bulletin, 17.*

Patented Medicine Prices Review Board. (2005). *Annual report: 2004.* Ottawa: Supply and Services Canada.

Pharmaceutical Manufacturers Association of Canada. (1975). *The performance of the Canadian pharmaceutical manufacturing industry.* Ottawa.

Pharmaceutical Manufacturers Association of Canada. (1997). *Code of marketing practice.* Ottawa.

Productivity Commission (2001). *International pharmaceutical price differences: Research report.* Canberra, AU: AusInfo.

Public Citizen's Congress Watch. (2002). America's other drug problem. A briefing book on the Rx drug debate. Washington, DC: Public Citizen.

Regush, N. (1982, October 25). How a suspect arthritis drug evaded government checks. *Montreal Gazette*, pp. A1, A6.

Restrictive Trade Practices Commission. (1963). *Report concerning the manufacture, distribution and sale of drugs*. Ottawa: Queen's Printer.

Royal Commission on Health Services. (1964). *Report*. Ottawa: Queen's Printer.

Sawatsky, J., & Cashore, H. (1986, August-September). Inside dope: The multi-million-dollar sellout of Canada's generic drug industry. *This Magazine, 20*, 4–12.

Schondelmeyer, S.W. (1993, January). *The cost of Bill C-91: An economic impact analysis of the elimination of compulsory licensing of pharmaceuticals in Canada*. Ottawa: Canadian Drug Manufacturers Association.

Scoffield, H. (2000, March 18). WTO upholds drug patent rule. *The Globe and Mail,* p. B3.

Shin, J.H., Haynes, R.B., & Johnston, M.E. (1993). Effect of problem-based, self-directed undergraduate education on life-long learning. *Canadian Medical Association Journal, 148*, 969–976.

Strang, D., Gagnon, M., Molloy, W., Bedard, M., Darzins, P., Etchells, E., & Davidson, W. (1996). National survey on the attitudes of Canadian physicians towards drug-detailing by pharmaceutical representatives. *Annals of the Royal College of Physicians and Surgeons of Canada, 29*, 474–478.

Taylor, K.M. (1991). The impact of the pharmaceutical industry's clinical research programs on medical education, practice and researchers in Canada: A discussion paper. In *Canadian pharmaceutical research and development: Four short-term studies*. Ottawa: Industry, Science & Technology Canada.

Temin, P. (1979). Technology, regulation, and market structure in the modern pharmaceutical industry. *Bell Journal of Economics, 10*, 429–446.

VanWoert, M.H. (1978). Profitable and nonprofitable drugs. *New England Journal of Medicine, 298*, 903–905.

Walton, H. (1980, June). Ad recognition and prescribing by physicians. *Journal of Advertising Research, 20*, 39–48.

Wiktorowicz, M. (2000). Shifting priorities at the health protection branch: Challenges to the regulatory process. *Canadian Public Administration, 43*(1), 1–22.

Wiktorowicz, M.E. (2003). Emergent patterns in the regulation of pharmaceuticals: Institutions and interests in the United States, Canada, Britain and France. *Journal of Health Politics, Policy and Law, 28*(4), 615–658.

Won Tesoriero, H., Brat, I., McWilliams, G., & Martinez, B. (2005, August 22). Liability trumps science at Merck trial. *The Globe and Mail,* p. B5.

Woods, D. (1986). PMAC to spend almost $1 million annually to reach "stakeholders." *Canadian Medical Association Journal, 134*, 1387–1389.

ENDNOTES

1. Canada's Research-Based Pharmaceutical Companies (Rx&D) currently has more than fifty member companies, including almost all the large multinationals operating in Canada. Fewer than twenty of its members are Canadian-owned companies, and these are generally small biotechnology companies. The Canadian Generic Pharmaceutical Association represents fourteen generic companies, the largest of which are Apotex and Novopharm.
2. In Canada and the United States the drug was called Oraflex.

3. The Health Protection Branch, now the Health Products and Food Branch, is the division of Health Canada charged with monitoring the safety and efficacy of prescription drugs. Before the HPFB allows a drug to enter the Canadian market, the manufacturer has to present evidence to it that the product is safe and effective for human use and that the manufacturing process meets appropriate standards.
4. The branch of the HPFB that regulates drugs was then the Drugs Directorate, then was renamed the Therapeutic Products Programme, and is now known at the Therapeutic Products Directorate.
5. In 1998, Pravachol had sales of $121 million, making it the sixth-leading drug in Canada in terms of dollar sales (*Scrip*, 1999).
6. At that time, companies had a monopoly on their product for seventeen years from the time that the patent was granted. In the late 1960s, it took about four years to get a drug to market, so the effective monopoly period was about thirteen years. The patent term is now twenty years from the date that the application for a patent is filed.
7. A compulsory license is essentially a permit that effectively negates a patent. Theoretically, the company owning the patent on a drug would be a monopoly seller until the patent expired. However, if other companies apply for, and are granted, a compulsory license against a drug, they can then market their own version of that drug before the patent has expired. The compulsory aspect means that the company owning the patent cannot block the license from being granted. Since 1923, companies in Canada have been able to get a compulsory license, allowing them to manufacture the drug in Canada, but because of the small size of the market few licenses were issued.
8. Although C-91 was passed in 1993, it was made retroactive to December 1991. Some people claim that this was a favour to Merck, the largest multinational subsidiary operating in Canada, because it disallowed a compulsory license on one of Merck's best-selling products.
9. It takes about eight years from the time a patent application is filed until a drug appears on the market.
10. As an example, five years after a drug appears, it may have sales of $100 million. Therefore, a generic that costs 25 percent less could lead to savings of up to $25 million. After twelve years, sales of the drug may be down to $50 million, and therefore generic savings would only be $12.5 million.
11. By and large, generic companies do not promote to doctors.

23

Ethics in Health Care in Canada

JANET STORCH University of Victoria

PATRICIA RODNEY University of British Columbia

ROSALIE STARZOMSKI University of Victoria

INTRODUCTION

In this chapter, we provide a social critique of contemporary ethics issues in health care in Canada. Although there is a rich literature of ethical analyses of these issues in the Canadian context (e.g., Baylis, Downie, Hoffmaster & Sherwin, 2004; Kluge, 2005; Roy, Williams & Dickens, 1994; Sherwin, 1992; Yeo & Moorhouse, 1996), these types of in-depth analyses will not be the focus of this account. Instead, in this chapter, we provide an overview of ethics and social policy issues, as well as selected ethical issues related to the context of health care and to the climate of health care. Health and social policy will be considered at three levels of analyses: the level of societal responsibilities for the health of the total population (the **macro level**), the level of institutional responsibilities for programs of care (the **meso level**), and the level of individual professional responsibilities for patients and families receiving health care (the **micro level**). We draw on theory and research from ethics and the health care professions to analyze these levels. We also draw on social science literature that critiques health care as well as health care ethics (e.g., Churchill, 1997; Coward & Ratanakul, 1999; De Vries, 2003; Fox & Swazey, 1992a, b; Weisz, 1990).

We begin with a discussion of societal values and ethical issues focused on health and social policy. Included in this discourse is a focus on ethics and human reproduction, genetics and genetic testing, organ donation and organ transplantation, end of life issues, public and global health ethics, and health research (including pharmaceutical research). Most of these issues would be considered the more sensational issues in ethics as opposed to the everyday ethics issues involved in the delivery of health care. In the second and shorter section of the chapter, we focus on contextual issues in the delivery of health care, including resource allocation and the moral climate of health care agencies. These issues are often regarded as less spectacular or non-spectacular issues in health ethics. They rarely grab the headlines, yet they are the issues of everyday ethics and system ethics that affect *all* individuals involved in health care. Finally, we conclude the chapter with a brief review of major themes emerging in health ethics issues, and provide some predictions about health ethics issues in the next decade.

SOCIETAL VALUES AND ETHICAL ISSUES – ETHICS AND SOCIAL POLICY

The interface of ethics, health, and social policy is important, both in terms of generating policies to address ethical issues in clinical practice and in critiquing the ethical implications of existing policies (Churchill, 2002; Kenny & Giacomini, 2005; Malone, 1999). All health and social policy issues include the balancing of individual and collective rights, as well as ethical justifications for restrictive practices. Examples of health policy examined here illustrate the breadth of ethics concerns raised by contemporary health policy issues.

Ethics and Human Reproduction – Should We Create Life?

SOCIETAL ISSUES

Less than 25 years ago, the range of ethical issues that would be collected under a heading such as "ethics and human reproduction" were fairly circumscribed. One could expect such a discussion to include contraception, sterilization, and abortion; a modest discussion about the control of genetic quality made possible through prenatal diagnosis; some discussion about care in childbirth; and a hint of concern about the ethical implications of the new frontiers in reproductive technology, such as "test-tube" babies (Storch, 1982). In Catholic hospitals, in particular, there were long-standing committees (often named medical-moral committees) to deal with contraception, sterilization, and abortion in accord with Catholic doctrine. But these were not the only health agency committees concerned about intervention in human reproduction. Therapeutic abortion committees were also operative in most major hospitals in Canada as the only legal route to permissible abortion (under section 221 of the *Criminal Code*). By 1988, that law was ruled unconstitutional through a legal challenge (*R. vs. Morgentaler*), and section 221 was struck from the *Criminal Code*. It was considered in violation of the *Canadian Charter of Rights and Freedoms* because it violated a woman's right to life and personal security (Keatings & Smith, 1995, p. 12). Thus, abortion became legalized in Canada.

The dialogue about abortion and other issues related to human reproduction have often been framed by the language of rights, that is, the rights of the woman versus the rights of the fetus (Sherwin, 1992; Tong, 1997). It is argued that women, as autonomous beings, should be free to choose their own destiny. When that choice jeopardizes another beginning life (a fetus), differing values lead to moral and legal controversy. Apart from the controversy that continues to surround abortion, the matter of a woman's choice has commanded more newsworthy attention in contemporary cases in which pregnant women are found to be engaging in behaviour that has a strong potential to be detrimental to the well-being of the fetus. In such cases, should a fetus be seen as a child in need of protection? Should child welfare laws be invoked to compel a pregnant mother to have treatment (Picard & Robertson, 1996)? In the Winnipeg case of Mrs. G., a young mother-to-be involved in sniffing glue (Baylis et al., 2004, pp. 398–400), this matter was tested in the courts. It was determined that a woman could not be compelled to enter into treatment to protect the fetus because under Canadian law, a fetus is not a person until it has been born. Therefore, birth is viewed as the necessary condition for legal personhood, and until birth the pregnant woman and her unborn child are legally one (Windwick, 1997).

Matters of non-therapeutic sterilization of mentally handicapped women also dominated much of the ethics discussion for decades. But it is the acceleration in the development of new reproductive technology that has been breathtaking. Current reproductive ethics discussions focus on a plethora of issues, including ovulation enhancement, gamete intrafallopian transfer, ovum donation and reception, in vitro fertilization, sex selection, surrogacy, cryo-banking, and a range of previously "unimagined" possibilities (Baylis et al., 1995b; Kluge & Lucock, 1991; Royal Commission on New Reproductive Technologies, 1993).

Central ethical concerns in the use of these technologies continue to be shaped in part by the language of rights; for example, the right of a child to know his or her origins, the right of couples to be parents, and so forth. For the most part, rights language tends to be limiting because it sets up a relationship of controversy. Many health care ethicists have found a focus on relationships to be a more helpful way of examining the ethics of human reproduction (Bergum, 1990; Bergum & Dossetor, 2005; Sherwin, 1992, 2002; Tong, 1997). Apart from the clinical issues about quality of life that these newer reproductive technologies raise, they also raise serious matters of health policy.

McTeer (1995) suggests that there are few areas of modern life where the challenge to find a "balanced relationship" between law, the public good, and the life of the individual is as great. Because human reproduction and genetic technologies are complex, powerful, and progressing at a rapid pace, a moral consideration of the questions implied about the integrity and definition of the human person is critical. At issue, as well, is the rightful place of the law in the regulation and enforcement of the use of these technologies.

POLICY RESPONSES

Burgeoning new reproductive technologies, and the serious societal-ethical questions raised by the use or anticipated use of these means to alter human reproductive capacity, led the government of Canada to establish a Royal Commission on New Reproductive Technologies in 1989. This commission consisted of seven members. Some viewed the concerns surrounding new reproductive technologies as problems of medical management, while others viewed the concerns as problems requiring societal value decisions (Kondro, 1992). In late 1993, the royal commission report was released (Royal Commission on New Reproductive Technologies, 1993). The general theme of the commission's recommendations was to "proceed with caution" in introducing these new reproductive technologies (NRTs). Market forces were not to determine how these NRTs would be used. A permanent regulatory and licensing body to govern everything from sperm banks to in vitro fertilization to research involving human zygotes was recommended (Kondro, 1993).

In July 1995, the federal Minister of Health declared a "voluntary moratorium" on applying nine reproductive technology procedures regarded as threatening to human dignity; presenting serious ethical, social, and health risks; and treating women as commodities. These technologies included sex selection; commercial surrogacy arrangements; buying and selling oocytes, sperm, or embryo; formation of animal-human gametes; retrieval of eggs from cadavers and fetuses for donation, fertilization, or research; creation of an artificial womb; germ-line genetic alteration; egg donation in exchange for in vitro fertilization (IVF) services; and human embryo cloning (Marleau, 1995). But in the absence of a definitive response by the federal government to regulate NRTs, the "voluntary" moratorium had limited effect.

It was not, however, until March 2004 that an act respecting assisted human reproduction and related research became law in Canada. This law is designed to 1) prohibit unacceptable practices such as human cloning, 2) protect Canadian families using assisted human reproduction (AHR) to help build their families in health and safety, and 3) to ensure that research related to AHR which may facilitate the treatment of infertility and other disorders takes place in a regulated environment. This Act prohibits a number of unacceptable activities in Canada including: human cloning; germ-line alterations; payment of surrogates; payment of donors of egg, sperm or in vitro embryos; creating chimeras; and using someone's reproductive material without their consent (Health Canada, 2004). In 2006 the Canadian government established the Assisted Human Reproduction Canada Agency to be the official federal regulator of AHR practices.

There are many future concerns about new reproductive technology policy. The matter of health insurance coverage for the use of these technologies is an important issue (Giacomini, Hurley & Stoddart, 2004). Some ethicists have framed this issue as a matter of becoming a society compassionate enough to allow women and men a choice about parenthood. Others have pointed out that the questions go beyond those of information and access, to questions about how new reproductive technologies will affect existing barriers to equality (Sherwin, 2002, p. 282).

Another policy matter that will require careful regulation is the issue of research on human cloning. Arguments for and against human cloning are powerful and will continue to raise serious concerns about the human values involved, including genetic determinism, the interests of the child, the risks involved in cloning, the use of clones as donors, and the regulation of this technology (National Bioethics Advisory Commission, 1999). Implementing and regulating the new AHR policy directives will be challenging given diverse interests, values, and views about new reproductive technologies, not the least of which is the interest in scientific pursuit through research on human subjects and human tissue.

Genetics and Genetic Testing – Should We Alter Our Genes?

SOCIETAL ISSUES

Similarly, the social, political, and ethical issues surrounding genetics and genetic testing are many. New genetic knowledge and techniques are changing the ways in which many people think about health and illness, personal risk, and family responsibility (Beardsley, 1996; Cox, McKellin & Burgess, 1995; Halsey-Lea, Jenkins & Francomano, 1998; Midgley, 2000; Nisker & Gore-Langton, 1995). New genetic knowledge is also creating high expectations for the future abolition of some inherited conditions and modification of others. This knowledge is developing rapidly, due in large part to the **human genome project**.

The human genome project was considered one of the most significant research endeavours of the 20th century. Launched in 1990, this was a multi-billion dollar international project, the purpose of which was to coordinate scientific discoveries, data, and methods related to genetic research with the goal of understanding the structure, function, and outcome of hereditary instructions within the human genome (Cox, 2004;

Halsey-Lea, Jenkins & Froncomano, 1998; Hoffman, 1994). As a result of the project, which involved researchers in a number of centres worldwide, large numbers of genes have been identified and new commercial tests are becoming available for genetic screening purposes. These discoveries raise a series of ethical questions for health research, for health care delivery, and for society as a whole. As Cox (2004) notes,

> Now that a draft of the human genome is complete, it is important to ask what this new knowledge and its application means for human health and well-being, as well as for social justice. Does the possession of a computerized catalogue containing the biochemical "recipes" for life enhance our ability to detect and treat common as well as rare forms of disease? Or do the predictive powers of the new genetics engender new anxieties around health and "normalcy" and contribute to new forms of discrimination and stigmatization? (pp. 279–380)

POLICY QUESTIONS

Other policy questions arise, for example, should researchers be setting any boundaries in this search for new genetic knowledge? Who should oversee the applications of this knowledge, and should some regulatory element be established to monitor such uses of this knowledge? How much funding should be devoted to the advancement of genetic science relative to other matters requiring research? To be able to adequately address these types of questions requires discussion about genetic research, policy development, regulation, testing, and caring for persons with genetic disorders (Kerr, Cunningham-Burley & Amos, 1998). A major concern raised at the Canadian Bioethics Society Conference in October 2005 was the amount of public and private monies allocated to research in genetics and genomics. Downie (2005) reported that in Canada, 48 percent of government research funding was allocated to genetic research while a large proportion of private funding was also earmarked for such research. What does that mean for societal expectations? For the channeling of scientific information? For all the other important research endeavours that cannot be undertaken because research funds are used up for this single area of focus?

The availability of genetic testing raises a host of difficult social and ethical issues for at-risk individuals and families, health care professionals, and society as a whole (Cox & Starzomski, 2005). Questions related to the confidentiality and privacy of genetic information, to informed consent and voluntary decision-making by patients and families, and to the potential for abuse of genetic information are emerging. When is the knowledge derived from such testing likely to be an appropriate social intervention? Who should know the results? How and when should information about hereditary risk be provided to other members of the family? These questions will, in turn, have important implications for the clinical management and support of families affected by genetic disorders.

A variety of other ethical issues and moral experiences (e.g., perceived responsibility in marital and reproductive planning, duty to provide caregiving) present themselves. In particular, it is important to understand from the perspective of individuals and families at risk for genetic disorders what the issues are and how they intersect with, and present new challenges for, the clinical management of the conditions. As studies of the social and ethical experiences of offering predictive genetic testing for other adult onset disorders (such as Huntington's chorea) have shown, one of the most prominent aspects of the experience is the profound importance of family and family dynamics (Cox, McKellin & Burgess, 1995; Hayes, 1992; Kessler, 1994; Wexler, 1996). The impact of predictive testing on families is discussed in genetic counseling sessions, but there are significant moral dimensions of this discussion that are not typically the responsibility of counselors or other service providers (e.g., future caregiving responsibilities for family members with Huntington's chorea). Moreover, it is often the case that participants' perceived responsibilities are not explicitly recognized as moral issues that have a significant bearing on the shape and outcome of predictive genetic testing (Cox, 2004; Cox & McKellin, 1999).

There is a need for continued research to better understand the social, ethical, and legal ramifications of new genetic knowledge. As Baylis and Robert (2004) point out, our goals are misdirected if our aim is to stop the development and use of genetic enhancement technologies. Rather, we need to "direct our energies to a systematic analysis of the scope of their use" (p. 457). And to that end, broad societal dialogue must occur.

Organ Transplantation and Organ Donation: Should We Replace Parts?

SOCIETAL ISSUES

Since the first successful kidney transplant, performed in Boston in 1954 between identical twins, transplantation has been considered an extremely controversial area, generating significant discussion in the health care arena and highlighting many of the issues that are central in the resource allocation debate. Transplantation has been viewed as a microcosm within which some of the most difficult ethical issues related to the evolution of technology and allocation of scarce resources are occurring (Dossetor, 2005; Fox & Swazey, 1992a, b; Murray, 1992; Starzomski, 1994, 1997, 2004).

Organ transplantation has been declared one of the greatest achievements of the 20th century, moving from the impossible to the commonplace, offering people with end-stage organ failure "a gift of life" (Murray, 1992). A successful transplant offers some people virtually complete physical rehabilitation and improvement in overall quality of life. However, others are not so fortunate. Some die while on transplant waiting lists; others reject their organs after transplantation and/or succumb to the many complications of the treatment (Dossetor, 2005; Murray, 1992; Starzomski, 1997, 2006). Although success rates are improving, they are still low for transplantation of some organs (for example, bowel and multiple organs). Some concerns about transplantation, particularly when the success rates are low or the procedures are considered experimental, are that transplantation consumes a large proportion of health care resources and benefits only a few (Starzomski, 1994, 1997).

As a result of the shortage of donor organs and of the human and financial resources required for transplantation, distributive justice questions analogous to those posed in the early years of transplantation are resurfacing: who will make the decisions about the resource commitment for transplantation, and who should be treated when all cannot be treated? Fox and Swazey (1992a, b) describe transplantation as epitomizing many of the issues that are part of the health care reform debate. Much of the debate about resource allocation in transplantation has focused narrowly on the methods required to procure organs sufficient to meet the demand rather than on discussions about the level of resources allocated for transplantation or on the views of the public and health care providers about how they think resources ought to be allocated (Starzomski, 1997, 2006).

POLICY QUESTIONS

The community at large is faced with fundamental questions at the macro or societal level about the level of resources to be allocated to life-saving technology (Brooks, 1993; Evans, 1992). Also at the macro level, an ongoing worldwide shortage of donor organs has raised questions about examining strategies for presumed consent (Sadler, 1992), using fetal tissue for transplantation (Martin, 1992), offering financial incentives for organ donation (Warren, 1993), engaging in buying and selling organs (Kazim et al., 1992), using anencephalic infant donors (Roy, Williams & Dickens, 1994), considering the use of xenografts (transplanting from one species to another) (Nicholson, 1996; Singer, 1992, Starzomski, 2004), and considering cloning to solve the problem of shortage of organs for human transplantation.

As research in the area of xenografting continues, questions about the level of regulation for this new technology are being discussed with the goal that the appropriate level of research and clinical application of xenograft technology will be identified prior to human trials in Canada. Given the potential risks of transmitting animal pathogens into humans (xenozoonosis), as well as the many ethical concerns about raising animals for transplant purposes, the need to proceed with caution and appropriate regulation is imperative. Health Canada has taken the position that, until some of the risks can be modified, clinical trials in humans will not be conducted in this country (Starzomski, 2004).

At the meso or institutional level of the health care system, questions are raised about the type of patients who should be the recipients of organ transplantation, and how selection criteria should be developed (Kilner, 1990; Kluge, 1993), as well as the proportion of an institutional budget devoted to transplantation compared with other programs (Balk, 1990; Starzomski, 1994, 2006).

Decisions at the micro level of the health care system are evident in questions about how health care providers decide whether or not a transplant is in a given patient's best interest. For example, health care providers make decisions about removing kidneys and parts of livers and lungs from individual living donors to be transplanted into specific recipients (Siegler, 1992). In addition, organs from unrelated donors are considered more frequently in transplant centres around the world (Spital, 1992, 1993). Finally, there is the question of how many re-transplants one individual is entitled to receive (Evans et al., 1993).

These are some of the most perplexing problems in transplantation today. These problems highlight concerns about autonomy and informed consent. Importantly, the critical principle of justice is embedded in many of the ethical issues about organ transplantation, exposing deep tensions about the societal sense of what is true or just (Kjellstrand & Dossetor, 1992).

In Canada, there has been ongoing discussion about the need to reduce the gap between the supply of donor organs and the increasing demand for organ transplants (Federal-Provincial Advisory Committee on Health Services, 1996; Molzahn, Starzomski

& McCormick, 2003; Standing Committee on Health, 1999). A Parliamentary committee on health, after several months of hearing from expert witnesses, released a report that outlined a comprehensive strategy for the reorganization of organ and tissue transplant services in Canada, including recommendations to develop a national organ-donation management network with federal and provincial cooperation (Standing Committee on Health, 1999). Within the report there was acknowledgment that at all levels of the health care system there needed to be a collaborative approach amongst consumers, health care providers, and governments to increase the number of organs available for transplantation and to ensure a high-quality Canadian organ and tissue donation system. As a result of these recommendations, the Canadian Council for Donation and Transplantation (CCDT) was established in the fall of 2001 to advise the Federal, Provincial and Territorial Conference of Deputy Ministers of Health. The CCDT supports efforts to coordinate federal, provincial, and territorial activities in the development of standards, policies, and best practices for organ and tissue donation and transplantation.

End of Life Issues – Should We Interfere with "Nature" at the End of Life?

SOCIETAL ISSUES

Not surprisingly, some of the most significant and pervasive issues in bioethics arise at the end of life. Societal challenges chronicled by early sociological studies have become articulated in terms of ethics. **Euthanasia, withholding and withdrawing treatment,** the concept of **futility,** and attempts to provide meaningful end of life care are issues that reflect a deep concern about the quality of living while dying.

Euthanasia has been a controversial issue in society. Given the psychological, social, and spiritual significance of death, it is no wonder that consideration of euthanasia is so difficult. As Roy et al. (1994) stated over a decade ago,

> Every discussion of euthanasia is bedeviled by the many different understandings of the term, as used in popular, academic, and professional discourse. It is very difficult for opponents and proponents of euthanasia to agree on a definition of the term. (p. 410)

This remains true today. The most widely accepted definition of euthanasia in Western health care is considered to be the "deliberate, rapid, and painless termination of a life of a person afflicted with incurable and progressive disease" (Roy et al., p. 411). **Assisted euthanasia** refers to advancing one's own death by requesting help from others either to provide lethal dosages of drugs with instructions about how to use them effectively, or requesting others to administer drugs or other mechanisms to bring about one's death (p. 412).

The issue of euthanasia is not new. Debates about euthanasia in Western society appeared in the literature as early as 1873 and were revisited in the 1920s, 1930s, and 1940s. Revelations at the military and medical crimes trials held at Nuremberg shortly after World War II "produced widespread revulsion against euthanasia, even when [it was] voluntary and for the purpose of relieving suffering" (Roy et al., 1994, p. 417). Most contemporary Western societies since then have continued to reject euthanasia as a policy option, although "over the past two decades, public opinion in Australia, Europe, and the United States suggests majority support... for the legalization of euthanasia and assisted suicide" (Johnstone, 2004, p. 236). While public support does not (and ought not) to necessarily translate directly into health care policy (Johnstone, 2004), it is important to note that there have been a number of initiatives emerging. Euthanasia and assisted suicide have been "officially tolerated and widely practiced" in the Netherlands for almost two decades (Jochemsen & Keown, 2003, p. 235). In Australia, the Northern Territory had a short-lived (1996–97) period in which euthanasia and assisted suicide were decriminalized (the period ended as a result of widespread political pressure) (Jochemsen & Keown, 2003; Johnstone, 2004). Several U.S. states along the Pacific coast, notably California, Washington, and Oregon, moved beyond discussion to a "series of ballot initiatives" (Moreno, 1995, p. 121). In 1994, Oregon became the first state to pass a law allowing assisted suicide (Moreno, 1995, pp. 120–167).

CANADIAN POLICY RESPONSES

In 1983, the Law Reform Commission of Canada recommended against decriminalizing euthanasia in any form, and in 1995, the Special Senate Committee on Euthanasia and Assisted Suicide upheld that recommendation, also recommending that programs of palliative care be made more available so that all patients and families could be supported in the dying process and not believe that euthanasia/assisted suicide were their only options. Concerns about inadequate pain relief for dying patients and institutional structures and workloads that made it difficult to provide appropriate care were raised in the Special Senate Committee report (1995), were echoed again by the Special Subcommittee (2000), and revisited again most recently by Senator Sharon Carstairs (2005) (see also Bernabei et al., 1998; Hunter, 2000). Two of the authors of this chapter have argued elsewhere that a policy permitting euthanasia would be particularly dangerous in our era of ongoing cost constraints (Ericksen, Rodney & Starzomski, 1995).

Nonetheless, this is not the end of the debate in either Canada or the rest of the Western world. Many members of the Canadian public – some of whom are part of "Right to Die" groups – argue compellingly for dignity and control at the end of life. While most health care professionals (as well as the Canadian Medical Association and the Canadian Nurses Association) believe that such dignity and control can be furnished through programs of palliative care, questions about euthanasia will continue to appear in the press, in government chambers, and in the courts. This is particularly likely when poignant cases of euthanasia arise, such as the Rodriguez and Latimer cases (McTeer, 1999; Sneiderman, 1994, 1997). In Fall 2005, for example, another private members bill (Bill C-407) was tabled in the House of Commons to allow euthanasia and assisted suicide. It faced a strong lobby, largely from groups representing disabled people for whom such legislation is perceived to hold significant dangers (*The BC Catholic,* November 7, 2005, p. 14); the Bill died on the Order paper when a federal election was called.

Meanwhile, in the 1980s and after, several hospitals began the development of "*Do Not Resuscitate*" (DNR) policies in an attempt to protect patients from the loss of dignity occasioned by prolongation of life and to protect health care professionals from potential legal liability should they determine that further treatment by resuscitation would be medically useless. This action eventually led to a common Canadian guideline by agreement of four major professional bodies (Canadian Medical Association, the Canadian Hospital Association, the Canadian Nurses Association, and the Canadian Bar

Association, 1995), followed by guidelines to deal with conflict in end of life situations (Canadian Healthcare Association, Canadian Medical Association, Canadian Nurses Association & Catholic Hospital Association, 1999).

It is important to note that these national Canadian guidelines are (at least partially) based on a notion of *futility* in order to limit treatment choices for patients. To say that treatment is futile is to say that it is impossible or unlikely to achieve its therapeutic goal or that there is something problematic about the goal (Browne, 2000, p. 2). Sneiderman, Jecker, and Jonsen (1990) believe that futility has two distinct components: physiological effect and benefit. From their point of view, some treatments can be futile because they do not produce a desired physiological effect or the anticipated goal of treatment. More specifically, *quantitative* futility occurs when physicians conclude from empirical data that they are not obligated to offer medical treatment to a patient. *Qualitative* futility occurs when physicians will not offer treatment because it will result neither in a return to consciousness nor in the ability to leave a critical care hospital unit (Sneiderman, Jecker & Jonsen, 1990). While these two categories of futility are useful to consider, research and clinical experience warn that supposedly "objective" determinations of futility are often laden with biases. When someone claims a treatment is "futile," communication amongst patients/residents, families, and health care team members can be shut down (Council on Ethical and Judicial Affairs & American Medical Association, 1999; Providence Health Care, 2005; Storch, 2004; Taylor, 1995).

Rather than subscribing to categories of levels of futility to drive decision-making, many health care agencies now have developed (or are developing) end of life guidelines tailored to patient needs. These guidelines often include a determination of *levels of intervention*, which are pre-selected sets of choices about treatment and care, creating categories ranging from full acute care (including critical care) to palliative interventions only (Providence Health Care, 2005; Rodney & Howlett, 2003). Resuscitation status is just one component of the categories. Levels of intervention are based on the premise that specific interventions may be either withheld or administered based on individual patient/resident needs, and that supportive comfort/palliative care ought to be integrated with all levels. Indeed, the Canadian Critical Care Society recently established guidelines for this kind of approach in critical care, as there is a growing interest in integrating palliative support with critical care, even when the focus is on saving lives (Rocker & Dunbar, 2000; Rocker, Shemie & Lacroix, 2000; Storch, 2004; see also Truog et al., 2001).

One other area where there has been considerable activity in Canadian policy over the past decade is around the use of **advance directives** (Dossetor & Cain, 1997; Wilson et al., 1996). An advance directive is "a written document containing a person's wishes about life-sustaining treatment" that "extend[s] the autonomy of competent patients to future situations in which the patient is incompetent" (Singer, 1994, p. 111). Advance directives, such as living wills and consultation with a proxy decision-maker who knows the patient well and speaks for his or her best interest, have the potential to facilitate communication about the withholding and withdrawal of treatment, even though these directives are not yet codified in law in every Canadian province (Blondeau et al., 2000; Storch, 2004).

At the same time as we are witnessing the evolution of various policy initiatives around end of life care, a growing number of ethicists and health care professionals are calling for a more compassionate approach to decision-making and care at the end of life (e.g., Kuhl, 1994; 2002; Lachs, 2003; Quill, 2000; Roy, 1994; Roy, Williams & Dickens, 1994; Storch, 2004). They want to take the principles and goals of palliative care and apply them more broadly to *all* patients who are, or might be, dying (Special Subcommittee, 2000).

But ethicists remain divided on matters of meaningful end of life care. Over the past twenty-five years, the Hastings Center in New York (an ethics think-tank of experts) has been actively involved in considering appropriate arrangements/processes for end of life care. They have issued at least three Special Supplements that underscore what we know about end of life decision-making and care. In 1995, the Center released a report titled *Dying well in the hospital: The lessons of SUPPORT* (the Study to Understand Prognosis and Preferences for Outcomes and Risks of Treatments). The SUPPORT study was designed to explore the extent to which patients' wishes and best interests were honoured in end of life care. The second and third Special Supplements are titled *Access to hospice care: Expanding boundaries, overcoming barriers* (2003), and *Improving end of life care: Why has it been so difficult?* (2005).

In the latter supplement, probing questions are raised about the failure of all the mechanisms noted previously to be as fully effective as they might be, and some ethicists suggest that the fundamental fear of death prevents people from engaging in discussions and recording their wishes for their end of life care (Callahan, 2005). Other ethicists maintain that autonomy has been over-emphasized in end of life care since there is great ambivalence about death (Burt, 2005). Still others suggest that the advent of even more powerful technologies, such as stem cell transplants, may well have moved physicians to once again sustain life at all costs because stem cells offer the hope of cure, and this new technology is becoming available (Callahan, 2005). Callahan suggests that this is an attitude reflective of the 1960s when technology was seen as the answer to our health problems (Callahan, 2005). Several authors in this collection of reflections on *Improving end of life care* make reference to the conflict surrounding Terry Schiavo's dying as indicative of the ongoing confusion noted in this section of this chapter, that is, poor understandings about euthanasia and withholding and withdrawing treatment, as well as a lack of meaning in end of life care (see *Hastings Center Report*, May-June 2005). They argue for a better system of care for the dying and system-wide decision-making.

In considering ways to rethink assumptions and set new directions for end of life care, Murray and Jennings (2005) make three key policy suggestions: that we should re-evaluate surrogate decision-making and advance directives; that independent mediation and counseling should be available in health institutions to assist families to deal with conflicts and disagreements that arise in end of life care; and that we should take a policy- and population-based approach to end of life care, and not simply a clinical approach.

Public Health and Global Health – Should We Care About Global Health?

SOCIETAL ISSUES

The need to take a policy- and population-based approach characterizes other ethical issues, including public health and global health. We know that health is determined primarily by social and environmental conditions, and that health is a socially mediated process that is greatly affected by intersecting vulnerabilities related to ethnicity, gender, income level, age, ability, housing security, substance use, and a number of other attributes (Anderson, 2004; Frankish, Hwang & Quantz, 2005; Lynam, 2005; MacDonald, 2002; Pauly, 2005). Yet, our traditional approaches to health care ethics do not effectively address such determinants i.e. determinants that raise fundamental questions about social justice (Rodney, Pauly & Burgess, 2004; Sherwin, 2002). While it is not within the scope of this chapter to examine public health and global health in their entirety, in what follows we will address a couple of contemporary issues.

It is well known that public health measures such as clean water and safe food products have done more to promote health than all the medical technologies combined (McKeown, 1979). Yet, it is only when these taken-for-granted utilities are in danger that people notice their importance. Events in Canada, most notably the Walkerton, Ontario incident of contaminated water that caused illness and death in May 2000 (Richards, 2005), have brought this reality to the forefront.

Likewise our taken-for-granted protection from communicable disease was common until the outbreak of HIV/AIDS in the early 1980s. Some have suggested that HIV/AIDS may be "the most devastating infectious disease in the world since the bubonic plague" (Beckman Murray, Zentner, Pangman & Pangman, 2006, p. 35). In Canada, an estimated 56,000 people were living with HIV in early 2003. A more recent and sudden threat to health was the outbreak of Sudden Acute Respiratory Syndrome (SARS) in Toronto in 2003 (Beckman Murray et al., 2006). SARS had a dramatic and devastating effect on the physical, economic, political, and social health of people in Toronto. Most importantly, it illustrated a lack of health system and public readiness to deal with an epidemic of massive proportions. Since then, the threat of epidemic, even pandemic, is evident in the spread of Asian flu beginning in the late 1990s; and more recently, the threat of super-bugs and the threat of a world pandemic have raised alarms for the safety and security of persons.

Reference is often made to the serious influenza epidemic, commonly known as the "Spanish Flu" that swept through the Western world following World War I (1918–19). In recounting the impact of this epidemic on Canada, Dickin McGinnis (1997) noted that this post-war epidemic spread rapidly and efforts to control it through quarantine and other health promoting measures had little public sympathy. In contrast to other outbreaks of the "flu," this particular influenza had a high morbidity (15–50%) and a high mortality (about 1% of those who contracted this flu died). Despite these threats to health, the public was largely non-cooperative in stemming the epidemic. They complained that quarantine was an injustice and that health department personnel were guilty of discrimination. Doctors were careless or indifferent to reporting cases because they thought other doctors were doing the same. McGinnis concludes her paper stating that the organization of health services was regarded as faulty. A positive outcome was that planning was effected to ensure that better protection and care would be available for a future outbreak. This same "effect" was seen in the wake of the SARS outbreak. Currently, governments at all levels in Canada are discussing and/or preparing for the possibility of a pandemic. These events have forced the public and public health officials alike to recognize the importance of moving from individualistic concerns to collective and global health concerns.

POLICY APPROACHES

One group actively involved in planning for the ethical issues that arise in public health, particularly epidemics and pandemics, is the Joint Centre for Bioethics in Toronto. Their working group on pandemic influenza published a paper on their web site entitled, *Stand on guard for thee: Ethical considerations in preparedness and planning for pandemic influenza* (2005). Citing the experience of the SARS crisis, where "decision-makers had to balance individual freedoms against the common good, fear for personal safety against the duty to treat the sick, and economic losses against the need to contain the spread of a deadly disease" (p. 4), the working group developed an ethical framework for decision-makers focusing on four key issues. These include: 1) the duty of health workers to provide care during a communicable disease outbreak, 2) the need to restrict the liberty of the public in the interest of public health by measures such as quarantine, 3) the need to set priorities in relation to scarce resources including vaccines and antiviral medicines, and 4) the need for acceptance of global governance including travel advisories (p. 5). In its ethical framework the group includes ten substantive values and five procedural values such as being reasonable, open and transparent, inclusive, responsive, and accountable (p. 8). More detail is required, however, about the needs of health providers on the front lines of care. Without corporate support to minimize their risks in the provision of care, it could be difficult for many nurses and others to fulfill their "duty to care" (B. Pauly, personal communication, March 16, 2006).

Given our highly individualistic society, the propensity to function with the public good in mind does not come naturally to many citizens, nor do directive communiqués from other countries fit well for most Canadians. Thus, the step from an ethical framework of any kind to international directives will likely be difficult for many to accept, particularly when one's own economic and social losses are at stake. Martin (2005) suggests that what is needed is an ethical framework for public health that incorporates four levels of ethics: personal responsibility, professional responsibility, institutional (government and non-governmental bodies) responsibility, and public (state and government) responsibility. She notes that medical ethics, bioethics, and research ethics combined will not provide an adequate framework for public health practice because they are considerably different from medical practice in that they deal with communities and populations. Martin proposes the development of a discrete code of ethics for public health.

Apart from the potential of pandemics calling us to pay attention to global health, a global ethic also requires that we take seriously our responsibilities in global health equity (Austin, 2004). Labonte, Schrecker, and Gupta (2005) note that despite the millennium development goals, there have been substantial reversals of the global trend toward improvements in health over the past 150 years. These authors call upon the G8 countries to ensure that debt cancellation, fairer trade, and a "rights based" approach to health and development are supported (p. 535): they note that "health is a human right and an essential investment for economic development" (p. 536; see also Labonte & Schrecker, 2004).

Health Research – How Risky Is Human Subject Research?

SOCIETAL ISSUES

Advances in medical and nursing science, and in the work of all health professionals involved in the delivery of health care, have required that people participate in research studies to determine the effect of health care interventions. A principal cause for concern is the fact that for many of the interventions being tested, there may be no known benefit (i.e., no known therapeutic benefit) to the participant (commonly called the research subject), and there may be significant risk. The necessity to test interventions on human beings prior to introducing those interventions into standard practice often conflicts with the risks involved for human beings as subjects. In order to ensure that the researcher does as little harm as possible while carrying out such research, standards for research involving human subjects, as well as mechanisms to monitor the use of these standards, are necessary.

Concerns about the protection of human subjects involved in research studies are well-founded. The history of abuses in health research became most apparent following World War II, when the reality of Nazi experimentation on prisoners in concentration camps became widely known. These abuses included starving inmates to study the physiology of nutrition, placing them in low-pressure chambers to determine the effects of rapid changes in altitude, infecting inmates with bacteria to study the course of disease, and exposing inmates to icy water or blizzards to test for revival after freezing (Pence, 1995; Brody, 1998). But these were not the only abuses of human subjects in research projects, and Germany is not the only country in which such inappropriate use of human subjects has occurred. Abuse in other countries has included injecting long-term-care patients with live cancer cells, injecting institutionalized mentally challenged children with hepatitis virus, and observing poor people of colour with syphilis to determine the effects of untreated syphilis long after effective treatment became available (Baylis et al., 1995c; Law Reform Commission of Canada, 1989). In Canada, the use of hallucinogenic drugs at the Allan Memorial Institute in Montreal for purposes of investigating brainwashing techniques is another example of the abuse of research subjects (Collins, 1988; Law Reform Commission of Canada, 1989). Common themes in these situations were that medical science had lost all ethical perspective, and that the health professionals entrusted to provide therapeutic care for patients betrayed that trust by conscripting clients for research without their consent.

As a result of these and other abuses of human subjects, codes of research ethics were developed by medical associations, government departments, nursing associations, and other groups. In Canada, the Medical Research Council (later to become the Canadian Institutes of Health Research) took the lead in developing guidelines for the protection of human subjects in medical research in 1987. The various codes and guidelines (or standards) included several key protections:

1. Human subject research should be undertaken only if the potential benefits outweigh the potential risks.
2. A subject's involvement in research must be informed and voluntarily given.
3. Confidentiality cannot be breached without the subject's consent.
4. The research must be designed and conducted to yield fruitful results.
5. The subject must be protected from harm, and any harm must be minimized.
6. The subject must be free to withdraw from the experiment at any time (Medical Research Council, 1993).

POLICY AND INSTITUTIONAL RESPONSES

In an attempt to establish mechanisms to deal with safeguarding human subjects and to operationalize ethical guidelines at the meso level, research ethics committees have been developed in universities and major health care agencies in Canada and the United

States. In the United States, where this type of development was pioneered, these committees are called institutional review boards (IRBs). In Canada, these committees have been named research ethics boards (REBs). Their purpose is to review research proposals to determine if adequate provision has been made for the protection of human subjects involved in the research. Key elements of the ethics review are the assurance of the consent of the research subject and attention to privacy and confidentiality. Research relevance and research design are also considered fundamental to a sound ethics review. Poorly designed research is unethical because resources are wasted and human subjects are used for no good purpose.

To assist research ethics boards in their task, a Canadian organization called the National Council on Bioethics in Human Research (NCBHR) was created in 1989. Initially a "child" of the Medical Research Council (MRC), the Royal College of Physicians and Surgeons of Canada, and Health Canada, the NCBHR was designed to be an independent body for the education of REB members and for the monitoring of MRC-funded research involving human subjects. When the MRC, the Social Sciences and Humanities Research Council (SSHRC), and the Natural Sciences and Engineering Council (NSERC) chose to unite in developing one common code for research ethics in Canada, the National Council on Bioethics in Human Research (NCBHR) changed its name to become the National Council on Ethics in Human Research (NCEHR) to serve all constituencies. NCEHR has published numerous papers to provide more detailed guidance to researchers and research ethics boards, including one on research involving children and another designed to clarify the issue of consent in research (informed choice) (NCEHR, 1993, 1996; Storch, 2001).

The creation of the Tri-Council Policy Statement, *Ethical Conduct for Research Involving Humans* (1998), referred to as a common code above, was a major national endeavour. The admonition of *respect for human dignity* is incorporated throughout the Tri-Council Policy Statement. The initiation and implementation of the Tri-Council Policy Statement has not been without challenge, however. Even as it was released, it was evident that revisions and significant additions were required. To ensure its continued development, evolution, interpretation, and implementation, the granting councils (SSHRC, NSERC & the new CIHR) formed an Interagency Advisory Panel on Research Ethics, now known as the Panel on Research Ethics (PRE).

In May 2000, the Law Commission of Canada released a report titled *The Governance of Health Research Involving Human Subjects (HRIHS)*, focusing on the ethical governance of research of HRIHS in Canada. Some significant conclusions of this study were that Canadians likely know more about how animals fare in research than about how human subjects are being treated, and that too much of the focus of ethics review has centered on the bureaucratic process of approving consent forms, which is suggested to be a review with "tunnel vision." Broader concerns about the promotion of beneficial research, the protection of human subjects, and the generation of trust are considered to be critical to the future of human research ethics in Canada. In mid-August 2007 the Sponsors Table for Human Research Participant Protection was formed. It is a group of organizations that share a common concern about the state of research ethics in Canada and whose goal it is to examine the current system and develop recommendations regarding structures needed to continue to promote high ethical standards in human research.

Meanwhile, the Canadian case of Nancy Oliveri continues to be cited as an example of how protection of human research subjects is inadequate. Nancy Oliveri, a medical researcher at the Hospital for Sick Children in Toronto, took considerable risks in exposing a situation of purported harm to research subjects when she decided to "blow the whistle" during the trial of a drug that was apparently having unexpected negative side effects. Conflict between the research sponsor (a pharmaceutical company), hospital financing, and the researcher's concerns was at issue in this case, which first emerged in the press in the fall of 1998 (Crelinston, 1999; Shuchman, 1999) and continues to be used as an example of the corporatization of health research. It appears that corporate interests in research (including health research) rather than scientific merit have too often covertly driven research agendas and the dissemination of research findings (Demont, 1998).

In the past several years, an apparent lack of knowledge and often a lack of accountability in pharmaceutical research have been the focus of much attention. The Law Commission of Canada findings cited earlier indicated that little is known about numbers of research subjects. An even greater problem is that little is known about the numbers of research studies underway within a country, province, or state at any given time. In an attempt to address this lack of sufficient information, consideration of the establishment of a clinical trials registry has been ongoing. For example, an Australian Clinical Trials Registry (2005) was recently established as a national, online register of "clinical trials being undertaken in Australia." Registrants are required to register a trial before the enrollment of the first patient in trials of "pharmaceuticals, surgical procedures, preventive measures, lifestyle, devices, treatment and rehabilitation strategies and complementary therapies." The information to be recorded includes the trial's objectives, main design, and sample size; treatments under investigation; outcomes assessed; principal investigators; and contact details. In the United States, a similar registry has been established and compliance in reporting is increasing, but as researchers (Zarin, Tse & Ide, 2005) note, there is substantial room for improvement in the completeness of data recorded. In Canada, such a registry is under discussion as this chapter is being written.

Finally, the policy challenges that lie ahead include the need to increase the faith of the public and researchers themselves in IRBs/REBs as a means of protecting humans in research. A January 26, 2006 article in the *The Washington Post* decried the lack of attention to the relevance of costly research, citing two types of studies (one on drugs, and one on baby sleeping position and sudden infant death); the article notes that the results of previous research in both of these areas has long been accepted practice. The journalist argues as follows:

> When a patient volunteers for a randomized clinical trial, he or she strikes an implicit bargain with the researcher. The patient may benefit, but even if he does not, others will. That is because the study will produce new knowledge. But if the question is already settled, then the patient's sacrifice and altruism are for naught. (p. A06)

While scholars will recognize the shortcomings of this analysis, the sentiment expressed merits careful attention by policy-makers in that public trust in the research enterprise is critical if health-related research is to succeed. The type of lack of oversight noted in the above article is telling of inadequate mechanisms in place. At an even deeper level, concerns about fraud in research and inappropriate corporate practices in pharmaceutical research are of serious concern in Canada and abroad (Lemmens, 2004). In March 2006, for example, Munro reported on scientific misconduct involving faked medical research as highly problematic at several Canadian universities. Featured in this CanWest News Service article published in *The Globe and Mail* (Abraham, 2005) was the fact that these studies had been funded by taxpayer's money, funds that could have been used in areas too commonly ignored in health research.

SOCIETAL VALUES AND ETHICAL ISSUES: CONTEXTUAL AND CARE ISSUES

Resource Allocation – Should There Be Limits to Medicine and Health Care?

SOCIETAL ISSUES

The growth in the size and complexity of health systems in the Western world is seen to present significant problems for economic viability. From a language of health management that focused primarily on expansion of services with no limits to the possibilities for medical advance, examining the appropriate limits of medicine gradually became the norm in the 1990s (Callahan, 1990; see also Rodney & Varcoe, 2001; also see chapter 7 in this book for a critique by Varcoe & Rodney.

Economic needs to sustain the current system in Canada paved the way for profound debate about sensible approaches to the provision of health services, for numerous government studies of provincial systems of care, and for suggestions to reduce benefits in Canadian medicare, with the all too convenient allegations of patients' abuse of the system to justify removal of services (Evans, Barer & Hertzman, 1991). The scope and magnitude of the subsequent changes in health care delivery have been unparalleled in Canadian history (Storch & Meilicke, 2006). Voices reminding the health establishment that it is responsible for encouraging patients to use the system and that it has accepted few limits to its modes of practice (Jecker, 1991) are not often either heard or acknowledged. Similarly ignored are the voices reminding the health establishment that disparities and inequities that have long existed may be worsened by the outcomes of the current debates (Blue et al., 1999).

POLICY RESPONSE

Beginning in the mid-1940s, Canadians gradually developed a framework for a Canadian health care system based upon values of equity. Although the explicit commitment to equity in health care was new at that time, the commitment was based on egalitarian principles that had shaped Canada as a nation since its inception (Saul, 1997). The belief that all persons should have access to required medical care and hospital services was enshrined in the legislation introducing hospital insurance and medical care in Canada in 1957 and 1968, respectively. The right to health care was further emphasized in the *Canada Health Act* of 1984 amid bitter disputes about the physician's right to independence versus the citizen's rights to access to care (Taylor, 1987). Despite its relative equity and effectiveness over the past forty years, however, the just allocation of health care resources is currently subject to serious political challenges (Douglas, 1993; Taft & Steward, 2000; Kenny, 2002; Pauly 2004).

By the late 1990s, most members of the Organization for Economic Co-operation and Development (OECD), composed of countries in Europe, North America, and the South Pacific, had launched a major reform of their health care systems (Evans et al., 1993, p. 35; National Forum on Health, 1997). The focus of the reform was to address issues and concerns about the allocation of health care resources, many of which have arisen as a result of the "spare no expense" philosophy in health care (Lomas, 1996; Starzomski, 1997). Therefore, determining the optimal methods for allocation of health care resources has become one of the most critical issues facing the system in the 21st century.

Fundamental questions of distributive justice have led to some of the most widely debated questions at all political levels in Canada. There is increasing discussion about the need to determine what Canadians wish to spend on health care, how resources should be allocated within federal and provincial health care budgets to meet the health care needs of citizens, how priorities should be determined within these budgets, and who will make the decisions about how resources will be allocated (National Forum on Health, 1997; Starzomski, 1997). It is believed that resolving these allocation dilemmas requires a partnership of consumers, providers, and government (Charles & DeMaio, 1993; National Forum on Health, 1997; Commission, 2002). It is important to note that in Canada, there has been widespread support for an egalitarian approach to health care (Commission, 2002). This is in contrast to the United States, where preservation of the autonomy of individuals in the health care marketplace has tended to militate against universal health care coverage (Storch, 1988, 1996).

In fact, in a report from the National Forum on Health (1997) it was noted (contrary to widely held public beliefs) that health care costs in Canada *decreased* from 10.3 percent of the GDP in 1992 to 9.5 percent in 1995. Further evidence for reduction in health care spending was reported in a health care study prepared for the Tommy Douglas Research Institute. This study showed a 1.1 percent decrease in health care spending between 1992 and 1997. The authors of this study note that "[t]his absolute decline is unprecedented" (Rachlis et al., 2000). Yet in the United States, health care costs increased from 14 percent of the GDP in 1992 to 14.5 percent in 1995 and have continued to rise. Total health care spending in Canada in 2004 comprised 70 percent of all public spending; in Great Britain, health care makes up 83 percent of public spending and in the United States it is 45 percent.

In Canada in the late 1990s, the federal government and all ten provincial governments examined various options to maximize resource usage by focusing on restructuring, re-engineering, decentralizing health care delivery systems, and the more effective use of health care services and personnel (Barer & Stoddart, 1992; National Forum on Health, 1997). It became clear that more health care does not necessarily mean better health for the population, and that there was a growing interest in moving to a health care model in which the broader determinants of health, such as social status and income, are central in the development of healthy public policy (Renaud, 1994). This interest was distinguished from traditional health care policy by being ecological in perspective, multidimensional in scope, and participatory in strategy (Milio, 1985; National Forum on Health, 1997; Commission, 2002). There also has been an increasing emphasis on the development of research that focuses on the outcomes of health care and the impact of new technology on the health care system (Deber, 1992; Goodman, 1992; Hadorn, 1993; National Forum on Health, 1997).

In 2002, two significant federal reports were released in Canada: one was a Parliamentary commissioned report on health care by Roy Romanow, the other a Senate authorized report by David Kirby. Although there were several common elements to these reports (namely, the need for increased funding in health care, accountability for funding and services provided, and the promotion of a National Health Council), the reports differ in substantial ways likely reflecting the dichotomous thinking in Canada today. Romanow, who heard from 40,000 Canadians in his consultation stressed the enduring value Canadians place on a publicly insured health care system that ensures solidarity in sharing burdens and benefits of health and illness; Kirby, who received input from 400 witnesses, left the door wide open for private sector involvement in health care (Storch & Meilicke, 2006).

Although the tenets of medicare (universality, comprehensiveness, accessibility, portability, and a publicly administered health care system) are considered sacred by most Canadians, these tenets are under siege. The reorganization of the health care system is rooted in the social ideology of each individual province. Decisions about allocation have been made primarily by governments, often in the form of cuts to programs, forcing rationing to occur at the meso level of health care agencies and institutions (Wilson, 1994, 1995). Moreover, some governments are examining methods (such as user fees, definitions of basic levels of care, and privatization of some health care services) that threaten to change the foundation upon which the Canadian health care system is built. These changes point to a need for public discussion about resource allocation in health care to assure that the best decisions are made, that all societal voices are heard in the debate, and that the decisions are made in a democratic fashion (Kenny, 2002).

Many hope that collaboration amongst stakeholders will ultimately improve the asymmetry in the relationship between provider and patient, and result in the best possible health care for Canadians. Clearly, this dialogue must continue (Anderson & Rodney, 1999; Charles & DeMaio, 1993; Kenny, 2002). Improved relationships have the potential to enhance the moral climate of health care agencies.

The Moral Climate of Health Care Agencies – Does the Moral Climate of a Health Agency Matter?

SOCIETAL ISSUES

As the previous analysis of resource allocation has illustrated, this is a time of unrest in health care in Canada. Consequently, contextual issues in the delivery of health care – which have always been important – are now impossible to ignore for those involved in the planning, delivery, and receiving of health care. We wish to explore some of the implications in terms of the moral climate of health care agencies.

Agencies such as hospitals, long-term-care facilities, community centres, and research institutes are characterized by hierarchy, a complex division of labour, administrative positions based on technical expertise and knowledge, collective outputs, reliance upon rules and policies, and multiple institutional and staff relationships (Buchanan, 1996, pp. 419–420). Health care agencies have responsibility and accountability that transcend those of individual health care providers. This means that health care agencies have a role in the resolution and creation of ethical problems in health care (see Chapter 7 in this text by Varcoe and Rodney).

Traditional bioethics has not effectively addressed these kinds of meso- and **macro-level** problems (Storch, 2004). Such problems are "everyday" rather than "quandary" issues, and hence do not get the same kind of attention that clinical health ethics issues such as end-of-life treatment, transplantation/organ donation, and genetics/genetics testing do. However, everyday contextual issues are as significant as clinical issues, and, indeed, the latter cannot be adequately addressed without attention to the former. For example, the previous discussion of end-of-life issues pointed out that one of the findings of the Special Senate Committee on Euthanasia and Assisted Suicide (1995) and the Special Subcommittee update (2000) was that inadequate pain relief at the end of life has at least in part led to requests for euthanasia. Inadequate pain relief is related to excessive workloads for providers and interdisciplinary team conflict (Ericksen, Rodney & Starzomski, 1995) – everyday problems that are commonplace in most health care agencies.

Finally, a serious contextual issue in the moral climate of health care agencies has to do with culture. Health care agencies take their own culture for granted and tend to marginalize patients and families whose culture is not from mainstream biomedicine (Coward & Ratanakul, 1999; Browne, A.J., 2005). As Burgess explains:

> health care services and health care ethics have complex assumptions comparable to cultural background or religious traditions. The fact that the health care context and much of industrialized society share many of these assumptions makes them difficult to recognize. (1999, p. 159)

Consequently, the communication required for value-based decisions is often fraught with unshared assumptions and divergent meanings (Burgess et al., 1999). Aboriginal Canadians who are giving "informed" consent, for instance, may have an understanding of their illness and treatment options that is different from that of their more powerful health care providers (Kaufert & O'Neil, 1990). Given the importance of informed consent in health care delivery and health research, difficulties negotiating informed consent in cross-cultural contexts are of concern.

Being oblivious to their own culture also means that health care agencies tend to be oblivious to systematic inequities in the accessibility and delivery of health care (Blue et al., 1999; Rodney, Pauly & Burgess, 2004; Stephenson, 1999). For example, immigrant women with a chronic illness such as diabetes who are employed in the lower echelons of the labour market may have difficulty in following the diet and blood glucose monitoring required to manage their disease, let alone in getting time off to attend appointments with their physicians (Anderson, Dyck & Lynam, 1997; see also Anderson, 2004; Lynam et al., 2003). These kinds of problems pose significant challenges in terms of social justice (Anderson & Rodney, 1999; Rodney, Pauly & Burgess, 2004; Watson, 1994).

POLICY AND INSTITUTIONAL APPROACHES

Fortunately, there are a number of initiatives in health care ethics in Canada that have made significant inroads into (or are on the threshold of) addressing many of the clinical and contextual issues articulated here. These include the generation of theoretical and empirical work addressing the moral climate of health care agencies, the creation of structures and mechanisms to foster ethical decision-making in practice, and the updating of professional codes of ethics.

Attending to the moral climate of health care agencies is a fairly new focus in ethics. A number of researchers and theorists claim that a better understanding is required of the morality of the complex organizational contexts within which ethics is enacted and within which professionals and providers, and patients and their family members, struggle to make ethical decisions (Hoffmaster, 1993; Jameton, 1990; Jennings, 1990; Liaschenko, 1993; McPherson et al., 2004; Pellegrino, 1990; Reiser, 1994; Rodney, 1997; Storch, 2006; Webster & Baylis, 2000; Weisz, 1990; Winkler, 1993). Research related to the context of health care ethics is beginning to proliferate. For example, in the United States, an ethnographic study evaluating a form used by physicians to elicit patients' preferences about treatment provided important information about institutional policies and practices (Ventres et al., 1997). In a study cited earlier in this chapter's analysis of genetics and genetics testing, researchers tried to understand the interface of consent for genetics testing with family history and dynamics (Cox, McKellin & Burgess, 1995). Another hopeful development toward change is the increased attention being accorded to organizational ethics in health care (see, for example, Blake, 1999; Weber, 2001; Persaud & Narine, 2000). This relatively recent phenomenon has the potential to influence the social organization of health care in significant and unprecedented ways. Many nursing researchers, including the authors of this chapter, are giving particular attention to the moral climate in health care (see Chapter 7 in this text by Varcoe and Rodney).

The creation of structures and mechanisms to foster ethical decision-making in practice have included (but are not limited to) the growth of ethics committees and the use of clinical ethics consultants. Ethics committees serve as an important resource for health care agencies in the areas of ethics education, case consultation, and policy formulation (McPherson et al., 2004; Storch et al., 1990; Storch & Griener, 1992). Interestingly, all three authors of this chapter have noted that while the initial focus of ethics committees since their inception in the late 1970s was on difficult decision-making at the **micro level,** a number of ethics committees are also beginning to grapple with meso-level decisions about the allocation of resources. Overall, ethics committees and ethics consultants seek to improve the moral climate of health care agencies. Thus, consultants – who may come from a variety of disciplinary backgrounds – serve as an important adjunct to committees (American Society for Bioethics and Humanities, 1998; Baylis, 1994).

Codes of ethics have served as a long-standing mechanism to improve decision-making in health care on matters of ethical concern. Codes of ethics set the standards by which the profession and the public can evaluate (and potentially discipline) individual members, and codes provide guidance for individual members about their own conduct. Codes also "inform the public about what they can expect from professional practitioners" (Du Gas, Esson & Ronaldson, 1999, p. 115; Storch, 2004; Yeo, 1996, p. 3).

Most health care professionals have such codes, and most codes have been substantially revised in the past decade to maintain currency and relevance to the broadening field of health care ethics (Baylis et al., 1999; Lamb, 2004; Storch, 1982; Yeo & Moorhouse, 1996). For instance, The Code of Ethics for Registered Nurses in Canada (CNA) was last revised in 2002 and is scheduled for release of its next revisions in June, 2008. The major changes in context between revisions are provided to explain the changes, additions, and other modifications in the Code (see Canadian Nurses Association, 2008). Although codes of ethics cannot address all issues, and cannot provide complete guidance to address the complexity of issues at micro, meso, and macro levels, they do play a noteworthy role in providing a standard for ethical behaviour, and in facilitating greater sensitivity to ethical issues (Baylis et al., 1999; Canadian Nurses Association, 2002, 2004).

CONCLUSION

The significance and complexity of the social, contextual, clinical, and policy issues noted in this chapter cannot be overemphasized. Many of these issues challenge the most precious values of Canadian society. As Canada becomes increasingly multicultural at the same time as experiencing an increased corporatization of health care and health research, the task of arriving at shared social and ethical values becomes an enormous challenge. What is morally right and what is morally wrong has never been more difficult to navigate. One thing, however, is clear. In order to develop solutions to the ethical problems that face it, the health care system will require a partnership of members of the public, health care providers, and government. The solutions will only become apparent if they collaborate.

Although some ethical issues tend to continually "catch the headlines" in health care, taking ethics seriously often results in seeing problems where we previously saw none. Thus, even some of the more mundane everyday issues of health care, such as those involving greater attention to patient autonomy and patient choice, have become serious concerns. Attention to these issues, in turn, has led to a re-examination of the relationships between health professionals and patients, and to the structures in which health care is delivered. The less spectacular issues in health care remain troublesome as the needs of health professionals, health institutions, government funding formulas, and patients are often in conflict. The more spectacular issues of health care continue to be unsettled as beliefs about the sanctity of life, quality of life, and appropriate medical interventions elicit polarized value positions. And, as we have explained in this chapter, looming over *all* these issues are pressing questions about the equitable and effective allocation of health care resources.

Fortunately, attention to improved ethical decision-making by all those involved in health care has never been greater. There have been tremendous strides made in ethics education for health professionals, in ethics committees, in guidelines for ethical decision-making, and in ethical standards and policies. It behooves all who have an interest in health care – providers, patients, families, communities, governments, and members of the public – to support such initiatives and to develop new and better ways to monitor and correct ethical violations, resolve ethical dilemmas, and relieve ethical distress. In the words of one health care ethicist:

> We want, as participants in [health care], to be able to notice our moral problems and to cope with them with sensitivity and integrity and to keep our health care institutions responsive to their moral goals. (Jameton, 1990, p. 450)

STUDY QUESTIONS

1. *What role can sociology play in our ability to understand, and ultimately improve, health ethics in Canada?*
2. *What is the difference between euthanasia and withholding or withdrawing treatment?*

3. *What are your opinions about the use of xenografts in transplantation?*
4. *How could ethical guidelines for public health be helpful to global health?*
5. *Why might corporate sponsorship of health research be problematic?*
6. *How might greater public participation in decisions about the provision of health care in Canada be accomplished?*
7. *Can you think of examples of problems in the allocation of resources that have worsened the moral climate of health care agencies?*

GLOSSARY

advance directives (personal directives) a person's written wishes about life-sustaining treatment, meant to assist with decisions about withholding and withdrawing treatment.

assisted euthanasia (assisted suicide) assisting a person in advancing his or her death at the request of that person.

euthanasia the deliberate, rapid, and painless termination of the life of a person afflicted with incurable and progressive disease (Roy, Williams & Dickens, 1994, p. 411).

futility two components exist: quantitative futility, in which physicians conclude through an appeal to empirical data that they are not obligated to offer medical treatment to a patient; and qualitative futility, in which physicians will not offer treatment because it will not result in either a return to consciousness or the ability to leave a critical care hospital unit (Schneiderman, Jecker & Jonsen, 1990; Taylor, 1995).

human genome project a project carried on worldwide in a number of research centres to coordinate scientific data in order to further understand the structure, function, and outcome of the hereditary instructions in the human genome.

macro-level approach the level of societal responsibilities for the health of the total population including a focus on large-scale social, political, economic, and cultural factors that impact health care and health care delivery.

meso-level approach the level of institutional responsibilities for programs of care.

micro-level approach the level of individual professional responsibilities for patients and families receiving health care.

withholding and withdrawing treatment reasoned clinical judgments identifying treatments that are or are not in the patient's best interest, determined on the basis of an assessment of the patient's personal, cultural, and spiritual values, as well as an assessment of the patient's prognosis, treatment options, and so forth (Moreno, 1999; Storch, 1999); withholding and withdrawing treatment used to be (misleadingly) called passive euthanasia.

REFERENCES

Abraham, C. (2005). Star scientist hatches cloning controversy. *Globe and Mail* (2005, November 25). B.C. Edition. A1 & A14.

American Society for Bioethics and Humanities. (1998). *Core competencies for health care ethics consultation.* Glenview, IL: Author.

Anderson, J.M. (2004). Lessons from a postcolonial-feminist perspective: Suffering and a path to healing. *Nursing Inquiry, 11*(4), 238–246.

Anderson, J.M., Dyck, I., & Lynam, J. (1997). Health care professionals and women speaking: Constraints in everyday life and the management of chronic illness. *Health, 1*(1), 57–80.

Anderson, J., & Rodney, P. (1999). Part IV [Health policy: A cross-cultural dialogue], Conclusion. In H. Coward & P. Ratanakul (Eds.), *A cross-cultural dialogue on health care ethics* (pp. 257–261). Waterloo, ON: Wilfrid Laurier University Press.

Austin, W. (2004). Global health challenges, human rights, and nursing ethics. In J. Storch, P. Rodney, & R. Starzomski (Eds.), *Toward a moral horizon: Nursing ethics for leadership and practice* (pp. 339–356). Toronto: Pearson-Prentice Hall.

Australian Clinical Trials Registry (2005). http://www.actr.org.au.

Balk, R. (1990). Should transplantation be part of a health care system? *Canadian Medical Association Journal, 36*, 1129–1132.

Barer, M., & Stoddart, G. (1992). *Toward integrated medical resource policies for Canada*. Report prepared for the Federal/Provincial/Territorial Conference of Deputy Ministers of Health. Winnipeg: Manitoba Health.

Baylis, F.E. (1994). A profile of the health care ethics consultant. In F.E. Baylis (Ed.), *The health care ethics consultant* (pp. 25–44). Totowa, NJ: Humana Press.

Baylis, F., Downie, J. & Dewhirst, K. (1999). *Codes of ethics* (2nd ed.). Toronto: Hospital for Sick Children.

Baylis, F., Downie, J., Freedman, B., Hoffmaster, B., & Sherwin, S. (1995b). Introduction [Assisted reproductive technologies]. In F. Baylis, J. Downie, B. Freedman, B. Hoffmaster, & S. Sherwin (Eds.), *Health care ethics in Canada* (pp. 450–455). Toronto: Harcourt Brace.

Baylis, F., Downie, J., Freedman, B., Hoffmaster, B., & Sherwin, S. (1995c). Introduction [Research involving human subjects]. In F. Baylis, J. Downie, B. Freedman, B. Hoffmaster, & S. Sherwin (Eds.), *Health care ethics in Canada* (pp. 320–325). Toronto: Harcourt Brace.

Baylis, F., Downie, J., Hoffmaster, B., & Sherwin, S. (Eds.) (2004). *Health care ethics in Canada* (2nd ed.). Toronto: Thomson Nelson.

Baylis, F., & Robert, J.S. (2004). The inevitability of genetic enhancement technologies. In F. Baylis, J. Downie, B. Hoffmaster, & S. Sherwin (Eds.), *Health care ethics in Canada* (2nd ed., pp. 448–460). Toronto: Thomson Nelson.

Beardsley, T. (1996, March). Vital data: Trends in human genetics. *Scientific American*, 100–105.

Beckman Murray, R., Zentner, J.P., Pangman, V., & Pangman, C. (2006). *Health promotion strategies through the lifespan*. Canadian Edition. Toronto: Pearson/Prentice Hall.

Bergum, V. (1990, April). Abortion revisited: What can pregnancy tell us about abortion? *The Bioethics Bulletin*, 3–5.

Bergum, V., & Dossetor, J. (2005). *Relational ethics: The full meaning of respect*. Hagerstown, MD: University Publishing Group.

Bernabei, R., Gambassi, G., Lapane, K., Landi, F., Gatsonis, C., Dunlop, R., Lipsitz, L., Steel, K., & Mor, V. (1998). Management of pain in elderly patients with cancer. *Journal of the American Medical Association, 279*(23), 1877–1882.

Blake, D.C. (1999). Organizational ethics: Creating structural and cultural change in health-care organizations. *Journal of Clinical Ethics, 10*(3), 187–193.

Blondeau, D., Lavoie, M., Valois, P., Keyserlingk, E.W., Hébert, M., & Martineau, I. (2000). The attitude of Canadian nurses towards advance directives. *Nursing Ethics, 7*(5), 399–411.

Blue, A., Keyserlingk, T., Rodney, P., & Starzomski, R. (1999). A critical view of North American health policy. In H. Coward & P. Ratanakul (Eds.), *A cross-cultural dialogue on health care ethics* (pp. 215–225). Waterloo, ON: Wilfrid Laurier University Press.

Brody, B.A. (1998). *The ethics of biomedical research: An international perspective.* New York: Oxford University Press.

Brooks, J. (1993). The heart of the matter: Dalton Camp and his controversial transplant. *Canadian Medical Association Journal, 149*(7), 996–1002.

Brown, D. (2006, January 2). Superfluous medical studies called into question. *The Washington Post,* A06.

Browne, A. (2000). When patients demand too much. *Health Ethics Today, 11*(1), 2–3.

Browne, J.A. (2005). Discourses influencing nurses' perceptions of First Nations' patients. *Canadian Journal of Nursing Research, 37*(4), 62–87.

Buchanan, A. (1996). Toward a theory of the ethics of bureaucratic organizations. *Business Ethics Quarterly, 6*(4), 419–440.

Burgess, M. (1999). Part III [Ethical issues in the delivery of health care services], Introduction. In H. Coward & P. Ratanakul (Eds.), *A cross-cultural dialogue on health care ethics* (pp. 157–159). Waterloo, ON: Wilfrid Laurier University Press.

Burt, R.A. (2005). The end of autonomy. In B. Jennings, G.E. Kaebnick, & T.H. Murray (Eds.). *Improving end of life care: Why has it been so difficult?* Special Report of the Hastings Center, S9–S13. New York: Hastings Center.

Callahan, D. (1990). *What kind of life: The limits to medical progress.* Toronto: Simon and Schuster.

Callahan, D. (2005). Death: "The distinguished thing." In B. Jennings, G.E. Kaebnick, & T. Murray (Eds.). *Improving end of life care: Why has it been so difficult?* Special Report of the *Hastings Center,* S5–S8. New York: Hastings Center.

Canadian Healthcare Association, Canadian Medical Association, Canadian Nurses Association, & Catholic Hospital Association. (1999). *Joint statement on preventing and resolving ethical conflicts involving health care providers and persons receiving care.* Ottawa: Authors.

Canadian Medical Association, Canadian Healthcare Association, Canadian Nurses Association, & Catholic Hospital Association of Canada (in co-operation with the Canadian Bar Association). (1995). *Joint statement on resuscitative interventions.* Ottawa: Authors.

Canadian Nurses Association. (2002). *Code of ethics for registered nurses.* Ottawa: Author.

Canadian Nurses Association. (2004). *Everyday ethics: Putting the code into practice* (2nd ed.). Ottawa: Author.

Canadian Nurses Association. (2008). *Code of ethics for registered nurses.* Ottawa: Author.

Carstairs, S. (2005). *Still not there: Quality end-of-life care: A progress report.* Ottawa: Author.

Charles, C., & DeMaio, S. (1993). Lay participation in health care decision making: A conceptual framework. *Journal of Health Politics, Policy and Law, 18*(4), 883–904.

Churchill, L.R. (1997). Bioethics in social context. In R.A. Carson & C.R. Burns (Eds.), *Philosophy of medicine and bioethics* (pp. 137–151). Dordrecht, Netherlands: Kluwer Academic.

Churchill, L.R. (2002). What ethics can contribute to health policy. In M. Danis, C. Clancy, & L.R. Churchill (Eds.). *Ethical dimensions of health policy* (pp. 51–64). New York: Oxford University Press.

Collins, A. (1988). In the sleep room: The story of the CIA brainwashing experiments in Canada. Toronto: Lester & Orpen Dennys Limited.

Commission on the Future of Health Care. (2002). *Building on values: The future of health care in Canada.* Final report. R. Romanow, Commissioner. Ottawa: Parliament of Canada.

Council on Ethical and Judicial Affairs & American Medical Association. (1999). Medical futility in end-of-life care: Report of the council on ethical and judicial affairs. *Journal of the American Medical Association, 281*(10), 937–941.

Coward, H., & Ratanakul, P. (Eds.). (1999). *A cross-cultural dialogue on health care ethics*. Waterloo, ON: Wilfrid Laurier University Press.

Cox, S. (2004). Human genetics, ethics, and disability. In J. Storch, P. Rodney, & R. Starzomski (Eds.), *Toward a moral horizon: Nursing ethics for leadership and practice* (pp. 378–395). Toronto: Pearson Canada.

Cox, S., & McKellin, W. (1999). "There's this thing in our family": Predictive testing and the social construction of risk for Huntington Disease. In P. Conrad & J. Gabe (Eds.), *Sociological perspectives on the new genetics* (pp. 121–145). Oxford: Blackwell.

Cox, S., McKellin, W., & Burgess, M. (1995). The medical genetics patient: Individual or family? Canadian Sociology and Anthropology Association Annual Meetings, Montreal.

Cox, S., & Starzomski, R. (2004). Genes and geneticization? The social construction of Autosomal Dominant Polycystic Kidney Disease. *New Genetics and Society, 23*(2), 137–166.

Crelinston, G. (1999). Adjudicating ethics in research: Independent review. *Canadian Medical Association Journal, 160*(3), 386–388.

Deber, R. (1992). Translating technology assessment into policy: Conceptual choices and tough issues. *International Journal of Technology Assessment in Health Care, 8*(1), 131–137.

Demont, J. (1998, November 16). Pressure point: Federal researchers say drug companies push hard for approvals. *Maclean's, 111*(46), 70–72.

De Vries, R. (2003). How can we help? From "Sociology in" to "Sociology of" bioethics. *Journal of Law, Medicine, & Ethics, 32*, 279–292.

Dickin McGinnis, J.P. (1977). The impact of epidemic influenza: Canada, 1918–1919. *Historical Papers* 120–130.

Dossetor, J.B. (2005). *Beyond the Hippocratic oath: A memoir on the rise of modern medical ethics*. Edmonton: University of Alberta Press.

Dossetor, J.B., & Cain, D.J. (Eds.) (1997). *A handbook of health ethics*. Edmonton: Bioethics Centre, University of Alberta.

Douglas, R. (1993). *Unfinished business*. Auckland, NZ: Random House Press.

Downie, J. (2005, October 22). Glass houses. Plenary presentation to the Canadian Bioethics Society Conference, Halifax.

Du Gas, B.W., Esson, L., & Richardson, S.E. (Eds.) (1999). The legal and ethical foundations of nursing practice. In *Nursing foundations: A Canadian perspective* (pp. 98–122). Scarborough, ON: Prentice-Hall.

Ericksen, J., Rodney, P., & Starzomski, R. (1995). When is it right to die? *Canadian Nurse, 91* (8), 29–34.

Evans, R.G., Barer, M.L., & Hertzman, C. (1991). The 20-year experiment: Accounting for, explaining, and evaluating health care cost containment in Canada and the United States. *Annual Review of Public Health, 12*, 481–518.

Evans, R.W. (1992). Need, demand, and supply in organ transplantation. *Transplantation Proceedings, 24*(5), 2152–2154.

Evans, R.W., Manninen, D., Dong, F., & McLynne, D. (1993). Is retransplantation cost effective? *Transplantation Proceedings, 25*(1), 1694–1696.

Federal-Provincial Advisory Committee on Health Services. (1996). *Organ and tissue distribution in Canada – A discussion document*. Ottawa: Health Canada.

Fox, R., & Swazey, J. (1992a). Leaving the field. *Hastings Center Report, 22*(5), 9–15.

Fox, R., & Swazey, J. (1992b). *Spare parts: Organ replacement in American society*. New York: Oxford University Press.

Frankish, C.J., Hwang, S.W., & Quantz, D. (2005). Homelessness and health in Canada: Research lessons and priorities. *Canadian Journal of Public Health, 96*(Supp 2), S23–S29.

Giacomini, M., Hurley, J., & Stoddart, G. (2004). The many meanings of deinsuring a health service: The case of in vitro fertilization in Ontario. In F. Baylis, J. Downie, B. Hoffman, & S. Sherwin (Eds.) *Health care ethics in Canada* (2nd ed., pp. 108–127). Toronto: Thomson Nelson.

Goodman, C. (1992). It's time to rethink health care technology assessment. *International Journal of Technology Assessment in Health Care, 8*(2), 335–358.

Hadorn, D. (1993). *Outcomes management and resource allocation: How should quality of life be measured*? Health Policy Research Unit Discussion Paper Series. Vancouver: University of British Columbia (HPRU 93:7D).

Halsley-Lea, D., Jenkins, J., & Francomano, C. (1998). *Genetics in clinical practice: New directions for nursing and health care*. Toronto: Jones and Bartlett.

Health Canada. (2004). Seeking input on a proposed approach for regulations concerning consent. Ottawa: Author.

Health Canada. (2001a). Guide to the proposals for legislation governing assisted human reproduction. Ottawa: Author.

Hoffman, E. (1994). The evolving genome project: Current and future impact. *American Journal of Human Genetics, 54*(1), 129–136.

Hoffmaster, B. (1993). Can ethnography save the life of medical ethics? In E.R. Winkler & J.R. Coombs (Eds.), *Applied ethics: A reader* (pp. 366–389). Oxford: Blackwell.

Hunter, S. (2000). Determination of moral negligence in the context of the undermedication of pain by nurses. *Nursing Ethics, 7*(5), 379–391.

Jameton, A. (1990). Culture, morality, and ethics: Twirling the spindle. *Critical Care Nursing Clinics of North America, 2*(3), 443–451.

Jecker, N.S. (1991). Knowing when to stop: The limits of medicine. *Hastings Centre Report, 21*(3), 5–8.

Jennings, B. (1990). Ethics and ethnography in neonatal intensive care. In G. Weisz (Ed.), *Social science perspectives on medical ethics* (pp. 261–272). Philadelphia: University of Pennsylvania Press.

Jennings, B., Kaebnick, G.E., & Murray, T. (Eds.) (2005). *Improving end of life care: Why has it been so difficult?* A Special Supplement of the *Hastings Center Report* (November-December), S1–S60.

Jennings, B., Ryndes, T., D'Onofrio, C., & Baily, M.A. (Eds.). (2003). *Access to hospice care: Expanding boundaries, overcoming barriers. A special supplement to the Hastings Center Report,* (March-April), S1–S60.

Jochemsen, H., & Keown, J. (2003). Voluntary euthanasia under control? Further empirical evidence from the Netherlands. In T.L. Beauchamp & L. Walters (Eds.), *Contemporary issues in bioethics,* (6th ed.; pp. 235–240). Belmont, CA: Thomson Wadsworth. (Reprinted from *Journal of Medical Science, 25*(1), 16–21, 1999).

Johnstone, M.-J. (2004). *Bioethics: A nursing perspective* (4th ed.). Sydney: Churchill-Livingstone.

Joint Centre for Bioethics. (2005). *Stand on guard for thee: Ethical considerations in preparedness and planning for pandemic influenza*. Toronto: Author

Kaufert, J.M, & O'Neil, J.D. (1990). Biomedical rituals and informed consent: Native Canadians and the negotiation of clinical trust. In G. Weisz (Ed.), *Social science perspectives on medical ethics* (pp. 41–63). Philadelphia: University of Pennsylvania Press.

Kazim, E., Al-Rukaimi, H., Fernandez, S., Raizada, S., Mustafa, M., & Huda, N. (1992). Buying a kidney: The easy way out? *Transplantation Proceedings, 24*(5), 2112–2113.

Keatings, M., & Smith, O. (1995). *Ethical and legal issues in Canadian nursing.* Toronto: W.B. Saunders.

Kenny, N.P. (2002). *What good is health care?* Ottawa: CHA Press.

Kenny, N.P., & Giacomini, M. (2005). Wanted: A new ethics field for health policy analysis. *Health Care Analysis 13*(4), 247–260.

Kerr, A., Cunningham-Burley, S., & Amos, A. (1998). The new genetics and health: Mobilizing lay expertise. *Public Understanding of Science, 7,* 41–60.

Kessler, S. (1994). Invited editorial: Predictive testing for Huntington Disease: A psychologist's view. *American Journal of Medical Genetics, 54,* 161–166.

Kilner, J. (1990). *Who lives? Who dies? – Ethical criteria in patient selection.* New Haven, CT: Yale University Press.

Kjellstrand, C., & Dossetor, J. (1992). *Ethical problems in dialysis and transplantation.* Boston: Kluwer Academic.

Kluge, E. (1993). Age and organ transplantation. *Canadian Medical Association Journal, 149*(7), 1003.

Kluge, E. (Ed.). (2005). *Readings in biomedical ethics: A Canadian focus* (2nd ed.). Toronto: Pearson/ Prentice-Hall.

Kluge, E., & Lucock, C. (1991). *New human reproductive technologies.* Ottawa: Canadian Medical Association.

Kondro, W. (1992). Canada: Controversy over Royal Commission on new reproductive technologies. *The Lancet, 340*(14), 1214–1215.

Kondro, W. (1993). Proposed curbs on reproductive technology. *The Lancet, 340,* 1477–1478.

Kuhl, D.R. (2002). *What dying people want: Practical wisdom for the end of life.* Toronto: Doubleday Canada.

Labonte, R., & Schrecker, T. (2004). Committed to health for all? How the G7/G8 rate. *Social Science and Medicine, 59,* 1661–1676.

Labonte, R., Schrecker, T., & Gupta, A.S. (2005). A global health equity agenda for the G8 summit. *British Medical Journal, 330,* 533–536.

Lachs, J. (2003). Dying old as a social problem. In G. McGee (Ed.), *Pragmatic bioethics* (2nd ed., pp. 207–217). Cambridge: MIT Press.

Lamb, M. (2004). An historical perspective on nursing and nursing ethics. In J. Storch, P. Rodney, & R. Starzomski (Eds.), *Toward a moral horizon: Nursing ethics for leadership and practice* (pp. 20–41). Toronto: Pearson-Prentice Hall.

Law Commission of Canada. (2000). The governance of health research involving human subjects (HRIHS). Ottawa: Author.

Law Reform Commission of Canada. (1983). *Report: Euthanasia, aiding suicide and cessation of treatment.* Ottawa: Author.

Law Reform Commission of Canada. (1989). *Biomedical experimentation involving human subjects.* Protection of Life Project. Working Paper 61. Ottawa: Author.

Lemmens, T. (2004). Leopards in the temple: Restoring scientific integrity to the commercialized research scene. *Journal of Law, Medicine & Ethics (International and Comparative Health Law and Ethics: A 25 Year Retrospective),* (Winter), 641–657.

Liaschenko, J. (1993). Feminist ethics and cultural ethos: Revisiting a nursing debate. *Advances in Nursing Science, 15*(4), 71–81.

Lomas, J. (1996). Devolved authority in Canada: The new site of health care system conflict? In J. Dorland & S.M. Davis (Eds.), *How many roads?...Decentralization of health care in Canada* (pp. 25–34). Kingston, ON: Queen's School of Policy Studies.

Longwoods Publishing Corporation. (2005). ehealthrecord.info. 2(25) retrieved December 31, 2005 from http://longwoods.com/website/eHealthRecord/index.html.

Lynam, M.J. (2005). Health as a socially mediated process: Theoretical and practical imperatives emerging from research on health inequalities. *Advances in Nursing Science, 28* (1), 25–37.

Lynam, M.J., Henderson, A., Browne, A., Smye, V., Semeniuk, P., Blue, C., Singh, S., & Anderson, J. (2003). Healthcare restructuring with a view to equity and efficiency: Reflections on unintended consequences. *Canadian Journal of Nursing Leadership, 16*(1), 112–140.

MacDonald, M.A. (2002). Health promotion: Historical, philosophical, and theoretical perspectives. In L.E. Young & V. Hayes (Eds.), *Transforming health promotion practice: Concepts, issues, and applications* (pp. 22–45). Philadelphia: FA Davis Company.

Malone, R.E. (1999, May-June). Policy as product: Morality and metaphor in health policy discourse. *Hastings Centre Report, 29*(3), 16–22.

Martin, D. (1992). Fetal tissue transplantation research: A Canadian analysis. *Health Law in Canada, 13*(1), 132–141.

Martin, R. (2005). The moral mandate of public health ethics and infectious disease. Presentation at the 3rd ICCHNR Conference, Tokyo, September 30-October 2.

Marleau, D. (1995, July 27). Health minister calls for moratorium on applying nine reproductive technologies and practices in humans. *News Release*. Health Canada.

McKeown, T. (1979). *The role of medicine: Dream, mirage, or nemesis*. Princeton, NJ: Princeton University Press.

McPherson, G., Rodney, P., Storch, J., Pauly, B., McDonald, M., & Burgess, M. (2004). Working within the landscape: Applications in health care ethics. In J. Storch, P. Rodney, & R. Starzomski (Eds.), *Toward a moral horizon: Nursing ethics for leadership and practice* (pp. 98–125). Toronto: Pearson-Prentice Hall.

McTeer, M. (1995). A role for law in matters of morality. *McGill Law Journal, 40*(4), 893–903.

McTeer, M. (1999). *Tough choices: Living and dying in the 21st century*. Toronto: Irwin Law.

Medical Research Council. (1993). *Guidelines on research involving human subjects*. Ottawa: Author.

Midgley, M. (2000). Biotechnology and monstrosity: Why we should pay attention to the "Yuk Factor." *Hastings Center Report, 30*(5), 7–15.

Milio, N. (1985). Healthy nations: Creating a new ecology of public policy for health. *Canadian Journal of Public Health, 76*(Suppl. 1), 79–87.

Molzahn, A., Starzomski, R., & McCormick, J. (2003). The supply of organs for transplantation: Issues and challenges. *Nephrology Nursing Journal, 30*(1), 17–28.

Moreno, J.D. (1995). *Arguing euthanasia*. New York: Touchstone.

Moskowitz, E., & Lindeman Nelson, J. (Eds.) (1995). *Dying well in the hospital: The lessons of SUPPORT. A Special Supplement of the Hastings Center Report* (November-December), S1–S36.

Munro, M. (2006, March 16). Scientific misconduct. *Times Colonnist*, A2. Can West News Service.

Murray, J. (1992). Human organ transplantation: Background and consequences. *Science, 256*, 1411–1416.

Murray, T.H., & Jennings, B. (2005). The quest to reform end of life care: Rethinking assumptions and setting new directions. In B. Jennings, G.E. Kaebnick, & T. Murray (Eds.), *Improving end of life care: Why has it been so difficult?*(S52–57). Special Report of the *Hastings Center*. New York: Hastings Center.

National Bioethics Advisory Commission. (1999). Executive summary: Cloning human beings. In J.D. Arras & B. Steinbock (Eds.), *Ethical issues in modern medicine* (5th ed., pp. 481–484). Mountain View, CA: Mayfield.

National Forum on Health. (1997). *Canada health action: Building on the Legacy (Volume 1&2).* Ottawa: National Forum on Health.

NCBHR. (1993). *Report on research involving children.* Ottawa: National Council on Bioethics in Human Research.

NCBHR. (1996). *Facilitating ethical research: Promoting informed choice.* Ottawa: National Council on Bioethics in Human Research.

Nicholson, R. (1996). This little pig went to market. *Hastings Center Report, 26*(4), 3.

Nisker, J.A., & Gore-Langton, R.E. (1995, March). Pre-implantation genetic diagnosis: A model of progress and concern. *Journal of the Society of Obstetricians and Gynaecologists of Canada*, 247–262.

Pauly, B. (2004). Shifting the balance in the funding and delivery of health care in Canada. In J. Storch, P. Rodney, & R. Starzomski (Eds.), *Toward a moral horizon: Nursing ethics for leadership and practice* (pp. 181–208). Toronto: Pearson Canada.

Pauly, B.M. (2005). *Close to the street: The ethics of access to health care.* Unpublished doctoral dissertation, University of Victoria.

Pellegrino, E.D. (1990). The medical profession as a moral community. *Bulletin of the New York Academy of Medicine, 66*(3), 221–232.

Pence, G.E. (1995). *Classic cases in medical ethics* (2nd ed.). Toronto: McGraw-Hill Ryerson.

Persaud, D.D., & Narine, L. (2000). Organizational justice principles and large-scale change: The case of program management. *Healthcare Management Forum, 13*(4), 10–16.

Picard, E., & Robertson, G. (1996). *Legal liability of doctors and hospitals in Canada.* (3rd ed.). Scarborough: Carswell.

Providence Health Care. (2005). *(Draft) Providence Health Care end of life guidelines: Acute and residential care.* Vancouver, BC: Providence Health Care.

Quill, T.E. (2000). Perspectives on care at the close of life: Initiating end-of-life discussions with seriously ill patients: Addressing the "elephant in the room." *Journal of the American Medical Association, 284*(19), 2502–2507.

Rachlis, M., Evans, L.G., Lewis, P., & Barer, M.L. (2000). *Revitalizing medicare: Shared problems, public solutions.* Vancouver: Tommy Douglas Research Institute.

Reiser, S.J. (1994). The ethical life of health care organizations. *Hastings Center Report, 24*(6), 28–35.

Renaud, M. (1994). The future: Hygeia versus Panakeia? In R.G. Evans, M.L. Barer, & T.R. Marmor (Eds.), *Why are some people healthy and others not? The determinants of health of populations* (pp. 317–334). Hawthorne: Aldine deGruyter.

Richards, A. (2005). The Walkerton health study. *Canadian Nurse, 101*(5), 17–21.

Rocker G., & Dunbar S. (2000). Withholding or withdrawal of life support: The Canadian Critical Care Society Position Paper. *Journal of Palliative Care, 16* (Supp), S53–S62.

Rocker, G.M., Shemie, S.D., & Lacroix, J. (2000). End-of-life issues in the ICU: A need for acute palliative care? *Journal of Palliative Care, 16*(Supp), S5–S6.

Rodney, P.A. (1997). *Towards connectedness and trust: Nurses' enactment of their moral agency within an organizational context.* Unpublished doctoral dissertation, University of British Columbia, Vancouver.

Rodney, P., & Howlett, J. (2003). Elderly patients with cardiac disease: Quality of life, end of life, and ethics. Paper in unpublished *Canadian Cardiovascular Society Consensus Document on the Elderly and Cardiac Disease.*

Rodney, P., & Varcoe, C. (2001). Toward ethical inquiry in the economic evaluation of nursing practice. *Canadian Journal of Nursing Research,* 33, 1, 35–57.

Rodney, P., Pauly, B., & Burgess, M. (2004). Our theoretical landscape: Complementary approaches to health care ethics. In J. Storch, P. Rodney, & R. Starzomski (Eds.), *Toward a moral horizon: Nursing ethics for leadership and practice* (pp. 77–97). Toronto: Pearson-Prentice Hall.

Rodney, P.A., & Street, A. (2004). The moral climate of nursing practice: Inquiry and action. In J. Storch, P. Rodney, & R. Starzomski (Eds.), *Toward a moral horizon: Nursing ethics for leadership and practice* (pp. 209–231). Toronto: Pearson Canada.

Roy, D., Williams, J., & Dickens, B. (1994). *Bioethics in Canada.* Scarborough, ON: Prentice-Hall.

Royal Commission on New Reproductive Technologies. (1993). *Proceed with care: Final report of the Royal Commission on new reproductive technologies.* Ottawa: Supply and Services.

Sadler, B. (1992). Presumed consent to organ transplantation: A different perspective. *Transplantation Proceedings, 24*(5), 2173–2174.

Saul, J.R. (1997). *Reflections of a Siamese twin: Canada at the end of the twentieth century.* Toronto: Penguin Books.

Sherwin, S. (1992). *No longer patient: Feminist ethics and health care.* Philadelphia: Temple University Press.

Sherwin, S. (2002). The importance of ontology for feminist policy-making in the realm of reproductive technology. *Canadian Journal of Philosophy, 28*(Supp), 273–295.

Shuchman, M. (1999). Independent review adds to controversy at Sick Kids. *Canadian Medical Association Journal, 160*(3), 386–388.

Siegler, M. (1992). Liver transplantation using living donors. *Transplantation Proceedings, 24*(5), 2223–2224.

Singer, P. (1992). Xenotransplantation and speciesism. *Transplantation Proceedings, 24*(2), 728–732.

Singer, P.A. (1994). Advance directives in palliative care. *Journal of Palliative Care, 10*(3), 111–116.

Sneiderman, B. (1994). The Rodriguez case: Where do we go from here – A multidimensional (6 layered) approach. *Health Law Journal, 2,* 1–38.

Sneiderman, B. (1997). The Latimer mercy killing case: A rumination on crime and punishment. *Health Law Journal, 5,* 1–26.

Sneiderman, L.J., Jecker, N.S., & Jonsen, A.R. (1990). Medical futility: Its meaning and ethical implications. *Annals of Internal Medicine, 112,* 949–954.

Special Senate Committee on Euthanasia and Assisted Suicide. (1995). *Of life and death: Report of the special Senate Committee on euthanasia and assisted suicide.* Ottawa: Senate of Canada.

Spital, A. (1992). Unrelated living donors: Should they be used? *Transplantation Proceedings, 24*(5), 2215–2217.

Spital, A. (1993). Living organ donation is still ethically acceptable. *Archives of Internal Medicine, 153*(4), 529.

Standing Committee on Health. (1999). *Organ and tissue transplantation in Canada: Report of the Standing Committee on health.* Ottawa: House of Commons.

Starzomski, R. (1994). Ethical issues in palliative care: The case of dialysis and organ transplantation. *Journal of Palliative Care, 10*(3), 27–33.

Starzomski, R. (1997). *Resource allocation for solid organ transplantation: Toward public and health care provider dialogue.* Unpublished doctoral dissertation, University of British Columbia, Vancouver.

Starzomski, R. (2004). The biotechnology revolution – A brave new world? The ethical challenges of xenotransplantation. In J.L. Storch, P. Rodney, & R. Starzomski (Eds.). *Toward a moral horizon: Nursing ethics for leadership and practice* (pp. 314–338). Toronto: Pearson Canada.

Starzomski, R. (2006). Ethical concerns in nephrology nursing. In A. Molzahn & E. Butera (Eds.), *Contemporary nephrology nursing: Principles and practices* (pp. 795–816). Pitman, NJ: American Nephrology Nurses Association.

Storch, J. (1982). *Patients' rights: Ethical and legal issues in health care and in nursing.* Toronto: McGraw-Hill Ryerson.

Storch, J. (1988). Major substantive ethical issues facing Canadian health care policy makers and implementers. *The Journal of Health Administration Education, 6*(2), 263–271.

Storch, J.L. (1996). Foundational values in Canadian health care. In M. Stingl & D. Wilson (Eds.), *Efficiency vs equality: Health reform in Canada* (pp. 21–26). Halifax: Fernwood.

Storch, J.L. (2001). Current status of human participant protection in research in Canada. *Annals, Royal College of Physicians and Surgeons of Canada,* 34, 4, 201–204.

Storch, J.L. (2004). End-of-life decision-making. In J. Storch, P. Rodney, & R. Starzomski (Eds.), *Toward a moral horizon: Nursing ethics for leadership and practice* (pp. 262–284). Toronto: Pearson-Prentice Hall.

Storch, J.L. (2004). Nursing ethics: A developing moral terrain. In J. Storch, P. Rodney, & R. Starzomski (Eds.), *Toward a moral horizon: Nursing ethics for leadership and practice* (pp. 262–284). Toronto: Pearson-Prentice Hall.

Storch, J.L. (2006). Ethical dimensions of leadership. In J.M. Hibberd & D.L. Smith (Eds.), *Nursing management in Canada* (3rd ed., pp. 395–414). Toronto: Elsevier Mosby.

Storch, J.L., & Griener, G.G. (1992, Spring). Ethics committees in Canadian hospitals: Report of the 1990 pilot study. *Healthcare Management Forum, 5,* 19–26.

Storch, J.L., Griener, G.G., Marshall, D.A., & Olineck, B.A. (1990, Winter). Ethics committees in Canadian hospitals: Report of a 1989 survey. *Healthcare Management Forum, 3,* 3–8.

Storch, J.L., & Meilicke, C.A. (2006). Political, social, and economic forces shaping the health care system. In J.M. Hibberd & D.L. Smith (Eds.), *Nursing management in Canada* (3rd ed., pp. 5–28). Toronto: Elsevier Mosby.

Storch, J.L., Rodney, P. & Starzomski, R. (Eds.). (2004). *Toward a moral horizon: Nursing ethics for leadership and practice.* Toronto: Pearson Prentice Hall.

Subcommittee to update "Of Life and Death" of the Standing Committee on Social Affairs, Science and Technology. (2000). *Quality end-of-life care: The right of every Canadian.* Ottawa: Author.

Taft, K., & Steward, G. (2000). *Clear answers: The economics and politics of for-profit medicine.* Edmonton: Duval.

Taylor, C. (1995). Medical futility and nursing. *Image, 27*(4), 301–306.

Taylor, M.G. (1987). *Health insurance and Canadian public policy.* Montreal: McGill-Queen's University Press.

Tong, R. (1997). *Feminist approaches to bioethics: Theoretical reflections and practical applications.* Boulder, CO: Westview Press.

Tri-Council Policy Statement. (1998, 2005). *Ethical conduct for research involving human subjects.* Ottawa: Supply and Services Canada.

Truog, R.D., Cist, A.F.M., Brackett, S.E., Burns, J.P., Curley, M.A.Q., Danis, M., et al. (2001). Recommendations for end-of-life care in the intensive care unit: The Ethics Committee of the Society of Critical Care Medicine. *Critical Care Medicine, 29*(12), 2332–2348.

Ventres, W., Nichter, M., Reed, R., & Frankel, R. (1997). Limitation of medical care: An ethnographic analysis. In N.S. Jecker, A.R. Jonsen, & R.A. Pearlman (Eds.), *Bioethics: An introduction to the history, methods, and practice* (pp. 218–231). Boston: Jones and Bartlett.

Warren, J. (1993). Financial incentive controversy continues. *Dialysis & Transplantation, 22*(3), 156–158.

Watson, S.D. (1994). Minority access and health reform: A civil right to health care. *Journal of Law, Medicine & Ethics, 22*, 127–137.

Weber, L.J. (2001). *Business ethics in health care: Beyond compliance.* Bloomington: Indiana University Press.

Webster, G.C., & Baylis, F.E. (2000). Moral residue. In S.B. Rubin & L. Zoloth (Eds.), *Margin of error: The ethics of mistakes in the practice of medicine* (pp. 217–230). Hagerstown, MD: University Publishing Group.

Weisz, G. (Ed.). (1990b). *Social science perspectives on medical ethics.* Philadelphia: University of Pennsylvania Press.

Wexler, A. (1996). Genetic testing of families with hereditary diseases. *Journal of the American Medical Association, 276*(14), 1139–1140.

Wilson, D. (1994). Ethics and the crisis in health care organization. *Bioethics Bulletin, 6*(1), 5–7.

Wilson, D. (1995). The values that sustain the Canadian health-care system. *Humane Medicine, 11*(4), 178–179.

Wilson, D.M. (2000). End-of-life care preferences of Canadian senior citizens with care giving experience. *Journal of Advanced Nursing, 31*(6), 1416–1421.

Wilson, D., Anderson, M., Dossetor, J., Lantz, H., & Lawrence, C. (1996). Advantages and disadvantages of Bill 35 – Personal care directives. *Health Law Review, 5*(1), 14–15.

Windwick, B.F. (1997). Recent Decisions: Winnipeg child and family services v. D.F.G, [1997] S.C.J. No. 96 (QL). *Health Law Review, 6*(2), 35–37.

Winkler, E.R. (1993). From Kantianism to contextualism: The rise and fall of the paradigm theory in bioethics. In E.R. Winkler & J.R. Coombs (Eds.), *Applied ethics: A reader* (pp. 343–365). Oxford, UK: Blackwell.

Yeo, M. (1996). Introduction. In M. Yeo & A. Moorhouse (Eds.), *Concepts and cases in nursing ethics* (2nd ed., pp. 1–26). Peterborough, ON: Broadview Press.

Yeo, M., & Moorhouse, A. (Eds.). (1996). *Concepts and cases in nursing ethics* (2nd ed.). Peterborough, ON: Broadview Press.

Zarin, D.A., Tse, T., & Nicholas, C.I. (2005). Trial registration at ClinicalTrials.gov between May and October 2005. *New England Journal of Medicine, 353*(26), 2779–2787.

24

Making the Gift of Life Safer: The Canadian Tainted Blood Scandal and Its Regulatory Consequences

ANDRÉ P. SMITH University of Victoria

JAY FIDDLER University of British Columbia

INTRODUCTION

Every year, **Canadian Blood Services** (CBS), the agency that manages Canada's blood system, supplies enough blood and blood products for about 600,000 transfusions for a wide ranging number of medical conditions; these conditions include blood loss from trauma injuries, cancer, major surgeries, organ transplants, and fractured hip/joint replacements (Canadian Blood Services [CBS], 2007a). While few risks are associated with the process of donation, the blood that is collected can carry pathogens that will contaminate transfusion recipients if they are not detected and eliminated from the blood supply. This risk has always existed since advances in transfusion technology made it possible for blood to be collected, stored, and transfused on a wide scale. In the late 1970s and early 1980s, two deadly viruses were introduced into blood supplies worldwide – the **Human Immunodeficiency Virus** (HIV), a then unknown virus which causes Acquired Immunodeficiency Syndrome (AIDS), and the **Hepatitis C** (HCV) virus. The consequences of this contamination were far-reaching and continue to this day. Between 5–10 percent of the worldwide cases of HIV infection have been transmitted through the transfusion of infected blood or tainted blood products (Bloodbook.com, 2007). At the height of the crisis in the early 1980s, about 12,000 Americans became infected with HIV from tainted transfusions and another 290,000 Americans with HCV (United States Congress House Committee, 1996). HIV infected an estimated 2,000 Canadians – the majority of them hemophiliacs – and the estimates of people infected by HCV range from 60,000 to as high as 160,000 individuals (Orsini, 2002, p. 475; Picard, 1998). HIV infections are almost always fatal while the consequences of HCV infection vary – approximately 90 percent of those infected go on to develop chronic Hepatitis and from these, 10 percent will develop cirrhosis of the liver or liver cancer after ten years; this proportion doubles after twenty years (Krever, 1997, p. 3). At least 6,000–12,000 people are likely to die in Canada as a result of having being transfused with blood tainted with HCV (Picard, 1998).

This public health crisis redefined the role of government vis-à-vis blood collection systems in industrialized countries, making them far more accountable for setting strict regulatory measures to ensure the safety of blood supplies. In Canada, this crisis – often referred to as the tainted blood scandal – sparked a public outcry that prompted an inquiry by the subcommittee on health issues of the *Standing Committee on Health and Welfare, Social Affairs, Seniors, and the Status of Women*. The subcommittee held hearings between November 1992 and April 1993, and concluded that the Canadian blood system did not respond to the HIV/AIDS threat as adequately as it could have. However, it was unable to determine the precise reasons for this delayed response because of its limited mandate, and thus recommended the creation of a more comprehensive public inquiry to investigate the circumstances that surrounded the contamination of the blood supply (Krever, 1997, pp. 4–5). In September 1993, this recommendation was endorsed by the federal, provincial (except for Québec's Minister of Health), and territorial ministers of health and, on October 4, an Order in Council was passed authorizing the *Commission of Inquiry on the Blood System in Canada*. Led by Ontario Court of Appeal Justice Horace Krever, the inquiry was to "review and report on the mandate, organization, operations, financing and regulation of all activities of the blood system in Canada, including the events surrounding the contamination of the blood system in Canada in the early 1980s" (Krever, 1997, p. 5). Justice Krever created several expert committees that examined the scientific knowledge upon which decisions to safeguard the system were based and provided advice on the changes needed to avoid a similar disaster in the future. He also held public hearings which heard lay witness testimony from groups such as the Canadian Hemophilia Society, Canadian AIDS Society, Association of Hemophiliac Clinic Directors of Canada, Hepatitis C group, and several others. In total, over 400 people testified. Justice Krever (1997, p. 3) characterized the tainted blood scandal as "a nationwide public health calamity" and offered a series of comprehensive recommendations that changed the face of **blood donation** in Canada.

This chapter offers an overview of the tainted blood scandal and its regulatory consequences. The first section takes a look at the Canadian blood system, briefly tracing its history from its inception under the Canadian Red Cross (Red Cross) to its current management by CBS. The second section summarizes key findings from the **Krever Inquiry** on the circumstances that surrounded the contamination of the Canadian blood supply and, in particular, focuses on the failure of the Red Cross to promptly react to the threat posed by the emergence of AIDS in the late 1970s and early 1980s. The third section critically examines the risk management practices that were put in place following the blood scandal. This section also surveys the complex roles played by stakeholder groups, regulatory bodies, blood collection agencies, the blood industry, and government, at the federal, provincial, and territorial levels, in creating the regulatory structures that govern the blood system and ensure the safety of the blood supply. The final section explores the consequences of those regulatory structures. As Roussel (2003, p. 124) points out, the period surrounding the tainted blood scandal marked the emergence of a precautionary culture in which public decision-makers were increasingly being denounced and held criminally responsible for their lack of foresight in managing new risks to public health. While Roussel spoke specifically about the tainted blood scandal in France, her comments equally apply to the Canadian situation, particularly in the light of recent criminal charges laid against the former head of the Red Cross, other health officials, and an American pharmaceutical company (Canadian Broadcasting Corporation, 2005, 2006).

THE CANADIAN BLOOD SYSTEM

Canada's blood system emerged through a partnership between the Red Cross and Connaught Laboratories, which at the time was attached to the University of Toronto's School of Hygiene. At the start of World War II, Connaught Laboratories developed a process to manufacture freeze-dried human serum for use in the battlefield. The Red Cross began its involvement in the blood system by supplying Connaught with blood it collected from volunteer donors. At the end of the war, the Red Cross expanded its wartime donor program nationally to supply blood free of charge to hospitals. By 1961, it had established sixteen blood centres across Canada and, by 1973, was receiving operational funding from federal and provincial governments to cover the costs of operating the blood system nationwide (Krever, 1997, pp. 43–46; Picard, 1998, pp. 18–35). By the 1980s, the Red Cross was operating seventeen blood centres and many more mobile clinics often held in churches, schools, legion halls, factories, and offices. It managed the blood supply through two services with separate administrative structures and responsibilities (Krever, 1997, p. 210). The transfusion service consisted of paid employees who were responsible for screening donors and for the collection, testing, storage, and distribution of blood and blood products. By contrast, donor services relied on a strong base of provincial, regional, and local volunteers to organize the activities that pertained to the recruitment of donors, including managing mobile blood clinics, greeting and registering donors, and caring for them post-donation. This organizational structure was designed to respond to the blood needs of Canadians by collecting many donations as quickly as possible from large donor bases in rural and urban centres across the country.

The Red Cross already had several measures in place to protect the blood supply prior to the HIV and HCV contamination crisis. For example, careful handling and storage procedures minimized the risks of bacterial contamination. As well, every donation was tested for known disease-causing pathogens, such as those causing syphilis and Hepatitis B (Krever, 1997, p. 208). There were also several strategies in place to protect the blood supply against pathogens for which no tests were available, including the deferral of donors who were in poor health, who had engaged in conduct that put them at risk of acquiring infectious disease, or who had been exposed to higher rates of infectious disease in other parts of the world.

Another key strategy was to collect donations from volunteer donors, who gave their blood for altruistic reasons. The belief was that such donors "were inherently safer than paid donors who had a financial motive for giving blood even if they were not healthy enough to do so" (Krever, 1997, p. 211). The value of this approach was further entrenched by the work of sociologist Richard Titmuss (1972) who used blood donation as a case study to demonstrate the moral and practical superiority of giving versus selling health care services. In his landmark work *The gift relationship: From human blood to social policy*, he argued that "a competitive, materialistic, acquisitive society based on hierarchies of power and privilege ignores at its peril the life-giving impulse towards altruism" (Titmuss, 1972, p. 7). For Titmuss, the voluntary donation of blood represented "the relationship of giving between human beings in its purest form, because people will give without expectations that they will necessarily be given to in return" (Titmuss, 1972, p. 8). He viewed a voluntary blood donation system as a form of institutionalized altruism that encouraged people to care for one another, thereby strengthening community bonds and, ultimately, contributing to a safer and more efficient blood supply.

THE TAINTED BLOOD SCANDAL

By 1982, AIDS had emerged as a significant threat to the safety of the blood supply, although the virus causing the disease had yet to be discovered. There was some degree of consensus early in the crisis amongst American public health experts that AIDS was caused by an infectious agent and was contaminating the blood supply (Krever, 1997, pp. 214–218). On December 10, 1982, the *Morbidity and Mortality Report,* published by the U.S. Centers for Disease Control, reported the first confirmed case of transfusion-associated AIDS in a twenty-month old child who had received multiple units of blood components at birth (Krever, 1997, p. 214). It was thus apparent early on in the emergence of the AIDS crisis that strong measures needed to be rapidly deployed to reduce the risk this new disease posed to the blood supply. Dr. Joseph Bove, chair of the American Association of Blood Banks (which included the American Red Cross), is quoted in the Krever report as saying: "I think we are under great pressure to do 'anything and everything' to curtail the spread of AIDS" (Krever, 1997, p. 215). By spring 1983, U.S. Blood Bankers had implemented several measures to prevent individuals at high risk of contracting AIDS from donating blood under the guidance of public health authorities (Krever, 1997, pp. 284–285). At the time, high risk groups were identified as homosexual or bisexual men with multiple partners, recent immigrants from Haiti, individuals with the signs and symptoms of AIDS, intravenous drug users, and sexual partners of persons at risk of contracting AIDS. Measures included a public information campaign targeting those groups, the distribution of pamphlets in blood clinics describing the groups at high risk of contracting AIDS and the symptoms of AIDS, requesting individuals belonging to those groups and/or having the symptoms of AIDS not to donate, and directly questioning individuals to ascertain whether or not they belonged to a high risk group or had the signs and symptoms of AIDS and excluding them on the basis of their answers.

By contrast, the Canadian response to the threat of AIDS was timid. The Red Cross rejected active screening and exclusion of high risk donors, preferring instead to rely on a policy of voluntary self-exclusion that placed the onus on the donors themselves to refrain from donating if they believed they presented a risk to the blood supply (Krever, 1997, p. 286). The success of this strategy obviously depended on the ability of the Red Cross to effectively inform donors who were at risk of contracting AIDS, or who already had been infected with disease, about the threat they posed to the blood supply. Unfortunately, this safety measure was not implemented in an effective manner. The Red Cross initially put together a "public information campaign" that essentially consisted of two press releases issued by its national office describing the groups at risk of contracting HIV and asking members of those groups not to donate blood. That the releases received scant media coverage has been confirmed by the Red Cross through its own analysis of newspaper reports, and these two ineffective news releases were not followed by further releases (Krever, 1997, p. 287). The Red Cross also contacted the representatives of high-risk groups in the regions it served to inform them about the risk posed by AIDS to the blood supply. However, the effectiveness of this strategy varied depending on the willingness and initiative of local medical directors and their level of comfort with discussing health issues pertaining to homosexuality (Krever, 1997, p. 288).

Following the lack of success of its public information campaign, the Red Cross decided to follow the American example and distribute an AIDS information pamphlet in its blood clinics. However, there were several problems with this strategy as well. First, the language used to describe persons at high risk of contracting AIDS was vague and confusing – making reference to homosexual and bisexual men with multiple partners but not specifying what was meant by "multiple." By contrast, the American Red Cross had revised their pamphlet to include a more specific description of individuals in non-monogamous relationships who had more than one sexual partner. Second, the pamphlet did not contain any description either of the symptoms of AIDS or its precursor states. Third, it was only available in English and French versions, despite the fact that there were significant numbers of donors in the cities where the incidence of AIDS was greatest who neither spoke nor read either language. A fourth issue centred on the lack of procedure to monitor how the pamphlet was distributed to individuals in clinics – some clinics provided the pamphlet as part of their pre-donation procedures, whereas other clinics handed out the pamphlet during the donation or afterwards. As Krever (1997) notes, blood donor recruitment staff "had little involvement in or understanding of the issues raised by AIDS" and "volunteers in the blood donor program were ill-suited to deliver a message concerning homosexuality that would result in the exclusion of donors" (p. 291). Finally, the pamphlet did not contain any information about how self-identified "high risk" donors could discretely remove themselves from the donation process without fearing public embarrassment. By contrast, the pamphlet used by the American Red Cross specified that high risk donors who had donated blood could contact their blood centres afterwards and request that their donation not be used. Indeed, it was not until November 1986, a full year after it had implemented HIV-antibody testing of all blood donations, that the Red Cross addressed these concerns. Further evidencing a lack of responsiveness to the AIDS threat, Red Cross officials delayed the implementation of HIV testing by eight months from the time the test was approved for use in the U.S. by the Food and Drug Administration (FDA). This delay resulted in 133 additional cases of HIV infection that could have been prevented had testing begun as soon as it was available (Weinberg et al., 2002, p. 313; Krever, 1997, p. 287).

Justice Krever (1997) concluded that "the Red Cross did not carry out risk-reduction measures assiduously" and called the measures taken "ineffective and half-hearted" (pp. 293–294). He singled out several reasons that accounted for this failure. First, Red Cross officials adhered to a rather narrow interpretation of existing evidence about the AIDS threat, citing the lack of definite proof about the link between AIDS and **blood transfusion** to justify using voluntary self-exclusion instead of the more aggressive approach of actively screening high risk donors. Krever (1997) noted that the Red Cross response was "characterized by a refusal to accept and act upon risks to which prudent blood services, elsewhere in the world, were responding" (p. 208). He concluded that the organization should have not required conclusive evidence and instead decisions could have been made on the basis of reasonable doubt that transfusion-associated AIDS constituted an impending threat to the blood supply. Another reason cited to explain this inadequate response was a desire on the part of the Red Cross "to answer the concern of the public that something had to be done to protect the blood supply from AIDS without having to take measures that would result in rejecting donors or that might give offence" (Krever, 1997, p. 292). Red Cross officials feared that the organization's reputation as a humanitarian service could be sullied by accusations that they were discriminating against high-risk groups such as Haitians or homosexual men. In his account of the tainted blood scandal, Parsons (1995) echoes the Krever Inquiry, noting that Red Cross officials were particularly concerned about avoiding "the kind of homophobic accusations that were prevalent at the time" (p. 144). Finally, Krever (1997, pp. 283–284) points to a lack of leadership on the part of federal regulatory agencies in offering guidelines to assist the Red Cross in dealing with transfusion-associated AIDS. In particular, Krever singled out the failure of the Bureau of Biologics (the regulatory arm of Health Canada that oversees blood and blood products) to monitor the purchase in the early 1980s of blood products from the United States to address a shortage in Canada. Those products increased the risk of contamination, particularly for Canadian hemophiliacs, because of the higher incidence of HIV infection in the United States coupled with the practice of American blood product manufacturers to collect plasma from prison inmates. The Bureau of Biologics ordered a switch to safer heat-treated products in October of 1984 but failed to ensure that the Red Cross complied with this directive. Presumably because of pervasive concerns about shortages, the Red Cross deliberately used up its American inventory of non-heated blood concentrates before making the safer products available, approximately eight months later (DeMont & Corelli, 1997). Judge Krever felt that if regulatory officials had acted according to their mandate, many hemophiliacs would have avoided HIV infection.

Overall, more than 2,000 Canadians were infected with HIV and tens of thousands infected with HCV (Picard, 1998, p. 179). Almost half of all Canadian individuals suffering from hemophilia became infected with HIV and/or HCV because of their reliance on contaminated blood products. In light of those tragic consequences, Justice Krever (1997, p. 1047) stipulated several guiding principles for the new blood system: blood should remain a public resource; donors of blood and plasma should not be paid for their donations, except in rare circumstances; whole blood, plasma, and platelets must be collected in sufficient quantities in Canada to meet domestic needs for blood components and blood products; Canadians should have free and universal access to blood components and blood products; and safety of the blood supply system is paramount.

On November 26, 1997, then Federal Minister of Health Allan Rock released the Krever report on behalf of the federal government. He also issued an apology for the government's role in the scandal: "We can't undo the damage – I wish we could – but we can express our profound sadness and our deep regret for the harm done to so many Canadians and their families. The federal government accepts its share of responsibility" (DeMont & Corelli, 1997, p. 20). Over four years and at a cost of an estimated $17 million, the Krever Inquiry heard from 427 witnesses, produced 50,000 pages of testimony, and issued 50 recommendations for revamping the Canadian blood system. Although the inquiry did not directly assign blame, it nevertheless won the right to identify individuals by names and publish findings that could serve as the basis for criminal prosecution, despite numerous legal challenges from the Red Cross, the federal government, six provinces, five pharmaceutical companies, and 64 individuals.

In 1998, two new organizations, Canadian Blood Services (CBS) and **Héma-Québec** (HQ), assumed the responsibility of managing the blood system from the Red Cross.

While those organizations differ on some of their policies and procedures, they are both regulated by Health Canada and must meet the same national regulatory standards. CBS was established in 1998 following a Memorandum of Understanding (MOU) signed by representatives of all of the provinces/territories (except Québec) and which made the organization responsible for collecting, processing, and distributing transfusion-ready blood and blood products. In 2005–2006, CBS collected 871,818 units of whole blood, with a frequency of 2.16 donations per donor (CBS, 2006a, p. 5). HQ came to being as a result of a series of recommendations issued by the Gélineau Committee, which had been struck by the Québec government to investigate effective ways to revamp the province's blood system. Like CBS, HQ is responsible for all blood donation and transfusion activities in the province of Québec. In 2005–06, HQ collected 248,386 units of whole blood, with a frequency of 1.6 donation per donor (Héma-Québec, 2006, p. 34).

BLOOD AND THE RISK SOCIETY

According to sociologist Anthony Giddens (1999), the term **risk society** denotes a society that is "increasingly preoccupied with the future (and also with safety), which generates the notion of risk" (p. 3). While risks have always existed, late modern society has been characterized by an expansion of risk that is produced by the progression of human activity associated with modernization. According to Giddens, this type of risk contrasts with "external risk" which occurs regularly and often enough to be predictable and insurable, such as in the case of illness, disability, or work injury. Because manufactured risk is an emergent product of scientific and technological development, it is also difficult to characterize and predict. Examples include the nuclear disaster at Chernobyl, the infection of bovine livestock with Bovine Spongiform Encephalopathy (BSE or Mad Cow Disease), and the tainted blood scandal.

For Giddens (1990), everyday life and the experience of risk in late modernity are influenced by three mechanisms: "time-space distanciation, disembedding mechanisms, and reflexivity" (p. 63). Time-space distanciation pertains to the process by which daily life is imbedded within complex interrelated sets of events and actions that occurred in the past and in several other locations. In the case of the tainted blood scandal, contamination of the blood supply occurred as the result of several events and actions linked to the transmission of HIV in several populations with members who were also donors. Two disembedding mechanisms or abstract systems facilitate time-space distanciation: symbolic tokens and expert systems. Symbolic tokens allow for the convenient storage and transmission of socially constructed values between individuals across time and space (Giddens, 1999, p. 24). For example, blood systems are able to collect blood from voluntary donors because of the value placed in society on altruistic gestures. Individual donors derive satisfaction and engage in repeat donations in part because such gestures are recognized by others as useful and are indicative of valued personality traits. The second mechanism pertains to expert systems, which are "systems of technical accomplishment or professional expertise that organize large areas of the material and social environments in which we live today" (Giddens, 1990, p. 27). One example would be the way contamination risks are managed in the blood system at several expertise levels, including regulatory health agencies, blood collection agencies and their donor and transfusion services, as well as blood testing technologies developed by biotechnology manufacturers.

Giddens (1990) argued that trust plays a central role in the way disembedding mechanisms operate. Because individuals lack the necessary expertise to evaluate the effectiveness of the expert systems on which they rely, they have no choice but to trust them "based upon the experience that such systems generally work as they are supposed to" (p. 29). However, expert systems have limitations and can fail to meet expectations. As Giddens (1990) puts it, the "realisation of the areas of ignorance which confront the experts themselves, as individual practitioners and in terms of overall fields of knowledge, may undermine or weaken that faith on the part of lay individuals" (p. 130). The third mechanism proposed by Giddens is reflexivity, which pertains to the ability of individuals and institutions to reflect upon their own circumstances and place in the world. Reflexivity lies at the roots of a cultural turn away from a passive deference to accredited authority and toward a more active and critical engagement of individuals in their dealings with abstract systems (Giddens, 1990, p. 144). This reflexive turn has rendered lay individuals more skeptical of the benefits of technological developments, thus requiring expert systems to actively engage in trust-earning activities and to adopt preventative measures to decrease the possibility of mishaps that could weaken existing levels of trust.

Giddens's theoretical approach to risk helps illuminate the tainted blood scandal broadly as a failure in the operation of the mechanisms of late modernity and, more specifically, as the consequence of localized failures in the expert systems that were mandated to manage risk to the blood system. Within blood systems, experts are faced with the particular challenge of protecting the blood supply from the threats of pathogens for which they have limited or non-existent knowledge about their nature, origins, and course. In the case of the tainted blood scandal, the failure to anticipate the threat posed by HIV/AIDS had immediate and tragic consequences for those transfused with contaminated blood and weakened the trust members of the public had placed in their blood systems and in the authorities overseeing their operations. This point was underscored by Justice Krever (1997) when he singled out the lack of foresight on the part of Red Cross officials in dealing with the AIDS transfusion crisis, which he attributed in large measure to the "rejection, or at least the non-acceptance, of an important tenet in the philosophy of public health: action to reduce risk should not await scientific certainty" (p. 989). As Roussel (2003) suggests, the public outcry and scrutiny associated with the tainted blood scandal have made it necessary for blood experts to look for more thorough and efficient ways of anticipating and responding to emergent risks in order to retain their legitimacy and, ultimately, rebuild public trust.

One way more efficient risk management can be achieved is through the use of the **precautionary principle**. In the field of public health, the precautionary principle relies on a strategy of "preventative anticipation" whereby risk control measures are taken in advance of scientific proof if further delays are judged to have the potential to cause serious and irreversible damage to individuals and society (Srinivas, 2007). In calling for the creation of a new agency to manage the blood supply, Krever (1997, p. 1049) recommended that the principle of safety should transcend all other principles and policies, and requested the use of the precautionary principle as a first line of defense against possible threats to the blood supply. The precautionary principle now underlies many of the regulatory activities of the CBS and the federal agencies that oversee blood safety. These activities involve several federal agencies beginning with the Centre for Infectious Disease Prevention and Control, which monitors international reports on potentially dangerous pathogens and the populations in which such pathogens are evident. This information is then sent to the Expert Advisory Committee on Blood Regulation, which provides the **Biologics and Genetic Therapies Directorate** with scientific, medical, ethical, and communications advice related to blood, blood components, and blood products. The Directorate then makes recommendations that are issued as policy directives by Health Canada. Those policies in turn guide CBS and HQ in taking the necessary course of action to protect the blood supply – typically by deferring individuals with patterns of activity or behaviour that are identified as posing a threat of contamination. For example, in 1999, Health Canada recommended the deferral of individuals who had spent six months in the United Kingdom (U.K.) between 1980 and 1996 from donating blood or plasma as a preventative measure to avoid potential contamination of the blood supply by a newly discovered form of Creutzfeldt-Jakob disease (CJD), a fatal degenerative brain disease. This new form of the disease, simply called variant Creutzfeldt-Jakob Disease (vCJD), is thought to be transmitted by consuming the nervous tissue of bovines infected with bovine spongiform encephalopathy or mad cow disease (Wilson et al., 2001, p. 61). This directive was later altered to reduce the length of travel time to three months (Health Canada, 2001). Both CBS and HQ followed this directive, although they differed on the length of traveling time allowable before a donor would be deferred – CBS deferred people who had spent a cumulative total of three months or more in the U.K. between January 1980, and December 31, 1996, whereas HQ relied on an exclusion criterion of one month (CBS, 2007b). This policy was expanded in 2002 to include individuals who traveled to France and expanded again in 2005 to include individuals who received a blood transfusion or medical treatment with a product made from blood in the U.K., France, or Western Europe since 1980 (CBS, 2007b).

Heeding Justice Krever's recommendation, CBS also implemented several mechanisms of public accountability to restore public confidence in the safety of the Canadian blood system. One mechanism involved giving public stakeholders a voice within CBS by establishing a National Liaison Committee as well as seven regional liaison committees across the country, made up of members of the public, stakeholders, and the medical community. Further public involvement was entrenched in the composition of the CBS Board of Directors, which comprises a Board Chair, consumer interest representatives, regional interest representatives, and representatives from the medical, technical, scientific, public health, and business communities (CBS, 2005, p. 73). A final mechanism was to make the CEO of the CBS the focal point of accountability by having this position report directly to the Board of Directors.

THE MORAL CONSEQUENCES OF REGULATING BLOOD DONATION

While Giddens has contributed fresh insights about the place of risk in contemporary society, there is a notable lack of attention paid to the link between risk and its moral dimensions. This link can be more thoroughly explored by using a Foucauldian perspective on governmentality. Foucault (1991) understood governmentality as an activity which attempts not only to guide the conduct of people but also to constitute them in such ways that they can be more easily governed. For Foucault (1993), "governing people is not a way to force people to do what the governor wants; it is always a versatile equilibrium, with complementarity and conflicts between techniques which assure coercion and processes through which the self is constructed or modified by himself" (p. 204). This concept provides a framework for understanding the practices of power through the instruments, procedures, and techniques of government. According to Foucault, governmentality marks a shift from "totalizing deterministic or oppressive forms of power" to a "micro-physics of power" in which techniques of power are diffused among individuals by way of social and economic institutions (Gordon, 1991, p. 3). For Foucault (1991), "it is the population itself on which government will act, either directly through large-scale campaigns, or indirectly through techniques that will make possible, without the full awareness of the people, the direction of the population" (p. 100).

While Foucault did not deal specifically with risk, several authors have used his work on governmentality to analyze the ways in which certain discourses, strategies, and practices serve to construct risk as an object of regulation (e.g., Lupton, 1999; Hunt, 2003; Castel, 1991). In particular, Lupton (1999) sees the Foucauldian perspective as useful for examining the relationship between risk and the technologies of normalization that provide "the guidelines and advice by which populations are surveyed, compared against norms, trained to conform with these norms and rendered productive" (p. 87). Risk designations allow regulatory organizations to manage risk using population control techniques. Thus, individuals posing a threat no longer need to be observed engaging in risk behaviour and instead can be detected with screening criteria that define the boundary between normality and deviance.

An example of this phenomenon is the use of deferral criteria to identify and exclude individuals posing a contamination risk to the blood supply. Although the exclusion of certain populations from donating has always occurred, the tainted blood scandal resulted in the inclusion of the notion of precaution, or theoretical risk, in risk management policy. This allowed for the deferral of specific populations on the basis of known as well as anticipated threats to the blood supply. While effective as a safety measure, the use of deferral criteria poses several challenges for blood systems. First, every new deferral criterion that is implemented results in a reduction of the donor base which, if significant, needs to be compensated with the aggressive recruitment of new donors to avoid possible shortages of blood. Another issue pertains to the potential psychological impact of the deferral process, particularly when newly introduced criteria result in the deferral of long term donors who derive a sense of self-worth from their altruistic actions. Finally, deferral criteria excluding donors on the basis of specific sexual practices or on the basis of particular geographical origins could be construed as discriminatory.

Another moral dimension of risk management pertains to the use of non-remunerated volunteer donations from "altruistic" donors. British sociologist Richard Titmuss (1971) examined the value of altruistic donation as a safety measure in his cross-institutional comparison of American and British blood systems. He found the British blood system, which collected blood from unpaid donors, to be more efficient and safer in comparison to the American system, which relied on both remunerated and non-remunerated donations. Titmuss claimed that donations from paid blood donors were more likely to be contaminated due to higher rates of alcoholism and drug addiction in the populations that relied on blood donation as a source of income. He also viewed voluntary blood donation as a unique social gift because the goodness of the gift largely depended on the honesty of the giver. By virtue of being selflessly motivated, volunteer donors would readily withdraw from the blood system when becoming aware that their donation posed a risk to the blood supply. According to Healy (1999), Titmuss's study was instrumental in moving the United

States toward adopting a voluntary donation system and, as a result, there has been essentially no commercial collection of whole blood in that country since 1974. In Canada, there has been a voluntary blood donation system since 1947, and Justice Krever further reaffirmed the value of this approach as one of several safety measures to protect the blood supply. Specifically, he stipulated that "donors of blood and plasma should not be paid for their donation, except in rare circumstances" because "well-informed, altruistic donors will not donate if there is the possibility that their donations will do harm rather than good" (Krever, 1997, p. 1047). However, according to Valentine (2005), the implicit relationship between voluntary donation and altruism has profound moral implications. She argues that voluntary donation systems introduce "a strictly defined and finite civil sphere which promises an identity of altruism and belonging to those who participate" (Krever, 1997, p. 116). Voluntary systems, thus, re-inscribe the boundaries of what constitutes civic belonging and introduce "a corollary of the bad or non-citizen, the donor who is not altruistic and who endangers the public sphere through inappropriate occupation of it" (Krever, 1997, p. 126). These systems create two categories of donors, altruistic ones with safe blood and paid donors whose blood is more likely to pose a threat to the blood supply. Yet, as Healy (1999) points out, it is still possible for altruistic donors to contaminate the blood supply if they harbour pathogens that have yet to be detected or if they have a poorly characterized risk profile as happened in the case of the HIV contamination crisis. Furthermore, a limited use of paid donors does not necessarily pose a tangible threat to the blood supply. As the Bayer Advisory Council on Bioethics (2000, p. 19) points out, Canada de facto uses a mixed (and safe) voluntary and commercial system by virtue of having to import American blood-derived plasma products manufactured from the donations of paid American plasma donors to address endemic shortages at home.

CONCLUSION

Giddens (1999) viewed modern society as being characterized by a growing exposure of its citizens to risk manufactured and mitigated by human activity. Arguably, the tainted blood scandal is a manufactured risk of modernity. While HIV and HCV entered the blood supply as the result of donations by unsuspecting donors, their devastating impact is partly the consequence of human and institutional negligence.

For Giddens, modern society is predominantly organized around the need to efficiently manage risk. The creation of an elaborate regulatory apparatus, a reliance on the precautionary principle and the extensive use of deferrals criteria provides evidence of this process within Canadian society. These measures have been remarkably effective in making blood safe. Indeed, the risk of contamination from a blood transfusion is now minuscule. According to Chiavetta et al. (2003) in 2000, "Canadian Blood Services collected 790,460 whole-blood and apheresis donations. Of these, only three were identified as positive for HIV. Among the first-time donations, HIV-positive rates of donation decreased significantly, from 9.6 per 100,000 in 1990 to 1.0 per 100,000 in 2000" (p. 769).

However, controlling one type of risk can sometime engender new risk management challenges. In this case of blood donation, stringent deferral criteria are excluding an increasingly larger segment of the population from donating. The inconvenience of submitting oneself to screening procedures could also discourage many from donating.

Could these safety measures thus pose a new risk to the blood supply – one of shortage? As CBS (2006b) warns in one of its numerous donation appeals, the demand for blood is outpacing the increase in the number of people who donate and shortages are looming in the near future unless the percentage of Canadians who regularly give blood significantly increases. Perhaps risk management experts in the Canadian blood system will be confronted at some point with an unenviable dilemma – the safer they continue to make the blood supply, the higher the risk will be of a scarcity of "safe" transfusable blood.

ACKNOWLEDGEMENTS

The writing of this chapter was supported by a Social Sciences Research Council of Canada Doctoral Fellowship and a Canadian Blood Services Graduate Fellowship for Jay Fiddler. The authors wish to acknowledge Dr. Ralph Matthews for his support and valuable insights on risk and society.

STUDY QUESTIONS

1. *What role does the precautionary principle play in the current Canadian blood system?*
2. *According to the Krever Inquiry, what factors accounted for the failure of the Canadian Red Cross to respond promptly to the threat to the blood supply posed by HIV?*
3. *What have been the moral consequences of strengthening the regulations that govern the safety of the Canadian blood supply?*
4. *In what way is blood donation a manufactured risk of modernity?*

GLOSSARY

Biologics and Genetic Therapies Directorate a Canadian federal authority that regulates biological drugs and health products, including blood and blood products, viral and bacterial vaccines, gene therapy products, tissues, organs, and xenografts, which are manufactured in Canada or elsewhere.

blood donation a medical procedure by which a donor voluntarily gives blood, typically at a local blood collection centre for processing, storage, and subsequent use in a blood transfusion. In Canada, blood donations are collected by Canadian Blood Services. Blood is made up mostly of plasma, red blood cells, white blood cells, and platelets, and is usually separated into these components after being donated to make the most use of it.

blood transfusion a medical procedure involving the transfer of blood or blood products into the circulatory system of a recipient to treat a medical condition, such as massive blood loss due to trauma or surgery, the aftermath of cancer treatment, and life-threatening disorders like hemophilia, sickle cell disease, and thalassemia.

Canadian Blood Services in 1998, two new organizations, Canadian Blood Services and Héma-Québec, assumed the responsibility of managing the collection and distribution of blood and blood products from the Red Cross. While these organizations differ on some of their policies and procedures, they are both regulated by Health Canada and must meet the same national regulatory standards.

Héma-Québec see definition for Canadian Blood Services.

Hepatitis C Hepatitis C is a blood-borne disease that is spread by blood-to-blood contact with an infected person's blood and which can cause liver inflammation, cirrhosis, and liver cancer. The estimates of people infected by transfusion-associated Hepatitis C range from 60,000 to as high as 160,000 individuals.

Human Immunodeficiency Virus commonly known as HIV, this retrovirus primarily attacks the human immune system and affects vital organs such as the kidneys, heart, and brain. HIV is transmitted through direct contact of a mucous membrane with a bodily fluid containing the virus. In a recent report, the Joint United Nations Programme on HIV and AIDS estimated that 40 million people were currently living with HIV worldwide, and that more than 28 million people have already died from the disease. Approximately 2,000 Canadians became infected with HIV as a result of receiving a tainted transfusion.

Krever Inquiry established by the Canadian Government in October 1993, the Royal Commission of Inquiry on the Blood System in Canada (commonly known as the Krever Inquiry) investigated the circumstances that surrounded the contamination of the Canadian blood supply by the HIV and Hepatitis C viruses. Headed by Justice Krever, the Inquiry tabled a report on November 26, 1997 that recommended the creation of a new blood agency (Canadian Blood Services) that would operate at arm's-length from the federal government.

precautionary principle the precautionary principle rests on the idea that it is better to avoid actions that are anticipated to have significantly negative consequences, even when the exact nature of those consequences cannot be predicted. In the field of public health, the precautionary principle is applied on the basis of preventative anticipation whereby measures may be taken in advance of scientific proof of evidence if further delays are judged to be potentially costly to society and individuals. The precautionary principle serves as an important first line of defense against threats to the safety of the blood supply and guides much of the regulatory activities of Canadian Blood Services, Héma-Québec, and the federal agencies that oversee the safety of the blood system.

risk society this type of society is the product of modernization and is organized in response to risks that are the product of human activity (manufactured risk). It is also characterized by a preoccupation with safety and the hazards and uncertainties associated with the management of risk.

REFERENCES

Bayer Advisory Council on Bioethics. (2000). Plasma product supply in Canada: A bioethical analysis. Ottawa: ON. Retrieved September 14, 2007, from http://www.bayer-bioethics.org/documents/Patient_Notification.pdf.

Bloodbook.com (2007). *Welcome to Bloodbook.com: Information for life.* Retrieved September 14, 2007, from http://www.bloodbook.com/.

Canadian Blood Services. (2006a). One day: Everyday. *A report to Canadians 2005/2006.* Ottawa, Ontario: Canadian Blood Services.

Canadian Blood Services. (2006). *Join other caring community partners in the CBS Life Link Program.* Retrieved April 14, 2006, from http://www.bloodservices.ca/centreapps/internet/uw_v502_mainengine.nsf/9749ca80b75a038585256aa20060d703/27cded70d5acf1fc85256c690049b699?OpenDocument.

Canadian Blood Services (2007a). Who needs blood? Retrieved September 14, 2007, from http://www.bloodservices.ca/centreapps/internet/uw_v502_mainengine.nsf/9749ca80b75a038585256aa20060d703/9ea67b6ef00db3e785256d8d005fd2f3?OpenDocument.

Canadian Blood Services (2007b). Deferral Policies for vCJD. Retrieved September 14, 2007, from http://www.bloodservices.ca/centreapps/internet/uw_v502_mainengine.nsf/web/4F7E837A2D7C079685256AB100501F20?OpenDocument.

Canadian Broadcasting Corporation – News online (2005, May 23). *Tainted blood scandal*. Retrieved April 19, 2006, from http://www.cbc.ca/news/background/taintedblood/.

Canadian Broadcasting Corporation. (2006, February 21). *Tainted-blood trial will go ahead: Crown*. Retrieved September 16, 2007, from http://www.cbc.ca/canada/story/2006/02/21/tainted-blood060221.html.

Castel, R. (1991). From dangerousness to risk. In G. Burchell, C. Gordon, and P. Miller (Eds.), *The Foucault effect: Studies in governmentality* (pp. 281–298). Chicago: University of Chicago Press.

Chiavetta, J.A., Escobar, M., et al. (2003). Incidence and estimated rates of residual risk for HIV, hepatitis C, hepatitis B and human T-cell lymphotropic viruses in blood donors in Canada, 1990–2000. *Canadian Medical Association Journal, 169*(8), 767–773.

DeMont, J., & Corelli, R. (1997, December 8). A harsh rebuke: The Krever report dissects the tainted blood scandal. *Maclean's, 110*, 20–24.

Ericson, R.V., & Doyle, A. (2003). *Risk and morality*. Toronto: University of Toronto Press.

Foucault, M. (1988). Technologies of the self. In L.H. Martin, H. Gutman, & P.H. Hutton (Eds.), *Technologies of the self: A seminar with Michel Foucault* (pp. 16–49). Amherst, MA: University of Massachusetts Press.

Foucault, M. (1991). Governmentality. In G. Burchell, C. Gordon, and P. Miller (Eds.), *The Foucault effect: Studies in governmentality* (pp. 87–104). Chicago: University of Chicago Press.

Foucault, M. (1993). About the beginnings of the hermeneutics of the self: Two lectures at Dartmouth. *Political Theory, 21*(May), 198–227.

Giddens, A. (1990). *The consequences of modernity*. Cambridge, UK: Polity Press.

Giddens, A. (1991). *Modernity and self-identity: Self and society in the late modern age*. Cambridge, UK: Polity Press.

Giddens, A. (1999). Risk and Responsibility. *The Modern Law Review, 62*(1), 1–10.

Gordon, C. (1991). Governmental rationality: An introduction. In G. Burchell, C. Gordon, and P. Miller (Eds.), *The Foucault effect: Studies in governmentality* (pp. 1–51). Chicago: University of Chicago Press.

Health Canada. (2001). Donor exclusion to address theoretical risk of transmission of variant Creutzfeldt-Jakob Disease (vCJD) through the blood supply. United Kingdom, France, and Western Europe. Ottawa: Canadian Government Publishing.

Healy, K. (1999). The emergence of HIV in the U.S. blood supply: Organizations, obligations and the management of uncertainty. *Theory and Society, 28*, 529–558.

Héma-Québec. (2006). *Annual report: 2005–2006*. Québec, Q.C.: Héma-Québec.

Hunt, A. (1991). Risk and moralization in everyday life. In R.V. Ericson & A. Doyle (Eds.), *Risk and morality* (pp. 117–144). Toronto: University of Toronto Press.

Joint United Nations Programme on HIV and AIDS. (2005). *UNAIDS 2004: Report on the global AIDS epidemic*. Geneva, Switzerland.

Krever, H. (1997). *Commission of inquiry on the blood system in Canada. Volumes 1, 2 & 3*. Ottawa: Canadian Government Publishing.

Lupton, D. (1999). *Risk*. London: Routledge Press.

Orsini, M. (2002). The politics of naming, blaming and claiming: HIV, hepatitis C and the emergence of blood activism in Canada. *Canadian Journal of Political Science, 35*(3), 475–498.

Parsons, V. (1995). *Bad blood: The tragedy of the Canadian tainted blood scandal.* Toronto: Lester Publishing.

Picard, A. (1998). *The gift of death: Confronting Canada's tainted blood tragedy.* Toronto: Harper Perennial.

Roussel, V. (2003). New moralities of risk and political responsibility. In R.V. Ericson & A. Doyle (Eds.), *Risk and morality* (pp. 117–144). Toronto: University of Toronto Press.

Srinivas, H. (2007). *Six basic concepts of precautionary principles.* Retrieved September 18, 2007, from http://www.gdrc.org/u-gov/precaution-6.html.

Titmuss, R. (1972). *The gift relationship: From human blood to social policy.* New York: Vintage Books.

United States Congress House Committee on Government Reform and Oversight. Subcommittee on Human Resources and Intergovernmental Relations. (1996). *Protecting the nation's blood supply from infectious agents: New standards to meet new threats: Hearings before the Subcommittee on Human Resources and Intergovernmental Relations of the Committee on Government Reform and Oversight, House of Representatives, One Hundred Fourth Congress, first session, October 12, and November 2, 1995.* (SuDoc number: Y 1.1/8:104–746). Washington, DC: U.S. Government Printing Office.

Valentine, K. (2005). Citizenship, identity, blood donation. *Body & Society, 11*(2), 113–128.

Weinberg, P.D., Hounshell, J., Sherman, L.A., Godwin, J., Ali, S., Tomori, C., & Bennett, C.L. (2002). Legal, financial, and public health consequences of HIV contamination of blood and blood products in the 1980s and 1990s. *Annals of Internal Medicine, 136*(4), 312–319.

Wilson, K., Hébert, P.C., Laupacis, A., Dornan, C., Ricketts, M., Ahmad, N., & Graham, I. (2001). A policy analysis of major decisions relating to Creutzfeldt-Jakob and the blood supply. *Canadian Medical Association Journal, 165*(1), 59–65.

25

PERSONAL AND STRUCTURAL DETERMINANTS OF HEALTH AND ILLNESS: LIFESTYLES AND LIFE CHANCES

B. SINGH BOLARIA University of Saskatchewan, University of Victoria

ROSEMARY BOLARIA Researcher and Medical Writer

INTRODUCTION

Lifestyles, healthy living, and health promotion have emerged as important areas of investigation in medical sociology. One of the issues that continues to receive considerable attention in the epidemiological, population health, and health promotion literature is the relative importance of the individual and structural determinants of health and illness. In this debate, a distinction is often made between societal factors that are beyond one's control and influence health, and individual behavioural factors, over which one presumably has control and for which one can make healthy choices. In the former approach, the focus is on the social-structural conditions, including economic and social inequality, that influence health status.

The latter approach focuses on overall aggregate patterns of health behaviour and health practices which constitute lifestyles, such as smoking, alcohol consumption, exercise, and diet. It is assumed that lifestyles are matters of individual choice, and that these choices have either positive or negative health consequences. Within this framework, the responsibility for staying healthy is shifted to individuals. It is argued that since the major risk factors for ill health are at the personal discretion of individuals, there would be a considerable reduction in mortality if individuals focused on changing aspects of their lifestyles that are injurious to their health. On the other hand, the studies from a historical, materialistic, epidemiological perspective argue that the solution lies in changing the social, economic, and environmental conditions that produce illness and mortality.

This debate points to the significance of both individual and structural determinants in the health status of a population. It also points to the need to further investigate consumer behaviour and lifestyle choices individuals make within the limits and constraints imposed upon them by the social and cultural environment and their material conditions, that is, their **life chances**. At a broader level, this constitutes the study of the relative importance of the role of structure (chances) and agency (choices) in shaping social behaviour in the structure-agency debate in the sociological literature. Structuralists give primacy to institutional factors, which both enable and constrain individuals to act, whereas agency refers to the ability of individuals to act and to choose their behaviours regardless of structural constraints (Cockerham, 2000).

Specific studies of health lifestyles and health behaviour would make significant contributions to the structure-agency debate. In addition, the sociological perspective broadens the scope of inquiry beyond individual psychology, to include the social, cultural, and normative context of people's lives and circumstances which influence lifestyles and social behaviour. A consideration of the social and material conditions, the circumstances of individuals' daily existence, and their coping responses to circumstances and societal forces beyond their control, is likely to provide a more complete picture of the persistence of certain behaviour patterns which have negative health consequences (Cockerham, 2000). The sociological perspective allows us to take into account social-structural factors in the discussion of lifestyles.

This chapter begins with a discussion of the reductionist orientation in medicine. It then considers conceptual and empirical issues and the relative importance of lifestyles and life chances in disease etiology and health. The chapter concludes with a discussion of the policy implications of individualist and structural perspectives concerning health promotion.

BACKGROUND TO REDUCTIONISM IN MEDICINE

To fully appreciate the current debate on personal and structural determinants of health, it is important to briefly consider the individualistic, biomedical, and reductionist orientations in medicine (Bolaria, 2002b, 1994). The clinical paradigm, widely accepted in medical practice, defines health and illness in individual terms, independent of the social context in which they occur. This paradigm decontextualizes medical problems; individuals are "atomized" and decontextualized for treatment. This individual-centred concept of disease has led to an essentially curative orientation, whereby people can be made healthy by means of "technological fixes." Many diseases are viewed as malfunctions – technical defects in body machinery – and treatments are oriented toward restoring the "normal" functioning of the human body. The response to psychological disorders is often pharmacological, including the use of antidepressants, stimulants, and tranquilizers (for review, see Bolaria, 2002b). Although the clinical paradigm has received critical scrutiny, individualized etiology and treatment have a pervasive and continuing influence in medical practice (see, in particular, Waitzkin, 1983; Navarro, 1986). This orientation is also reflected in medical research. There has been a heavy emphasis on an individualized etiology of disease, rather than on social and environmental factors, such as occupational and environmental exposure to pollutants, chemicals, and other harmful agents (Waitzkin, 1983; Navarro, 1986; Firth, Brophy & Keith, 1997).

This mechanistic-individualistic conception of disease, which engenders a disease-centred, high-technology orientation in medical practice and research, also largely absolves the economic and political systems of responsibility for disease, and denies the social foundations and **social causation** of disease. A similar reductionist approach has emerged that emphasizes individual lifestyle. In Canada in 1974, the publication of a federal policy paper gave prominent attention to health risks associated with individual lifestyles and consumption patterns (Lalonde, 1974). Lifestyle was also one of the foci of another official policy paper (Epp, 1986). Whereas the clinical model attributes disease to the malfunctioning of the human body, this reductionism introduced the idea that the causes of disease lie in individual lifestyles and behaviours. In the former case, the normal functions of the human body can be restored through "technological and chemical fixes," while in the latter, the solution lies primarily in changing individual behaviours and patterns of consumption. This approach, too, obscures the social nature of disease and fails to recognize the important relationships between social and material conditions, and health and sickness. Both the biomedical-clinical paradigm and the individual lifestyle approach share a common orientation in disease etiology. With a focus on individuals, they tend to neglect the social context of individuals' lives and the social and material conditions that produce sickness and disease. **Social epidemiology** and the environmental approach to health are in conflict with the biological and individual orientation of the predominant paradigm.

LIFESTYLES AND LIFE CHANCES

In recent years, the study of lifestyles and the interplay between social-structural conditions, lifestyles, and health behaviour has received considerable attention (Abel, 1991; Chaney, 1996; Bunton, Nettleton & Burrows, 1995; Cockerham, 2000; Townsend, 1990). The growing body of literature addresses a wide range of theoretical and empirical questions, as well as public health policy and health promotion issues.

An early discussion of lifestyles is found in Max Weber's work on social stratification, particularly in the distinction Weber makes between class and status (Weber, 1978; Garth & Mills, 1958). Class stratification, according to Weber, represents economic inequality, whereas status groups are distinguished by their specific lifestyle or style of life, which is manifested in their distinct consumption patterns. Status groups share similar lifestyles. As Weber (1978, p. 933) states: "One might thus say that classes are stratified according to their relations to the production and acquisition of goods; whereas status groups are stratified according to the principles of their consumption of goods as represented by special styles of life." Weber also recognized the importance of life chances in realizing specific lifestyles. Lifestyle choices, however, are not made in a vacuum; rather, these choices are influenced by life chances, which set the social parameters within which choices are realized. Life chances are structured by one's social situation. In short, lifestyle choices are constrained by life chances (Frohlich & Potvin, 1999; Cockerham, 2000). Yet, the social context of lifestyles and the social-structural constraints within which lifestyle choices are made have often been ignored in epidemiological and health promotion literature.

The term "lifestyle" is used to refer to certain individual behaviours such as smoking, drinking, and drug abuse, which are considered sources of illness (Frohlich & Potvin, 1999). In this context, health problems and health outcomes are linked to personal choices, lifestyles, and behaviours that are presumably within individual discretion and control. Therefore, individual effort and responsibility are required to achieve and maintain health; conversely, individuals are blamed for their ill health and sickness. Thus, to be healthy, one has to "work at it"; otherwise, one faces a risk of disease and premature death (Cockerham, 2000). This focus on individual responsibility for health and self-care is attributed to a number of factors, including the public recognition of the limitations of modern medicine in curing chronic diseases, state policies that emphasize personal responsibility for health, mass media attention, and educational campaigns by health professionals (Cockerham, 1998, 2000; Segall & Chappell, 2000).

Despite the current popularity of lifestyles in epidemiological studies and health promotion, this emphasis has received considerable criticism on conceptual, empirical, and ideological grounds. The term "lifestyle" is used rather loosely (Abel, 1991), and it is often not clear whether it refers to discrete individual health practices or an aggregate of a number of discrete behaviours.

The tendency to treat lifestyles and health behaviour as matters of individual choice has received considerable criticism. Furthermore, the focus on individual lifestyles and self-imposed risks tends to downgrade the importance of social, economic, and environmental factors in the production of illness. Social-structural conditions in society can both enable and constrain individual lifestyle choices. In other words, lifestyles and life choices are influenced by life chances (Frohlich & Potvin, 1999; Cockerham, 1998, 2000). Cockerham states: "Health lifestyles are collective patterns of health-related behavior based on choices from options available to people according to their life chances. A person's life chances are determined by their socioeconomic status, age, gender, race, ethnicity, and other factors that impact on lifestyle choices" (1998, p. 85). Personal health practices and lifestyles are closely linked to social and economic life circumstances, and "lifestyle and health behaviours vary with one's position in a social hierarchy" (Frankish, Milligan & Reid, 1998, p. 288).

Studies show that those with higher socio-economic status, particularly as reflected in educational level, have better health habits and lifestyles than those with lower socio-economic status. For instance, those with higher educational achievement are more likely to engage in positive health behaviours such as exercising, moderate drinking, not smoking, avoiding obesity, and they are more likely to have preventive health checkups. Education enables people to have healthy lifestyles. High educational achievement is key to gaining rewarding jobs with considerable control and autonomy over work and better income, and hence to gaining a better position in the social hierarchy. These factors increase individuals' sense of control over their lives and provide motivation to live a healthy lifestyle (Mirowsky, Ross & Reynolds, 2000). Based upon their review of extensive research, Mirowsky, Ross, and Reynolds draw the following conclusions:

> First, higher social status protects and improves health. Second, the primary aspects of social status that improve health include education, employment, autonomous and fulfilling work, and the absence of economic hardship. Third, those aspects of social status improve health by developing and reinforcing a sense of mastery and control and by encouraging and enabling a healthy lifestyle. (2000, p. 56)

That individual lifestyles are constrained by specific life solutions and social and material conditions is commonly recognized. The World Health Organization (WHO) conceptualizes lifestyle "as a way of life, a socio-cultural phenomenon arising from interactions between patterns of behaviour and specific life situations rather than individual decisions to avoid or accept certain health risks" (Dean, 1989, p. 137). Abel (1991, p. 901) defines health lifestyles as "patterns of health related behaviour, values, and attitudes adapted by groups of individuals in response to their social, cultural and economic environments." In short, individual choices are made in the context of specific life situations. Lifestyles are not simply matters of freedom of choice and individual decisions to choose between healthy and unhealthy practices, but are made in the specific context within which people live.

More importantly, as Berliner (1977, p. 119) has stated, "focusing on lifestyle serves only to reify the lifestyle as an entity apart from the social conditions from which it arises"; and "discussing changes in lifestyles without first discussing the changes in social conditions which give rise to them, without recognizing that lifestyle is derivative, is misleading and, in effect, is victim blaming." Health status and health outcomes are not just a matter of individual lifestyle and health behaviour but are also closely linked to one's socio-economic status and other social, economic, and environmental conditions (Frankish, Milligan & Reid, 1998). In other words, there is a need to consider both the personal and the structural determinants of health and the combined impact of life circumstances and life choices (Segall & Chappell, 2000, pp. 82–86, 154; Gunning-Scheppers & Hagen, 1987; Blaxter, 1990; Frankish, Milligan & Reid, 1998).

In summary, lifestyles are shaped by life chances. Yet, the material and social context, which both enables and constrains chosen lifestyles, is often ignored. The focus on individuals and their choices and lifestyles also obscures the social and material production of health and illness. The empirical reality is that socio-economic inequalities produce social variability in health status. Social determinants are the primary determinants of health status differences amongst Canadians.

SOCIAL-STRUCTURAL DETERMINANTS OF HEALTH

There is extensive and pervasive evidence that social-structural factors such as income, education, food security, employment and work, and housing produce differences in health status for Canadians. Lifestyle and behavioural factors play a minor role in health status outcomes (Raphael, 2004a, b; Raphael, Bryand & Rioux, 2006; Marmot & Wilkinson, 2006). In Canada and elsewhere, socio-economic status remains the most important link to health status. People who are advantaged in socio-economic status are also advantaged in health status (Raphael, 2002; Auger et al., 2004; Phipps, 2003; Krieger & Fee, 1993, 1994; Link & Phelan, 2000; Mirowsky, Ross & Reynolds, 2000; Ross & Roberts, 1999; see also Bolaria & Bolaria, 1994a, b). The evidence of association between social class and longevity was provided several years ago by Antonovsky (1992, p. 28): "The inescapable conclusion is that class influences one's chances of staying alive." Based upon a review of numerous international studies, Wilkinson (1996, p. 3) concluded that "in the developed world, it is not the richest countries which have the best health but the most egalitarian." Cockerham (1998, p. 53) concludes: "The fact remains that people at the bottom of the society have the worst health of all, regardless of what country they live in, what type of insurance they have, and the level of health care they receive." The relationship between social class and health is attributed to the differential exposure to physical and social environments by members of different socio-economic levels. Social inequality leads not only to differential exposure to health risks but also to unequal access to the social, economic, and other resources needed to deal with these risks. In short, **structured inequality** produces **inequality of conditions** and differential opportunity and life chances.

Other structural factors such as living and working conditions "are the most powerful factors affecting health" (Millar & Hull, 1997, p. 148). Research in Canada on health status indicates the persistence of social variability in health status and that social factors are "the most important determinants of health status" (Coburn & Eakin, 1993, p. 86). Denton and Walters (1999, p. 1229) also conclude that "these analyses suggest that the structural determinants of health play a greater role than the behavioural or lifestyle determinants in shaping the health status of Canadians." The Whitehall studies provide strong evidence of the association of health status and mortality within the social hierarchy of British civil servants (Marmot et al., 1978, 1984, 1991): each group of civil servants had worse health than the group above it in the hierarchy. What is also significant is that only a small portion of differences in coronary heart disease (CHD) mortality could be explained by personal health habits and lifestyles such as cigarette smoking, physical activity, and blood pressure. Social hierarchy in the civil service appears to be an important gradient in differences in mortality amongst various grades.

Epidemiological data clearly demonstrates the differential health status of the population by socio-economic status (Federal, Provincial and Territorial Advisory Committee on Population Health, 1999a, b). The health gap between the rich and the poor continues to exist in Canada, where the principle of universality was a major impetus to the introduction of medicare in the 1960s. Upper-income Canadians live longer, healthier, and more disability-free lives on average than do poor Canadians. This gap in health status is primarily due to the "debilitating conditions of life that poverty forces upon people" (National Council of Welfare, 1990, p. 6). Poor social and material conditions, such as poor housing, poor nutrition, poor neighbourhoods, and poor environment, contribute to high mortality in the low-income population (Bolaria, 2002a; Bolaria & Bolaria, 2002). The high mortality, high disability, and low health status of Aboriginal people is associated with their poor environmental, economic, social, and living conditions (Shah, 2004). In short, social determinants remain the most important factors determining the health status of individuals and populations.

TARGET INDIVIDUALS OR CONDITIONS

The level of analysis is crucial in any discussion of population health-promotion policies. If health problems are blamed on individuals and their lifestyles, then policies and programs need to target individuals and their harmful lifestyle behaviours. But if health problems are considered to be the product of social and material inequalities and conditions embodied in group-level characteristics, then the policies to improve population health need to target those inequalities and conditions (Taylor, 1989; Eakin et al., 1996; Matcha, 2000, p. 127). Individual-level solutions seem to be easier to implement than are social structural changes. Eakin and colleagues (1996, p. 161) comment: "Health related problems that are believed to reside in the individual are seen to be easier to address than those residing in such intangible and unyielding places as the environment, social interaction, economic systems, and social class." Within the individualistic framework, group-level characteristics (e.g., social class, race, and gender) related to health are "collapsed into handy individual risk factors that can be remedied by changing personal habits" (Conrad, 1987, p. 265).

Health promotion policies cannot be divorced from social and ideological contexts. Health promotion approaches and perspectives are embedded in prevailing ideologies, policies, and practices (Bryant, 2006; Raphael, 2003). The state is intimately involved in the health promotion movement. The individual-centred approach – individual etiology and individual solutions – has received considerable support and promotion in many Western countries (for review, see Bolaria, 1994).

In times of economic constraint, when the situation becomes even more critical and the health care crisis deepens, government programs promoting this type of individual emphasis gain dominance over others. An attempt is made "to shift the responsibility for disease back onto the worker, in this case through **victim-blaming epidemiology** and of individual solutions for the workers" (Berliner, 1977, p. 119). As Doyal and Pennell (1979, p. 296) put it: "Thus it is said that individuals are to blame for their own health problems and it is up to them to adopt a healthier lifestyle. The Victorian notion of 'undeserving poor' is being replaced by the equally inappropriate notion of 'the undeserving sick.'" This has strong implications for health care policy.

Health promotion strategies and educational campaigns are primarily oriented toward changing individuals and their lifestyles. These strategies continue to focus on lifestyle behavioural changes (Mechanic, 1999), and the emphasis remains at the individual level of lifestyles and behavioural changes. As McQueen (1989, p. 342) states:

> How else can one explain a public health rhetoric which argues that social conditions affect health outcomes and then, in turn, argues that the appropriate solution is to eat better, exercise more, drink less and give up smoking?

Relatively little attention is given to the transformation of the physical and social environment, of the health care system, or of public policy (McDowell, 1986). This response to crises in health care strengthens the **ideology of individualism**, emphasizes individual responsibility for one's social and economic position and health status, and masks the social production of inequality and social variability in health (Navarro, 1986). A focus on individuals displaces responsibility for health. For instance, a focus on workers' lifestyles diverts attention from unhealthy and unsafe work environments (Berliner, 1977). By promoting individual responsibility, this strategy distracts attention away from the illness-generating economic and social environment. A popularization of this strategy, in the long run, would be instrumental in preparing the public to accept further reductions in health services, "to tighten their medical care belts" (Berliner, 1977, p. 116). It is likely to have adverse effects.

Healthy lifestyles, "wise living," and self-care, although positive choices, cannot substitute for professional health services when they are required (Waitzkin, 1983). Self-care is considered by many a "conservative idea that could strengthen arguments for the dismantling of the welfare state" (Kickbusch, 1989, p. 125). With regard to Epp's health promotion policy paper, McDowell (1986, p. 448) states: "Self-care and the assistance of neighbours are laudable, but are made here to sound like a cheap alternative to professional health care....Epp is trying to reduce the demand for health services, rather than the need for them."

Therefore, the burden of health crises may be borne by individuals, to the extent that they are willing to accept the proposition that socially, economically, and politically caused conditions can be solved individually, either by medical intervention or by self-care and changes in lifestyle. This approach promotes a policy of "health education in prevention and clinical medicine in cure," rather than drawing attention to the organization of health care delivery systems or to the nature, function, and composition of the health sector, and the economic and political forces that influence the state of healthiness.

Health promotion policies have also been severely criticized when certain social groups are targeted. Analysis is extended from the individual to the collective way of life of a particular group; for instance, the health problems of minorities may be attributed to their cultural practices and beliefs rather than to their socio-economic position and the institutional racism to which they are subject (Douglas, 1995). Educative approaches are often based upon broad generalizations and stereotypes of cultural differences between mainstream and minority communities. Minority groups are often considered to have "special" health problems requiring "special" intervention. Well-intended, culturally sensitive approaches to health education and promotion only strengthen the cultural stereotypes, and in the process they often further marginalize these communities.

Another critique of health promotion comes from feminist groups that are critical of educative programs based upon gender stereotypes that view caring and nurturing as "natural" to women, and that target women as a homogeneous group (Daykin & Naidoo, 1995). Gender inequalities affect all women and constrain women's lives and opportunities. Women of colour and poor women are further disadvantaged. Such constraints and divisions need to be considered in health promotion; otherwise, "the current vogue for addressing women as consumers able to exercise personal choice over lifestyles and health care services is inappropriate, given the constraints on most women's lives" (Daykin & Naidoo, 1995, p. 69).

In some cases, health promotion policies penalize the most disadvantaged. For instance, poor women smokers are most affected by increases in tobacco and cigarette costs. Educational programs that target certain groups of women create negative self-images and self-blame. For instance, pregnant women, who are often the target of health education about smoking, drinking, and substance abuse, are made to feel guilty and responsible for their children's poor health outcomes (Burrows, Nettleton & Bunton, 1995; Daykin & Naidoo, 1995). This has the effect of contributing to their marginalization, moral condemnation, and social stigmatization (Conrad, 1994). Nettleton and Bunton (1995, pp. 51–52) further elaborate on this point:

> Whilst the discourse of health promotion emphasizes the merits of providing people with knowledge and information so that they can make healthy choices, the structural critique suggests that the notion of individual choice is a mythical one and draws attention to the fact that health promotion makes people feel responsible and culpable for their own health.

It is also pointed out that although the targets of health promotion are often disadvantaged groups, it is the structurally advantaged groups that benefit the most from lifestyle changes (Nettleton & Benton, 1995; Blaxter, 1990). Health promotion may further exacerbate the existing inequalities in health.

The focus on individuals and collectivities may also have the effect of extending medical surveillance, monitoring, and control to their bodies, lifestyles, and health behaviour, particularly for groups that are "problematized" (Conrad & Walsh, 1992; Nettleton & Bunton, 1995; O'Brien, 1995). The structural argument suggests that any attempt to prevent illness and promote health must consider the political economy that produces illness in the first place. Health promotion discourse that focuses on individuals fails to consider the social and material conditions of people's daily existence (Corin, 1994; McKinlay, 1993, 1994; Grace, 1991; Raphael & Bryant, 2000; Rutten, 1995). Resources that enhance participation in healthy lifestyles and promote a healthy existence are greater amongst the middle and upper classes (Cockerham, 1998; Blaxter, 1990). The argument advanced by structuralists is that the target of intervention should be the conditions that make people unhealthy and the societal conditions and forces that induce high-risk behaviours (Corin, 1994).

CONCLUSION

A growing body of literature on the determinants of health and illness addresses a wide range of theoretical and conceptual questions as well as public health policy and health promotion issues. Both the biomedical-clinical paradigm and the individual lifestyle approach share a common reductionist orientation, and they tend to ignore the social context of individuals' lives and the social and material conditions that produce health and illness. The literature on lifestyles and life chances indicates that lifestyles are shaped by life chances. Social and material conditions both enable and constrain chosen lifestyles. A focus on lifestyles and self-imposed risks ignores the social basis of lifestyles and health and illness. The empirical reality is that socio-economic inequalities produce social variability in health status.

The level of analysis also becomes crucial in public health policy. If the source of health problems is individual lifestyles, then programs and policies need to target individuals and their harmful lifestyles. On the other hand, if health problems are considered to be a product of social and material inequalities, then health promotion campaigns need to target the inequalities. Health promotion policies that primarily focus on changing individuals and their lifestyles are criticized on several grounds. A focus on individuals shifts the responsibility for health and illness onto them, and diverts attention from illness-generating conditions and a degraded environment. This also makes people feel responsible and guilty for their own health, producing negative self-images and self-blame.

A focus on individuals and collectivities often marginalizes and stigmatizes these individuals and groups. The primary structural argument suggests that the target of intervention must be the political economy that produces illness and induces high-risk behaviour in the first place.

Finally, a complete picture requires a consideration of both the personal and structural factors, and a further investigation into the social behaviours and lifestyle choices of individuals within the structured constraints of their lives. The sociological perspective broadens the scope of inquiry to include the social, cultural, and normative contexts of people's lives, contexts that shape lifestyles and social behaviours. It enables researchers to understand the persistence of certain behaviour patterns, even when such behaviour has negative health consequences. The knowledge gained from specific studies of lifestyles would make a significant contribution to the structure-agency debate in sociology.

STUDY QUESTIONS

1. *Discuss the ideological and health policy implications of a focus on individual lifestyles and self-imposed risks.*
2. *Discuss the limitations of the persistence of the biomedical clinical paradigm in the understanding of health and illness.*
3. *How do biomedical lifestyle approaches obfuscate the significance of social-structural factors in the understanding of morbidity and mortality?*
4. *Briefly discuss the relationship between socio-economic inequality and health status inequalities.*
5. *Discuss the evidence that people who are more socially advantaged also enjoy health advantages.*
6. *Discuss the statement that improving the health of vulnerable populations lies in altering the social-structural causes of inequalities in health and not in altering individual behaviour and lifestyles.*

GLOSSARY

ideology of individualism the idea that individual qualities such as hard work, motivation, initiative, and intelligence determine one's station in life.

inequality of conditions differences in access to, and the availability of, material and social resources.

life chances opportunities to acquire material goods, services, and desirable living conditions.

lifestyles the individual behaviours and consumption patterns associated with health and disease.

social causation the social-structural factors and social conditions that produce different mortality and morbidity patterns in society.

social epidemiology the social, economic, political, and cultural forces that shape patterns of disease and death in human populations.

structured inequality an arrangement of social position whereby one's location in the social structure has important bearings on one's opportunities in life, or life chances.

victim-blaming epidemiology a focus on individual health behaviours and lifestyles that places responsibility for illness on individuals and shifts the blame from a social causation of illness and disease to those who are ill and suffer.

REFERENCES

Abel, T. (1991). Measuring health lifestyles in a comparative analysis: Theoretical issues and empirical findings. *Social Science and Medicine, 32*(8), 899–908.

Antonovsky, A. (1992). Social class, life expectancy and overall mortality. In E.G. Jaco (Ed.), *Patients, physicians and illness* (pp. 5–30). New York: Free Press.

Auger, N., Raynault, M.-F., Lassard, R., & Choiniere, R. (2004). Income and Health in Canada. In D. Raphael (Ed.), *Social determinants of health: Canadian perspective* (pp. 39–52). Toronto: Canadian Scholars' Press.

Berliner, H.S. (1975). A large perspective on the Flexner report. *International Journal of Health Services, 5*, 573–592.

Berliner, H.S. (1977). Emerging ideologies in medicine. *Review of Radical Political Economics, 9*(1), 116–124.

Blaxter, M. (1990). *Health and lifestyles.* London: Tavistock/Routledge.

Bolaria, B.S. (2002a). Income inequality, poverty, food banks and health. In B.S. Bolaria & H.D. Dickinson (Eds.), *Health, illness and health care in Canada* (3rd ed., pp. 131–143). Toronto: Thomson Nelson.

Bolaria, B.S. (2002b). Sociology, medicine, health and illness: An overview. In B.S. Bolaria & H.D. Dickinson (Eds.), *Health, illness, and health care in Canada* (3rd ed., pp. 1–18). Toronto: Thomson Nelson.

Bolaria, B.S. (1994). Lifestyles, material deprivation and health. In B.S. Bolaria & R. Bolaria (Eds.), *Racial minorities, medicine and health* (pp. 67–84). Halifax and Saskatoon: Fernwood.

Bolaria, B.S., & Bolaria, R. (Eds.). (1994a). *Racial minorities, medicine and health.* Halifax and Saskatoon: Fernwood.

Bolaria, B.S., & Bolaria, R. (Eds.). (1994b). *Women, medicine and health.* Halifax and Saskatoon: Fernwood.

Bolaria, B.S., & Bolaria, R. (2002). Personal and structual determinants of health and illness: Lifestyles and life chances. In B.S. Bolaria & H.D. Dickinson (Eds.), *Health, illness and health care in Canada* (3rd ed., pp. 445–459). Toronto: Thomson Nelson.

Brown, P. (2000). Environment and health. In C.E. Bird, P. Conrad, & A.M. Fremont (Eds.), *Handbook of medical sociology* (5th ed., pp. 143–158). Upper Saddle River, NJ: Prentice-Hall.

Bryant, T. (2006). Politics, public policy and population health. In D. Raphael, T. Bryant, & M. Rioux (Eds.), *Staying alive: Critical perspectives on health, illness and health care* (pp. 193–216). Toronto: Canadian Scholars' Press.

Bunton, R., Nettleton, S., & Burrows, R. (Eds.). (1995). *The sociology of health promotion: Critical analysis of consumption, lifestyle and risk.* London: Routledge.

Burrows, R., Nettleton, S., & Bunton, R. (1995). Sociology and health promotion. In R. Bunton, S. Nettleton, & R. Burrows (Eds.), *The sociology of health promotion: Critical analysis of consumption, lifestyle and risk* (pp. 1–9). London: Routledge.

Chaney, D. (1996). *Lifestyles.* London: Routledge.

Coburn, D., & Eakin, J. (1993). The sociology of health in Canada: First impressions. *Health and Canadian Society, 1*, 83–110.

Cockerham, W.C. (1997). Lifestyles, social class, demographic characteristics and health behavior. In D. Gochman (Ed.), *Handbook of health behavior research I: Personal and social determinants* (pp. 253–265). New York: Plenum Press.

Cockerham, W.C. (1998). *Medical sociology* (7th ed.). Upper Saddle River, NJ: Prentice-Hall.

Cockerham, W.C. (2000). The sociology of health behavior and health lifestyles. In C.E. Bird, P. Conrad, & A.M. Fremont (Eds.), *Handbook of medical sociology* (5th ed., pp. 159–172). Upper Saddle River, NJ: Prentice-Hall.

Cockerham, W.C., Rutten, A., & Abel, T. (1997). Conceptualizing contemporary health lifestyles: Moving beyond Weber. *Sociological Quarterly, 38*, 321–342.

Conrad, P. (1994). Wellness as a virtue: Morality and the pursuit of health. *Culture, Medicine and Society, 18*, 385–401.

Conrad, P., & Walsh, D.C. (1992). The new corporate health ethic: Lifestyle and the social control of work. *International Journal of Health Sciences, 22*, 89–111.

Corin, E. (1994). The social and cultural matrix of health and disease. In R.G. Evans (Ed.), *Why are some people healthy and others not? The determinants of health in populations* (pp. 93–132). New York: Aldine deGruyter.

Crawford, R. (1977). You are dangerous to your health: The ideology and politics of victim blaming. *International Journal of Health Services, 7*(4), 663–680.

Daykin, N., & Naidoo, J. (1995). Feminist critiques of health promotion. In R. Bunton, S. Nettleton, & R. Burrows (Eds.), *The sociology of health promotion: Critical analysis of consumption, lifestyle and risk* (pp. 59–69). London: Routledge.

Dean, K. (1989). Self-care components of lifestyle: The importance of gender, attitudes and the social situation. *Social Science and Medicine, 29,* 137–152.

Denton, M., & Walters, V. (1999). Gender differences in structural and behavioral determinants of health: An analysis of the social production of health. *Social Science and Medicine, 48,* 1221–1235.

Douglas, J. (1995). Developing anti-racist health promotion strategies. In R. Bunton, S. Nettleton, & R. Burrows (Eds.), *The sociology of health promotion: Critical analysis of consumption, lifestyle and risk* (pp. 70–77). London: Routledge.

Eakin, J., Robertson, A., Poland, B., Coburn, D., & Edwards, R. (1996). Towards a critical social science perspective on health promotion research. *Health Promotion International, 11*(2), 157–165.

Epp, J. (1986). Achieving health for all: A framework for health promotion. *Canadian Journal of Public Health, 77*(6), 393–407.

Federal, Provincial and Territorial Advisory Committee on Population Health. (1999a). *Statistical report on the health of Canadians.* Ottawa: Minister of Public Works and Government Services Canada.

Federal, Provincial and Territorial Advisory Committee on Population Health. (1999b). *Toward a healthy future: Second report on the health of Canadians.* Ottawa: Minister of Public Works and Government Services Canada.

Firth, M., Brophy, J., & Keith, M. (1997). *Workplace roulette: Gambling with cancer.* Toronto: Between the Lines.

Frankish, C., Milligan, C., & Reid, C. (1998). A review of the relationship between active living and determinants of health. *Social Science and Medicine, 47,* 287–301.

Frohlich, K.L., & Potvin, L. (1999). Collective lifestyles as the target for health promotion. *Canadian Journal of Public Health, 90*(Suppl. 1), 511–514.

Garth, H.H., & Mills, C.W. (1958). *Max Weber: Essays in sociology.* New York: Galaxy.

Grace, V.M. (1991). The marketing of empowerment and the construction of the health consumer: A critique of health promotion. *International Journal of Health Services, 21*(2), 329–343.

Kickbusch, I. (1989). Self-care in health promotion. *Social Science and Medicine, 29*(2), 125–130.

Lalonde, M. (1974). *A new perspective on the health of Canadians.* Ottawa: Information Canada.

Link, B.G., & Phelan, J.C. (2000). Evaluating the fundamental cause explanation for social disparities in health. In C.E. Bird, P. Conrad, & A.M. Fremont (Eds.), *Handbook of medical sociology* (5th ed., pp. 33–46). Upper Saddle River, NJ: Prentice-Hall.

Lynch, J.W., Davey-Smith, G.; Kaplan; G.A.; and House, J.S. (2000). Income inequality and morality: Importance to health of individual income, psychological environment, or material conditions. *British Medical Journal, 320,* 1220–1224.

Marmot, M., Rose, G., Shipley, M., & Hamilton, P. (1978). Employment grade and coronary heart disease in British civil servants. *Journal of Epidemiology and Community Health, 32,* 244–249.

Marmot, M., Shipley, M., & Rose, G. (1984). Inequalities in death – Specific explanations of a general pattern. *Lancet, 1*(83), 1003–1006.

Marmot, M., Smith, G.D., Stanfield, S., Patel, C., North, F., Head, J., White, I., Brunner, E., & Feeney, A. (1991). Health inequalities among British civil servants: The Whitehall II study. *Lancet, 337*(8754), 1387–1393.

Matcha, D.A. (2000). *Medical sociology*. Toronto: Allyn and Bacon.

McDowell, I. (1986). National strategies for health promotion. *Canadian Journal of Public Health, 77*(6), 448.

McKinlay, J.B. (1993). The promotion of health through planned sociopolitical change: Challenges for research and policy. *Social Science and Medicine, 36*(2), 109–117.

McKinlay, J.B. (1994). A case for refocussing upstream: The political economy of illness. In P. Conrad & R. Kern (Eds.), *The sociology of health and illness: Critical perspectives* (4th ed., pp. 509–523). New York: St. Martin's Press.

McQueen, D. (1989). Thoughts on the ideological origins of health promotion. *Health Promotion, 4*(4), 339–342.

Mechanic, D. (1999). Issues in promoting health. *Social Science and Medicine, 48*, 711–718.

Millar, J., & Hull, C. (1997). Measuring human wellness. *Social Indicators Research, 40*, 147–158.

Mirowsky, J., Ross, C.E., & Reynolds, J. (2000). Links between social status and health status. In C.E. Bird, P. Conrad, & A.M. Fremont (Eds.), *Handbook of medical sociology* (5th ed., pp. 47–67). Upper Saddle River, NJ: Prentice-Hall.

Muntaner, C., Borelli, C., Kunst, A., Chung, H., Benach, J., & Ibrahim, S. (2006). Social class inequalities in health: Does welfare state regime matter? In D. Raphael, T. Bryant, & M. Rioux (Eds.), *Staying alive: Critical perspectives on health, illness and health care* (pp. 139–158). Toronto: Canadian Scholars' Press.

National Council of Welfare (1990). *Health, health care and medicare*. Ottawa: Supply and Services Canada.

Navarro, V. (1986). *Crisis, health, and medicine*. New York: Tavistock.

Nettleton, S., & Bunton, R. (1995). Sociological critique of health promotion. In R. Bunton, S. Nettleton, & R. Burrows (Eds.), *The sociology of health promotion: Critical analysis of consumption, lifestyle and risk* (pp. 41–58). London: Routledge.

O'Brien, M. (1995). Health and lifestyle: A critical mess: Notes on the dedifferentiation of health. In R. Bunton, S. Nettleton, & R. Burrows (Eds.), *The sociology of health promotion: Critical analysis of consumption, lifestyle and risk* (pp. 191–205). London: Routledge.

Pederson, A., & Raphael, D. (2006). Gender, race, and health inequalities. In D. Raphael, T. Bryant, & M. Rioux (Eds.), *Staying alive: Critical perspectives on health, illness and health care* (pp. 159–192). Toronto: Canadian Scholars' Press.

Phipps, S. (June, 2003). The impact of poverty on health. Ottawa: Health Canada, Canadian Population Health Initiative, Canadian Institute for Health Information.

Poland, B., Coburn, D., Robertson, A., & Eakin, J. (1998). Wealth, equity and health care: A critique of a population health perspective on the determinants of health. *Social Science and Medicine, 46*, 785–798.

Raphael, D. (2002). Poverty, income inequality and health in Canada. Toronto: Centre for Social Justice Foundation for Research and Education (CSJ). http://www.socialjustice.org/index.php?page=poverty-income-inequality-and-health-in-canada.

Raphael, D. (2003). Addressing the social determinants of health in Canada: Bridging the gap between research findings and public policy. *Policy Options, 24*(3), 35–40.

Raphael. D. (2004a). Introduction to the social determinants of health. In D. Raphael (Ed.), *Social determinants of health: Canadian perspective* (pp. 1–18). Toronto: Canadian Scholars' Press.

Raphael, D. (Ed.). (2004b). *Social determinants of health: Canadian perspectives*. Toronto: Canadian Scholars' Press.

Raphael, D., & Bryant, T. (2000). Putting the population into population health. *Canadian Journal of Public Health, 91*(1), 9–12.

Raphael, D., Bryant, T., & Rioux, M. (Eds.). (2006). *Staying alive: Critical perspectives on health and illness, and health care*. Toronto: Canadian Scholars' Press.

Ross, C.E., & Bird, C.E. (1994). Sex stratification and health lifestyle: Consequences for men's and women's perceived health. *Journal of Health and Social Behaviour, 35*, 161–178.

Ross, D.P., & Roberts, P. (1999). *Income and child well-being: A new perspective on the poverty debate*. Ottawa: Canadian Council on Social Development.

Rutten, A. (1995). The implementation of health promotion: A new structural perspective. *Social Science and Medicine, 41*(12), 1627–1637.

Segall, A., & Chappell, N.L. (2000). *Health and health care in Canada*. Toronto: Prentice-Hall.

Shah, C.P. (2004). The health of aboriginal peoples. In D. Raphael (Ed.), *Social determinants of health: Canadian perspective* (pp. 267–280). Toronto: Canadian Scholars' Press.

Taylor, R.C.R. (1989). The politics of prevention. In P. Brown (Ed.), *Perspectives in medical sociology* (pp. 368–388). Belmont, CA: Wadsworth.

Townsend, P. (1990). Individual or social responsibility for premature death? Current controversies in the British debate about health. *International Journal of Health Services, 20*(3), 373–392.

Waitzkin, H. (1983). *The second sickness: Contradictions of capitalist health care*. New York: Free Press.

Weber, M. (1978). *Economy and society* (2 vols.). G.F. Roth & C. Wittick (Eds. & Trans.). Berkeley: University of California Press.

Wilkinson, R.G. (1996). *Unhealthy societies*. London: Routledge.

INDEX

A page number appearing in bold refers to a glossary definition of the term. A page number with an italized '*t*' or '*f*' refers to a table or figure.

CREDITS

This page constitutes an extension of the copyright page. We have made every effort to trace the ownership of all copyrighted material and to secure permission from copyright holders. In the event of any question arising as to the use of any material, we will be pleased to make the necessary corrections in future printings. Thanks are due to the following authors, publishers, and agents for permission to use the material indicated.

Chapter 1. 16: Courtesy of Canadian Public Health Association.

Chapter 2. 34: From Federal Transfers in Support of the 2000/2003/2004 First Ministers' Accords <www.fin.gc.ca/FEDPROV/fmAcce.html>. Reproduced with the permission of the Minister of Public Works and Government Services, 2007.

Chapter 4. 57–58: Excerpts from "Health Indicators Framework: a) Health Status b) Non-Medical Determinants of Health," adapted from Statistics Canada publication *Health Indicators*, Catalogue 82-221, 2003. **59:** "Life Expectancy at Birth in Canada, By Sex, Selected Years, 1931–2001," data is adapted in part from Statistics Canada publications *Infant Mortality Table from Canada at a Glance*, Catalogue 12-581, 2006 Edition. Release date: March 10, 2006. URL: www.statcan.ca/english/freepub/12-581-XIE/12-581-XIE2005001.pdf. **60:** Excerpts from "Life Expectancy at Birth, By Sex, By Province," adapted from Statistics Canada website http://www40.statcan.ca/l01/cst01/ health 26.htm. **60:** "Causes of Death Among Children Under 5 (2002–2003)," *World Health Day Toolkit*, 7 April 2005, p. 8. Copyright © 2005 World Health Organization. **61:** Courtesy of Canadian Public Health Association. **65:** Courtesy of National Aboriginal Health Organization (NAHO). **66:** Courtesy of National Aboriginal Health Organization (NAHO). **67–68:** Courtesy of National Aboriginal Health Organization (NAHO).

Chapter 5. 79: Courtesy of UBC Centre for Health Services & Policy Research. **80:** "Figure 11: Percentage of IENs by Country of Graduation, Canada, 2003," *Workforce Trends of Registered Nurses in Canada*, p. 30. © 2004, Canadian Institute for Health Information (CIHI). All rights reserved. **82:** "Figure 8: Number of Physicians Who Moved Abroad or Returned From Abroad, Canada, 1969–2005," (URL: http://secure.cihi.ca/cihiweb/dispPage.jsp?cw_page=statistics_results_topic_physicians_e&cw_topic=Health%20Human%20Resources&cw_subtopic=Physicians). © 1996–2007, Canadian Institute for Health

Information (CIHI). All rights reserved. **84:** "Figure 4: Percentage of RNs with Secondary Registrations by Location of Employment," *Workforce Trends of Registered Nurses in Canada*, 2003, p. 17. © 2004, Canadian Institute for Health Information (CIHI). All rights reserved.

Chapter 9. 173: From *Poverty Profile, 2002 and 2003*, 2006, p. 15. Published by the National Council of Welfare. **174:** From *Poverty Profile, 2002 and 2003*, 2006, p. 15. Published by the National Council of Welfare. **176:** Courtesy of Canadian Association of Food Banks.

Chapter 11. 205: Table 11.1: "Proportion of Visible Minorities, Canada, Provinces and Territories, 1991, 1996 and 2001," adapted from Statistics Canada website http://www.12.statcan.ca/english/census01/products/analytic/companion/etoimm/tables/provs/vmhist.cfm. **206:** Table 11.2: "Proportion of Foreign-born Population, By Census Metropolitan Area (1991 to 2001 Censuses)," adapted from Statistics Canada website <http://www40.statcan.ca/I01/cst01/demo47a.htm. **207:** Table 11.3: "Major Religious Denominations, Canada 1991 and 2001," adapted from Statistics Canada website <http://www12.statcan.ca/english/census01/Products/Analytic/companion/rel/canada.cmf#overview>.

Chapter 12. 229: Courtesy of United Nations Population Fund (UNFPA). **230**: "Trafficking in Women: The Canadian Perspective." Reprinted from CMAJ 05-Jul-05; 173 (1), Pages 25–26, by permission of the publisher. © 2005 Canadian Medical Association.

Chapter 13. 246: Reprinted with permission of CP.

Chapter 16. 317: Courtesy of Dr. Bernard Schissel, University of Saskatchewan. **318:** Courtesy of Dr. Bernard Schissel, University of Saskatchewan. **321:** Courtesy of Dr. Bernard Schissel, University of Saskatchewan.

Chapter 17. 343: CORNERED © 1999 Mike Baldwin. Reprinted with permission of UNIVERSAL PRESS SYNDICATE. All rights reserved.

Chapter 20. 399: Reprinted from *Social Science and Medicine*, Vol. 61, 2005. L.M. Hall and D. Kiesners "A Narrative Approach to Understanding the Nursing Work Environment in Canada," pp. 2482–2491. Copyright © 2005. Reprinted with permission from Elsevier.

Chapter 22. 444: Lexchin, J., "Relationship between Pharmaceutical Company User Fees and Drug Approvals in Canada and Australia: A Hypothesis-generating Study," *The Annals of Pharmacotherapy*, December 2006, 40:2218. © 2006, The Annals of Pharmacotherapy. **446:** "Effect of Generic Drug Competition on the Price of Prescription Drugs in Ontario" – Figure 1 reprinted from *CMAJ*, 1 January 1993; 148(1), Page(s) 35–38 by permission of the publisher. © 1993 Canadian Medical Association. **447:** "Changes in the Ration of GDP and Prescription Drug Prices," original data is adapted from the Statistics Canada report: *Financial Performance Indicators for Canadian Business*, Vol. 1, 2001–2003, Catalogue #61-224-XCB.